Analysis and Design of Digital Integrated Circuits

Ronak Desai.

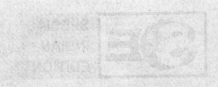

Analysis and Design of Digital Integrated Circuits

Roopak Desai
Roopak Desai

Analysis and Design of Digital Integrated Circuits

In Deep Submicron Technology

THIRD EDITION

David A. Hodges
University of California, Berkeley

Horace G. Jackson
University of California, Berkeley

Resve A. Saleh
University of British Columbia

Tata McGraw Hill Education Private Limited

NEW DELHI

McGraw-Hill Offices

New Delhi New York St Louis San Francisco Auckland Bogotá Caracas
Kuala Lumpur Lisbon London Madrid Mexico City Milan Montreal
San Juan Santiago Singapore Sydney Tokyo Toronto

Tata McGraw-Hill

ANALYSIS AND DESIGN OF DIGITAL INTEGRATED CIRCUITS: IN DEEP SUBMICRON TECHNOLOGY, THIRD EDITION

Tata McGraw-Hill Edition 2005

Ninth reprint 2012
RCCLRRCHRYADD

Adapted by Tata McGraw-Hill in India by arragement with the McGraw-Hill Companies Inc., New York

Sales Territories: India, Pakistan, Nepal, Bangladesh, Sri Lanka and Bhutan

ISBN-13: 978-0-07-059375-6
ISBN-10: 0-07-059375-2

Published by Tata McGraw Hill Education Private Limited,
7 West Patel Nagar, New Delhi 110 008, typeset in Times at Script Makers,
19, A1-B, DDA Market, Paschim Vihar, New Delhi 110 063 and printed at
Pushp Print Services, Delhi 110 053

Cover printer: SDR Printers

About the Authors

David A. Hodges is the Daniel M. Tellep Distinguished Professor of Engineering Emeritus at the University of California, Berkeley. He earned the B.E.E. degree at Cornell University and the M.S. and Ph.D. degrees at the University of California, Berkeley. In 1970 he joined the faculty in Electrical Engineering and Computer Sciences at UC Berkeley. Following a year as Chair of the EECS Department, he served as Dean of the College of Engineering from July 1990 through June 1996. Professor Hodges was the winner of the 1997 IEEE Education Medal and the 1999 ASEE Benjamin Garver Lamme Award. He was the founding editor of the *IEEE Transactions on Semiconductor Manufacturing,* and a past editor of the *IEEE Journal of Solid-State Circuits.* Professor Hodges is a Fellow of the IEEE and a Member of the National Academy of Engineering. He is a Director of Silicon Image, Inc. and a former Director of Mentor Graphics.

Horace G. Jackson was born and educated in England. In 1947 he went to Canada, where until 1956 he was engaged in nuclear physics research at the Chalk River Laboratories of Atomic Energy of Canada. In 1956 he joined the Lawrence Berkeley Laboratory of the University of California, where he worked as a Senior Staff Scientist, as well as serving as a Resident Lecturer in the Department of Electrical Engineering and Computer Sciences until his retirement. He has published widely in nuclear science and electronic engineering journals and is coauthor on two books. His research interests are in high frequency analog and high-speed digital integrated circuits.

Resve A. Saleh currently holds the NSERC/PMC-Sierra Chair in the Department of Electrical and Computer Engineering at the University of British Columbia. Dr. Saleh obtained his M.S. and Ph.D. degrees in electrical engineering from the University of California, Berkeley. He received the prestigious Presidential Young Investigator Award in 1990 from the National Science Foundation in the United States. Dr. Saleh has published two books and over 60 journal articles and conference papers. He was an Associate Editor of IEEE Transactions on Computer-Aided Design and technical program chair of the Custom Integrated Circuits Conference. He has also served on numerous program committees. He is a founder and former

Chairman of Simplex Solutions (Sunnyvale, CA). Prior to starting Simplex, Dr. Saleh spent nine years as a Professor in the Department of Electrical and Computer Engineering at the University of Illinois in Urbana. He also spent one year at Stanford University on a sabbatical leave. Before embarking on his academic career, Dr. Saleh worked for Mitel Corporation in Ottawa, Canada, Toshiba Corporation in Japan, Tektronix in Beaverton, Oregon, and Nortel in Ottawa, Canada. At present, he is directing research at UBC in the System-on-Chip Research Laboratory.

Contents

Preface to the Third Edition

Motivation for a Third Edition

Since the publication of the second edition over 15 years ago, the integrated circuit (IC) industry has undergone a tremendous amount of change. The most significant trend is the emergence of CMOS as the dominant IC technology. Other technologies such as NMOS, bipolar, and GaAs, have given way to CMOS due to considerations such as power, level of integration, and cost. The tools, technologies, and know-how in CMOS are so pervasive that it will continue to lead the industry for the next decade.

A second important trend is that scaling is continuing its relentless pace according to Moore's Law. The industry reached the 1 μm minimum line width around the time of publication of the second edition. This was once considered to be a physical and psychological limit of scaling. However, it was quickly realized that transistors could be fabricated with minimum dimensions well below 1 μm and this ushered in the submicron era. Since then, we have been witness to six generations of technology scaling: 0.8 μm, 0.5 μm, 0.35 μm, 0.25 μm, 0.18 μm, and 0.13 μm.

At roughly the 0.35 μm technology node, we entered the deep submicron era where a number of fundamental changes were encountered in behavior of transistors and wires. Devices experienced a number of short-channel effects, perhaps the most important of which is velocity saturation. Interconnect began to control many of the electrical properties of the design such as delay, noise, power, and reliability. As a result, the transition from 0.18 μm to 0.13 μm also triggered a wholesale switch from aluminum to copper to mitigate these new interconnect issues. With all of these fundamental changes in the IC industry, there was a need to completely revise this book.

What's in the New Edition?

- We have focused on CMOS technology.
- The content is based on 0.18 μm and 0.13 μm CMOS technologies.

- Most recent CMOS fabrication processes are described, including shallow-trench isolation, copper interconnect, and low-k dielectrics.
- Two important chapters have been added on deep submicron interconnect.
- New material has been added on logical effort that is useful for back-of-the-envelope calculations of optimal gates sizes in high-speed CMOS design.
- Advanced material has also been added on Flash memories, field-programmable gate arrays, and content-addressable memories.
- A chapter has been added on advanced power grid design, clock design, and phase-locked loops.
- A new section has been added on BSIM3 modeling and simulation.
- This edition uses short-channel MOS device equations with velocity saturation throughout the book. New equations have been derived for noise margins and switching thresholds.
- Junction capacitance modeling has been updated to include shallow-trench isolation effects.
- A SPICE tutorial has been provided in Appendix A.
- Gallium arsenide has been removed from this edition.

With these changes, the new edition of the book will be valuable for many years to come.

Why Buy This Book?

This book will teach you how to think like a designer. It is the product of the design know-how of many of the leaders in the field. This edition also contains extremely valuable information for practicing engineers in the semiconductor industry. The real value of the book is that it starts with the fundamentals of semiconductor devices and sequences in a step-by-step fashion to the key issues of digital IC design in deep submicron technologies. Like the previous editions, it is intended to be used as a fourth-year university textbook, with some of the latter material suitable for first-year graduate courses.

This book retains the readability and accessibility of previous editions that led to its widespread use. While the goal is to provide the reader with the key concepts and equations for digital IC design, it provides much more detail than other books in the field. Concepts are introduced in a logical sequence and then reinforced throughout the book. Complex equations are reduced to simple design equations that can be used to carry out rapid hand calculations.

There are many derivations, worked examples, exercises, and SPICE simulations to allow the student and practicing engineer to build a solid understanding of the material in each chapter. There are problems at the back of the chapter to gain experience with the material and explore other topics not directly covered in the chapter. The chapter summaries are in the form of useful equations and parameters from each chapter. The inside front and back covers provide useful parameters, scale factors, and conversion factors that are used throughout the book.

Website for the Book

A website for the textbook is available through McGraw-Hill. The website contains solutions, supporting material, color diagrams, illustrations, design problems, and errata. The website is valuable in constructing lecture material for a course based on this book.

Advanced CMOS Technologies

The material in this book is built around the 0.18 μm and 0.13 μm technology nodes. Both technologies are covered in enough detail to select one or the other as the primary technology for a course based on this book. Since SPICE is the simulation tool used in this book, it is necessary to have access to device models for one of these two technologies for the course. All of the SPICE examples are based on 0.18 μm, while the worked problems are based on both 0.18 μm and 0.13 μm technologies. The textbook is also suitable for technologies below 0.13 μm, with appropriate changes in the examples and problems at the back of the chapters.

Advanced Topics

Advanced topics are included for students wishing to go beyond the basic material of this text and gain insight into the issues in industry. They are designated with an asterisk (*) and may be skipped without loss of continuity.

How to Use This Book

Chapters 1–3 comprise the foundational material upon which the rest of the book is based. Chapters 4–7 are the main body of the text where all of the transistor-level design issues are described in detail. Chapter 8 focuses on an application of all material covered in the book, specifically in static memory design. Chapter 9 describes advanced topics in semiconductor memory design. The book continues with a detailed treatment of deep submicron interconnect issues in Chapter 10 and concludes with power grid and clock design in Chapter 11.

For a 15-week semester course, with 3 hours of lecture time each week, the entire text may be covered at the rate of about one chapter each week. For a 12-week course, there is sufficient time to cover Chapters 1–8, Chapter 10, and selected topics in Chapters 9 and 11.

In a 10-week course, only Chapters 1–8 and Chapter 10 can be covered assuming that much of the advanced topics are skipped. Depending on the background of the students entering the course, instructors should use their own discretion in selecting the appropriate material and sequencing of this book.

A chapter-by-chapter outline of the topics follows.

Chapter 1
Deep Submicron Digital IC Design
In the first chapter, we provide a perspective on digital design in the deep submicron era and motivate the topics in the rest of the book. We briefly review important concepts of logic gates primarily to provide notational context for the book, including the ideal logic element, static input-output characteristics, noise margin, and propagation delay time. Then we elaborate on the key issues in deep submicron such as power dissipation, velocity saturated transistors, interconnect resistance, coupling capacitance, and inductance. The role of computer-aided design tools such as SPICE is described. The chapter concludes with the challenges ahead as described in the technology roadmap.

Chapter 2
Transistors & Devices—MOS and Bipolar
The short-channel device models to be used in the rest of this book are described in this chapter. To begin the treatment, rudimentary device physics concepts are covered to explain the threshold voltage equation and the transistor current equations. Both long- and short-channel models are derived. Then the oxide and junction capacitance models are described. The Bipolar transistors and circuits are described in brief. The structure and operation of BJTs and SBDs are summarized. Thereafter, an introduction to the most widely used circuits, based on them, is given to complete the chapter.

Chapter 3
Fabrication, Layout, and Simulation
This chapter describes the relationship between fabrication, layout, and simulation in the integrated circuit design process. The topics of fabrication and layout are important to IC designers and should be well-understood. However, for this course, it serves more as a background for the rest of the text. The more important subject is simulation with SPICE. The model parameters for SPICE are detailed in this chapter. A brief user manual is provided in Appendix A for those unfamiliar with the basics of SPICE. We also provide some advanced material on MOS transistors and fabrication technologies of the future.

Chapter 4
MOS Inverter Circuits
This is a core chapter on MOS digital inverters and introduces concepts of voltage transfer characteristics, noise margins, inverter configurations, and simple timing and power calculations. Analytical equations are derived for noise margin parameters and switching thresholds of inverters for a number of MOS inverters.

Chapter 5
Static MOS Gate Circuits
This is another core chapter of the book. It examines the static design issues for NANDs, NORs, and complex gates. It develops extensions to inverter design to size the transistors in CMOS gates. Sequential elements, such as flip-flops and latches,

are described in this chapter. The chapter concludes with a detailed treatment of the various components of power dissipation in logic gates.

Chapter 6
High-Speed CMOS Logic Design

This chapter describes the issues involved in high-speed logic design. It develops useful equations for switching delay calculation for step and ramp inputs. This involves the use of the large-signal on-resistance of gates, and the calculation of the loading capacitance, both of which are detailed. The total capacitance can be computed using two key parameters for input and output capacitance. Gate sizing for equal delay and minimal delay are described. The thrust of the latter half of this chapter is high-speed logic optimization using logical effort.

Chapter 7
Transfer Gate and Dynamic Logic Design

In this chapter, we explore dynamic design techniques using transmission gates and precharged logic. The important concepts of charge-sharing, bootstrapping, feedthrough, and charge leakage are elaborated in this chapter. Domino logic is described in detail as it is the most common form of dynamic logic in use today. These concepts lay the groundwork for the operation of many of the memory circuits discussed in the next two chapters.

Chapter 8
Semiconductor Memory Design

This chapter addresses the analysis and design of VLSI memories, commonly known as semiconductor memories. In this chapter, we classify the different types of memory, examine the major subsystems, and then focus on the static RAM (SRAM) design issues. This topic is particularly suitable for our study of CMOS digital design as it allows us to apply many of the basic concepts presented in earlier chapters. The entire design process for static RAMs is described in detail.

Chapter 9
Additional Topics in Memory Design

This chapter explores a variety of other semiconductor memories, their architectures, access mechanisms, and cell configurations. We begin by examining content-addressable memories, since they are a derivative of the SRAM architecture. We also cover an important application of SRAM cells in the growing market segment of programmable logic called field-programmable gate-arrays (FPGAs). The chapter sequences through dynamic RAMs, mask-programmable ROMs, erasable programmable ROMs, electrically-erasable ROMs and Flash memories, and concludes with a look at memory cells based on ferroelectric materials called FRAMs.

Chapter 10
Interconnect Design

This chapter is devoted to the study of interconnect issues that the IC designer faces when designing in deep submicron technologies. It addresses the issues associated with *RLC* aspects of wires in detail. We begin by re-examining the *RC* delay calculation using the Elmore delay, and address the issue of buffer insertion in long wires. Then we examine the capacitances associated with 3D interconnect which leads to a discussion of the effect of coupling capacitance on delay and crosstalk in logic circuits. The chapter continues with a discussion of inductance effects, and concludes with a look at antenna effects.

Chapter 11
Power Grid and Clock Design

In this chapter, we address two chip-level design issues that are dominated by interconnect: power system distribution and clock distribution. This chapter addresses advanced issues such as power routing, *IR* drop, *Ldi/dt*, and the impact of voltage drop on timing. The chapter highlights the interaction of the power system with the clock design. It also addresses clock generation and phase-lock loop (PLL) circuits to conclude the chapter.

Acknowledgments

The authors acknowledge the many colleagues and students who aided us in the preparation of all editions of this book over two decades. This extensively revised and augmented third edition has been developed by Professor Resve Saleh over the past three years. Much of the new material was developed in the Spring of 2000 when Professor Saleh taught at Stanford University. Professor Mark Horowitz at Stanford provided the original blueprint for a new course on deep submicron digital IC design which ultimately found its way into this edition. It was indeed a pleasure to work with him during that year to gain his insights into the important issues in circuit design today. His approach to digital integrated circuit design and his methods of teaching served as inspiration for this book. We gratefully acknowledge his impact and thank him for his contributions. Professor Gu-Yeon Wei of Harvard University also participated as an instructor for the first course. He prepared early versions of materials that eventually wound up herein. In addition, Professor Bruce Wooley of Stanford University provided valuable course materials.

There were a number of faculty and students at the University of British Columbia who made significant contributions to the book with suggestions, corrections, and proofreading of various chapters. We appreciate the efforts of Professors Steve Wilton, Shahriar Mirabbasi, and David Pulfrey, and students Jess Chia, Payam Lajevardi, Gary Lim, Louis Hong, Laura Ishkintana, Roberto Rosales, Sean Safarpour, and Marwa Hamour. In addition, Sandy Scott assisted with many of the administrative duties associated with the book.

A number of industry professionals have also had an impact on the book, most notably those associated with Simplex Solutions. David Overhauser, Narain Arora, Steffen Rochel, Peter McCrorie, Sandy Taylor, and Michael Benoit were extremely helpful in many aspects of the material presented in this book. Pallab Chatterjee of SiliconMap provided useful technology insights for upcoming generations of CMOS.

Many people were involved in reviewing this project and offered valuable feedback. We would like to acknowledge the assistance of following people:

Philip Allen, *Georgia Institute of Technology*
R. Jacob Baker, *University of Idaho*
Anantha Chandrakasan, *MIT*
Kyusun Choi, *Pennsylvania State University*
P. David Fisher, *Michigan State University*
Jim Frenzel, *University of Idaho*
Arvin Grabel, *Northeastern University*
Jeffrey L. Gray, *Purdue University*
Edwin Greeneich, *Arizona State University*
Paul Hurst, *University of California–Davis*
Shrinivas G. Joshi, *Marquette University*
Thottam S. Kalkur, *University of Colorado, Colorado Springs*
Hong Koo Kim, *University of Pittsburgh*
Ivan Kourtev, *University of Pittsburgh*
Hisham Z. Massoud, *Duke University*
Martin Margala, *University of Alberta*
Boris Murmann, *Stanford University*
Kelvin F. Poole, *Clemson University*
Ahok Srivastava, *Louisiana State University*
Dennis Sylvester, *University of Michigan*
John Uyemura, *Georgia Institute of Technology*
Chin-Long Wey, *Michigan State University*
Mona Elwakkad Zaghloul, *George Washington University*

Jan Willis and Janet Greene provided the cover material for this book and their contributions are gratefully acknowledged. We also acknowledge the support of PMC-Sierra for the writing of this book. The folks at McGraw-Hill were a pleasure to work with and we acknowledge the efforts of Emily Lupash and Joyce Watters, and countless others, who made this book possible.

We would especially like to thank Professors Richard Newton and Don Pederson of the University of California, Berkeley, for their continuous support and encouragement over the years.

The authors dedicate this book to our families who have supported us through several editions so that we can continue to inspire the next generation of IC engineers.

Deep Submicron Digital IC Design

1.1   Introduction

Integrated circuits (ICs) are part of virtually every electronic component in the world today, such as cell phones, personal digital assistants, pagers, personal computers, printers, set-top boxes, automobiles, and so on. Most of these IC chips are "digital" in nature, with an increasing presence of "analog" circuitry. This text-book addresses the design of digital circuits in deep submicron (DSM) technologies. If you have taken a design course on very large-scale integration (VLSI), you will recognize many of the circuit issues covered in this book. However, the main objective of this book is to train you to "think like a circuit designer." The goal is to give you the intuition and models that you need to be able to analyze existing circuits and create interesting new circuits. We aim to provide some real-world experience in how circuits are designed in industry, and how to make design trade-offs to achieve a good balance among speed, power consumption, and reliability. We strive to provide the understanding needed to anticipate the likely improvements and potential difficulties that may be encountered with future technologies.

Before we can talk about circuits, we need to understand the basic digital components and tools that we use to analyze them. We need to look at technology trends and what types of problems have been introduced due to technology scaling. This will provide the motivation for the topics that are described in the rest of this book.

The design of modern digital systems requires contributions from several engineering specialists. First, a *system designer*, or *system architect*, determines the desired characteristics for the overall system and prepares a detailed specification that defines all inputs, outputs, environmental conditions, operating speeds, etc. The system is then implemented using a register-transfer level (RTL) language such as VHDL or Verilog.[1] This RTL description is translated into a logic design that can meet the functional requirements. The output of this step is referred to as the *gate-level* design. Once the gate-level design is completed, it is converted to the circuit level where transistors are used to implement each logic gate. Finally, the transistor schematic is converted to an integrated circuit in the form of geometric layout usually represented in GDS-II stream format.[2]

Good system design requires that design decisions result in the appropriate balance among system characteristics, logic design, circuit design, layout design, and fabrication technology. Since compromises must usually be made and alternatives evaluated, it is important that the various specialists mentioned above have some knowledge of the related fields.

The task of the *circuit design engineer* is to design transistor circuits that implement the required logic functions. Whenever many copies of the desired system are to be manufactured, it is important to achieve high reliability of operation and a proper balance among cost and performance characteristics, such as timing, power, and area. The design must also operate properly in the presence of process variations, supply fluctuations, and changes in the environmental conditions. The chapters that follow address in depth the issues of microelectronic design that determine these characteristics. Of particular concern is the tradeoff between timing and power in ICs since designs today are either high speed or low power.

Today, virtually all digital systems are based on integrated circuit technology. Various design options and tradeoffs exist. Choices must be made among circuit families, level of integration (the number of circuits on a chip), and programmable versus fixed-function ("hard-wired") circuits. A wide variety of IC technology is in use today. The most prevalent technology is the metal-oxide-semiconductor (MOS) process. Other technologies such as bipolar, GaAs, and SiGe are also available but represent a smaller part of the total market. The various integrated circuit technologies have widely differing characteristics. In the bipolar category, transistor-transistor logic (TTL) and emitter-coupled logic (ECL) have seen widespread use in the past. In the last 20 years, a dramatic transition has been made to MOS technology due to its high density of integration. In fact, integrated circuit *process and device engineers* continue to make major improvements in these technologies every 2 or 3 years. Through the 1970s, *n*-channel MOS (NMOS) technology was

---

[1] VHDL and Verilog are hardware description languages used to describe large digital systems.
[2] GDS-II is an industry standard format for describing the geometric objects in a layout.

commonplace. Since 1980, complementary MOS (CMOS) has become the dominant technology due to its low-power characteristics.

Some understanding of integrated circuit fabrication techniques is required to compare the relative characteristics of different circuit families, such as NMOS and CMOS. An appreciation for the direction and rate of change in fabrication technology is important if product designs are to provide good possibilities for evolutionary improvements. Furthermore, the statistical variation in the process must be well understood to design modern circuits. The fabrication process and transistor structure have changed over the last 10 years and we will examine these changes. While it is not the purpose of this book to describe the details of IC fabrication, it is necessary to describe the basic processing steps used today to understand both the layout of MOS circuits and the origins of the important parameters for simulation tools used for their analysis.

Computer-aided design (CAD) tools are essential in design and analysis of digital integrated circuits. We will examine the types of tools that are typically used in industry, but focus on circuit simulation that is important for cell library characterization and custom IC design. The primary workhorse tool for detailed circuit analysis is SPICE.[3] We will spend time understanding MOS models for hand analysis and comparing their results against circuit simulation to validate the hand analysis. In effect, we want models that are suitable for hand analysis but accurate enough to provide insight into the actual circuit operation. Detailed circuit simulation can be used to examine the second-order issues, and address other first-order issues such as process, temperature, and supply variations.

1.2   Brief History of IC Industry

The IC industry started in the late 1960s and early 1970s with a *ten micron technology*. This technology node was identified by the minimum geometry that could be printed on the chip. We refer to designs of that era as small-scale integration (SSI) and medium-scale integration (MSI), meaning that only a few gates, or a few hundred gates, could be integrated on a single chip. Every 3 years or so, technology dimensions were scaled by a factor s, which has historically been found to be equal to 0.7. This meant that a chip that was 1 mm $\times$ 1 mm = 1 mm^2 could be reduced to 0.7 mm $\times$ 0.7 mm $\approx$ 0.5 mm^2 in the next generation. Another way to look at it is that twice the number of transistors could be integrated on the same 1 mm^2 chip as compared to the previous technology node. Because of this, the cost per logic function decreased with each new generation. This trend came to be known as *Moore's law*, perhaps the most important observation in the history of ICs. Many have predicted the end of Moore's Law several times in the past 30 years and have been proved wrong to this day.

During the 1970s, the ability to integrate thousands of gates on a single chip became feasible. This was the era of large-scale integration (LSI). Designers began

---

[3] SPICE is an acronym for Simulation Program with Integrated Circuit Emphasis, originally developed at the University of California—Berkeley in the 1970s.

to develop microprocessors with significant processing capability, and memories with large storage capacities. Integrated circuits began to show up in pocket calculators, computers, and television sets. By the end of this decade, the enormous potential of integrated circuits was well understood. Around 1980, a revolution began in the microelectronics industry with major advances in IC processing technology, microprocessor design, memory design, and computer-aided design (CAD). This was driven by a whole host of consumer products including personal computers, printers, and VCRs. The name coined for this era was, of course, very large-scale integration (VLSI). The term *VLSI* captured everyone's imagination of the unlimited possibilities of this technology. The ability to place 1 million (1M) transistors on a single chip was within reach and the race began to develop chips that were capable of using this level of integration.

Through the 1980s, available technologies were mostly in the 5 μm to 1 μm range. This dimension nominally refers to the *channel length* of the transistor. It also refers to the minimum resolvable geometry on a given layer of metal in the integrated circuit, specifically, the metal line widths or metal-to-metal spacing (metal *pitch*). Advances in photolithography, the key process that defines the minimum dimension in a technology, eventually led to line widths that were below 1 μm. This was referred to as the *submicron* era, at one time thought unreachable. However, scaling continued aggressively to the point where 0.5 μm and 0.35 μm line widths were achieved by the mid-1990s. At the same time, the number of layers of metal continued to increase. Metal layers composed of aluminum and tungsten were used to connect transistors. The industry began with only one layer of metal for all connections. As the number of transistors increased, there was a need to increase the number of levels of metal so that all required connections could be made. Figure 1.1 shows a four-layer metal process in 0.35 μm technology.

Many argued that 0.35 μm technology would be a physical limit for photolithography since the wavelength of light is approximately equal to this value. However, further advances allowed scaling below this barrier. At this point, the term *deep submicron* (DSM) was coined to emphasize that we had gone beyond another scaling limit, and well below the 1 μm barrier. The device behavior was largely controlled by a number of new *short-channel effects*. In addition, new problems began to arise concerning the metal interconnect. The wires connecting the transistor began to introduce additional RC delays in the circuit due to increased resistance. Furthermore, coupling between lines caused delay variations and noise injection. The increases in resistance in the power distribution system led to voltage drops in the power grid, commonly referred to as IR drop. The reliability of the aluminum metal lines began to degrade due to metal migration resulting from high current levels. Collectively, these issues were referred to as signal integrity problems and they characterize what we call the *deep submicron era*.

While these problems were not completely resolved, scaling continued its relentless pace to 0.25 μm, 0.18 μm, 0.15 μm, and by the year 2001, to 0.13 μm. We entered a new era where aluminum lines with tungsten vias gave way to a dual-Damascene *copper* process, as shown in Figure 1.2, to mitigate the interconnect issues mentioned above. New dielectric materials were introduced, the so-called *low-k dielectrics*, to reduce coupling effects between wires. This period goes by many names, for example, very deep submicron (VDSM) and ultra-deep submicron

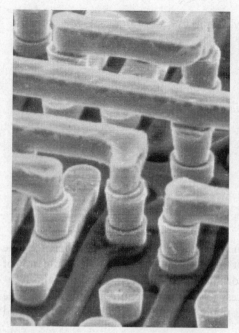

Figure 1.1
Four-layer aluminum wires with tungsten vias in 0.35 μm technology.
[Courtesy: IBM Corporation. Unauthorized use not permitted.]

Figure 1.2
Copper interconnect.
[Courtesy: IBM Corporation. Unauthorized use not permitted.]

(UDSM). Because of the fine geometries, a change of units from microns to nanometers seemed appropriate. In this book, we will often refer to 0.13 μm as 130 nm technology, and vice versa. Initial developments are already underway for the 90 nm and 65 nm technology nodes.

DSM technologies have introduced new problems in both devices and interconnect. A partial list is provided in Table 1.1. While the issues that have been encountered with devices are similar in number to the list shown for interconnect, the interconnect issues have caused more failures in CMOS designs over the past few years. Many now believe that interconnect is more important than devices. We will give the two roughly equal billing in this book. The reader should note that many of the problems are not fully resolved, as yet. One purpose is to provide sufficient detail so that future designers are well-equipped to deal with these and other deep submicron issues.

This book addresses digital integrated circuit design primarily in 0.18 μm and 0.13 μm technologies. The 130 nm technology features copper wires with low-k dielectrics, twin-wells for the devices, and shallow trench isolation (STI). This technology is quite different from its predecessors, due to changes in materials, but similar to its successors in the next two technology generations, 90 nm and 65 nm. There are also many similarities with 0.18 μm technologies when examining the fundamental principles. In 0.18 μm technology, the materials are aluminum wires and

Table 1.1

A short list of major DSM device and interconnect issues

DSM Devices	DSM Wires
Short-channel effects on V_T	RC delays
Velocity saturation	IR drop
Thin-oxide (tunneling/breakdown)	Ldi/dt
Subthreshold current	Capacitive coupling
DIBL	Inductive coupling
Hot-carrier effects	Electromigration
Thin-oxide gate leakage	Antenna effects

tungsten vias. STI is also used at 0.18 μm and below. Except for these differences, the design and analysis methods described in this book apply equally well. At the time of the writing of this book, 0.18 μm is the dominant technology so coverage of this technology is appropriate. Furthermore, access to 0.18 μm technology files is available through a number of websites. Therefore, many examples from 0.18 μm are included in this book.

1.3   Review of Digital Logic Gate Design

1.3.1   Basic Logic Functions

As we embark on the design of digital integrated circuits, we start by reviewing the basic logic elements that are used in the design process[4] and elaborate on some of the notation and symbols used in the book. Digital logic gates implement Boolean functions such as the inverter (INV), NAND, and NOR. Any logic function can be constructed from these basic gates. These *combinational* gates and their corresponding truth tables are shown in Figure 1.3.

Logic functions are represented in one of two canonical forms: sum-of-products or product-of-sums. For example, a sum-of-products representation takes the form:

$$F = AC + BC + AD + BD$$

whereas a product-of-sum form for the same function would be

$$F = (A + B)(C + D)$$

The sum function is always represented using the "+" symbol. The product function may be represented as "*" or "·", or it may be left out altogether. Typically, we will employ the sum-of-products form, but both are useful. Other useful combinational gates such as the exclusive OR (XOR), exclusive NOR (XNOR), and multiplexers

---

[4] Although the treatment is brief, those familiar with this subject may choose to skip this section.

XOR $A \oplus b = Y = A \cdot \bar{B} + \bar{A} \cdot B$ or $(A+B) \cdot (\bar{A} \cdot \bar{B})$
= odd one dector

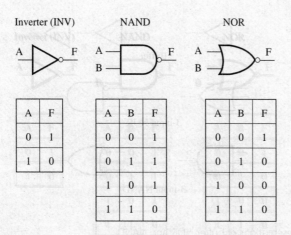

Figure 1.3

Basic logic gates.

(MUX) can be easily implemented using the basic gates of Figure 1.3. For example, the XOR gate has the function:

$$F = A \oplus B = A\bar{B} + \bar{A}B$$

A bar over a literal indicates the complement of a variable. Assuming that only A and B are available as inputs, the function can be implemented using two NAND gates, one NOR gate, and five inverters. A more efficient version would use three NANDs and only two inverters.

Also important is the multiplexer which is a selection of a particular input, A or B in this case, based on the value of select input S:

$$F = AS + B\bar{S}$$

Another common circuit function is the buffer, which is a gate that produces an output that is the same as its input. Using the gates in Figure 1.3, we would implement this function using two inverter stages. There are two possible symbols for a buffer, as shown in Figure 1.4. Since the intent of the gate is to perform a buffering operation, we would like to reflect this in the logic circuit somehow. We can either use a buffer symbol, or cascade two inverters and place a bubble in front of the second gate, instead of a bubble at the end (as shown in Figure 1.4). Simply having two inverters in series may lead to confusion later in the design process.

Similarly, NAND and NOR gates have two possible representations depending on the placement of the bubbles, as shown in Figure 1.4. These two representations can be constructed using DeMorgan's Laws. Recall that DeMorgan's Laws, in their most basic form, can be stated as:

$$\overline{(a + b)} = \bar{a} \cdot \bar{b}$$
$$\overline{(a \cdot b)} = \bar{a} + \bar{b}$$

$$(1.1)$$

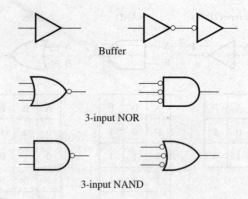

Figure 1.4
Alternative representations of buffer, NOR, and NAND.

In general, DeMorgan states that the complement of a function can be obtained by replacing each variable or element with its complement, and then exchanging the AND and OR functions. It also tells us that we can represent NOR and NAND gates in two ways, as illustrated in Figure 1.4. Both sets of gates function identically.

Which representation is preferred? It depends on the intended function of the gate. If the intent of the function is to perform a logical "AND" operation, the designer should use the AND function with bubbles on the input (rather than the NOR function). If the intent of the function is to perform a logical "OR" operation, the designer should use the OR function with bubbles on the input (rather than the NAND function). Imagine the confusion when debugging if the intended logic function and the actual logic implementation look different. To avoid this, we always use the gate representation that captures design intent.

Exercise 1.1   Draw the detailed logic circuits for the following gates using only the gates of Figures 1.3 and 1.4: AND, OR, XOR, XNOR, 2-input multiplexer.

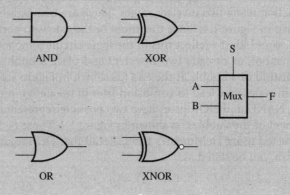

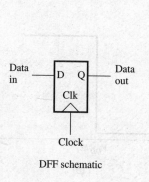

Clk	D	Q (old)	Q (new)
0	X	0	0
0	X	1	1
0 → 1	0	X	0
0 → 1	1	X	1
1	X	0	0
1	X	1	1
1 → 0	X	0	0
1 → 0	X	1	1

Excitation table

Data in   D   Q   Data out
           Clk

Clock

DFF schematic

Figure 1.5

Positive-edge triggered D-type flip-flop.

Sequential logic elements, such as flip-flops and latches, can be constructed from the basic logic elements described above using feedback. A wide variety of flip-flops exist: D-flip-flop, JK-flip-flop, T-flip-flop, SR-flip-flop, etc. These elements act to store logic values until the input changes and a clock signal activates them to read new data. Figure 1.5 shows a simple D-type flip-flop (DFF) and its corresponding excitation table. When the clock switches from low to high, the value at the data input is read into the DFF, and then propagated and held at the output. Under all other conditions, the output value is held at its previous value. This is a so-called positive-edge triggered flop, meaning that the input is sampled only on the positive edge of the clock. The X state in the table refers to a "don't care" state indicating that the output is not dependent on the value of the corresponding input.

1.3.2   Implementation of Logic Circuits

Electronic circuits are used to implement these and more complex gates. Figure 1.6a shows an ideal logic gate. It operates from a single power source, from which it draws a minimum amount of power (ideally zero, of course).

The two binary output levels are at zero (logic 0) and at the supply voltage V_{DD} (logic 1). The output impedance is low so that large currents may be driven into external resistive or capacitive loads without altering the output voltage level. The transition between states at the output occurs abruptly for an input level equal to one-half the supply voltage, as in Figure 1.6b. There is negligible time delay between the input and output transitions. Virtually any number of inputs are available; the input impedance is high so that the circuit imposes little loading on the driving signal. Of course, all practical logic elements fall short of the ideal performance

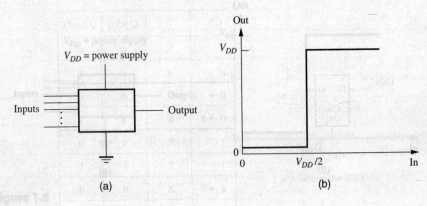

(a)   (b)

Figure 1.6
Ideal digital circuit.

defined here, but depending upon the application, some are better than others. Thus there are opportunities for good engineers to make useful tradeoffs as a part of circuit design.

The first shortcoming to realize is that the signals associated with actual implementations are continuous whereas the truth table values are discrete. Therefore, certain important characteristics are desired of electronic circuits for processing digital information.

1. The binary output signal must be a prescribed function of the binary input or inputs of the gate.

2. Quantization of amplitudes within the normal range of operating voltage is required, as illustrated in Figure 1.7a. This implies strong nonlinearities in circuit operation. Amplitudes within the boxed regions in Figure 1.7a represent each of the two binary states. At the circuit input, the uncertain region between the two boxed regions should be as small as possible.

3. Amplitude levels should be regenerated in passing from the input to the output of a digital circuit, as illustrated in Figure 1.7b. This requirement dictates a voltage transfer characteristic in the general shape shown in Figure 1.7c or Figure 1.7d. Voltage gain should be greater than unity somewhere between the logic states. The two nominal output levels are denoted V_{OH} and V_{OL}, as in Figure 1.7c or Figure 1.7d. The input voltages V_{IL} and V_{IH} are defined by the points at which the magnitude of the slope of the voltage transfer characteristic is unity.

4. Directivity is required for a useful logic circuit. Changes in an output level should not appear at any unchanging input of the same circuit; that is, there must be an explicit, unilateral cause-effect relationship between input(s) and output(s).

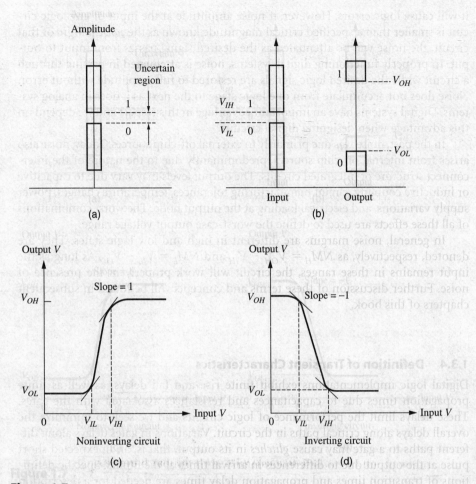

Figure 1.7
Logic abstraction of continuous signals.

5. The output of one circuit must be capable of driving more than one input of similar circuits. The number that can be driven is termed the *fanout* of the circuit. Similarly, for general use, digital circuits must be capable of accepting more than one input. The number of independent input nodes is termed the *fanin*.

1.3.3   Definition of Noise Margin

The word *noise,* in the context of digital circuits and systems, means unwanted variations of voltages or currents at logic nodes. Today, there are a wide variety of noise sources that may affect circuit performance. We want to define a *metric* that can be used to assess the effect of noise on a circuit. If the magnitude of noise is too great, it will cause logic errors. However, if noise amplitude at the input of any logic circuit is smaller than a specified critical magnitude known as the *noise margin* of that circuit, the noise will be attenuated as the desired signal passes from input to output. In properly functioning digital systems, noise is attenuated in passing through a circuit while the desired logic signals are restored to full amplitude without error. Noise does not accumulate from one logic stage to the next as it does in analog systems. Digital systems have an important advantage in this respect and we depend on this advantage when designing digital circuits.

In the past, noise was due primarily to external off-chip sources. Today, noise also arises from internal on-chip sources, predominantly due to the nature of the interconnect structure of integrated circuits. The output levels may vary due to capacitive or inductive coupling, circuit manufacturing tolerances, temperature changes, power supply variations, and electrical loading at the output node. The worst combinations of all these effects are used to define the worst-case output voltage range.

In general, noise margins are different in high and low logic states. They are denoted, respectively, as $NM_H = V_{OH} - V_{IH}$ and $NM_L = V_{IL} - V_{OL}$. As long as the input remains in these ranges, the circuit will work properly in the presence of noise. Further discussion of these terms and concepts will be found in subsequent chapters of this book.

1.3.4 Definition of Transient Characteristics

Digital logic implementations exhibit finite rise and fall delays, as well as finite propagation times due to capacitances and resistances associated with the gates. These delays limit the performance of logic circuits and we seek to minimize the overall delays along critical paths in the circuit. Variations in gates delays along different paths to a gate may cause *glitches* in its output, that is, an unexpected short pulse at the output due to differences in arrival times at the inputs. Specific definitions of transition times and propagation delay times are needed for a description of the switching characteristics of logic circuits. Once such definitions are established, calculations of these times can be made.

Standard definitions of digital circuit delay times are illustrated in Figure 1.8. Rise and fall times t_r and t_f are defined between the 10 and 90% points of the total voltage transition at the input of an inverter or gate. The total voltage range at both input and output is taken to be V_{OL} to V_{OH}, because this is the nominal situation when identical inverters or gates are cascaded. Input transition voltages V_{IL} and V_{IH} are not normally used in specification of transient performance.

High-low and low-high transition times at the output of a gate are defined as t_{HL} and t_{LH}, again between the 10 and 90% points, as seen in Figure 1.8a. Propagation delay times from input to output, denoted t_{PHL} and t_{PLH}, are defined between the 50% points of the input and output pulse waveforms. Cycle time t_{cycle} is the time between identical points of successive cycles in the signal waveform as seen at any single node, as in Figure 1.8a. Often cycle time is specified in terms of its reciprocal, clock frequency f_{clk}. Practical digital systems operate with cycle times 20 to 50 times the propagation delay of a single gate circuit.

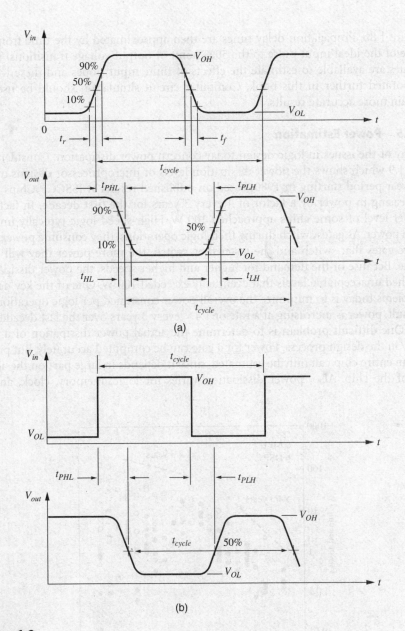

Figure 1.8

Definitions of transition and delay times. (a) Actual transient voltages. (b) Idealized transient voltages for hand calculations.

In hand calculations, it is difficult to take into account the finite rise and fall times of signals at inverter or gate inputs. Consequently, it is common to use an ideal pulse input with zero rise and fall times, as in Figure 1.8b. This ideal input signal is positioned with its edges at the 50% points of an actual input signal, as illustrated in

Figure 1.8b. Propagation delay times are then approximated by the time from the edge of the ideal input pulse to the 50% point of output voltage transitions. Techniques are available to estimate the effects of finite input slopes and these will be elaborated further in this book. Computer circuit simulation should be used to obtain more accurate results.

1.3.5   Power Estimation

Many of the issues in logic design today concern power dissipation. Consider Figure 1.9 which shows the power dissipation levels of microprocessor designs over a 25-year period starting in 1980, based on published results at ISSCC.[5] Chips were increasing in power by a factor of 4 every 3 years for the first decade. In fact, the power level of some chips approached 100 W. High-speed logic typically implies high power. As gates switch during their logic operations, they consume power. The more gates that switch and the faster they switch, the more power they will consume. Because of the demand for higher and higher speeds, the power dissipation reached unacceptable levels that eventually exceeded 100 W. One of the key design problems today is to minimize the overall power consumed per logic operation. As a result, power is increasing at a rate of 1.4× every 3 years over the last decade.

One difficult problem is to determine the actual power dissipation of a chip early in the design process. Power for a gate can be computed accurately, but power for an entire chip can only be estimated, since it depends in large part on the activity of the chip. Also, power dissipation varies for logic, memory, clock, analog

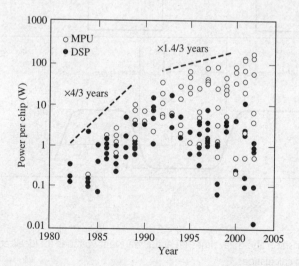

Figure 1.9

Power dissipation of processors over a 20-year period. [After Sakurai.]

[5] International Solid-State Circuits Conference held annually by the Solid-State Circuits Society.

blocks, etc. Therefore, a variety of methods may be required to have a reasonable estimate of the total power.

The basic power equation is

$$P = I \times V_{DD} \tag{1.2}$$

where I is the current flowing from V_{DD} to ground. The power dissipation of a logic gate may be broadly categorized into static and dynamic power. Static power involves power dissipation when the gate is not switching. Dynamic power involves the power during switching operations. The total power is a combination of the static power and the dynamic power:

$$P_{total} = P_{static} + P_{dynamic} \tag{1.3}$$

For the static case, I is simply the steady-state current when there is no switching. This can be due to any dc current that may exist or leakage currents in the circuit:

$$P_{static} = (I_{DC} + I_{leakage})V_{DD} \tag{1.4}$$

Dynamic power is associated with switching from high-to-low and low-to-high. The power dissipated is a function of the voltage swing, capacitance, and switching frequency. In the dynamic case, we will find that

$$P_{dynamic} = CV_{DD}^2 f \tag{1.5}$$

where f is the switching frequency of the gate and C is the output capacitance driven by the gate. In circuit design, we attempt to design high-performance circuits that dissipate low power. However, high-speed implies a large f and requires large transistors with a large C. This unfortunately increases the overall power dissipation. Clearly, a power-delay tradeoff exists and we can only hope to balance the desired speed with the maximum allowable power dissipation. Even though this is a simple example, it provides some insight into the type of compromises that are involved in circuit design.

1.4 Digital Integrated Circuit Design

Simply stated, design is the effective management of a large number of engineering tradeoffs. This is true in virtually all engineering disciplines, but it is particularly true in design of integrated circuits where a large number of tradeoffs are possible. The main tradeoffs relate to timing, power, and area. Today, timing and power are the two most important specifications for the design, with area being a lower priority due to the scaling of technology and the level of integration that is possible. Other important issues include noise tolerance, testability, yield, temperature, supply fluctuations, short-term and long-term reliability, time-to-market, cost, and packaging considerations. Each design may have a different set of priorities relative to these issues, but all of these factors will influence the design decisions in one way or another.

As mentioned earlier, the goal of this book is to teach you to think like a designer. While all of the above issues cannot be fully described in one book, the art of making engineering tradeoffs can be conveyed. This involves the use of simple models that allow you to carry out "back-of-the-envelope" calculations. This will also help to develop intuition about circuits and how they work. Other techniques will be described that allow you to quickly optimize a circuit for speed and assess different alternatives for a particular function. A popular misconception is that good circuit design involves new and innovative circuit topologies. In contrast, industrial circuit design is more concerned with getting a chip to work the first time in the presence of process and environmental variations, and at low cost. It must also be delivered within a market window and operate properly for the expected lifetime of the chip. While there is a place for new circuit configurations, this book addresses mainstream circuit design techniques.

1.4.1 MOS Transistor Structure and Operation

We now turn our attention to the MOS transistors that will be used to implement logic gates. At a very high level, the MOS transistor essentially behaves as a *switch*. It has two major states: *on* or *off*. When it is *on*, it is conducting current; in the *off* state, there is no current flow. This basic transistor action can be used to build up complex logic functions. For example, parallel combinations of these switches can be used to implement the OR function, while series combinations can be used to implement the AND function. We will illustrate, in later chapters, how a collection of transistors can be configured to operate as an inverter, buffer, NOR, NAND, MUX, D-flip-flop, etc. At this stage, we simply need to understand the structure and operation of the transistor, so that some of the design issues can be elaborated further.

The structure of an NMOS transistor is shown in Figure 1.10. The acronym MOS refers to the vertical layers of metal-oxide-semiconductor. The metal is usually a silicon-based material called polysilicon.[6] The oxide is silicon-dioxide with a thickness of t_{ox} as shown in the figure. The transistor is comprised of two heavily doped n^+ regions diffused in a lightly doped p-type substrate. The n^+ regions have a large supply of mobile electrons available for current flow, while the p-type region has a large supply of mobile holes. The n^+ regions are separated by a distance, L, referred to as the channel length. The other important dimension of the transistor is the channel width, W, which goes into the page (not shown). This device is called an NMOS transistor since it has two n^+ regions, referred to as the *source* and *drain*. The other two terminals of the device are the *gate* at the top and the *substrate* at the bottom.

In the figure, the source and substrate terminals are both grounded. The gate terminal has voltage V_{GS} applied to it and the drain terminal has voltage V_{DS} applied to it. When V_{GS} is 0 V, the transistor is said to be in the "off" condition. This is because there is no current flow between the drain and source regions. In this condition, there is no path between the source and drain for electrons to flow. In fact, there are more holes than electrons in the region between the source and drain.

---

[6] The use of the word metal is somewhat of a misnomer. In the early days, aluminum was used as the metal gate but the industry quickly switched to polysilicon due to yield problems. The acronym MOS has remained with us in spite of the change in material.

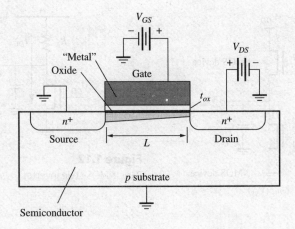

Figure 1.10
Basic transistor structure.

When a sufficiently high, positive value of V_{GS} is applied at the gate node, it will invert the surface of the semiconductor. The gate voltage at which this inversion occurs is called the *threshold voltage*, V_T, of the device. Under these conditions, a bridge of mobile electrons exists extending from source to drain. The transistor is considered to be "on" in this condition. Current will flow if a potential difference is created between the source and drain nodes using V_{DS}. This is an *n-channel* transistor since the polarity of the carriers in the channel is negative. A similar but opposite transistor, the *p-channel* transistor, can be created by diffusing two heavily doped p^+ regions into a lightly doped *n*-type substrate. For the PMOS device, a negative voltage V_{GS} of sufficient magnitude will invert the surface, and a negative potential difference for V_{DS} will initiate hole current flow.

1.4.2   CMOS Versus NMOS

With this basic understanding of the NMOS and PMOS devices, we can construct our first logic gate: the CMOS inverter. As shown in Figure 1.11, a CMOS inverter is comprised of an *n*-channel device and a *p*-channel device. The inverter is connected between the positive power supply voltage, V_{DD}, and ground, which we refer to as *Gnd* throughout the text (V_{SS} is also used for this reference node). The PMOS device is the *pull-up* device connected to V_{DD}. Its role is to pull the output to a high value. The NMOS *pull-down* device is connected to Gnd, and its role is to pull the output to a low value. The input, V_{in}, is connected to the gate terminal of both devices, while the output, V_{out}, is the drain terminal of both devices. When the input is at V_{DD}, the NMOS device is *on* while the PMOS device is *off*. Hence, the drain current of the NMOS device flows through a highly conductive channel and discharges the output capacitance. The result is that V_{out} is 0 V. When the input is at 0 V, the NMOS device is off while the PMOS device is conducting to pull the output to V_{DD}. Clearly, this configuration functions as an inverter.

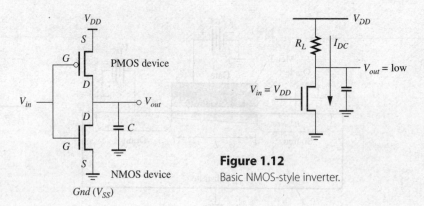

Figure 1.12
Basic NMOS-style inverter.

Figure 1.11
CMOS inverter schematic.

In either the high or low state, CMOS inverters dissipate very little power because one of the transistors is always off. The tiny steady-state power consumption of CMOS is its most attractive feature.

In the 1970s and early 1980s, NMOS technology was dominant. In this technology, p-channel devices were not allowed, since n-channel devices were known to be superior to p-channel devices. All gates were constructed from n-channel transistors. An example of an NMOS inverter is shown in Figure 1.12. Here, the pulldown device is the same as in the CMOS inverter, but the pull-up device is shown as a resistance, R_L. The resistance was implemented with a special type of n-channel transistor that remained *on* all the time, referred to as a *depletion-mode device*. When the input to this inverter is low, the resistor pulls the output to a high value since the pull-down device is off. When the input is high, the pull-down device attempts to pull the output low, while the resistor tries to pull the node high. The sizing of the devices ensures that a valid low output is established. However, when the output is low, there is dc current flowing from V_{DD} to Gnd given by $(V_{DD} - V_{OL})/R_L$. As a result, the gate dissipates steady-state power when the output is low, as shown in Figure 1.12.

When the scaling of MOS technology permitted several hundred thousand gates on the chip, it began to signal the demise of NMOS technology. The reason is that if half the gates on the chip had a low output, then they would be dissipating power. In the standby condition where no logic switching takes place, high levels of power would be dissipated unnecessarily. As the number of gates increases in accordance with Moore's Law, the power continues to increase. In the case of CMOS gates, very little standby power is dissipated whether the output is high or low. If fact, even with a number of notable disadvantages of CMOS, its low standby power eventually won out and led to the extinction of NMOS-only technologies.

In keeping with its technology dominance, this book focuses on CMOS digital circuits. It covers many different types of CMOS logic gates, their implementation and their design tradeoffs. While there have been many types of interesting CMOS circuits devised over the years, this book aims to provide coverage on the logic families that have emerged in mainstream design. However, there are new issues to address associated with deep submicron interconnect providing a second major focus for this book. This is highlighted in the next section. The hope is that, with a solid understanding of CMOS logic design and interconnect design concepts covered in the chapters to follow, the reader will be able to quickly grasp almost any new circuit topology or interconnect issue in the open literature.

1.4.3   Deep Submicron Interconnect

We now turn our attention to the wires in deep submicron technology. These wires, commonly known as *interconnect,* are used to provide connections between gates and also to route the power supply and ground to all the gates on the chip. In the early days of integrated circuit design, the connection between the transistors that form the logic gates was a simple routing exercise. Only one or two metal layers were available to wire up the devices. Since there were only a few thousand gates on the chip, the wiring process was rather straightforward, and the capacitances and resistances associated with these wires could be safely ignored. With technology scaling, the transistor density increased tremendously following Moore's Law. A new problem arose due to routing congestion. As the routing capacity of each layer was exhausted, the addition of many more levels of interconnect was needed to complete the routing. Meanwhile, the length of the wires increased to the point where the capacitance-to-ground of the wires could no longer be neglected. For example, to compute the delay of the inverter shown in Figure 1.11, calculation of capacitance value at the output required the inclusion of wire capacitance for any wire with an appreciable length.

Figure 1.13 provides an indication of the sheer density of interconnect in ICs today. Wires on a particular layer run in one direction while wires on another layer run in an orthogonal direction. In the past few years, the number of layers of interconnect has grown to more than eight.

More importantly, the introduction of multilayer interconnect and scaled dimensions have caused numerous problems. Interconnect issues now dominate the performance, reliability, and power distribution of advanced integrated circuits and, in some sense, interconnect is more important than the devices carrying out the logic operations.

Two prominent effects of scaling are shown in Figure 1.14. First, narrow wires have a nonnegligible resistance associated with them as illustrated in Figure 1.14a. This was noticed in earlier technologies but it became a problem at the 0.35 μm technology node. Second, the wires are getting thinner but not decreasing as rapidly in height. This produces wires that look like tall thin conductors. When placed next to one another they form parallel plate capacitors that couple two signals together. This capacitance was present in earlier generations, but its value was negligible. In present day technology, this *coupling capacitance* is significant, as seen in Figure 1.14b. This is also reflected in Figure 1.13 by the number of parallel lines adjacent to one another. These lines are tightly coupled due to the large capacitances between them.

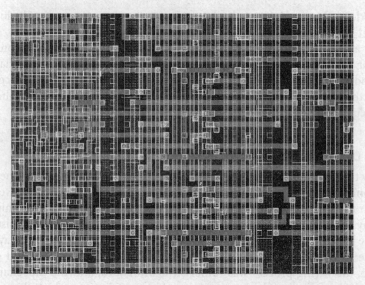

Figure 1.13

Example of integrated circuit layout dominated by routing.

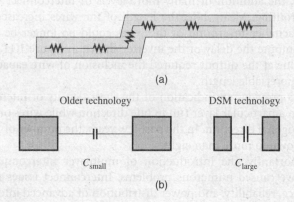

(a)

Older technology   DSM technology

C_{small} C_{large}

(b)

Figure 1.14

Wire resistance and coupling capacitance.

In Figure 1.15, we show two effects of increased resistance. The delay of a signal can no longer be computed with the wire capacitance alone. Wire resistance must now be included (Figure 1.15a) to determine the delay accurately. The increased resistance in the power supply lines, as shown in Figure 1.15b, causes voltage drops along the wire, referred to as *IR drop*. This may affect the timing and functionality of gates connected to the power lines if the drop becomes too significant.

An increase in wire resistance can sharply increase the delay along the interconnect as the length increases. For long wires, the interconnect delay is propor-

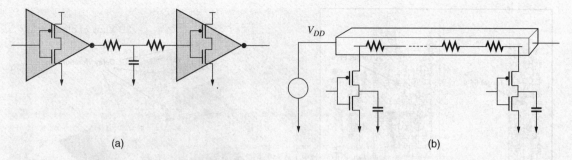

Figure 1.15
Effect of interconnect resistance. (a) RC delay. (b) IR drop.

tional to the square of the length. At some point the interconnect delay overtakes the gate delay. This is not an acceptable situation when the wire delay is larger than the delay of the gate driving it.

A number of new design techniques were introduced to mitigate this problem. For example, copper was introduced as wire material due to its lower resistivity. Another effective approach for long wires is to insert large buffers at intervals along the wire to keep the delay from being larger than the gate delay. By inserting buffers, the interconnect lengths are effectively shortened, thereby reducing the delay.

Clock design has become a major challenge due to the size of chips, the number of flip-flops to be driven, and the interconnect effects. The clock is an important signal that must be routed to almost all points of the chip. Differences in the arrival times of the clock to their target flip-flops is called *clock skew*. To minimize delay and skew, the interconnect lengths can be shortened by inserting buffers at certain intervals along the wire and ensuring that the delay to all points is roughly the same.

Figure 1.16 illustrates the impact of interconnect on clock design. A buffered clock tree and its corresponding delay diagram is shown in the figure. On the left, the clock root node is situated in the lower portion of the design and the main spine is routed from this point to the various blocks on the chip. The clock signal is then delivered to the target flip-flops in each block. A three-dimensional view of the delay from the clock root to various points on the chip is shown on the right side. This delay plot is color-coded such that clocks that arrive early are shaded white and gray, and late-arriving signals are darker. In the figure, there are a number of late-arriving signals with a high skew as evidenced by the many dark peaks.

Increased resistance in the power grid leads to IR drop, as illustrated in Figure 1.17. This is a contour plot of the voltage drop across the chip. The ideal supply voltage exists only at the boundaries of the chip, with reduced values available to gates inside the chip. If the voltage drops below 10% of the ideal value of V_{DD}, the circuit may not operate as expected. A different shade is used for each voltage range starting with a lighter shade for voltages near V_{DD}. The dark shading near the center of the chip indicates a violation of the noise budget of 10% calling for a redesign of the power grid.

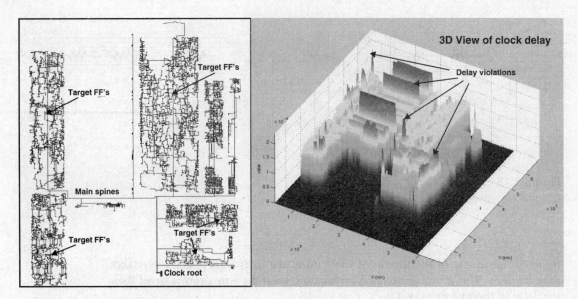

Figure 1.16
Clock tree and 3D delay plot. Plots courtesy of Simplex Solutions, Inc.

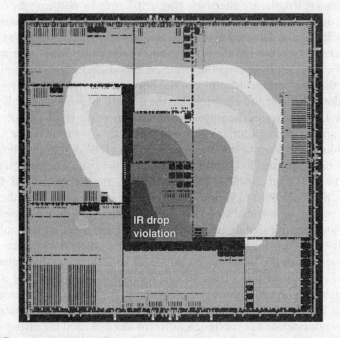

Figure 1.17
Contour plot of IR drop on a digital IC. Plots courtesy of Simplex Solutions, Inc.

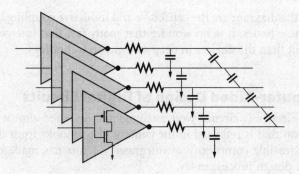

Figure 1.18
Effect of coupling capacitance.

The next issue to examine is the effect of coupling capacitance. A circuit representation of coupling capacitances along interconnect lines is shown in Figure 1.18. Problems occur when one or more gates switch. The switching of a given gate can affect the neighboring lines in two ways. First, the delay may be unpredictable since the effective coupling capacitance may be large or small depending on the switching characteristics of the neighboring lines. Second, noise may be injected into the neighboring lines and upset their logic values. These two problems became serious issues in 0.25 μm designs, and continue to plague designs at 0.18 μm and below. To combat this problem, designers will space out the wires to reduce capacitance. In addition, new low-k dielectrics are under development to replace oxide as the insulating material between metal lines.

If this is not enough, recently, the issues of self and mutual inductive effects have been encountered. In the power grid, an additional voltage drop of $L di/dt$ is observed in addition to the aforementioned IR drop. This term is important due to the large rates of change of the current seen in advanced high-speed designs. There are also documented occurrences of mutual inductive coupling effects in multibit busses which have led to intermittent failures in the design. A realistic scenario for the power and signal lines today is illustrated in Figure 1.19. Not shown due to the

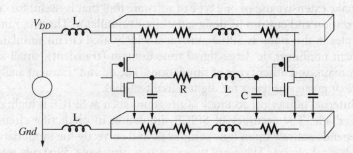

Figure 1.19
Power and signal lines in DSM logic circuits.

complexity of the diagram are the capacitive and inductive coupling between wires. Given all of these issues, it is no wonder that many feel that interconnect is truly more important than the devices in deep submicron technology.

1.5   Computer-Aided Design of Digital Circuits

Prior to 1970, electronic circuits were analyzed and designed almost exclusively by hand, a situation that is reflected in the content of textbooks from that era. Rapid growth in the feasible complexity of integrated circuits has made computer aids essential to the design process today.

In the 1980s and early 1990s, CAD tools revolutionized the way that circuits were designed. Broadly speaking, there are two categories of design tools: front-end and back-end tools. The front-end tools take a high-level description of the design and translate it to a gate-level design via logic synthesis. The back-end tools take the gate-level design and carry out the physical design to produce a layout containing the geometric artwork in GDS-II format. This flow which is intended for application-specific integrated circuits (ASIC) is a highly automated process. While this flow does not produce the highest performance ICs, it does allow designs to be implemented in a short time frame.

The other extreme relative to the ASIC flow is the custom IC design flow. Here, the designer is handcrafting almost every transistor. However, there is extensive use of repetitive structures for memory and datapath designs. The custom design process produces the highest performance designs, but it can be time-consuming since the circuits are handcrafted rather than being automatically generated. The purpose of this book is to describe the necessary details of circuit design to allow you to carry out custom design where required, and ASIC design wherever possible.

Figure 1.20 illustrates the complexity of a deep submicron physical design flow. Description of all the types of computer-aided design tools is beyond the scope of this book. However, we provide this generalized flow so that the reader can refer back to it when a particular tool is described in this book.

1.5.1   Circuit Simulation and Analysis

We will make extensive use of one type of software tool that is useful for cell library characterization and custom IC design: the circuit simulator. The program used for the examples in this book is SPICE, the most widely used circuit simulator. SPICE can perform nonlinear dc, large-signal time domain (transient), small-signal frequency domain, and other types of simulations. The dc and transient analysis capabilities are of greatest interest for digital circuit studies.

The internal numerical accuracy of programs such as SPICE is high; errors seldom exceed 1%. The accuracy of SPICE simulation in predicting circuit performance depends entirely upon how completely and correctly the input data describe the real physical circuit. There are two aspects to this issue. First, we must have a mathematical or numerical *model* that adequately represents each physical device. Usually the model for a device is stated as equations that relate voltages and cur-

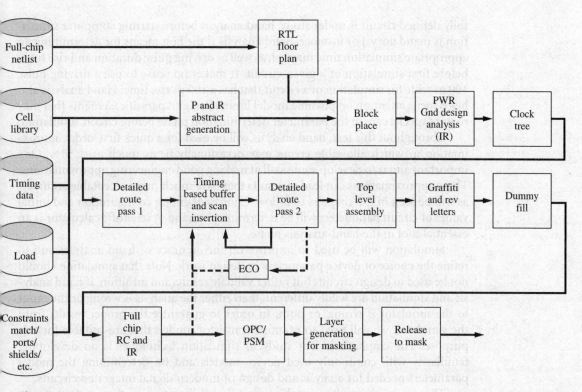

Figure 1.20

Deep submicron physical design flow. Flow courtesy of Silicon Map, LLC.

rents. For instance, the model equation for a single linear resistor is $i(t) = v(t)/R$, and for a single linear capacitor, $i(t) = C\,dV/dt$. Model equations for transistors are much more complex, because these devices exhibit nonlinear resistive and capacitive characteristics. Second, we must have practical means for determining numerical values applying to each device, for instance, R and C for the examples just cited.

The next few chapters devote much attention to the models used to represent integrated circuit devices, including the simplifications and approximations that are a practical necessity in the development of these models. Also described are means of measuring or calculating device parameters in forms suitable for hand analysis and computer simulation. By working carefully, one can usually obtain simulation results that are within $\pm 20\%$ of measurements for propagation delays and other transient characteristics.

Shortly after learning how to use a computer circuit simulator, many students develop the mistaken idea that skill in hand analysis is no longer necessary. Computer simulation appears to be much quicker and more accurate than hand analysis, especially for complex circuits with many nonlinearities. However, even when a fully defined circuit is under study, hand analysis before starting computer simulation is mandatory. For instance, hand analysis is the best means for determining an appropriate simulation time interval, as well as driving pulse duration and rise time, before first simulation of a given circuit. It makes no sense to use a driving pulse 100 ns wide for simulation of a circuit that has a 100 ps rise time! Hand analysis also helps focus attention on possible model limitations and parasitic elements that may require special care in the parameter determination phase before circuit simulation.

Throughout this text, hand analysis will be used for a quick first-order approximation in which allowable errors may occasionally be as much as $\pm 50\%$. One important aim is to develop some skill at making good engineering approximations. These approximations can lead to results that have much more acceptable accuracy, as will be seen in the chapters to follow. Choices of circuit configuration and initial values of circuit parameters will be determined by hand. A scientific calculator is an essential tool in the hand-analysis phase.

Simulation will be used to improve on the accuracy of hand analyses and to refine the choice of device parameters in design work. Note that simulation should not be used to design circuits but rather validate results and intuition. If hand analysis and simulation are wildly different, then either the analysis is wrong or the input to the simulator is wrong, or both. In order to guarantee the proper results from the simulator, we will need to examine transistor models that are suitable for this purpose. The emphasis in our study of simulation techniques is on developing familiarity with commonly used device models and on determining the model parameters needed for analysis and design of modern digital integrated circuits.

There is much emphasis in the circuit design literature on the creation of new circuits that are "better" in some context than previous circuits. Many new designers would like to invent a clever circuit that demonstrates their insight and abilities. However, there is a lot to be said for using well-known and well-understood circuit topologies because the CAD tools are readily available for mainstream design techniques. Furthermore, getting a working chip to market quickly is perhaps the most important design specification today. In industry, the focus is on getting circuits to work reliably across large process variations, supply variations, temperature variations, in the presence of signal integrity issues, and over the lifetime of the chip. Tools like SPICE prove to be extremely useful for this purpose.

*1.6   The Challenges Ahead

Many of the issues in deep submicron remain unresolved today. There are a number of significant challenges in the years ahead in process technology, design technology, and computer-aided design tools to continue scaling according to Moore's Law. This section describes some of the key issues to provide the reader with a perspective on what design challenges exist today, and what lies ahead. The issues are quite advanced and many of the terms used will not be elaborated further in this section. However, it is intended to familiarize the reader with the issues and to motivate the topics in the rest of the book.

Table 1.2
Technology roadmap based on the ITRS

Year	Technology Node (nm)	V_{DD} (V)	V_{th} (V)	t_{ox} ($\text{Å} = 10^{-10}$ m)	No. of Transistors
1995	350	3.3	0.6	75	10M
1997	250	2.5	0.55	50	20M
1999	180	1.8	0.5	35	40M
2001	130	1.2	0.4	22	100M
2004	90	1.0	0.35	20	250M
2007	65	0.7	0.3	14	500M
2010	45	0.6	0.25	11	1B
2013	32	0.5	0.22	10	2B
2016	22	0.4	0.2	9	4B

We begin with the semiconductor technology roadmap shown in Table 1.2. This is based on the International Technology Roadmap for Semiconductors (ITRS) but has been simplified to convey the key messages.[7] In this table, the values for the technology node, supply voltage, threshold voltage, oxide thickness, and expected number of transistors on the chip are reported. Each technology node, representing the minimum line width, is scaled by a factor of 0.7 relative to the previous node. In order to maintain constant fields and low-power dissipation, the supply voltage is also reduced. The threshold voltage is reduced but not at the same rate as the other factors. The same is true for the oxide thickness. In the final column, the number of useful transistors that can be integrated on one chip are reported. According to this projection, we will see a billion (1B) transistor chip before the decade is out!

Unfortunately, the path to 1B transistor chips is not straightforward. The first major problem is to generate the fine line widths that are projected in the technology node column. The limits of techniques such as optical proximity correction (OPC) and phase-shift masks (PSM) may soon be reached. A new generation of photolithographic equipment will be necessary. The table also reports that the oxide thickness beyond 2010 is roughly 10 Å, an extremely small value. The oxide is supposed to act as an insulator, but current tunneling through oxide occurs at much higher oxide thicknesses. This gives rise to a gate current that is not permitted in the classical operation of the MOS transistor. High-k dielectrics are under development to replace oxide as the gate insulator.

A second major issue facing the industry is the rapid increase in the subthreshold current. This is the current flowing through the transistor when it is nominally *off*, often called the I_{off} current. In this context, the current when the transistor is *on* is referred to as the I_{on} current. Ideally, we would like to have a high I_{on} and a very

---

[7] Complete documentation on the ITRS may be found at the website http://public.itrs.net.

low I_{off}. If I_{off} is large for a single transistor, then having a few hundred million devices leaking current would produce an unacceptably large static power dissipation. There is a tradeoff between these two requirements, since both of these currents depend on $(V_{GS} - V_T)$. If this value is large, both I_{on} and I_{off} are large. However, if it is small, both currents are small. As we scale V_{DD}, it is not possible to scale V_T as quickly since the I_{off} current reaches unacceptable levels. On the other hand, a larger V_T makes I_{on} smaller.

Further problems exist in terms of mobility degradation, dopant profile control in the channel region, substrate currents, and device reliability, both short term and long term. Another set of issues surround interconnect. The switch to copper and low-k dielectrics is continuing to encounter problems. Achieving low-k dielectrics in the range of 2 will be difficult. Reliability issues of copper vias, self-heating effects, the thickness of the barrier layer versus the copper material, and antenna effects are still under investigation. Technology advances are necessary with new materials and device structures, such as *high-k* dielectrics, *fin-fets (dual-gate fets)*, *vertical transistors, strained-silicon,* and *silicon-on-insulator (SOI)* to address these problems.

In the design arena, there are a number of thrust areas in the near future. As supply voltages shrink, designing digital circuits and mixed analog/digital circuits with very small values of V_{DD} presents a challenge. This is especially true in dynamic circuits, where logic values are determined by the amount of charge on a capacitor. As the supply voltage is reduced, the stored charge will be small. With larger subthreshold leakage currents, coupling noise, etc., it will be a challenge to get these circuits to operate properly. In addition, standard CMOS designs will continue to deal with process variations, capacitive and inductive coupling issues, supply fluctuations due to IR and Ldi/dt effects, and chip-wide timing synchronization.

As mentioned earlier, dynamic power is continuing to increase with each generation of technology. The reason for this is shown in Figure 1.21. The supply voltage is decreasing with each technology node. However, increases in performance can only be achieved with a corresponding increase in current. This results in an increase in the overall power. Furthermore, subthreshold current must be reduced using circuit design techniques in the near term, such as source degeneration or multi-V_T CMOS. Note that the historical rate of power increase can not be followed after 2005 due to economic, thermal, and packaging considerations. Today, performance is still the most important design objective. Over the next few years, low-power design methods will become more important than performance.

Another looming issue is the recurring problem of design productivity. While the ITRS forecasts 1B transistors by 2010, the design of chips with this staggering number of gates will take more time and more resources than in previous generations. A major *productivity gap* exists today due to the unprecedented levels of integration possible, and continues to widen as technology shrinks. One view of this productivity gap is shown in Figure 1.22 from ITRS. It shows the growth of logic transistors on a chip in the upper graph (58%) and the increase in productivity in the lower graph (21%). The difference between the two lines is known as the productivity gap.

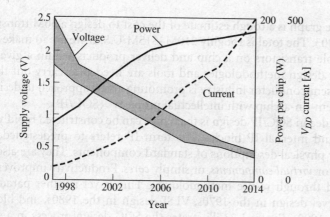

Figure 1.21

Supply voltage and current, chip power trends from ITRS.

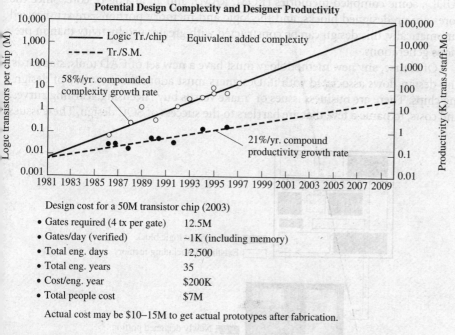

Design cost for a 50M transistor chip (2003)

- Gates required (4 tx per gate)   12.5M
- Gates/day (verified)   ~1K (including memory)
- Total eng. days   12,500
- Total eng. years   35
- Cost/eng. year $200K
- Total people cost $7M

Actual cost may be $10–15M to get actual prototypes after fabrication.

igure 1.22

RS productivity chart and design cost.

Below the graph is a rough estimate of the cost to design a 50M transistor chip in the year 2003. The total is roughly $10M–$15M U.S. If we are to make use of all of the available transistors on a chip and deliver products within a given market window, new design methodologies and tools are needed to carry out these large designs. The semiconductor industry is promoting a new approach to design that is dubbed "system-on-a-chip with intellectual property" (SOC/IP).

The key idea in SOC/IP design is that chips can be constructed rapidly by using third-party and internal IP blocks. The term IP refers to predesigned, reusable behavioral or physical descriptions of standard components. They are also referred to as *IP cores* or *virtual components*, or simply *cores*. Productivity improvements are accomplished through re-use methodologies. This is yet another paradigm shift from logic-level design in the 1970s, VLSI design in the 1980s, and block-based design of the 1990s. Figure 1.23 illustrates the SOC design process in a simplified form. The SOC is constructed using a combination of existing IP and user-defined logic (UDL). The user-defined logic can itself be comprised of newly designed blocks and some reusable blocks, as well as memory. The memory is generated with a memory compiler so it is considered to be a "reusable" block. Using this approach, designs can be assembled hierarchically with a much greater productivity level than before.

An example of an SOC design is shown in Figure 1.24. It contains a processor core (MCU), a number of digital signal processing cores (DSP), user-defined logic (UDL), some compiled memories (ROM, RAM), and an analog IP core. Since the cores are predesigned blocks, and the logic and memory portions are synthesized automatically, this design can be constructed with greater productivity than in previous generations.

Of course, any new methodology must have a new set of CAD tools, standards, and design flows associated with it. Designers must adopt this new way of designing chips. There are business issues of "make versus buy," licensing, learning curves, and costs, to name a few, that are barriers to the success of SOC design. These issues

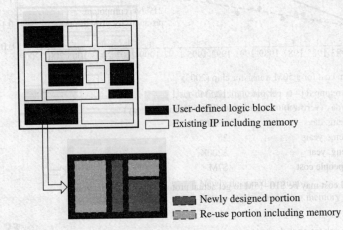

User-defined logic block
Existing IP including memory

Newly designed portion
Re-use portion including memory

Figure 1.23
System-on-chip design hierarchy

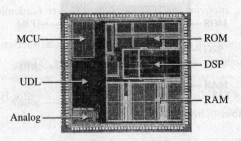

Figure 1.24
Example of SOC design.

will require time to resolve, but this is the direction that the industry has aggressively undertaken. In one form or another, this SOC design philosophy will emerge to propel the semiconductor industry forward to fully utilize the billion transistors available on a chip in the future.

1.7   Summary

Back in the 1970s, gate-level design techniques allowed the designer to start thinking of digital circuits at a higher level. In the VLSI era, the chip designer became a system-level designer and made use of ASIC design flows to implement chips (typically using a third party). As technology continued to scale, the problems of deep submicron emerged that required close interaction between the system-level design and the physical design teams to produce working circuits. With the advent of system-on-chip technologies, the chip designer continues to move to higher and higher levels of abstraction. However, the issues of deep submicron that have been overviewed in this chapter are forcing designers back to the silicon level. The designers of tomorrow must be able to design working chips in the presence of all the issues described above in a cost-effective and timely manner. A *design gap* exists today because of the trend to move to higher and higher levels of abstraction, while the problems actually lie at the lower levels. As such, this textbook serves to bridge the design gap by going back to the fundamentals of circuit design. It is hoped that the integrated circuit designers of tomorrow are well-equipped for the upcoming challenges upon reading and studying this material.

REFERENCES

1. J. Rabaey, A. Chandrakasan, and B. Nikolic, *Digital Integrated Circuits—A Design Perspective,* 2nd ed., Prentice-Hall, New Jersey, 2003.

2. N. Weste and K. Eshraghian, *Principles of CMOS VLSI Design,* Addison-Wesley, Reading, MA, 1993.

3. H. Veendrick, *Deep-Submicron CMOS ICs,* 2nd ed., Kluwer Academic Publishers, Boston, 2000.

4. M. Keating and P. Bricaud, *Reuse Methodology Manual,* 3rd ed., Kluwer Academic Publishers, Boston, 2002.

5. H. Chang et al., *Surviving the SOC Revolution,* Kluwer Academic Publishers, Boston, 1999.

6. D. D. Gajski, *Principles of Digital Design,* Prentice-Hall, New Jersey, 1997.

7. S. Edwards, *Languages for Digital Embedded Systems,* Kluwer Academic Publishers, Boston, 2000.

8. W. Wolf, *Modern VLSI Design: System-on-Chip,* 3rd ed., Prentice-Hall, New Jersey, 2002.

9. ITRS 2001 documents, http://public.itrs.net.

PROBLEMS

P1.1. Simplify the following functions and express each (a) as a sum of products and (b) as a product of sums:

(i) $F = CB\bar{A} + C\bar{B}A + \bar{C}BA + CBA$

(ii) $F = DC\bar{A} + \bar{D}CA + D\bar{C}\bar{A} + \bar{D}\bar{C}A$

P1.2. A light in a long hallway is to be controlled by three switches A, B, and C. If the switch is up, its logic value is 1. If an odd number of switches are up, the light is on; if an even number, the light is off. Design the logic circuit for F ($F = 1$ for light on) from A, B, and C (a) as an all-NAND circuit and (b) as an all-NOR circuit.

P1.3. Implement the following functions using only NAND, NOR, and INV:

(a) $F = AB + BC$

(b) $F = A \oplus B \oplus C$

P1.4. A "half adder" has the following truth table:

A	B	Sum	Carry
0	0	0	0
0	1	1	0
1	0	1	0
1	1	0	1

Table P1.4

(a) Using Karnaugh Map (K-Map) techniques, transform this table into two Boolean expressions, one for Sum and one for Carry.

(b) Sketch the associated gate equivalent for (a).

P1.5. Design the "full adder" truth table and repeat steps (a) and (b) as in Problem P1.4.

P1.6. Find the complement of the following functions by applying DeMorgan's Law:

(a) $F = \bar{A}\bar{B}C + \bar{A}B\bar{C} + AB\bar{C}$

(b) $F = ABC + \bar{A}\bar{B}C$

P1.7. An inverter has a measured delay of 2 ns.

(a) If five identical inverters are connected in series as shown in Figure P1.7a, what is the delay from *a* to *b*?

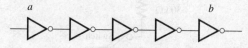

Figure P1.7a

(b) If the *a* and *b* are now connected as shown in Figure P1.7b, such that the voltage at *a* will now oscillate like a clock,

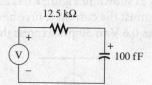

Figure P1.7b

(i) What is the period of oscillation?

(ii) What is the frequency of oscillation?

P1.8. A step input from 0 V to 1.2 V is applied to the RC circuit as shown in Figure P1.8. Calculate the time required for the voltage across the capacitor to: (a) reach 0.6 V, (b) reach 1.2 V, (c) go from 10% to 90% of 1.2 V.

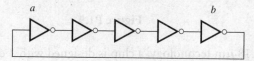

Figure P1.8

P1.9. A switch is used to control a capacitor's connection to either V_{DD} or Gnd through a resistor as shown in Figure P1.9. The resistor connected to V_{DD} has a resistance of 30 kΩ while the resister connected to Gnd has a resistance of 12.5 kΩ.

(a) If the switch has been connected to R2 for a long time, so that the capacitor's voltage is 0 V, and the switch is then connected to R1 at $t = 0$, calculate the time it takes for the capacitor's voltage to reach 0.6 V ($V_{DD}/2$).

(b) If the switch has been connected to R1 for a long time, so that the capacitor's voltage is 1.2 V, and the switch is then connected to R2 at $t = 0$, calculate the time it takes for the capacitor's voltage to reach 0.6 V ($V_{DD}/2$).

(c) Calculate the ratio of delays between (a) and (b).

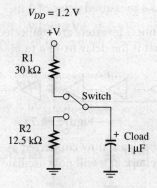

Figure P1.9

P1. 10. In a 0.18 μm technology, a chip is designed with 1 cm by 1 cm dimensions containing 50 million transistors. At 0.13 μm, how many transistors can be integrated on the same chip according to Moore's Law?

P1. 11. If the current high-speed desktop processors run at 2 GHz (10^9 Hz), and if the processor speeds doubles every technology node, how many technology nodes will it take for processor speeds to reach 10 GHz? If the time between each technology node is 3 years, how long will this take?

P1. 12. A capacitor C with an initial voltage of 0 V is suddenly connected to a current source I as shown in Figure P1.12. If the capacitor has a value of 25 fF, how large must the current source be so that the voltage across the capacitor reaches 0.6 V in 30 ps? Express the answer in mA.

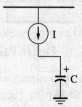

Figure P1.12

Transistors and Devices— MOS and Bipolar

2.1   Introduction

This chapter focuses on the semiconductor devices used in mainstream integrated circuits. MOS devices, *pn* junctions, device capacitances and bipolar transistors and circuits are all covered here. We will also examine basic physics and modeling of MOS transistors. It is an important chapter in that it lays the foundation for many of the design equations to be used throughout the book. Of course, it is difficult to have complete coverage of the background needed to grasp the device physics in one chapter. Readers who are unfamiliar with the terms and concepts presented here should consult the references for the prerequisite material. It is expected that many students embarking upon a study of this text will have had a course in semiconductor devices, including the MOS transistor. However, even these students should study this subject matter because the emphasis is on the specific character-istics of MOS devices that are important to VLSI digital circuit design.

We begin with MOS device characteristics that lead to the derivation of the threshold voltage equation, current equations, and capacitance models. MOS tech-nology is the basis for most of the very large-scale integrated (VLSI) digital mem-ory and microprocessor circuits. It is the dominant technology in the IC industry today, with bipolar technology a distant second. The most important advantage of

MOS circuits over bipolar circuits for VLSI is that more transistors and more circuit functions may be successfully integrated on a single chip with MOS technology. An individual MOS transistor occupies less chip area and transistor scaling continues to increase the chip density by a factor of two with each new generation. As a result, MOS VLSI circuits are significantly cheaper to manufacture than bipolar circuits of equivalent function and, consequently, MOS VLSI circuits make up a dominant percentage of the total market for digital ICs.

The first MOS circuits, made in metal-gate *p*-channel (PMOS) technology in the early 1970s, required special supply voltages and functioned only at very low digital data rates. The change to *n*-channel (NMOS) silicon-gate technology and other improvements resulted in LSI circuits that required only a single standard supply and operated at much higher data rates. In NMOS technology, all gates on the chip were constructed from two types of *n*-channel transistors. One type of device had a turn-on voltage above 0 V. This device was referred to as an *enhancement-mode* device. The other type of device had a turn-on voltage that was less than 0 V, which implied that it was always *on*. This was the *depletion-mode* device that played a supporting role on the chip since it could be used as a load resistor for the logic gates. Many chips were designed in NMOS technology and, in fact, this technology dominated the decade of the 1970s.

Since the early 1980s, complementary MOS (CMOS) has been the most prevalent MOS technology. This technology provides both *n*- and *p*-channel devices in one chip at the expense of some increase in fabrication complexity and chip area compared to basic NMOS. The great advantage of CMOS digital circuits is that they may be designed with low static power consumption in the steady-state condition. Power is consumed primarily when circuits switch between the two logic states; the average CMOS power consumption is much smaller than for NMOS circuits. In fact, the power consumption problems of NMOS led to a wholesale conversion of the industry from NMOS to CMOS. Today, CMOS is widely used in almost every type of microelectronic application including personal computers, personal digital assistants, cell phones, Internet applications, and a variety of other communication equipment.

The analysis and design of integrated circuits depends heavily on the use of suitable mathematical models for the devices. This is true in hand calculations, where fairly simple models are generally used, and in computer analysis, where much more complex models are utilized for high accuracy. The importance of "back-of-the-envelope" or hand calculations cannot be overemphasized. Designers must be able to gain quick insight into a new circuit configuration in terms of speed, power, and area, as well as many other important characteristics. If a simple model is not available, then design becomes an iterative process with a CAD tool.

Since any analysis or design is only as accurate as the models, it is essential that the circuit designer have a thorough understanding of the models commonly used and the degree of approximation involved in each. If we know the detailed models, and the approximations used to derive the simple models, we can safely use the simplified models and gain a tremendous insight into the behavior of complex devices. Keep this in mind as you work your way through the material in this chapter.

2.2   The MOS Transistor

2.2.1 Structure and Operation of the MOS Transistor

A simplified view of an *n*-channel polysilicon-gate MOS transistor is shown in Figure 2.1. In simple terms, there are two operating modes for this transistor: *on* and *off*. This is true of all transistors. We must use the terminals provided on the device to place it in these two possible conditions. The four terminals are the *gate, drain, source,* and *bulk* (or *body,* or *substrate*). The schematic symbol for the NMOS device is shown with these four terminals labeled as *G, D, S,* and *B,* respectively. In the *on* condition, electron current flows from source to drain. In the *off* condition, no current flows in the device. To turn it on, a voltage is applied to the gate node to set up an electric field that creates a conductive channel between heavily doped *n*-type (n^+) source and drain regions,[1] and current flows when a potential difference exists between these two nodes.

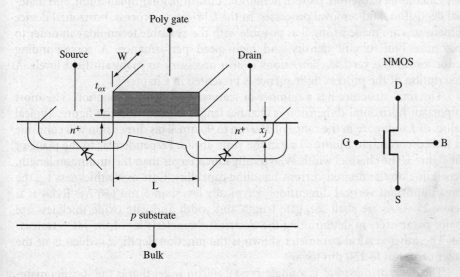

Figure 2.1

NMOS transistor structure and symbol.

---

[1] The notation n^+ implies doping $>10^{18}/cm^3$, n^- implies doping $<10^{15}/cm^3$, and *n* is not specific. The same convention applies for designations of *p*-type material.

Since it is based on the use of an electric field, the device is one form of field-effect transistor (FET). Note that the gate is completely insulated from the other electrodes. This fact leads to the designation insulated-gate field-effect transistor (IGFET). Another name, although much older, is unipolar transistor. This name arises from the fact that only a single type of charge carrier (electrons in NMOS) is necessary for device operation. The mobile holes in the *p*-type substrate of an NMOS transistor are not involved in normal transistor operation. A variety of terms have been used to reference this device including FET, IGFET, MOST, and MOSFET. We will use the more recent terms, *MOS transistor* or *MOS device, NMOS device,* and *n-channel* transistor, when referring to the device in Figure 2.1.

As mentioned in Chapter 1, the acronym *MOS* is derived from the metal-oxide-semiconductor structure that forms the gate of the device. In the early days of PMOS technology, a metal gate was used but it was difficult to align the metal over the channel precisely. An offset in one direction or the other would create a non-functioning transistor (either a short or an open). To overcome these alignment problems, a polycrystalline silicon material was introduced to serve as the gate. This so-called *poly* gate would be deposited before the source and drain material. When the source and drain diffusions were created, they would align with the gate, rather than the other way around. The yield of such devices went up significantly compared to metal-gate technology, and today, polysilicon is used almost exclusively as the gate material. It is heavily doped to keep its resistance low since it is supposed to behave like a metal material.

The device structure shown in Figure 2.1 is formed by a complex sequence of steps including oxidation, pattern definition, diffusion, ion implantation, and material deposition and removal processes. In the fabrication process, horizontal device dimensions are made as small as possible with the available technology in order to maximize both circuit density and high-speed performance. A corresponding reduction in the vertical dimensions is also necessary to maintain field levels. A description of the processing sequence is presented in Chapter 3.

The final structure has a number of features that deserve mention. The most important horizontal dimension is channel length L, shown in the figure. Typical values of L today are in the range of 350 nm to 90 nm. This dimension will continue to scale according to Moore's Law in the years ahead. Perpendicular to the plane of the figure is the channel width W, typically much larger than the minimum length, depending on the desired current-handling capability. Gate oxide thickness t_{ox}, the most important vertical dimension, is typically less than 5 nm (50 Å). Today it is below 25 Å. As we shall see, gate length and width and gate oxide thickness are major parameters in determining the electrical characteristics of the MOS transistor. The other vertical parameter shown is the junction depth, x_j, which is of the order of 70 nm to 150 nm today.

The *body*, or *substrate*, is a single-crystal silicon wafer that is the starting material for circuit fabrication and provides physical support for the final circuit. The *p*-type substrate doping density is a factor in device electrical behavior, as described in the next section. The silicon surface is comprised of *active* and *field* regions. The active region contains the transistor, while the field region serves to isolate transistors. The main requirement on the field regions is that they should never permit conduction between separate active regions. In NMOS, all conduction is via electrons, so the field region fulfills its purpose if electrons can never pass through it. In addition, a thick layer of silicon dioxide over the field regions is used to minimize unwanted capacitance from interconnecting metal to the body.

The transistor regions in the body comprise n^+ source and n^+ drain regions separated by p-type material in the channel region. Typical devices are symmetrical, just as the one shown in Figure 2.1; source and drain are interchangeable. *Strictly speaking, the source and drain can be only identified after the polarities of applied voltages are established.* In NMOS, the more positive node is defined as the drain. With no external voltages applied, the path from drain to source has two pn^+ junction diodes in series, back to back, with the body as a p region common to them. These junctions should never be forward-biased. In fact, the subtrate should be connected to the lowest possible potential in the circuit, typically a ground potential, called V_{SS} or Gnd. The only current that is permitted to flow across the junctions is diode reverse leakage current.

Now consider the result when source, drain, and body are all tied to ground and a positive voltage is applied to the gate. From simple concepts of electrostatics, a positive gate voltage will tend to draw electrons from the substrate into the channel region. The n^+ source and drain regions also provide nearby copious sources of electrons. Once electrons are present in the channel region, a conducting path is present between drain and source. Current will flow from drain to source if there is a voltage difference between them. That is, electrons will flow from source to drain in this condition.

To first-order, the conducting channel does not form for very small positive gate voltages. The electrostatic potential at the surface of the p-type material in the channel region must be made positive by application of a larger gate-source voltage. The gate voltage needed to initiate formation of a conducting channel is termed the *threshold voltage* V_T. This important device parameter is analyzed in the next section.

Now consider the structure of the device in Figure 2.2, called the p-channel or PMOS device. It has complementary characteristics to the NMOS device. While the structure is the same as the NMOS device, the doping is opposite. The heavily doped regions in the body comprise p^+ source and p^+ drain regions separated by lightly doped n-type material in the channel region. Again, the source and drain are interchangeable and can be identified only after the polarities of applied voltages are established. In PMOS, *the more positive node is defined as the source.* This is represented in the schematic of Figure 2.2 by reversing the positions of the source and drain.

The *substrate* is an n-type material that must be created in advance of placing the source and drain regions. It is often referred to as an *n-well* or *n-tub*, especially if it is created in a silicon wafer that is initially doped with a p-type background material. In this case, it would be called an n-well process. If both n-channel and p-channel devices are created in their own wells, it is referred to as a *double-well* or *twin-tub* process. Again, the path from drain to source has two p^+n junction diodes in series, back to back, with the body as an n region common to them. The

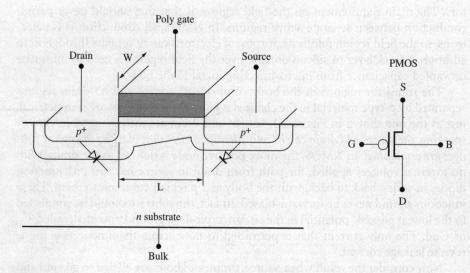

Figure 2.2

PMOS transistor structure and symbol.

only current that can flow is diode reverse leakage. They should never be forward-biased. Therefore, the *n*-well must be tied to the highest voltage in the system, called V_{DD}. In a twin-tub process, the *p*-well must be tied to Gnd or V_{SS} for the same reason. These connections of the wells to V_{DD} or Gnd are sometimes referred to as *tub-ties* or *well-plugs*.

Consider the *p*-channel device when source, drain, and body are all tied to V_{DD}. If a low voltage is applied to the gate, it will tend to draw holes into the channel region. Once holes are present in the channel region, a conducting path is present between drain and source. Current will flow from source to drain if there is a voltage difference between them. That is, holes will flow from the source to the drain if the drain has a lower potential than the source. By definition, the source is the terminal with the higher potential in PMOS devices. In effect, the PMOS device has a negative threshold since the gate must be at a lower voltage than the source to invert the channel.

The fact that the *p*-channel device has a negative threshold, and is therefore opposite to the NMOS device, is captured in the symbol for the device by placing a circle on the gate input. Many books use a slightly different symbol for this device, but we will use this one consistently throughout the book.

NMOS and PMOS transistors that have no conducting channel at zero gate-source voltage are termed *enhancement-mode* devices, meaning that gate-source voltage of the same polarity as drain-source voltage (positive for NMOS, negative for PMOS) is required to initiate conduction. NMOS *depletion-mode* devices have

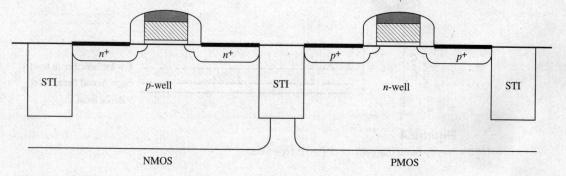

Figure 2.3
CMOS transistors structure.

negative thresholds, but in CMOS designs, we rarely (if ever) use depletion-mode devices today.

Figure 2.3 shows a cross-sectional view of a modern silicon-gate CMOS structure. While it is not drawn to scale, it represents the typical profile after fabrication of a twin-tub CMOS process, the details of which are left to Chapter 3. We now know that the PMOS devices are symmetrical but opposite to NMOS devices in terms of doping and voltage polarities. In CMOS circuits, all devices are assumed to be enhancement-mode devices. They are separated by oxide regions using a method called shallow-trench isolation (STI). The NMOS device has a positive threshold voltage while the PMOS device has a negative threshold voltage. The equations to be derived in the sections to follow are based on the NMOS device, but apply equally to the PMOS device after the appropriate sign changes.

2.2.2   Threshold Voltage of the MOS Transistor

In order to fully understand the mechanisms behind the threshold voltage derivation, we must examine the energy-band diagram of a material as shown in Figure 2.4. This diagram is a representation of the allowable energy states for electrons. Two distinct levels are defined: the conduction band, E_C, and the valence band, E_V. In order to have electrical conduction, an electron must move from the valence band to the conduction band and, in doing so, must surmount the *bandgap* associated with the material. In *metals*, the two energy levels overlap making the bandgap effectively zero; electrons can freely move from one band to another. In *insulators*, the energy levels are very far apart and the barrier is insurmountable. In *semiconductors*, the gap is relatively small, 1.1 eV for silicon. Since there are no allowed states in the bandgap region, electrons must have enough energy to jump from the valence band to the conduction band. However, since the gap is relatively small, energetic

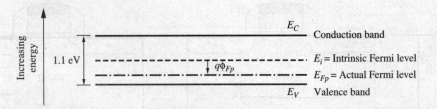

Figure 2.4
Energy-band diagram for doped *p*-type silicon.

electrons are able to surmount this barrier from time to time due to thermal excitation.

In an undoped semiconductor, the total number of electrons that are able to surmount this barrier is termed the *intrinsic carrier concentration*, n_i. This depends on the number of available states in the conduction band and the probability of occupancy of these states, which depends on the temperature. For example, n_i at room temperature is

$$n_i = 1.45 \times 10^{10}/\text{cm}^3 \qquad (2.1)$$

The relationship between the intrinsic carrier concentration and the holes and electrons at equilibrium is given by the *mass action law*:

$$np = n_i^2 \qquad (2.2)$$

where n is the mobile electron concentration and p is the mobile hole concentration. This equation tells us that the mobile electrons and mobile holes must have equal concentration in undoped silicon at equilibrium. To represent this on the energy band diagram, we define the *intrinsic Fermi level* as a line where the probability of electron occupancy of an empty state is 50%. This is denoted E_i in Figure 2.4 and is located roughly midway between the conduction band and the valence band.

More generally, the probability of electron occupancy of an allowable state is based on the doping level in the semiconductor. As we increase the doping level, N_A, of silicon with *p*-type acceptor impurities such as boron, the probability of electrons in the conduction band is reduced and the actual Fermi level (50% probability point) shifts below the intrinsic Fermi level. This is because we are adding holes to the semiconductor and reducing the likelihood that an electron will surmount the barrier. The mass action law can be used to support this fact. If $p = N_A \gg n_i$, then the mobile electron concentration is reduced to

$$n = \frac{n_i^2}{N_A}$$

which is much smaller than n_i. Since there are fewer mobile electrons, the probability that the empty states in the conduction band will be occupied decreases.

The amount of shift in the Fermi level due to the doping is called the electrostatic potential. Conventionally, the equilibrium electrostatic potential ϕ_F in a semiconductor is defined as the difference between the intrinsic Fermi level and the actual Fermi level in the p-type or n-type doped semiconductor:[2]

$$\phi_{Fp} = \frac{kT}{q} \ln \frac{n_i}{p} \qquad (2.3a)$$

or

$$\phi_{Fn} = \frac{kT}{q} \ln \frac{n}{n_i} \qquad (2.3b)$$

where the equilibrium majority mobile carrier concentration is assumed to be equal to the doping concentration $p = N_A$ for p-type material, or $n = N_D$ for n-type material.

The kT/q term is called the thermal voltage, V_{th}, which is approximately 26 mV at room temperature. (Do not confuse this with the threshold voltage, V_T, which is a completely different quantity!) By convention, ϕ_F is negative for p-type semiconductor material and positive for n-type material. For example, in a p-type material, we would have:

$$\phi_{Fp} = \frac{kT}{q} \ln \frac{n_i}{N_A} \qquad (2.4)$$

Since N_A is the doping level in the p-substrate, and the value of $N_A \gg n_i$, the electrostatic potential is negative.

Now that the energy band diagram has been reviewed, its application to the threshold voltage derivation can be described. Recall that the MOS structure is comprised of a metal material (polysilicon), a gate oxide, and the silicon body. The gate and body of the MOS transistor form the plates of a capacitor with silicon dioxide, SiO_2, as a dielectric. The gate-oxide capacitance per unit area is defined as:

$$C_{ox} = \frac{\varepsilon_{ox}}{t_{ox}} \qquad (2.5)$$

where ε_{ox} is the permittivity of oxide and t_{ox} is the oxide thickness.

The threshold voltage for a long-channel enhancement-mode NMOS device can be derived using the transistor cross-section shown in Figure 2.5. Consider the body, source, and drain connected to ground and a voltage V_{GS} (initially zero) applied to the gate. As V_{GS} changes from zero to a positive value, positive charge accumulates on top of the gate and negative charge accumulates as electrons in the substrate under the gate. This actually happens gradually as the gate voltage moves

---

[2] p-type silicon is obtained by adding acceptor impurities such as boron. n-type silicon is obtained by adding donor impurities such as phosphorus or arsenic.

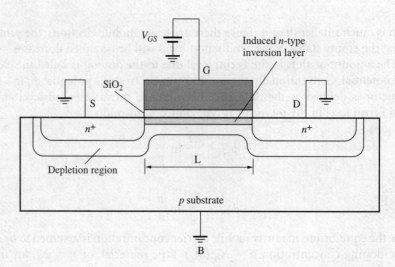

Figure 2.5
Idealized NMOS device cross section with positive voltage applied showing depletion regions and the induced channel.

from 0 V to the threshold voltage. Initially, the negative charge in the p-type body is manifested by creation of a *depletion region*[3] in which mobile holes are pushed down under the gate, leaving behind negatively charged immobile acceptor ions.

As the gate voltage continues to increase, the depletion-layer thickness increases and eventually an initial layer of mobile electrons appears at the surface of the silicon in the so-called *weak inversion* condition. Further increases in the gate voltage increases the concentration of the mobile carriers in the channel until the concentration of electrons at the surface equals the concentration of holes in the substrate, a condition known as *strong inversion*.[4] For gate voltages above this point, the depletion-layer thickness remains approximately constant while the additional charge on the gate is matched by additional mobile carriers in the channel region that are drawn from the source and drain regions—where an abundant supply of such carriers exists.

The value of gate voltage V_{GS} required to produce strong inversion is called the *threshold voltage, V_T*. We will present the main components of this voltage and then go back and describe the origin of each component. There are three main terms:

1. A voltage term, ϕ_{GC}, represents the difference in work functions between the gate (G) material and the silicon substrate on the channel (C) side. The work function for a material is the amount of energy needed to move an electron

---

[3] This is the same type of depletion region that appears in a pn junction.
[4] This is a somewhat arbitrary but important definition of strong inversion. The surface is inverted relative to the substrate since the carrier concentrations are equal and opposite.

from the Fermi level to free space level E_0, as shown in Figure 2.6. When two materials with different Fermi levels are brought together into one system, the Fermi levels are aligned at equilibrium. The work function difference tells us how "misaligned" they are to begin with. When equilibrium is reached, the conduction and valence bands will bend to accommodate the work function difference. For silicon-gate devices

$$\phi_{GC} = \Phi_{G\,(polysilicon\ gate)} - \Phi_{C\,(substrate)}$$

2. There is always an undesired positive charge Q_{ox} present in the oxide and at the interface between the oxide and the bulk silicon. This charge is due to impurities and/or imperfections such as sodium ions in the oxide, Q_{Na^+}, and dangling bonds at the interface, Q_{SS}. We combine these two terms into one term called Q_{ox} and place the equivalent charge at the oxide-silicon interface as in Figure 2.6. Since there is positive charge effectively on the bottom plate of the MOS capacitor, the top plate must provide negative charge to compensate for it. Therefore, it contributes a negative quantity to the threshold voltage of $-Q_{ox}/C_{ox}$.

3. A gate voltage $(-2\phi_F - Q_B/C_{ox})$ is needed to change the surface potential to the strong inversion condition and to offset the induced depletion-layer charge Q_B. This is shown in Figure 2.7.

Now that the terms are defined, we explain the inversion process in detail. Consider what happens when the MOS system is first brought together. At equilibrium, there is a certain amount of band-bending that occurs to make the Fermi levels constant throughout the entire system. We need to know exactly how much band-bending has taken place in order to provide a meaningful reference point for the strong inversion condition. Therefore, the bands are first flattened by a *flat-band* voltage, V_{FB}. The name comes from the fact that application of this voltage at the gate produces flat

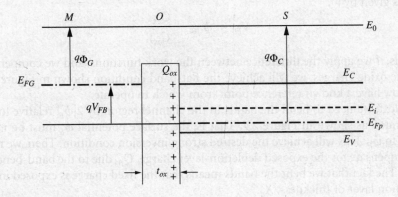

Figure 2.6
Flat-band condition in the MOS system.

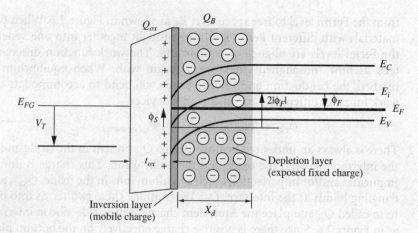

Figure 2.7
Energy bands in the strong inversion condition.

energy bands in the metal-oxide-semiconductor system, as shown in Figure 2.6. This figure shows the MOS energy band diagrams depicting the conduction band, E_C, valence band, E_V, the intrinsic Fermi level, E_i, and the actual Fermi level in the p-type semiconductor, E_{Fp}. The work functions associated with the gate, $q\Phi_G$, and the semiconductor, $q\Phi_C$, are also shown here. The Fermi level in the gate material, E_{FG}, depends on the doping level in the polysilicon gate material. If the gate is heavily doped with n^+ material, the position of E_{FG} is near E_C. However, if it is heavily doped with p^+ material, E_{FG} is near E_V. For an NMOS device, usually an n^+ doping is used in the poly gate whereas a p^+ doping is used for PMOS devices. This polarity of doping is consistent with the doping of the drain and source regions, so they can be doped at the same time.

The amount of band "unbending" that is needed to reach this flat-band condition is given by

$$V_{FB} = \phi_{GC} - \frac{Q_{ox}}{C_{ox}} \qquad (2.6)$$

That is, if we apply the difference between the work functions, and we compensate for the oxide charges, we will achieve the flat-band condition shown in Figure 2.6. We now have a known reference point from which to operate.

Next, we need to bend the bands in the channel region by $2|\phi_F|$ relative to the substrate,[5] as shown in Figure 2.7. That is, the surface potential ϕ_S must be made equal to ϕ_F. This will achieve the desired strong inversion condition. Then, we need to compensate for the exposed depletion-layer charge, Q_B, due to the band-bending itself. The fact that we bent the bands means that the fixed charge is exposed in the depletion layer of thickness, X_d.

---

[5] We drop the electronic charge q for convenience in Figure 2.7.

A simple analysis can be applied to find the depletion-layer charge by first determining the thickness X_d of the depletion region between the channel and the substrate as a function of the electrostatic potential ϕ_S at the silicon surface. To create the shaded depletion region shown in Figure 2.7, mobile holes must be pushed back into the substrate. The thickness of the depletion layer in the p-type material is given by

$$X_d = \left(\frac{2\varepsilon_{si} |\phi_S - \phi_F|}{qN_A} \right)^{1/2} \tag{2.7}$$

The doping density in the p-type substrate is denoted as N_A, and ε_{si} is the permittivity of silicon. The immobile charge per unit area due to acceptor ions that have been stripped of their mobile holes is given by

$$Q_B = qN_A X_d = -\sqrt{2qN_A \varepsilon_{si} |\phi_S - \phi_F|} \quad \text{for } |\phi_S - \phi_F| \geq 0 \tag{2.8}$$

In order to invert the surface of the p-type semiconductor, the voltage V_{GS} is used to attract mobile electrons to the channel region. As V_{GS} is increased in the positive direction,[6] the potential ϕ_S at the silicon surface increases from its original (negative) equilibrium value of ϕ_{Fp}, through zero, until $\phi_S = -\phi_{Fp}$. Under this condition the density of mobile electrons at the surface is equal to the density of mobile holes in the original substrate or body. The surface potential has changed by $-2\phi_{Fp}$ relative to the substrate.

The value of V_{GS} needed to cause this $-2\phi_{Fp}$ change in surface potential is defined as the *threshold voltage V_T* for a MOS transistor. This condition is known as *strong inversion*. In essence, the semiconductor surface that is normally p-type becomes n-type. Further increases in gate voltage produce only slight changes in ϕ_S and the depletion-layer thickness. However, it increases the electric field across the gate oxide and increases the electron concentration in the channel. The additional electrons are drawn into the inversion layer from the strongly n-type source or drain, with the positive surface potential as the attractive force.

Band-bending at Strong Inversion   **Example 2.1**

Problem:

A 130 nm technology employs carrier concentrations in the p-well in the range of 3×10^{17} cm^{-3}. Estimate the degree of band-bending required for strong inversion at room temperature, relative to the flat-band condition.

---

[6] The positive direction for the gate voltage is actually pointing downward in the energy band diagram of Figure 2.7. It bends the bands downwards. The flat-band voltage is negative since it will "unbend" the bands from its equilibrium condition.

Solution[7]:

$$2|\phi_{Fp}| = \frac{2kT}{q}\left|\ln\frac{n_i}{p}\right| = 2(0.026)\left|\ln\frac{1.45\times10^{10}}{3\times10^{17}}\right| \cong 0.88 \text{ V}$$

As long as there is only a small voltage difference between drain and source, the induced layer of electrons extends continuously from source to drain, producing a continuous region with mobile electrons. The conductivity of the channel thus formed can be increased or decreased (*modulated*) by increasing or decreasing the gate voltage. In the presence of an inversion layer, and with no body bias ($V_{SB} = 0$), the depletion region contains a fixed negative charge that may be found by using (2.8) together with the fact that $\phi_S = -\phi_F$.

$$Q_{B0} = -\sqrt{2qN_A\varepsilon_{si}\,|-2\phi_F|} \tag{2.9a}$$

If there is a voltage V_{SB} between source and body (V_{SB} is normally positive for n-channel and negative for p-channel devices), a slight modification is required. The surface potential required to produce inversion becomes $|-2\phi_F + V_{SB}|$ and the charge stored in the depletion region in this case is

$$Q_B = -\sqrt{2qN_A\varepsilon_{si}\,|-2\phi_F + V_{SB}|} \tag{2.9b}$$

Example 2.2   **Depletion Layer Fixed Charge Calculation**

Problem:

A p-type well in a 130 nm technology has $N_A = 3\times10^{17}$ cm^{-3}. Find the limiting value of depletion-layer width and the total charge contained in the depleted region.

Solution:

From Example 2.1, we already know that

$$2|\phi_{Fp}| = \frac{2kT}{q}\left|\ln\frac{n_i}{p}\right| = 0.88 \text{ V}$$

$$= |\phi_s - \phi_F|$$

From Equation (2.7),

$$X_d = \sqrt{\frac{2(11.7)8.85\times10^{-14}(0.88)}{1.6(10^{-19})\times3(10^{17})}} = 6\times10^{-6}\text{cm} = 60\text{ nm}$$

---

[7] Note that ϕ_{Fp} is negative for n-channel devices and ϕ_{Fn} is positive for p-channel devices. This can be confusing so we usually take the absolute value of this quantity.

From Equation (2.9a),

$$Q_{B0} = -(2 \times 1.6 \times 10^{-19} \times (3)10^{17} \times 1.0 \times 10^{-12} \times |-0.88|)^{1/2}$$

$$\approx -3 \times 10^{-7} \, C/cm^2$$

The complete expression for the threshold voltage V_T is given by

$$V_T = V_{FB} - 2\phi_F - \frac{Q_B}{C_{ox}} \tag{2.10}$$

Expanding V_{FB} and rearranging, we obtain

$$V_T = \phi_{GC} - 2\phi_F - \frac{Q_B}{C_{ox}} - \frac{Q_{ox}}{C_{ox}}$$

$$= \phi_{GC} - 2\phi_F - \frac{Q_{B0}}{C_{ox}} - \frac{Q_{ox}}{C_{ox}} - \frac{Q_B - Q_{B0}}{C_{ox}} \tag{2.11}$$

$$= V_{T0} + \gamma\left(\sqrt{V_{SB} + |2\phi_F|} - \sqrt{|2\phi_F|}\right)$$

where Equation (2.9a) has been used to simplify the expression and V_{T0} is the threshold voltage with $V_{SB} = 0$ called the *zero-bias threshold voltage*. The parameter γ (gamma) is termed the *body-effect coefficient* or *body factor*. Comparing Equation (2.9) to Equation (2.11), we see that γ is given by

$$\gamma = \frac{1}{C_{ox}}\sqrt{2q\varepsilon_{si}N_A} \tag{2.12}$$

Computation of C_{ox} and γ   **Example 2.3**

Problem:

Determine values of C_{ox} and γ, if $t_{ox} = 22$ Å and $N_A = 3 \times 10^{17} \, cm^{-3}$.

Solution:

To compute C_{ox} we use Equation (2.5):

$$\varepsilon_{ox} = 4\varepsilon_o$$

$$\therefore C_{ox} = \frac{\varepsilon_{ox}}{t_{ox}} = \frac{(4)(8.85 \times 10^{-14})}{22 \, \text{Å}} = 1.6 \times 10^{-6} \, F/cm^2$$

Apply this value to the equation for γ:

$$\gamma = \sqrt{2q\varepsilon_{si}N_A}/C_{ox}$$

$$\gamma = \sqrt{(2)(1.6 \times 10^{-19})(11.7)(8.85 \times 10^{-14})(3 \times 10^{17})}/1.6 \times 10^{-6}$$

$$\approx 0.2 \, V^{1/2}$$

Table 2.1

Signs in threshold voltage equation

Parameter	NMOS	PMOS
Substrate	p-type	n-type
V_{T0}	+	−
ϕ_{GC}:		
n^+ polysilicon gate	−	−
p^+ polysilicon gate	+	+
Φ_F	−	+
Q_{B0}, Q_B	−	+
Q_{ox}	+	+
γ	+	−
X_d, C_{ox}	+	+
V_{SB}	+	−

It is easy to become confused about the signs of the various terms in the threshold voltage equations (if not the terms themselves!). Equations (2.10–2.12) give correct results for NMOS and PMOS if the signs shown in Table 2.1 are used.

Example 2.4

Threshold Voltage Calculation

Problem:

Calculate the zero-bias threshold voltage (i.e., $V_{SB} = 0$) for an NMOS silicon-gate transistor that has well doping $N_A = 3 \times 10^{17}$ cm^{-3}, gate doping $N_D = 10^{20}$ cm^{-3}, gate-oxide thickness $t_{OX} = 22$ Å, and 2×10^{10} cm^{-2} singly charged positive ions per unit area at the oxide-silicon interface. Assume that the gate doping is n^+ and explain why it is appropriate.

Solution:

$$V_{T0} = \phi_{GC} - 2\phi_{FP} - \frac{Q_{B0}}{C_{ox}} - \frac{Q_{ox}}{C_{ox}}$$

$$\phi_{Fp} = \frac{kT}{q} \ln\frac{n_i}{N_A} = 0.026 \ln\frac{1.4 \times 10^{10}}{3 \times 10^{17}} = -0.44 \text{ V}$$

$$\phi_{GC} = \phi_{Fp} - \phi_{G(gate)} = -0.44 - 0.55 = -0.99 \text{ V}$$

$$\varepsilon_{ox} = 4\varepsilon_0 = 3.5 \times 10^{-13} \text{ F/cm}$$

$$C_{ox} = 1.6 \times 10^{-6} \text{ F/cm}^2$$

$$Q_{B0} = 3 \times 10^{-7} \text{ C/cm}^2$$

$$\frac{Q_{B0}}{C_{ox}} = \frac{3 \times 10^{-7}}{1.6 \times 10^{-6}} = 0.188 \text{ V}$$

$$\frac{Q_{ox}}{C_{ox}} = \frac{2 \times 10^{10} \times 1.6 \times 10^{-19}}{1.6 \times 10^{-6}} = 0.002 \text{ V}$$

$$V_{T0} = -0.99 - (-0.88) - (-0.188) - 0.002 = +0.08 \text{ V}$$

In the above solution, we assumed that the n^+ gate doping is so high that the Fermi level in the gate is coincident with the conduction band, which implies an electrostatic potential of $\phi_{FG(gate)} = 0.55$. If the gate doping were p^+, the value for V_{T0} would be 1.18 V which is well above the desired levels. Therefore, the doping of the poly gate must be n^+ to keep it below the target value. For the same reason, the poly gate for p-channel devices is doped with p^+ material. Of course, the value computed above is not very satisfactory for an NMOS device. We require a value closer to $V_{T0} = 0.4$ V.

The small positive value of threshold voltage calculated above is not desirable for use in digital circuits. Although in principal the threshold voltage may be set to any value by proper choice of doping concentrations and oxide capacitance, considerations such as breakdown voltage and junction capacitance frequently dictate the desirable specifications for these variables. Therefore, the final value of V_{T0} is determined during circuit fabrication by ion implanting dopant atoms into the channel region.

A p-type threshold implant, using boron for example, will make the threshold voltage more positive. On the other hand, an n-type threshold implant, using phosphorus for example, makes the threshold voltage more negative. NMOS threshold voltages are adjusted using a p-type implant until the desired positive value is reached. The PMOS thresholds are all adjusted with n-type implants until they are at the desired negative value.

Extra p-type impurities are implanted to make $V_{T0N} = +0.4$ V for n-channel enhancement devices in our generic 130nm process. By implanting n-type impurities in the channel region of a p-channel device, we try to achieve a $V_{T0P} = -0.4$ V. If Q_I is the charge density per unit area in the channel region due to the implant, then the threshold voltage, V_{T0}, given by (2.10) and (2.11) is shifted by Q_I/C_{ox}. It is assumed that all implanted ions are electrically active.

Threshold Voltage Implant Dosage Calculation   **Example 2.5**

Problem:

Continuing on with the previous example, since the NMOS threshold voltage is not close to the desired value, calculate the ion-implant doses N_I needed to achieve a threshold voltage of 0.4 V in unit of ions/cm^2.

Solution:

We know that V_T will be shifted by $Q_I/C_{ox} = qN_I/C_{ox}$.

$$\therefore N_I = \frac{Q_I}{q} = \frac{C_{ox}\Delta V}{q} = \frac{C_{ox}(0.4 - (+0.08))}{1.6 \times 10^{-19}} = 3.2 \times 10^{12} \frac{\text{ions}}{\text{cm}^2}$$

The above calculations of threshold voltage do not give exact quantitative results in practical cases. Reasons for this include the fact that body doping may vary near the oxide interface, the oxide thickness and dielectric constant may vary due to process variations, and oxide charge is not exactly controlled. Considerations such as hot-electron effects, junction breakdown voltages, junction capacitances, and punchthrough dictate the desirable specifications of the doping levels in the channel region. For our purposes, calculations of threshold voltage are useful for predicting how V_{T0} varies as a function of doping levels and dimensions. Furthermore, the values given above are for illustrative purposes only. As a practical matter for circuit design, nominal values and statistical variations of the threshold voltage and body-effect coefficient must be determined by direct measurements of actual devices.

2.2.3   First-Order Current-Voltage Characteristics

The next step is to derive the large-signal characteristics of long-channel MOS transistors for dc or slowly changing applied signals. We assume an NMOS device with source grounded and bias voltages V_{GS}, V_{DS}, and V_{BS} applied as shown in Figure 2.8. If V_{GS} is greater than V_T, a conducting channel is present and V_{DS} causes a drift current I_{DS} to flow from drain to source. The voltage V_{DS} causes a larger reverse bias from drain to body than that present from source to body, and thus a wider depletion layer exists at the drain. However, for simplicity we assume that the voltage drop along the channel is small so that the threshold voltage and depletion-layer width are approximately constant along the channel.

At a distance y along the channel, the voltage with respect to the source is $V(y)$, where $0 \leq V(y) \leq V_{DS}$, and the gate-to-channel voltage at that point is $V_{GS} - V(y)$. In order to have any inversion-layer charge, the gate-to-channel voltage must be higher than V_T. The amount of charge induced by a given voltage is $Q = CV$. We assume that this voltage $V_{GS} - V(y)$ exceeds the threshold voltage V_T, and thus the induced charge per unit area at the point y in the channel is the charge density:

$$Q_n(y) = C_{ox}\left[V_{GS} - V(y) - V_T\right] \tag{2.13}$$

In basic terms, current is simply charge in motion. Since Equation (2.13) determines how much charge exists in the channel, the drain-source current I_{DS} is given

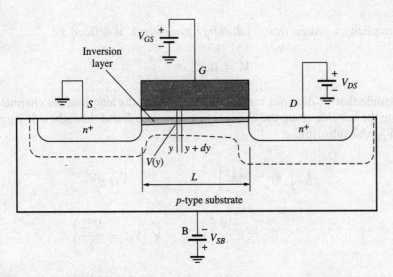

Figure 2.8
NMOS device with bias voltages applied.

by the charge density times the carrier velocity, v, times the channel width, W, perpendicular to the plane of Figure 2.8.

$$I_{DS} = Q_n \times v \times W \qquad (2.14)$$

The carrier velocity in cm/s is determined by the horizontal electric field, E, which is in units of V/cm and is directed from drain to source. For the first-order model, we assume that the velocity is linearly proportional to the magnitude of the E field:

$$v = \mu E \quad \text{where} \quad E = \frac{dV(y)}{dy} \qquad (2.15)$$

and μ is the carrier mobility which is the ratio of carrier (electron or hole) velocity to electric field. Its dimensional units are cm/s over V/cm, or cm²/V-s.

To continue with the analysis of MOS transistor conduction, we substitute Equation (2.15) into (2.14):

$$I_{DS} = C_{ox} \left[(V_{GS} - V(y)) - V_T \right] \times \mu_n E \times W$$

Further substitution and minor rearrangement produces:

$$I_{DS} \, dy = W \mu_n C_{ox} \left(V_{GS} - V(y) - V_T \right) dV$$

For simplicity, a *process transconductance parameter* k' is defined as:

$$k' = \mu_n C_{ox} = \frac{\mu_n \varepsilon_{ox}}{t_{ox}} \tag{2.16}$$

We assume that V_T does not vary significantly along the length of the channel. Integrating the left side along the channel from $y = 0$ to L and the right side from $V = 0$ to V_{DS} and substituting:

$$I_{DS} \int_0^L dy = Wk' \int_0^{V_{DS}} (V_{GS} - V - V_T)\, dV \tag{2.17a}$$

$$I_{DS} = k' \frac{W}{L} \left[(V_{GS} - V_T) V_{DS} - \frac{V_{DS}^2}{2} \right]$$

The *device transconductance parameter* is defined as $k = k'(W/L)$. Substituting this in the above yields

$$I_{DS} = \frac{k}{2} \left[2(V_{GS} - V_T) V_{DS} - V_{DS}^2 \right] \tag{2.17b}$$

for the so-called *linear* region of operation. This equation is an important one since it describes the current-voltage (*I-V*) characteristics of the long channel MOS transistor, assuming a continuous channel is present from source to drain.

As the value of V_{DS} is increased, the induced conducting channel charge Q_n decreases near the drain. Equation (2.13) indicates that Q_n at the drain end approaches zero as V_{DS} approaches $V_{GS} - V_T$. When V_{DS} equals or exceeds $V_{GS} - V_T$, the channel is said to be *pinched off*. Increases in V_{DS} above this critical voltage produce little change in I_{DS}, and Equation (2.17a) no longer applies. In fact, if Equation (2.17b) is plotted as I_{DS} versus V_{DS} with different values of V_{GS}, the curves would reach a peak and then "roll over" as V_{DS} is increased since it is a quadratic equation. This characteristic, shown in Figure 2.9a, is nonphysical and inaccurate. It is due to Equation (2.13) reversing its polarity when $V(y)$ is greater than $V_{GS} - V_T$. This produces positive charge in the channel after the pinch-off point, as shown in Figure 2.9b, something that is quite impossible!

Since the current equation is only valid up to the pinch-off point, we will call this the saturation voltage:

$$V_{Dsat} = V_{GS} - V_T \tag{2.18}$$

Beyond this value, I_{DS} is obtained by substituting $V_{DS} = V_{GS} - V_T$ in Equation (2.17b), giving

$$I_{DS} = \frac{k}{2} (V_{GS} - V_T)^2 \tag{2.19}$$

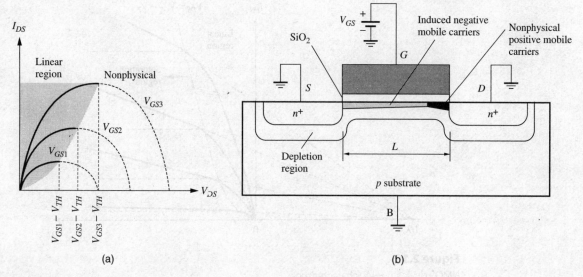

Figure 2.9
Nonphysical region of the drain current equation beyond pinch-off.

for the MOS transistor operating in this so-called *saturation* region.[8] The word *saturation* is used because I_{DS} reaches a limit, or saturates, at the level given by Equation (2.19). Figure 2.10 shows the currents in the linear and saturation regions of operation.

The drain current of an MOS transistor in the saturation region in fact is dependent on V_{DS}, because the depletion layer at the drain widens as V_{DS} increases, shortening the electrically effective value of L. Also, there is significant electrostatic coupling between the drain and the mobile charge in the channel, such that increasing the drain voltage increases Q_n above the value given by Equation (2.13). Each of these effects acts to increase the drain current as drain voltage increases. An empirical approximation to the actual drain current can be used to model this increase as

$$I_{DS} = \frac{k}{2}\,(V_{GS} - V_T)^2(1 + \lambda V_{DS}) \qquad (2.20)$$

where the channel-length modulation parameter λ (lambda) represents the influence of V_{DS} on I_{DS} in saturation. To avoid discontinuities in the $I_{DS} - V_{DS}$ characteristic, the $1 + \lambda V_{DS}$ term may be included for both saturated and linear regions with negligible error. Usually the value of λ has little effect on the operating characteristics of digital MOS circuits.

---

[8] The consequences of the earlier assumption of V_T constant along the channel may now be understood. In fact, V_T increases with $V(y)$ due to body effect. The result is that saturated drain current I_D is 10 to 40% smaller than the value given by Equation (2.19b). However, good accuracy is obtained in circuit design if the value used for k' is determined from data taken with the transistor operating in saturation.

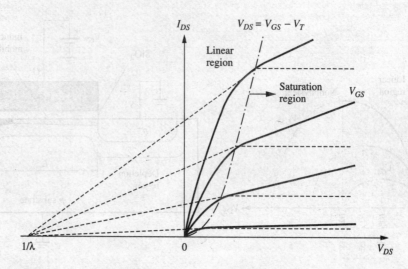

Figure 2.10
NMOS device $I_D - V_{DS}$ characteristics.

We summarize the results thus far using the I_{DS} versus V_{DS} plot for an NMOS transistor shown in Figure 2.10. Below pinch-off the device behaves as a nonlinear voltage-controlled resistor. This is termed the *linear, resistance, triode,* or *nonsaturation* region of operation. This book will refer to it as the linear region. Above pinch-off, the device approximates a voltage-controlled current source. The channel-length modulation parameter in the figure is much larger than usual, leading to a steeper slope for $I_D - V_{DS}$ in saturation than is usually observed. The slopes of all the curves in saturation converge at $1/\lambda$ along the V_{DS} axis.[9]

There is also a noticeable quadratic relationship between the current I_{DS} and V_{GS} in the saturation region. This makes sense since there is a $(V_{GS} - V_T)^2$ term in the current expression in saturation, so the current must increase quadratically with V_{GS}. This is an important characteristic associated with long-channel devices in saturation.

The separation between linear and saturation regions is also plotted in Figure 2.10. It is defined as the point where V_{DS} is equal to $V_{GS} - V_T$ for all the curves. Throughout the study of the material in this book, it will be important to quickly ascertain the region of operation of a device. As a rule of thumb, if V_{DS} is large relative to V_{GS}, then it is probably in saturation. If V_{GS} is large relative to V_{DS} then it is probably in the linear region. If the two are equal, then the device is definitely in saturation. This intuitive approach to determining the region of operation is useful as an initial guess, but it must be validated using Equation (2.18).

A similar set of plots can be generated for the PMOS device. As noted before, for PMOS devices, all polarities of voltages and current are reversed. When check-

---

[9] In bipolar transistors, this is referred to as the *Early* voltage.

ing for the region of operation, it is important to use the proper magnitudes of the voltages. Otherwise, incorrect results will be obtained.

MOS digital circuits are usually designed with MOS transistors as the only circuit elements. The values of V_T are usually given for the NMOS and PMOS devices but can be adjusted with body-bias, V_{BS}. All of the other parameters are process-dependent. As a consequence, the transistor width W and length L are typically the only design parameters available. Since L is usually selected as the minimum value possible, the only practical degree of freedom is the selection of W. Therefore, it is useful to relate most of the equations for the MOS transistor in terms of W. As we proceed through this chapter and subsequent chapters, useful coefficients will be computed relative to the W of the device.

2.2.4   Derivation of Velocity-Saturated Current Equations

The quadratic model derived above is valid for long-channel devices (typically $>$ 1 μm) and has served the IC industry well for many years, especially for hand calculations. However, it is not as suitable for today's deep submicron (DSM) technologies. The primary reason is that, in modern devices, the transistor channel lengths have been scaled to the point where the vertical and horizontal electric fields are large and they interact with one another. Furthermore, the assumption that saturation occurs at the pinch-off point is no longer correct. Saturation in DSM devices occurs when the carriers reach velocity saturation—that is, when they reach the speed limit of the carriers in silicon.

The effect on the current-voltage characteristics is illustrated in Figure 2.11 for a 0.18 μm device, for which V_{DS} and V_{GS} are swept from 0 to 1.8 V. Notice that the relationship between I_{DS} and V_{GS} is more linear than quadratic. This can be seen by visual inspection of the plot of I_{DS} versus V_{DS}, or directly in the plot of I_{DS} versus V_{GS}. This behavior is not predicted by the equations that we have derived thus far. As a result, a more suitable model is necessary for hand calculations.

Another observation is that the saturation voltage is smaller than what is predicted by the first-order model. The plot of I_{DS} versus V_{GS} indicates that the threshold voltage is around 0.5 V (x-intercept of plot). For the uppermost curve of I_{DS} versus V_{DS}, with $V_{GS} = 1.8$ V, the saturation condition of Equation (2.18) requires that $V_{DS} = V_{GS} - V_T = 1.8$ V $- 0.5$ V $= 1.3$ V. However, the curve saturates well before 1.3 V. It is closer to 0.6 V by inspection. This early saturation is true for all three curves in this plot and is due to velocity saturation. We now revisit the current derivations taking into account the high fields and velocity saturation.

2.2.4.1 Effect of High Fields

Consider the following trends in the horizontal and vertical fields. The horizontal field occurs in the y-direction which is in the direction of the channel pointing from drain to source. The vertical field occurs in the x-direction from the gate to the channel. The horizontal field is given by $E_y = V_{DS}/L$. Shown in the following are estimates of the horizontal field for three different years. We can see that the

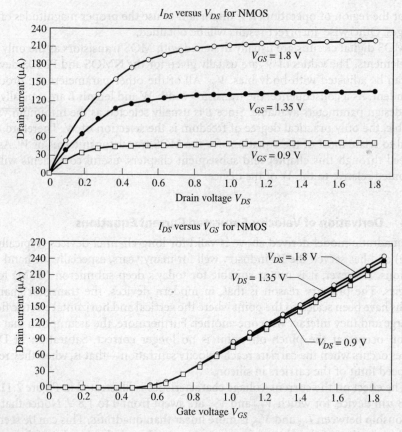

Figure 2.11
Current-voltage characteristics of a 0.18 μm process.

horizontal field has increased over the years by an order of magnitude and has remained approximately at 10^5 V/cm since 1995. The horizontal field acts to push the carriers to their velocity limit and this causes early saturation, which in turn degrades the mobility. The carrier velocity and the electric field no longer have a linear relationship as was assumed in the long-channel case.

1980	1995	2001
$E_y = \dfrac{5V}{5\,\mu m} = 10^4\,\text{V/cm}$	$E_y = \dfrac{3.3V}{0.35\,\mu m} = 9.4 \times 10^4\,\text{V/cm}$	$E_y = \dfrac{1.2V}{0.1\,\mu m} = 1.2 \times 10^5\,\text{V/cm}$

The vertical field can be approximated as $E_x = V_{DD}/t_{ox}$. Shown in the following are estimates of the vertical field for three different years. We can see that the vertical field has also increased by an order of magnitude and has remained approximately at 5×10^6 V/cm.

1980	1995	2001
$E_x = \dfrac{5V}{1000\ \text{Å}} = 50 \times 10^4\ \text{V/cm}$	$E_x = \dfrac{3.3V}{75\ \text{Å}} = 4.4 \times 10^6\ \text{V/cm}$	$E_x = \dfrac{1.2V}{22\ \text{Å}} = 5.5 \times 10^6\ \text{V/cm}$

For high gate voltages, a large number of mobile carriers are induced in the inversion layer near the interface. The mobility of these carriers decreases due primarily to electron scattering caused by dangling bonds at the Si-SiO$_2$ interface. The effect of the vertical field on mobility can be modeled to first-order as follows:

$$\mu_e = \frac{\mu_0}{1 + \left(\dfrac{V_{GS} - V_T}{\theta \cdot t_{ox}}\right)^{\eta}} \tag{2.21}$$

Here, μ_0 is the nominal mobility in the presence of low fields, typically 540 cm^2/V-sec for NMOS devices, and θ and η are empirical values. The equation uses a term based on the vertical electric field, $(V_{GS} - V_T)/t_{ox}$, to reduce the nominal mobility value. As an example of mobility degradation, let $\theta = 3.6 \times 10^6$ V/cm and $\eta = 1.85$ in a 0.13 μm technology. Then, with $t_{ox} = 22$ Å and $V_{GS} - V_T \approx 1.2$ V $-$ 0.4 V $=$ 0.8 V, we find that the mobility, $\mu_e \approx 270$ cm^2/V-sec, is reduced by a factor of 2 relative to μ_0. This effective value of mobility can be used to account for the high vertical field. The effective mobility for PMOS devices is 70 cm^2/V-sec which is about four times smaller than NMOS devices.

The horizontal field acts to reduce the mobility even further. We assumed that as E_y goes up, the carriers continue to increase in speed. Actually their velocity saturates (or reaches a velocity limit) at approximately $v_{sat} = 10^7$ cm/s. Consider Figure 2.12, which shows the relationship between the carrier velocity and horizontal electric field. Initially, as we increase the E_y field, the carrier velocity also increases. The linear proportionality constant between the velocity and the electric field is, of course, the mobility. Note that as the field increases beyond a certain critical electrical field, E_c, the carrier velocity saturates at its limit in silicon. The fields are so high in DSM devices that they tend to saturate very quickly as V_{DS} increases. This is the basic difference between long- and short-channel devices.

Figure 2.13 shows the experimental results for drift velocities, of holes and electrons in silicon. The saturation velocity for both electrons and holes is 8×10^6

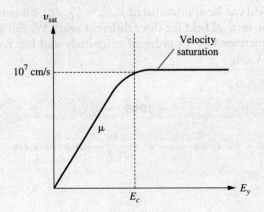

Figure 2.12
Carrier velocity versus electric field.

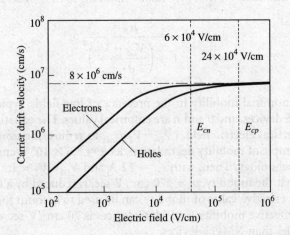

Figure 2.13
Plot of carrier drift velocity versus electric field at 400° K. (From Sze.)

cm/sec at $T = 400°$ K, and is independent of the doping level. This value is used in most of the analysis that follows. From the curves, we estimate the critical field values to be

$$E_{cn} = 6 \times 10^4 \ \frac{\text{V}}{\text{cm}} \text{ for electrons}$$

$$E_{cp} = 24 \times 10^4 \ \frac{\text{V}}{\text{cm}} \text{ for holes}$$

(2.22)

As the temperature decreases, the saturation velocity increases. For $T = 300°$ K, $v_{sat} \approx 10^7$ cm/s.

The next step is to somehow incorporate the effects of the high fields on mobility into a set of equations suitable for hand calculation. We first include the effect of the vertical field by using Equation (2.21). To account for the horizontal field, we can express the velocity as a piecewise continuous function of the horizontal electric field, E_y, as follows:

$$v = \mu_e \frac{E_y}{\left(1 + \dfrac{E_y}{E_c}\right)} \qquad E_y < E_c \qquad (2.23a)$$

$$v = v_{sat} \qquad E_y \geq E_c \qquad (2.23b)$$

That is, the relationship between the carrier velocity and the field is divided into two segments with a boundary defined by E_c, the critical field. Before the critical field is reached, the value of v is given by Equation (2.23a). Beyond E_c, the velocity saturates at v_{sat}. This captures the basic behavior of the curve but we should remember that it is only a model of the true behavior.[10] In order to ensure continuity at the boundary, where $E_y = E_c$, we can plug in this condition (2.23a) and set $v = v_{sat}$.

$$v = \mu_e \frac{E_y}{\left(1 + \dfrac{E_y}{E_c}\right)} = \frac{\mu_e E_c}{2} \qquad (2.24)$$

$$\therefore E_c = \frac{2v_{sat}}{\mu_e}$$

This sets up the relationship between E_c and v_{sat}. Note that this relationship is the result of the modeling approach described above as opposed to a fundamental relationship between the critical field and the saturated velocity. It holds true only in the context of Equation (2.23).

2.2.4.2 Current Equations for Velocity-Saturated Devices

To derive more suitable MOS current equations, we use Equation (2.14) and set v based on the region of operation using the conditions specified in Equations (2.23a) and (2.23b).

---

[10] This model slightly underestimates the velocity below the critical field and slightly overestimates the velocity above the critical field. But the model leads to simple current equations that are accurate enough for hand calculations.

In the linear region of operation,

$$I_{DS} = W \times Q_n \times v$$

$$= W \times C_{ox}(V_{GS} - V_T - V(y)) \left(\frac{\mu_e E_y}{1 + \dfrac{E_y}{E_c}} \right)$$

Reorganizing the equation and applying the relationship between field and potential, we obtain

$$I_{DS} = \left(\frac{W}{1 + \dfrac{E_y}{E_c}} \right) C_{ox}(V_{GS} - V_T - V(y)) \mu_e E_y$$

where $E_y = \dfrac{dV(y)}{dy}$

Plugging in and re-arranging produces

$$I_{DS}\, dy = W\mu_e \left[C_{ox}(V_{GS} - V_T - V(y)) - \frac{I_{DS}}{W\mu_e E_c} \right] dV(y)$$

After integration, we obtain

$$I_{DS} = \frac{W}{L} \frac{\mu_e C_{ox}}{\left(1 + \dfrac{V_{DS}}{E_c L} \right)} \left(V_{GS} - V_T - \frac{V_{DS}}{2} \right) V_{DS} \qquad (2.25)$$

This expression for the linear region is very similar to the previously derived equation except for the extra multiplier in the denominator. This is very convenient since we are only required to remember one additional term to obtain a more accurate current expression.

The next step is to determine the expression for the saturation region of operation. Saturation occurs when the carriers are moving at v_{sat}:

$$I_{DS} = W \times Q_n \times v_{sat} \qquad (2.26)$$

Since the current is the same throughout the channel we can set $V(y) = V_{DS}$ and write

$$I_{DS} = W \times C_{ox} (V_{GS} - V_T - V_{DS})v_{sat} \qquad (2.27)$$

We can further simplify it by equating the expressions of I_{DS} in linear (2.25) and saturation (2.27) regions to obtain V_{Dsat}:

$$V_{Dsat} = \frac{(V_{GS} - V_T)\, E_c L}{(V_{GS} - V_T) + E_c L} \qquad (2.28)$$

The difference between this expression and the first-order expression for V_{Dsat} is the extra multiplier (recall that $V_{Dsat} = V_{GS} - V_T$ in the first-order model). The new factor $E_cL/(V_{GS} - V_T + E_cL) < 1$, so the value of the V_{Dsat} will always be lower than the first-order model. This is the effect of velocity saturation—devices saturate faster and deliver less current than the quadratic model would predict.

If we now substitute this new V_{Dsat} into our saturation current equation of (2.27) we obtain

$$I_{DS} = W\upsilon_{sat}C_{ox} \frac{(V_{GS} - V_T)^2}{(V_{GS} - V_T) + E_cL} \qquad (2.29)$$

Again, this equation is similar to the first-order current equation and will be easy to remember. It is different from Equation (2.19) but has a familiar quadratic form in the numerator.

Consider the limiting cases for this equation. What happens if $E_cL >> V_{GS} - V_T$ (i.e., a long-channel device)? The equation reduces to our quadratic expression:

$$I_{DS} = \frac{W}{2L} \mu_e C_{ox} (V_{GS} - V_T)^2$$

Now consider what happens if $E_cL << V_{GS} - V_T$, that is, if we have a very short channel. We obtain an equation where the current is linear in $V_{GS} - V_T$, as we would expect for very short-channel devices:

$$I_{DS} = W\upsilon_{sat}C_{ox}(V_{GS} - V_T)$$

NMOS and PMOS Saturation Voltages for 0.18 μm Technology   **Example 2.6**

Problem:

Consider a 0.18 μm technology. Compute the values of V_{Dsat} for the NMOS and PMOS device assuming $V_{GS} = 1.8$ V, $V_{TN} = 0.5$ V, $V_{TP} = -0.5$ V. Assume the channel length is 200 nm for convenience.

Solution:

Using (2.22), we find that $E_{cn}L_n = 6 \times 10^4 (0.2\ \mu m) \approx 1.2$ V and $E_{cp}L_p = 24 \times 10^4 (0.2\ \mu m) \approx 4.8$ V. Using (2.28),

NMOS: $V_{Dsat} = \dfrac{(1.8 - 0.5)(1.2)}{(1.8 - 0.5 + 1.2)} \approx 0.6$ V

PMOS: $V_{Dsat} = \dfrac{(1.8 - 0.5)(4.8)}{(1.8 - 0.5 + 4.8)} \approx 1.0$ V

The value computed for the NMOS device is consistent with the plot shown in Figure 2.11.

The results of Example 2.6 are important in device sizing. The fact that the PMOS device saturates at a higher voltage implies that it will be able to supply a

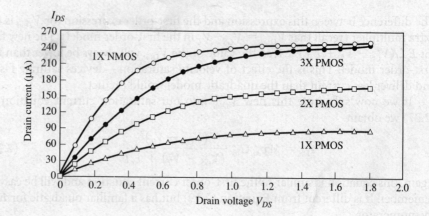

Figure 2.14
Effect of mobility and velocity saturation on device sizes.

higher than expected amount of current. To illustrate this, we plot the current for both NMOS and PMOS devices with the minimum (W/L) ratio in Figure 2.14. These two cases are labeled as 1X devices. In addition, we plot a 2X PMOS device and a 3X PMOS device. The 1X NMOS device and the 3X PMOS device deliver the same current in saturation even though mobility difference between the two 1X devices is 4:1. The device ratio is only 3:1 since the PMOS device saturates at a higher voltage.

To compare with hand analysis, consider the current ratio of the two 1X devices using Equation (2.29):

$$\frac{I_{DsatN}}{I_{DsatP}} = \frac{W_N \, v_{sat} \, C_{ox} \, (V_{GS} - V_{TN})^2 / (V_{GS} - V_{TN} + E_{CN}L_N)}{W_P \, v_{sat} \, C_{ox} \, (V_{GS} - V_{TP})^2 / (V_{GS} - V_{TP} + E_{CP}L_P)}$$

Plugging in our nominal values, we obtain

$$\frac{I_{DsatN}}{I_{DsatP}} = 2.4$$

Therefore, the required device ratio to deliver the same current in saturation is about 2.4X rather than 4X due to the difference in V_{Dsat}. Hand analysis underestimates the current ratio in saturation.

Example 2.7   **NMOS and PMOS Currents in Saturation for 0.13 μm Technology**

Problem:

Compute the saturation currents per micron of width for a 0.13 μm technology. Assume a channel length of 100 nm, $t_{ox} = 22$ Å, $V_{TN} = 0.4$ V, $V_{TP} = -0.4$ V, $V_{DD} = 1.2$ V. Use $v_{sat} = 8 \times 10^6$ cm/s.

Solution:

Using (2.22), we find that $E_{cn}L_n = 6 \times 10^4$ V/cm (0.1 μm) ≈ 0.6 V and $E_{cp}L_p = 24 \times 10^4$ V/cm (0.1 μm) ≈ 2.4 V.

Then, for the n-channel device:

$$I_{DS} = W v_{sat} C_{ox} \frac{(V_{GS} - V_T)^2}{(V_{GS} - V_T) + E_c L}$$

$$\therefore \frac{I_{DS}}{W} = v_{sat} C_{ox} \frac{(V_{GS} - V_T)^2}{(V_{GS} - V_T) + E_c L}$$

$$= (8 \times 10^6)(1.6 \times 10^{-6}) \frac{(1.2 - 0.4)^2}{(1.2 - 0.4) + 0.6} = 585 \ \mu A/\mu m$$

For the p-channel device,

$$\therefore \frac{I_{DS}}{W} = v_{sat} C_{ox} \frac{(V_{GS} - V_T)^2}{(V_{GS} - V_T) + E_c L}$$

$$= (8 \times 10^6)(1.6 \times 10^{-6}) \frac{(1.2 - 0.4)^2}{(1.2 - 0.4) + 2.4} = 256 \ \mu A/\mu m$$

To summarize the equations for deep submicron devices, we should first decide whether a device is in the linear region or saturation using the following inequalities:

$$\text{if } V_{DS} \geq \frac{(V_{GS} - V_T) E_c L}{(V_{GS} - V_T) + E_c L} \Rightarrow \text{saturation}$$

$$\text{if } V_{DS} < \frac{(V_{GS} - V_T) E_c L}{(V_{GS} - V_T) + E_c L} \Rightarrow \text{linear}$$

If we are in the saturation region, we should use the equation

$$I_{DS} = W v_{sat} C_{ox} \frac{(V_{GS} - V_T)^2}{(V_{GS} - V_T) + E_c L} \quad \text{saturation}$$

Note that there is still a channel length modulation effect, which we can capture as we did before. This involves the use of a parameter, λ, as follows:

$$I_{DS} = W v_{sat} C_{ox} \frac{(V_{GS} - V_T)^2}{(V_{GS} - V_T) + E_c L} (1 + \lambda V_{DS}) \quad \text{saturation}$$

The use of this equation is perhaps too cumbersome for hand calculations. Therefore, we will drop the last term and ensure that the I_{DS} is computed using the average value in saturation. For convenience, we set $\lambda = 0$.

If we are in the linear region, we should use the equation

$$I_{DS} = \frac{W}{L} \cdot \frac{\mu_e C_{ox}}{\left(1 + \frac{V_{DS}}{E_c L}\right)} \left(V_{GS} - V_T - \frac{V_{DS}}{2}\right) V_{DS} \quad \text{linear}$$

Example 2.8   **Current Ratio for 0.13 μm Process**

Problem:

Consider a 0.13 μm technology where the channel length is 100 nm. Using (2.22), $E_{cn}L_n = 0.6$ V and $E_{cp}L_p = 2.4$ V, and assuming that $V_{GS} = 1.2$ V and $V_{TN} = 0.4$ V, $V_{TP} = -0.4$ V, compute V_{Dsat} and the current ratio of two 1X devices in saturation.

Solution:

Using (2.28) we find that

NMOS: $V_{Dsat} = \dfrac{(1.2 - 0.4)(0.6)}{(1.2 - 0.4 + 0.6)} = 0.34$ V

PMOS: $V_{Dsat} = \dfrac{(1.2 - 0.4)(2.4)}{(1.2 - 0.4 + 2.4)} = 0.6$ V

The current ratio of the two 1X devices is

$$\frac{I_{DsatN}}{I_{DsatP}} = \frac{W_N \upsilon_{sat} C_{ox} \, (V_{GS} - V_{TN})^2 / (V_{GS} - V_{TN} + E_{CN}L_N)}{W_P \upsilon_{sat} C_{ox} \, (V_{GS} - V_{TP})^2 / (V_{GS} - V_{TP} + E_{CP}L_P)}$$

Plugging in our nominal values, we obtain

$$\frac{I_{DsatN}}{I_{DsatP}} = 2.3$$

---

*2.2.5 Alpha-Power Law Model

Another approach for a hand-calculation model is to empirically fit the real data to the following form of I_{DS} in saturation:

$$I_{DS} = K_S \frac{W}{L} (V_{GS} - V_T)^\alpha \tag{2.30a}$$

In this formulation, we can set K_S and α based on measured data. Clearly, α should be set to a value that is closer to 1 than 2. Today, α is approximately 1.25 but it will continue to approach 1 as technology scales.

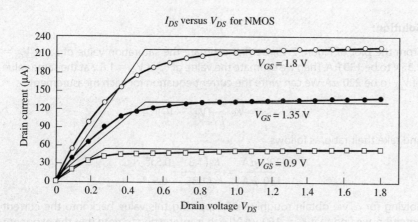

Figure 2.15
Alpha-power law modeling of MOS transistor.

Note that this model does not account for the behavior of the device in the linear region. Therefore, a simple model must be developed for the alpha-power law that fits both the linear and saturation regions, without a mismatch at the boundary between the two regions. An example of such a model for the linear region is to set

$$I_{DS} = K_L \frac{W}{L} (V_{GS} - V_T) V_{DS} \qquad (2.30b)$$

V_{Dsat} can be obtained by equating (2.30a) to (2.30b):

$$V_{Dsat} = \frac{K_S}{K_L} (V_{GS} - V_T)^{\alpha-1} \qquad (2.31)$$

The current versus voltage plots based on alpha-power law modeling is shown in Figure 2.15. The transistor characteristics in the saturation region are described by (2.30a) while the linear region is given by (2.30b). The interface between the two regions is obtained from (2.31). This model is suitable for hand calculations only after curve fitting is performed with the data points in the figure. If a new technology is developed, a new set of parameters must be extracted. The model derived earlier based on velocity saturation is a more general model and will be the primary model used in the rest of this book.

Parameters for Alpha-Power Law   **Example 2.9**

Problem:

Find K_S and α based on Figure 2.15 for the NMOS device using the saturation region alpha-power law model. Assume $(W/L) = 1$ and $V_T = 0.5$ V.

Solution:

From the plot of Figure 2.15, we first estimate the saturation value of I_{DS} at $V_{GS} = 1.35\,V$ to be $130\,\mu A$. Then we estimate the value of I_{DS} at $V_{GS} = 1.8\,V$ at the same value of V_{DS} to be $220\,\mu A$. We can write the current equation for each measurement as

$$I_{DS} = K_S \frac{W}{L} (V_{GS} - V_T)^\alpha$$

and take their ratio, as follows:

$$\frac{220\ \mu A}{130\ \mu A} = \frac{K_S(1.8 - 0.5)^\alpha}{K_S(1.35 - 0.5)^\alpha}$$

Solving for α, we obtain roughly 1.25. Applying this value back into the current equation, we find that $K_S = 160\ \mu A/V^{1.25}$. It is interesting to note that the exponent is close to 1. This is expected since the long-channel device has an exponent of 2 and a very short-channel device would have an exponent of 1.

One way to check the results would be to compute the current for the case when $V_{GS} = 0.9\,V$:

$$I_{DS} = 160\ \frac{\mu A}{V^{1.25}}\ (1)(0.9 - 0.5)^{1.25} \approx 50\ \mu A$$

This value is close to the expected value based on Figure 2.15.

2.2.6 Subthreshold Conduction

So far, there has been an implicit assumption that the current I_{DS} in the cutoff region is zero. In actual fact, there is appreciable transistor current even if $V_{GS} < V_T$, especially for deep submicron transistors. This section explores this previously negligible component of current that is increasingly important as technology scales. The magnitude of the current is small compared to the current when $V_{GS} > V_T$. However, if we have millions of such devices all leaking current, the standby power dissipation will be large. This is becoming a big concern for deep submicron technologies. As we will see in later chapters, this leakage current will prove to be problematic for dynamic logic circuits and dynamic memories, as it will discharge capacitances that store logic values. In technologies prior to 0.18 μm, this current was considered a second-order effect, but it is now a first-order concern and deserves some attention in this book.

In the derivation of the threshold voltage expression, the strong inversion condition was defined (somewhat arbitrarily) as the point at which the surface potential is $2|\phi_F|$ below the level in bulk silicon. However, in practice, surface inversion occurs well before this point and there are mobile carriers in the channel region capable of conducting current. The term *subthreshold region* is preferred to describe the case where $V_{GS} < V_T$, rather than *cutoff*, since there is current flow. As shown in Figure 2.16, I_{DS} is a continuous function of V_{GS} and drops off in a logarithmic fashion in the subthreshold region as V_{GS} is decreased. Figure 2.16 illustrates all three regions of operation and the associated current characteristics of the NMOS and PMOS devices.

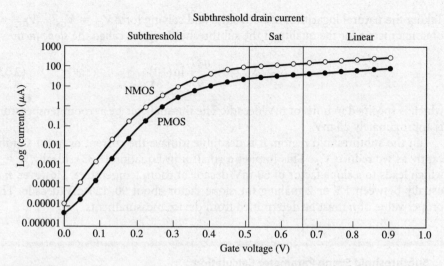

Figure 2.16
MOS current versus V_{GS}.

The mechanism for subthreshold current flow is due to the diffusion of minority carriers when the gate voltage is several thermal voltages less than V_T. In the subthreshold region, the MOS transistor behaves more like a (lateral) bipolar transistor (see Appendix B). The substrate is the base region, while the source and drain act as the emitter and collector, respectively. Therefore, modeling of the current can be carried out using a derivation based on bipolar modeling. In particular, the current equation in this region takes the form:

$$I_{sub} = I_s e^{\frac{q(V_{GS} - V_T - V_{offset})}{nkT}} \left(1 - e^{\frac{-qV_{DS}}{kT}}\right) \tag{2.32}$$

where I_s represents a current coefficient, V_{offset} is the sum of a number of voltage terms and lies in the range -0.1 to 0.1, and the factor n is a subthreshold swing parameter, typically ranging from 1 to 2. We can determine the value of n by considering how much voltage change in V_{GS} produces an *order of magnitude* change in the subthreshold current:

$$\frac{10\, I_{sub}}{I_{sub}} = \frac{I_s e^{\frac{q(V_{GS1} - V_T - V_{offset})}{nkT}} \left(1 - e^{\frac{-qV_{DS}}{kT}}\right)}{I_s e^{\frac{q(V_{GS2} - V_T - V_{offset})}{nkT}} \left(1 - e^{\frac{-qV_{DS}}{kT}}\right)}$$

$$\therefore 10 = \frac{e^{\frac{q(V_{GS1} - V_T - V_{offset})}{nkT}}}{e^{\frac{q(V_{GS2} - V_T - V_{offset})}{nkT}}} = e^{\frac{q(V_{GS1} - V_{GS2})}{nkT}}$$

Taking the natural logarithm of both sides and solving for $\Delta V_{GS} = V_{GS} - V_{GS2}$, we obtain a metric for the quality of the subthreshold region, called the *slope factor*:

$$S = \Delta V_{GS} = \frac{nkT}{q} \ln(10) \qquad (2.33)$$

which is specified in units of mV/decade. The thermal voltage at room temperature is approximately 26 mV.

In the subthreshold region, it is desirable to have the current drop off significantly as we reduce V_{GS}. This implies a small n in Equation (2.33). Ideally, $n = 1$ which leads to a slope factor of 60 mV/decade at room temperature. However, n is usually between 1.5 or 2 making the slope factor about 90–120 mV/decade. The proper value of n must be determined from device measurements.

Example 2.10   **Subthreshold Swing Parameter Calculation**

Problem:

From the plot of $\log(I_{DS})$ versus V_{GS} in Figure 2.16 with $V_{DS} = 1.8$ V, find n and the slope factor in the subthreshold region for the PMOS device.

Solution:

By measuring the subthreshold current at 10 nA and 100 nA the values for V_{GS} are

	V_{GS} (V)
10 nA	0.140
100 nA	0.212

From these points, $n = 1.2$ for PMOS. The slope factor is approximately $S = 60$ mV/decade $\times$ 1.2 = 72 mV/decade, which is close to the ideal value.

2.2.7   Capacitances of the MOS Transistor

The switching speed of MOS digital circuits is limited by the time required to charge and discharge the capacitances at internal nodes. Within VLSI circuits most of these capacitances are so small that they are difficult to measure directly. For circuit analysis, these capacitances must be calculated from device dimensions and dielectric constants. The capacitance values are usually specified in femto-Farads per μm of width (i.e., fF/μm). In the description to follow, the subscripts will be lowercase to imply these units. Total capacitance values use uppercase subscripts.

Figure 2.17 shows the significant capacitances between nodes of an MOS transistor. There are two basic types of nonlinear or voltage-dependent capacitances in the structure: thin-oxide capacitances and junction capacitances. The thin-oxide capacitances comprised of C_{gs}, C_{gd}, and C_{gb} are represented by C_g. The junction

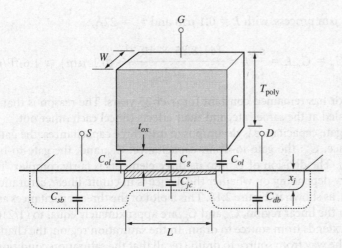

Figure 2.17
Capacitances of the MOS transistor.

capacitances are shown as C_{sb}, and C_{db}. In addition, there are two overlap capacitances, C_{ol}, which are linear and voltage-independent. Finally, the depletion layer capacitance under the channel, C_{jc}, is associated with C_{gb}, although a small part of this capacitance is associated with the drain and source on either edge. These types of capacitances are described in more detail in the sections below.

2.2.7.1 Thin-Oxide Capacitance

The thin-oxide capacitance is perhaps the most important capacitance in the MOS system. The two plates of the capacitance are defined as the gate and the channel. The dielectric material is the oxide sandwiched between these two plates. The total capacitance of the thin-oxide is:

$$C_G = WLC_{ox} = WL\frac{\varepsilon_{ox}}{t_{ox}} = WC_g \qquad (2.34)$$

where C_{ox} is the capacitance per unit area of the gate dielectric as defined in Equation 2.5. It is interesting to examine the factor, C_g. In a 5 μm technology, the oxide thickness was approximately 1100 Å. Therefore,

$$C_g = C_{ox}L = \frac{\varepsilon_{ox}}{t_{ox}}L = \frac{(4)(8.85 \times 10^{-14})}{1100}(5 \ \mu m) \cong 1.6 \ fF/\mu m$$

In a 0.35 μm process, with $t_{ox} = 75$Å,

$$C_g = C_{ox}L = \frac{\varepsilon_{ox}}{t_{ox}}L = \frac{(4)(8.85 \times 10^{-14})}{75}(0.35 \ \mu m) \cong 1.6 \ fF/\mu m$$

In a 0.13 μm process, with $L = 0.1$ μm and $t_{ox} = 22$Å,

$$C_g = C_{ox}L = \frac{\varepsilon_{ox}}{t_{ox}}L = \frac{(4)(8.85 \times 10^{-14})}{22}(0.1 \ \mu m) \cong 1.6 \ \text{fF}/\mu m$$

This factor has remained constant for over 25 years! The reason is that both L and t_{ox} are scaled at the same rate, and their effects cancel each other out.

The gate capacitance is decomposed into three capacitances: the gate-to-source capacitance, C_{gs}; the gate-to-drain capacitance, C_{gd}; and, the gate-to-bulk capacitance, C_{gb}. The division of C_g into its three elements is fairly complex. The components vary depending on whether the device is in cutoff, linear, saturation, or accumulation, as shown in Figure 2.18. This a plot of the three capacitances as a function of V_{GS}. In the linear region, C_{gs} and C_{gd} are approximately equal to $(1/2)C_g$ since the channel extends from source to drain. In the saturation region, the channel extends most of the way from source to drain (recall that the saturation condition is defined by the carriers reaching velocity saturation), so most of the gate capacitance can be attributed to the source node, and a negligible amount to the drain node. For this region, a detailed analysis would show the capacitances to be $C_{gs} = (2/3)C_g$ and $C_{gd} = 0$.

When the device is in cutoff, then $C_{gs} = C_{gd} = 0$. All of the capacitance is attributed to C_{gb}, the gate-to-bulk capacitance. However, in this regime, there is a depletion region under the gate and we have C_g in series with C_{jc}, which is the channel junction capacitance. As a result, the total capacitance is less than C_g (since it is in series with C_{jc}) until we reach the accumulation region. At this point, the channel is positively charged while the gate is negatively charged producing a total capacitance

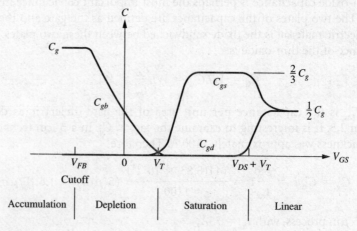

Figure 2.18
Capacitances based on region of operation.

of C_g. In normal operation, we are not usually concerned with the accumulation region of operation, but it is included for completeness. Note that when $V_{GS} = 0$, the value of C_{gb} is about $1/2$ C_g. It does not reach C_g until the gate voltage is equal to the flat-band voltage.

Thin-Oxide Capacitance Calculation   **Example 2.11**

Problem:

Compute the gate capacitance in the cutoff, linear, and saturation regions for a PMOS device with $t_{ox} = 22$ Å and device dimensions of $W = 400$ nm and $L = 100$ nm. Assume that $V_{GS} = 0$ in the cutoff region.

Solution:

The total capacitance is $C_g W = 1.6$ fF/μm $\times$ 0.4 μm $= 0.64$ fF.
In cutoff: $C_{GS} = 0, C_{GD} = 0, C_{GB} \cong 0.64$ fF/2 $= 0.32$ fF
In linear: $C_{GS} = 0.32$ fF, $C_{GD} = 0.32$ fF, $C_{GB} = 0$
In saturation: $C_{GS} = 0.43$ fF, $C_{GD} = 0, C_{GB} = 0$

2.2.7.2 *pn* Junction Capacitance

The source and drain regions and the substrate form *pn* junctions that give rise to two additional capacitances. The capacitances C_{sb} and C_{db} are n^+p source/drain junction capacitances for NMOS devices and are readily calculated using layout information. For PMOS devices, the capacitances are due to p^+n source/drain junctions. In addition, there is a junction capacitance between the inverted channel and the substrate, C_{jc}. Since the *pn* junction is a diode, it is worth revisiting some of the basic physics for this diode circuit element.

The current-voltage characteristic of a diode is given by

$$I_D = I_S(e^{V_J/V_{th}} - 1) \tag{2.35}$$

where I_S is the reverse saturation current of the diode, V_J is the voltage drop across the diode, and V_{th} is the thermal voltage. In normal operation, the *pn* junctions are all reverse-biased in a MOS transistor. When specifying the voltages at the source/drain and bulk terminals, we must ensure that the bulk is connected to the lowest voltage for NMOS devices. Similarly, for PMOS devices, the bulk voltage must be the highest potential in the system. Otherwise, we risk forward-biasing the diode.

Since $V_J < 0$, the exponential term in Equation (2.35) is small. In essence, for our MOS devices,

$$I_D = -I_S \tag{2.36}$$

This represents the *leakage* current of the MOS transistor, which is unwanted current flow from source/drain regions into the substrate. The actual value of leakage

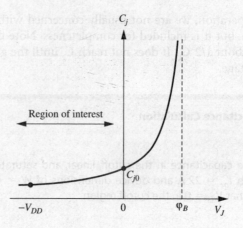

Figure 2.19
Plot of junction capacitance versus applied voltage.

is relatively small and depends on the area and the doping levels on each side of the junction.

The built-in junction potential for a diode is another important quantity in *pn* junction theory. It is computed using the equation:

$$\phi_B = \frac{kT}{q} \ln \frac{N_A N_D}{n_i^2} \tag{2.37}$$

Now we return to the more important discussion of junction capacitance. The depletion region of the diode has a capacitance effect associated with it since the modulation of diode voltage V_J changes the charge that is exposed or "covered up" in this *space-charge region*. This is equivalent to the action of a capacitor. The basic expression for junction capacitance is given by

$$C_J = \frac{C_{j0} A}{\left(1 - \frac{V_J}{\phi_B}\right)^m} \tag{2.38}$$

where C_{j0} is the zero-bias junction capacitance, A is the area of the junction, ϕ_B is the built-in junction potential, and m is the junction grading coefficient, which is approximately 1/2 for abrupt junctions (p^+n or n^+p). This function is plotted in Figure 2.19. The built-in junction potential defines the point where C_j asymptotically approaches infinity.[11] We can see that C_{j0} is an important quantity since it

---

[11] This would not occur in practice. The capacitance would reach some level and begin to "roll-over" as V_J increases. In any case, we are mostly interested in the reverse-biased region of operation where $V_J < 0$.

represents the value of junction capacitance when the external bias is 0 V. Its value is computed using the equation

$$C_{j0} = \sqrt{\frac{\varepsilon_{si} q}{2\phi_B} \frac{N_A N_D}{N_A + N_D}} \qquad (2.39)$$

For a one-sided step junction, where one region has a much higher doping level than the other region, we can simplify the expression. For an $n^+ p$ junction of the NMOS device, the equation is

$$C_{j0} = \sqrt{\frac{\varepsilon_{si} q N_A}{2\phi_B}} \qquad (2.40)$$

Since the junctions in a MOS transistor are normally reverse-biased, the junction capacitances are usually less than C_{j0}. This quantity is in units of fF/μm^2 and therefore it must be multiplied by the area of the junction to obtain the actual capacitance. The denominator of Equation (2.38) can be viewed as an adjustment factor due to the applied voltage. In our case, this is V_{BS} or V_{BD}, which is either zero or a negative quantity but never positive (otherwise we would have a forward-biased source/drain junction). Note that we are operating in the range of $V_J = 0$ to $-V_{DD}$ in normal mode for NMOS transistors, as indicated in Figure 2.19.

In order to compute the capacitance associated with the source and drain, we need to examine the transistor layout. Shown in Figure 2.20 is a very simple layout

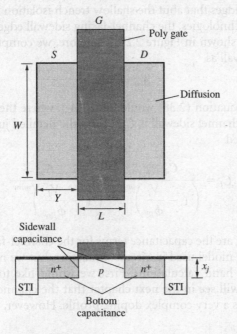

Figure 2.20

Junction capacitances from layout data.

of a MOS transistor in plan view and, below it, the corresponding cross-sectional view. In the layout view, there is a shaded polysilicon gate on top of a diffusion region. The intersection of polysilicon and diffusion forms a transistor. The gate (G), drain (D), and source (S) terminals are shown, along with the W, L, and Y dimensions of the transistor. The source/drain junction capacitances we seek are associated with the diffusion region, and so it is sometimes called the *diffusion* capacitance.

There are two types of junction capacitances that need to be computed for the NMOS device, namely the *bottom* capacitance and the *sidewall* capacitance. In the case of the bottom capacitance, we need to compute the area of the bottom region and the zero-bias value, C_{jb}, from the parameters for the n^+p junction. Looking at the layout, the area calculation for the bottom capacitance is as follows

$$A_b = WY$$

where W is the device width and Y is the diffusion extension from the poly gate edge. The junction is an n^+p junction so the numerator of Equation (2.38) would be equal to $C_{jb}A_b$.

For the sidewall capacitance, we need to take each edge of the junction and then multiply by the junction depth, x_j, to obtain the sidewall areas. A total of four faces need to be considered. Three edges are associated with the interface of the n^+ region and the shallow trench isolation,[12] and a fourth edge is due to an n^+p junction for the sidewall facing the channel.

Since the three edges that abut the shallow trench isolation have a small capacitance in modern technologies, the channel-facing sidewall edge is the only one we need to consider, as shown in Figure 2.20. Therefore, we compute the area for the channel-facing sidewall as

$$A_{sw} = Wx_j$$

The numerator of Equation (2.38) would be $C_{jsw}A_{sw}$, where the zero-bias junction capacitance for the channel sidewall is C_{jsw}. Now, the detailed junction capacitance equation can be stated

$$C_J = \frac{C_{jb}\, A_b}{\left(1 - \dfrac{V_J}{\phi_{Bb}}\right)^{mj}} + \frac{C_{jsw}\, A_{sw}}{\left(1 - \dfrac{V_J}{\phi_{Bsw}}\right)^{mjsw}} \tag{2.41}$$

where $mjsw$ and ϕ_{Bsw} are the capacitance terms for the channel-facing sidewall. This equation reflects the model used in circuit simulators, but we need to simplify the equation for use in hand calculations. First we would like to combine the two terms together. We will see in the next chapter that the channel-facing edge (i.e., the second term) has a very complex doping profile. However, if we consider it to

---

[12] Shallow-trench isolation will be described in more detail in Chapter 3.

be primarily an n^+p junction, then we can combine the two terms together. In fact, only a small error is made with this simplification

$$C_J = \frac{C_{jb}A_b + C_{jb}A_{sw}}{\left(1 - \frac{V_J}{\phi_B}\right)^{mj}} = \frac{C_{jb}(A_b + A_{sw})}{\left(1 - \frac{V_J}{\phi_B}\right)^{mj}}$$
(2.42)

Next, we would like to remove the voltage dependence of the term in the denominator of Equation (2.42) to produce a large-signal equivalent value. To do this, we can look back at Figure 2.19 and realize that the only region of interest is when $V_J \leq 0$, since the junctions are normally reverse-biased. If $V_J = 0$, then the denominator of Equation (2.42) is equal to one. If there is a reverse-bias of $-V_{DD}$, the denominator is between 1 and 2. One way to handle the voltage dependence is to define a new parameter, K_{eq}, which adjusts the zero-bias capacitance, C_{jb}, based on the expected bias voltage across the junction.

Since the voltage in digital circuits is expected to switch from low-to-high and vice-versa, we can use this fact to compute K_{eq}. To this end, we define an equivalent voltage-independent capacitance C_{eq} that requires the same change in charge as the nonlinear capacitance for a transition between two voltages V_1 and V_2 applied to the junction:

$$C_{eq} = \frac{Q_j(V_2) - Q_j(V_1)}{V_2 - V_1} = \frac{\Delta Q}{\Delta V}$$

where

$$\Delta Q = \int_{V_1}^{V_2} C(V)dV = \int_{V_1}^{V_2} C_{jb}\left(1 - \frac{V}{\phi_B}\right)^{-m} dV$$

Thus

$$C_{eq} = -\frac{C_{jb}\phi_B}{(V_2 - V_1)(1 - m)}\left[\left(1 - \frac{V_2}{\phi_B}\right)^{1-m} - \left(1 - \frac{V_1}{\phi_B}\right)^{1-m}\right]$$

We are now able to define K_{eq}, the dimensionless constant used to relate C_{eq} to C_{jb} for specified values of V_1 and V_2. In the case of an abrupt junction, $m = 1/2$, and therefore

$$K_{eq} = \frac{C_{eq}}{C_{jb}} = \frac{-2\phi_B^{1/2}}{V_2 - V_1}[(\phi_B - V_2)^{1/2} - (\phi_B - V_1)^{1/2}]$$
(2.43)

Fortunately, this complicated equation is required in only one case. Once computed, the simplified equation for hand calculations is as follows:

$$C_J = K_{eq}(C_{jb}WY + C_{jb}x_jW) = K_{eq}(C_{jb}Y + C_{jb}x_j)W = K_{eq}C_{jb}(Y + x_j)W$$
(2.44)

All the leading terms of the capacitance can be combined to produce a relatively straightforward equation for hand calculations:

$$C_J = K_{eq}C_{jb}(Y + x_j)W = C_jW \qquad (2.45)$$

Note that if the voltage switches from one level to the other, $K_{eq} \cong 0.75$. However, if there is a fixed voltage across the junction then we do not need to use Equation (2.43) to determine K_{eq}. In NMOS devices, if a source or drain node is close to Gnd, then $V_{SB} = 0$ so we can set $K_{eq} = 1.0$. If a node is close to V_{DD} we should use the capacitance value at $V_J = -V_{DD}$. For this case, we should set $K_{eq} \cong 0.5$ since there is a large voltage drop across the junction. Similar considerations apply for PMOS devices with similar capacitance values.

One final note on junction capacitance: the channel junction capacitance, C_{jc}, shown in Figure 2.18 uses the same formulation as given in Equation (2.38). This term is associated mainly with the gate-to-bulk capacitance. There is a small portion of it that is charged from the source and drain, but it is negligible and usually ignored.

Example 2.12   **Junction Capacitance Calculations**

Problem:

(a) Find ϕ_B and C_{jb} for an n^+p junction diode with $N_D = 10^{20}$ cm^{-3} and $N_A = (3)10^{17}$ cm^{-3}.

Solution:

From Equation (2.37),

$$\phi_B = \frac{kT}{q} \ln \frac{N_A N_D}{n_i^2} = 0.026 \ln \left(\frac{3(10^{17})(10^{20})}{(1.45(10^{10}))^2} \right) = 1 \text{ V}$$

From Equation (2.39)

$$C_{jb} = \sqrt{\frac{\varepsilon_{si}q}{2\phi_B} \frac{N_A N_D}{N_A + N_D}} \approx \sqrt{\frac{\varepsilon_{si}qN_A}{2\phi_B}}$$

$$= \sqrt{\frac{11.7 \times (8.85)(10^{-14}) \times 1.6(10^{-19})(3)(10^{17})}{2(1.0)}} \approx 1.6 \frac{fF}{\mu m^2}$$

Problem:

(b) For a 0.13 μm process, $W = 400$ nm, $L = 100$ nm, $x_j = 50$ nm, and the diffusion extension is $Y = 300$ nm. Using the layout of Figure 2.20, find C_J in units of fF for and $V_J = 0$ and $V_J = -1.2$ V.

Solution:

For $V_J = 0$, the value is obtained by multiplying C_{jb} with $(Y+x_j)W$

$$C_J = C_{jb}(Y + x_j)W = 1.6 \text{ fF}/\mu m^2 \times (0.3\mu m + 0.05\mu m) \times 0.4\mu m \approx 0.22 \text{ fF}$$

For $V_J = -1.2$,

$$C_J = \frac{C_{jb}(Y + x_j)W}{(1 - V_J/\phi_B)^m}$$

$$= \frac{1.6 \text{ fF}/\mu\text{m} \times (0.3 \ \mu\text{m} + 0.05 \ \mu\text{m}) \times 0.4 \ \mu\text{m}}{(1 + 1.2/1.0)^{1/2}} = 0.16 \text{ fF}$$

Problem:

(c) Find K_{eq} for $V_1 = -1.2$ V, $V_2 = 0$ and then compute the large-signal effective C_J.

Solution:

From Equation (2.43),

$$K_{eq} = \frac{-2(1)^{1/2}}{0 - (-1.2)} \left[(1 - 0)^{1/2} - (1 - (-1.2))^{1/2} \right] = 0.8$$

To compute C_J, we use

$$\therefore C_J = K_{eq}C_{jb}(Y + x_j)W$$

$$= 0.8 \times 1.6 \text{ fF}/\mu\text{m}^2 \times (0.3 \ \mu\text{m} + 0.05 \ \mu\text{m}) \times 0.4 \ \mu\text{m} \approx 0.18 \text{ fF}$$

Overlap Capacitance

The overlap capacitance, C_{ol}, shown on both sides of the gate in Figure 2.17 is due to *lateral diffusion* and *fringing* components. This voltage-independent capacitance is connected from gate-to-drain and from gate-to-source. In the older technologies, there was significant diffusion of the heavily doped source and drain regions under the gate. This gave rise to the overlap capacitance, C_{ov}. However, over the years, the fringing capacitance, C_f, between the sidewall of the polysilicon and the surface of the drain and source has increased and must also be taken into account. It is difficult to separate out the components due to lateral diffusion and fringing so the combination of the two is referred to as C_{ol}.

$$C_{ol} = C_{ov} + C_f \tag{2.46}$$

The two components are shown in Figure 2.21. They should always be included in the capacitance calculation to obtain accurate results. We can try to estimate this overlap capacitance for hand calculations as follows. The fringing component can be approximated by the formulation

$$C_f = \frac{2\varepsilon_{ox}}{\pi} \ln \left(1 + \frac{T_{poly}}{t_{ox}} \right) \tag{2.47}$$

where T_{poly} is the thickness of the polysilicon material that sits on the oxide.

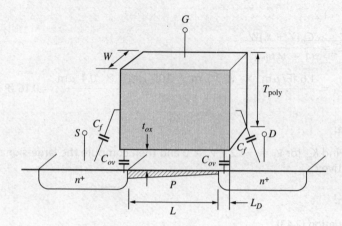

Figure 2.21
Overlap capacitance components.

The capacitance due to lateral diffusion is computed as

$$C_{ov} = C_{ox} \times L_D$$

where L_D is a lateral diffusion term illustrated in Figure 2.21.

Example 2.13	**Overlap Capacitance Calculations**

Problem:

Compute the overlap capacitance, C_{ol}, for a 0.13 μm technology with $T_{poly}/t_{ox} = 100$ and a lateral diffusion of 10 nm. Specify the solution in units of fF/μm of width.

Solution:

If we apply the ratio T_{poly}/t_{ox} to (2.47), then

$$C_f = \frac{2(4)(8.85 \times 10^{-14})}{3.14} \ln (1 + 100) \approx 0.1 \text{ fF}/\mu\text{m}$$

If $L_D = 10$ nm, then $C_{ov} = C_{ox}L_D \approx 0.15$ fF/μm. Therefore, for convenience we will use

$$C_{ol} = 0.1 \text{ fF}/\mu\text{m} + 0.15 \text{ fF}/\mu\text{m} = 0.25 \text{ fF}/\mu\text{m}$$

This value is multiplied by the width of the device to obtain the total overlap capacitance.

2.2.8 Summary

Operating voltages for the NMOS and PMOS devices:

NMOS Voltages	PMOS Voltages
$V_{TN} \geq 0$ V	$V_{TP} \leq 0$ V or $|V_{TP}| \geq 0$ V
$V_{GS} \geq 0$ V	$V_{GS} \leq 0$ V or $|V_{GS}| \geq 0$ V
$V_{DS} \geq 0$ V	$V_{DS} \leq 0$ V or $|V_{DS}| \geq 0$ V
$V_{BS} \leq 0$ V or $V_{SB} \geq 0$ V	$V_{BS} \geq 0$ V

The NMOS threshold voltage can be computed as follows (with appropriate changes for PMOS device):

$$V_T = V_{T0} + \gamma \left(\sqrt{|2\phi_F| + V_{SB}} - \sqrt{|2\phi_F|} \right)$$

$$V_{T0} = \phi_{GC} - 2\phi_F - \frac{Q_{B0}}{C_{ox}} - \frac{Q_{ox}}{C_{ox}} + \frac{Q_I}{C_{ox}}$$

$$\phi_F = \frac{kT}{q} \ln \frac{n_i}{p} \quad (p\text{-type substrate})$$

$$\gamma = \frac{1}{C_{ox}} \sqrt{2q\varepsilon_{si}N_A}$$

For long-channel devices, the current equations are as follows:

If $V_{GS} \geq V_T$

if $V_{DS} \geq (V_{GS} - V_T)$ saturation region $I_{DS} = \dfrac{k}{2} (V_{GS} - V_T)^2 (1 + \lambda V_{DS})$

if $V_{DS} < (V_{GS} - V_T)$ linear region $I_{DS} = \dfrac{k}{2} \left[2(V_{GS} - V_T)V_{DS} - V_{DS}^2 \right]$

If $V_{GS} < V_T$

subthreshold conduction region $I_{DS} = 0$

For the velocity saturated short-channel devices, use

If $V_{GS} \geq V_T$

if $V_{DS} \geq \dfrac{(V_{GS} - V_T)E_cL}{(V_{GS} - V_T) + E_cL}$ saturation region $I_{DS} = Wv_{sat}C_{ox} \dfrac{(V_{GS} - V_T)^2}{(V_{GS} - V_T) + E_cL}$

if $V_{DS} < \dfrac{(V_{GS} - V_T)E_cL}{(V_{GS} - V_T) + E_cL}$ linear region $I_{DS} = \dfrac{W}{L} \dfrac{\mu_e C_{ox}}{\left(1 + \dfrac{V_{DS}}{E_cL} \right)} \left(V_{GS} - V_T - \dfrac{V_{DS}}{2} \right) V_{DS}$

If $V_{GS} \leq V_T$

subthreshold conduction region $\quad I_{DS} = I_s e^{\frac{q(V_{GS} - V_T - V_{offset})}{nkT}} \left(1 - e^{\frac{-qV_{DS}}{kT}} \right)$

Simple expressions for total MOS capacitances associated with thin oxide:

	Cutoff	Linear	Saturation
C_{GS}	0	$\frac{1}{2}C_{ox}WL$	$\frac{2}{3}C_{ox}WL$
C_{GD}	0	$\frac{1}{2}C_{ox}WL$	0
C_{GB}	$C_{ox}WL$	0	0

Equations for junction capacitances:

$$C_J = \frac{C_{j0}A}{\left(1 - \dfrac{V_J}{\phi_B}\right)^m}$$

$$C_J = \frac{C_{jb}(A_b + A_{sw})}{\left(1 - \dfrac{V_J}{\phi_B}\right)^{mj}}$$

$$C_J = K_{eq}C_{jb}(Y + x_j)W = C_j W$$

where $C_j = K_{eq}C_{jb}(Y + x_j)$

Complete table of MOS transistor capacitances (including C_{ol} and C_{jc}) in fF/μm of width:

	Cutoff	Linear	Saturation
C_{gs}	C_{ol}	$C_{ol} + \frac{1}{2}C_g$	$C_{ol} + \frac{2}{3}C_g$
C_{gd}	C_{ol}	$C_{ol} + \frac{1}{2}C_g$	C_{ol}
C_{gb}	$(1/C_g + 1/C_{jc} < C_{gb} < C_g)$	0	0
C_{sb}	C_{jSB}	$C_{jSB} + \alpha_1 C_{jc}$	$C_{jSB} + \beta_1 C_{jc}$ (α, β small)
C_{db}	C_{jDB}	$C_{jDB} + \alpha_2 C_{jc}$	$C_{jDB} + \beta_2 C_{jc}$ (α, β small)

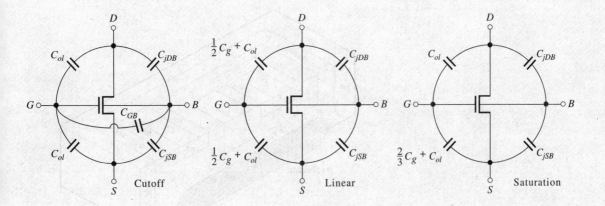

Cutoff   Linear   Saturation

2.3   Bipolar Transistors and Circuits

2.3.1   The Bipolar Junction Transistor

Before manufacturable MOS technologies were developed, digital integrated circuits were based upon bipolar junction transistors (BJTs) and Schottky-barrier (metal-semiconductor) diodes (SBDs). The word *bipolar* refers to the fact that both electrons and holes are required for normal operation of the BJT. For MOS transistors (sometimes termed *unipolar*), only one type of mobile carrier is required for normal operation.

This section provides a brief summary of the structure and operation of BJTs and SBDs, and an introduction to the most widely used digital circuits based upon them. A short summary of the model representations for BJTs and SBDs in the SPICE circuit simulation program is also included.

An *npn* bipolar junction transistor is made by forming two *pn* junctions in a single silicon crystal, such that the *p* region is common and very narrow ($\leq 0.5\ \mu$m). This is shown in cross section in Figure 2.22(a), where the two *n* regions, the emitter *E* and the collector *C*, sandwich the *p* region, the base *B*. The analysis that follows is idealized in that a one-dimensional structure is assumed. The dashed lines in Figure 2.22(a) show where such a region may be assumed to exist.

The biasing batteries as shown in Figure 2.22(b) cause the transistor to operate in the forward active mode. That is, the base-emitter junction is forward-biased by V_{BE} being positive at the base, and the base-collector junction is reverse-biased by V_{CB} being positive at the collector. The emitter must be much more heavily doped (*n-type*) than the base (*p-type*) to achieve effective operation.

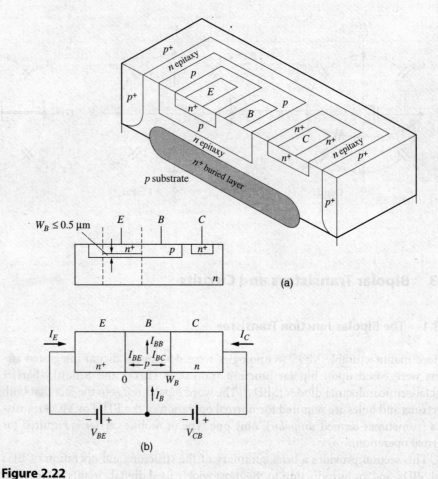

Figure 2.22
(a) Cross section of *npn* bipolar junction transistor. (b) *npn* transistor structure biased in the forward active mode.

As we forward-bias the emitter junction, electrons (the majority carriers in the emitter of this *npn* example) are thus injected (emitted) into the base, where they become minority carriers since the base is a *p* region. At the reverse-biased collector junction, electrons are swept out (collected) by the positive collector and are seen as collector current, I_C.

The steady-state distribution of injected electrons across the base is shown in Figure 2.23. During transit, a small fraction of the electrons in transit (typically less than 1%) are lost to recombination and are seen as current at the base, I_B. The injected electron current, the emitter current I_E, crosses the base region primarily by *diffusion* driven by the electron concentration gradient from left to right. The ratio

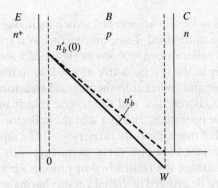

Figure 2.23

Excess minority carrier concentration in neutral base region; *npn* transistor biased in forward active mode.

of I_C/I_B is the dc common emitter forward current gain, β_F. A typical value is $\beta_F = 100$. The ratio of I_C/I_E is the dc forward current gain; $\alpha_F \approx 0.99$ is typical.

Because the emitter-base junction is a normal *pn* junction, we can relate the emitter current I_E to the base-emitter voltage V_{BE} using

$$I_E = I_S(e^{V_{BE}/V_T} - 1) \qquad (2.48)$$

where I_S the reverse saturation current of the emitter-base diode, and V_T is the thermal voltage given by kT/q. (Note: this is not the threshold voltage of the MOS device.) A typical value for an integrated circuit transistor is $I_S = 10^{-16}$ A.

Below, when we discuss the dynamic properties of the junction transistor, we will make use of the charge-control expressions. This will require a knowledge of the *excess minority carrier charge* Q_F stored in the neutral base region. Consider a steady-state condition and neglect the small loss due to recombination. The integral of the triangular area under the charge distribution shown in Figure 2.23 can be interpreted as being proportional to Q_F. The slope of the distribution can be interpreted as being proportional to flux of charge, or current I_C. For a fixed base width W, current I_C and charge Q_F must be in direct proportion, with a constant of proportionality having dimensions of time. Thus we define the relationship:

$$Q_F = \tau_F I_C \qquad (2.49)$$

We term the constant τ_F as the *mean forward transit time* of the minority carriers in the base. It is the mean time for the minority carriers to diffuse across the neutral base region from the emitter to the collector.

Simply considering the geometry in Figure 2.23, it is clear that if the current (slope) is held constant while base width W is increased, the charge (area) must increase in proportion to W^2. To achieve fast switching in digital circuits, the charge to be moved should be minimized. Thus, minimizing W is important.

If the emitter and collector connections in Figure 2.22 are reversed, the transistor would be operating in the reverse active mode. Due to the extremely asymmetric geometry of emitter and collector in the physical structure of Figure. 2.22a, the inverse current gain β_R is very low and the reverse transit time τ_R is much larger than for forward active operation. The fact that the collector is more lightly doped than the base means that more minority carriers would be injected from the base to the (much larger) collector than vice versa. Removing such carriers to turn off a conducting reverse transistor is a relatively slow process. Reverse operation of integrated circuit BJTs must be avoided in digital circuits having any speed requirement.

Bipolar transistors have pn junction capacitances that are derived in the same way as for MOS transistors (see Section 2.2.7.2). BJTs also have (undesired) small resistances in series with all electrode connections.

2.3.2 The Schottky-Barrier Diode

Very useful diodes can be made by forming a microscopically clean contact between certain metals and a lightly doped ($N_D \leq 10^{16}$ cm^{-3}) n-type semiconductor, as illustrated in Figure 2.24. Because practical means of forming the necessary clean interface were not developed until about 1970, Schottky-barrier diodes[13] were not used in early integrated circuits. Included in Figure 2.24 is the circuit symbol for a Schottky diode.

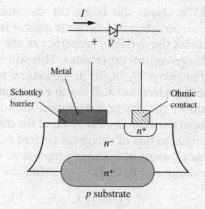

Figure 2.24

Cross section of Schottky-barrier diode.

---

[13] Named for W. Schottky, a pioneer in the study of metal-semicondutor interfaces.

The principal advantage of Schottky diodes is that all conduction is via electrons flowing in metal or n-type silicon. That is, only majority carriers contribute to current flow. Hence there are no minority carrier storage effects, and their limitations on diode switching speed are completely eliminated.

A detailed understanding of the Schottky diode generally involves energy-band theory, which is beyond the scope of this section. For every metal-semiconductor contact there is a characteristic potential barrier ϕ_B which depends only on the two materials. This is the *Schottky barrier*. It is not a function of semiconductor doping and is only a weak function of temperature. The barrier potential blocks the flow of electrons from the metal toward the semiconductor.

In the neutral semiconductor, far from the barrier, and with no externally applied potentials, the electron potential energy in the semiconductor is $\phi_n = V_T \ln(N_D/n_i)$. The potential difference $\phi_B - \phi_n = \phi_0$ is simply the equilibrium difference in energy for electrons in the metal compared to electrons in the semiconductor. It is analogous to the built-in junction potential for the pn junction diode. Externally applied reverse bias adds to ϕ_0 and increases the width of the depletion region, which extends entirely into the semiconductor. Depletion layer width, capacitance, etc., are identical to those for an abrupt p^+n junction diode.

Forward bias subtracts from ϕ_0, allowing electrons to flow from the n-type semiconductor into the metal. Although holes do not take part in forward conduction, the roles of electrons, ϕ_0 and V, are identical to the case of the pn junction diode. Hence it is not surprising that detailed analysis, omitted here, yields

$$I = I_0(e^{V/V_T} - 1) \tag{2.50}$$

A typical approximate value for the saturation current of a 20 μm^2 titanium silicide-n^- silicon barrier as often used in BJT integrated circuits is 10^{-10} A. A corresponding typical value for pn junction diodes of the same area is 2×10^{-17} A. The larger values of I_0 for Schottky diodes result in smaller forward voltage drops at any fixed current density. From the diode Equation (2.50) we have the useful rule of thumb that forward voltage drop for a fixed current at room temperature decreases by 60 mV for each factor of 10 increase of I_S or I_0. Thus for these typical values of saturation current, the difference in forward voltage between Schottky and pn junction diodes at the same forward current is about 0.4 V.

Not all metal-semiconductor contacts have diode characteristics. When the semiconductor is heavily doped (N_A or $N_D > 10^{18}$ cm^{-3}), the depletion layer becomes so narrow that carriers can travel in either direction through the potential barrier by a quantum-mechanical carrier transport mechanism known as *tunneling*. Under these conditions, current flows equally well in either direction, resulting in what is usually described as an *ohmic contact*. In fact, this is the physical explanation for most all ohmic contacts to semiconductor devices.

The diode model used in SPICE applies just as well for the Schottky-barrier diode, but with $I_0 = I_S$, and $\tau_T = 0$. SBDs and junction diodes have depletion layer capacitance represented by the same equations.

2.3.3   BJT Model for Circuit Simulation

As with the MOS transistor, accurate simulation of circuits using BJTs and SBDs requires that the devices be modeled in mathematical terms. The dc characteristics of the intrinsic BJT are modeled by nonlinear current sources I_C and I_E as shown in Equations 2.51.1a, 2.51.1b, and 2.51.2. (Terms for both forward and reverse operation are included for completeness.) The equations used in SPICE may be simplified to yield the classic Ebers-Moll equations

$$I_E = \frac{I_S}{\alpha_F}(e^{V_{BE}/V_T} - 1) - I_S(e^{V_{BC}/V_T} - 1) \qquad (2.51.1a)$$

$$I_C = I_S(e^{V_{BE}/V_T} - 1) - \frac{I_S}{\alpha_r}(e^{V_{BC}/V_T} - 1) \qquad (2.51.1b)$$

$$I_S = \alpha_F I_{ES} = \alpha_R I_{CS} \qquad (2.51.2)$$

The ohmic resistances of the neutral base, collector, and emitter regions of the BJT are modeled by linear resistors r_b, r_c, and r_e.

Charge storage in the BJT is modeled by the two nonlinear charge storage elements Q_{BE} and Q_{BC}, which are determined by the equations

$$Q_{BE} = \tau_F I_S(e^{V_{BE}/V_T} - 1) + C_{je0}\int_0^{V_{BE}}\left(1 - \frac{V}{\phi_e}\right)^{-m_e}dV \qquad (2.51.3a)$$

$$Q_{BC} = \tau_R I_S(e^{V_{BC}/V_T} - 1) + C_{jc0}\int_0^{V_{BC}}\left(1 - \frac{V}{\phi_c}\right)^{-m_c}dV \qquad (2.51.3b)$$

Equivalently, these elements can be represented by voltage-dependent capacitors, since

$$C_{BE} = \frac{dQ_{BE}}{dV_{BE}} = \frac{\tau_F I_S}{V_T}e^{V_{BE}/V_T} + \frac{C_{je0}}{[1 - (V_{BE}/\phi_e)]^{m_e}} \qquad (2.51.4a)$$

$$C_{BC} = \frac{dQ_{BC}}{dV_{BC}} = \frac{\tau_R I_S}{V_T}e^{V_{BC}/V_T} + \frac{C_{jc0}}{[1 - (V_{BC}/\phi_c)]^{m_c}} \qquad (2.51.4b)$$

The charge storage elements Q_{BE} and Q_{BC} model the charge stored in the neutral base region Q_F and Q_R as well as the charge stored in the depletion regions Q_{je} and Q_{jc}.

Charge storage in the depletion regions is represented by V_{BE} and the model parameters C_{je0}, ϕ_e, and m_e for the emitter junction and V_{BC}, C_{jc0}, ϕ_c, and m_c for the collector junction.

Charge storage due to minority carrier injection across the junctions is described by the exponential terms in Equations 2.51.3a and 2.51.3b. The effect is modeled by the transit time parameters τ_F for the emitter junction and τ_R for the collector junction.

The model equations are complete for a discrete BJT. For an integrated circuit transistor we must add one more component. As illustrated in Figure 2.22a, isolation of transistor collectors from each other and from the substrate is achieved using a reverse-biased diode. Assuming it remains reverse-biased, we find that this diode may be modeled by a current source (representing the diode leakage current) in parallel with a voltage-dependent depletion-layer capacitance.

For an integrated circuit *npn* transistor, this isolation diode is effectively connected between the collector and substrate. The substrate is common to all the components in the integrated circuit. This diode is modeled as a capacitance between the collector and substrate (C_{CS}) and is added to the basic model for the transistor in the forward active mode, as follows

$$C_{CS} = \frac{C_{js0}}{[1 - (V_{SC}/\phi_s)]^{m_s}} \tag{2.51.5}$$

2.3.4 Bipolar Transistor Inverter

Bipolar transistor technology has been succeeded by MOS technology for virtually all new designs of digital circuits and systems. However, discrete bipolar transistors, or combinations of a very few BJTs, still are used in digital systems. Examples include applications with external loads requiring drive current more than 0.1 A or load voltages more than 10 V. Bipolar devices driven by a MOS integrated circuit often are employed in such cases. Bipolar devices are readily available for switching up to 100 A or 1000 V. The elementary building block in such situations is a bipolar transistor logic inverter.

The discussion below also supports a subsequent description of historical TTL bipolar logic configuration, so the examples typically refer to 5 V operation with milliampere currents. Bear in mind that operation at higher voltages and currents is entirely feasible.

A simple but practical configuration of a bipolar transistor logic inverter is shown in Figure 2.25. Listed are some typical data for the transistor in this circuit.

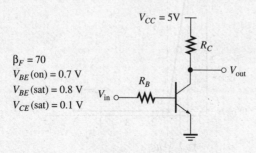

$\beta_F = 70$
$V_{BE}(\text{on}) = 0.7\ \text{V}$
$V_{BE}(\text{sat}) = 0.8\ \text{V}$
$V_{CE}(\text{sat}) = 0.1\ \text{V}$

Figure 2.25
Bipolar transistor inverter.

We assume that these data are independent of collector current, but with $I_C = 0.01\ I_{C\,(EOS)}$, and $V_{in} = V_{BE(on)}$, where (EOS) stands for edge of saturation. It can be seen from the circuit that, with the input voltage V_{in} less than the turn-on voltage $V_{BE(on)}$ for the transistor, the collector current will essentially be zero and the output voltage V_{out} will be equal to V_{CC}; that is, the transistor will be cut off.

When the input voltage is increased above $V_{BE(on)}$, the transistor turns on and enters the forward active region, where the collector current is related to the base current as $I_C = \beta_F I_B$. Now $V_{out} = V_{CC} - I_C R_C$. Therefore as the input voltage increases, the output voltage decreases; the direction of the voltage change is inverted. With sufficient input voltage, when the output voltage (which is in fact V_{CE} of the transistor) has fallen sufficiently, the transistor enters the saturation region. In the saturation region the output voltage shows little, if any, change as the input voltage is further increased.

Confusion arises from the different uses of the word *saturation* in MOS and bipolar circuit contexts. In the bipolar case, a transistor is said to be operating in saturation when the collector-emitter voltage is near zero, almost independent of output current. (In the MOS case, the transistor is in saturation when the output current is constant, nearly independent of the output voltage.)

2.3.5 Voltage Transfer Characteristics

The *voltage transfer characteristic* for the transistor inverter is shown in Figure 2.26, where straight-line asymptotes are used to join the two main breakpoints of the characteristic. At BP1, the input voltage is just at the point of turning the transistor on, but the output voltage is still very close to the cutoff value; that is, the collector current is very small. At BP2, the input voltage is now great enough to bring the

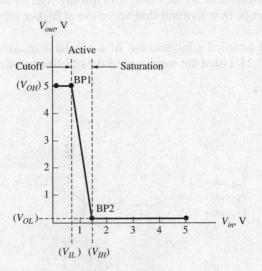

Figure 2.26
Voltage transfer characteristic.

transistor to the edge of the saturation region. The collector current is now at, or very nearly at, its maximum value, since any further increase in the input voltage results in hardly any change in the output voltage. Observe that the two breakpoints separate the following three regions of operation for the transistor:

1. Cutoff

2. Active

3. Saturation

The coordinates of BP1 are V_{IL} and V_{OH}, and for BP2 they are V_{IH} and V_{OL}, where these quantities have the same definitions as in Chapter 4, Section 4.2. Determining values for these quantities in a bipolar inverter is easy, as follows. From the circuit of Figure 2.25:

1. V_{OH}, which is equivalent to V_{CE} with the transistor at the edge of the cutoff region, that is, V_{CC}. For the given example it is 5 V. Hence,

$$V_{OH} = V_{CC}$$

    However, V_{OH} is usually measured with $V_{in} = V_{OL}$.

2. V_{OL}, which is equivalent to V_{CE} with the transistor at the edge of the saturation region, that is, $V_{CE(sat)}$. In the example it is 0.1 V. Thus,

$$V_{OL} = V_{CE(sat)}$$

    V_{OL} is commonly measured with $V_{in} = V_{OH}$.

3. V_{IL}, which is the input voltage just sufficient to turn the transistor on. In this example it is $V_{BE(on)}$, which is given as 0.7 V. Therefore,

$$V_{IL} = V_{BE(on)}$$

4. V_{IH}, which is the input voltage just sufficient to saturate the transistor. Now with the transistor just at the edge of saturation, $I_C = I_{C(EOS)}$, where

$$I_{C(EOS)} = \frac{V_{CC} - V_{CE(sat)}}{R_C} \tag{2.52.1}$$

But since the transistor is also at the edge of the forward active region,

$$I_{C(EOS)} = \beta_F I_{B(EOS)} \tag{2.52.2}$$

where, with the input at V_{IH},

$$I_{B(EOS)} = V_{IH} - \frac{V_{BE(sat)}}{R_B} \tag{2.52.3}$$

Therefore, solving for V_{IH} using Equations (B.5.2) and (B.5.1),

$$V_{IH} = V_{BE(sat)} + \frac{R_B}{R_C} \frac{V_{CC} - VC_{CE(sat)}}{\beta_F} \tag{2.52.4}$$

Using the numeric values,

$$V_{IH} = 0.8 + 10\,\text{k}\Omega/1\,\text{k}\Omega\ 5 - 0.1/70 = 1.5\,\text{V}$$

Hence the coordinates of BP1 are $V_{in} = 0.7$ V and $V_{out} = 5.0$ V; for BP2 they are $V_{in} = 1.5$ V and $V_{out} = 0.1$ V.

Note that the slope of the characteristic in Figure B.5 relates to the voltage gain of the transistor inverter, since the voltage gain is given as

$$a_v = \Delta V_{out}/\Delta V_{in} \qquad (2.52.5)$$

In the cutoff and saturation regions the slope is zero as is, of course, the voltage gain. But in the active region the slope directly indicates the voltage gain. Now straight-line asymptotes have been used in the voltage transfer characteristic to uniquely identify the breakpoints. More accurately, these breakpoints define the points on the characteristic curve where the small-signal voltage gain is 1.0; they are then identified as the *unity-gain points*. In particular, we note from Figure B.5 that to the left of BP1 and to the right of BP2 the voltage gain is <1.0, but to the right of BP1 and to the left of BP2, that is, in the active region, the voltage gain is >1.0.

2.3.6 Schottky-Clamped Inverter

As mentioned earlier, to minimize switching delays bipolar integrated circuits must be designed to prevent the collector-base junction from ever becoming appreciably forward biased. A Schottky-barrier diode (SBD) connected between the base and the collector of the inverter transistor, as in Figure 2.27, is an effective solution. By extending the base metal to contact the more lightly doped collector region, this extra diode is included by a simple addition to the fabrication procedure.

The Schottky clamp effectively prevents the transistor from saturating; hence there is no saturation delay time for the inverter circuit. When the transistor approaches saturation, because of a high voltage level at the input, any base current in excess of $\beta_F I_B$ is diverted from the base through the Schottky diode and then into the collector of the transistor. The forward voltage drop of the Schottky diode is less than the voltage drop of the base-collector junction diode of the transistor. At room temperature the forward voltage drop of a titanium silicide to n-type silicon Schottky diode is about 0.3 V. Thus for a clamped inverter circuit, and a transistor with $V_{BE(on)} = 0.7$ V, with the SBD conducting the voltage between collector and emitter, $V_{CE} = 0.7 - 0.3 = 0.4$ V. This is to be compared with $V_{CE(sat)} = 0.1$ V for the transistor without a Schottky diode. In the saturation mode, both junctions of the transistor are forward-biased. Hence, with $V_{BE(sat)} = 0.8$ V and $V_{CE(sat)} = 0.1$ V, $V_{BC(sat)} = 0.7$ V.

The Schottky diode effectively limits the minimum base-collector voltage to 0.4 V; therefore, although the base-collector junction is forward-biased (by 0.4 V), it is conducting little current. The Schottky diode is forward-biased, but as noted above there is no minority carrier charge storage in a SBD. Despite the fact that the

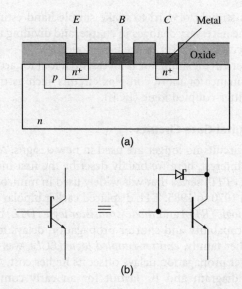

Figure 2.27

(a) Cross section of Schottky-clamped transistor. (b) Circuit symbol for Schottky-clamped transistor.

collector-base junction itself is not conducting significantly, this operating point still may be referred to as "saturation".

While the inclusion of the Schottky diode has improved the transient characteristics of the bipolar transistor inverter, unfortunately it has an opposite effect on the static characteristics. In particular, the low noise margin NM_L has been made worse because V_{OL} is increased from 0.1 to 0.4 V. Hence, NM_L has been decreased by the same amount. The Schottky diode has a minimal effect on the high noise margin NM_H.

2.3.7 BJT Inverter Switching Times

The transient behavior of a bipolar transistor inverter is limited by charge storage in depletion layer capacitances of the base-emitter, base-collector, and collector-substrate junctions. When a Schottky-barrier clamp is included, its depletion layer capacitance adds in parallel with the collector-base pn junction capacitance. All these depletion layer capacitances are modeled in the same way as the pn junction depletion layer capacitances of the MOS transistor, as described in Section 2.2.

In addition, there is charge stored in the base of the BJT, denoted as $Q_F = \tau_F I_C$, as explained earlier in this Section. This charge must be delivered to turn on the transistor and removed to turn it off. The base-emitter and base-collector depletion layer charges and Q_F all must be delivered to and removed from the base terminal. The base-emitter voltage change during switching usually is only a few tenths of a volt. Therefore, it is straightforward to make simple hand estimates of switching time by adding up the necessary changes in charge, and dividing the sum by the current the external circuit can deliver to the base node.

SPICE or another circuit simulator is an essential tool for accurately computing the transient performance of more complex circuits such as transistor-transistor logic (TTL) and emitter-coupled logic (ECL).

2.3.8   Bipolar Digital Gate Circuits

Bipolar digital gate circuits no longer are used in new designs. As a matter of technical and historical interest, here we briefly describe the first member of the *transistor-transistor logic (TTL)* series that was widely used in minicomputers and other digital systems from 1970 to 1985. TTL displaced earlier bipolar logic families such as *resistor-transistor logic (RTL)* and *diode-transistor logic (DTL)* because it provided better load driving capability and shorter propagation delays for the same power consumption. Another family, *emitter-coupled logic (ECL)*, was used in a few systems where its shorter propagation delays offset its higher cost.

The schematic diagram and IC layout for an early commercial *transistor-transistor logic (TTL)* circuit are shown in Figure 2.28. This was known as the Series 74, exemplified here as a 2-input NAND gate, where $F = \overline{AB}$. Schottky clamps had not yet been developed. The input terminals of the TTL gate are connected to separate emitters of transistor Q_1, performing the AND function immediately in a relatively small area. Q_1 violates the rule that base-collector junctions never should be forward-biased, but detailed analysis shows that in this particular case the reverse stored charge in Q_1 speeds turn-off of Q_2. Transistor Q_2 provides voltage of opposite phase to the bases of output transistors Q_3 and Q_4 so that only one of these is turned *on* in each of the two logic states. Diode D_1 provides additional voltage drop to minimize the current spike from supply to ground during switching between states. Resistor R_2 is the path for current to turn off Q_3.

The active pull-down (Q_3) and pull-up circuits (Q_4), familiarly known as a *totem-pole* output circuit, provide more current to discharge and charge parasitic capacitance associated with the load, thus decreasing the transition times at the turn-on and turn-off of these digital gates. The layout of Figure 2.28(b) shows a dual 4-input TTL NAND gate.

2.3.9   Voltage Transfer Characteristics

The voltage transfer characteristic of the standard TTL NAND gate is displayed in Figure 2.29. In describing the characteristic we assume the usual typical values, that is

$$V_{BE(on)} = 0.7 \; V$$

$$V_{BE(sat)} = 0.8V$$

$$V_{CE(sat)} = 0.1V$$

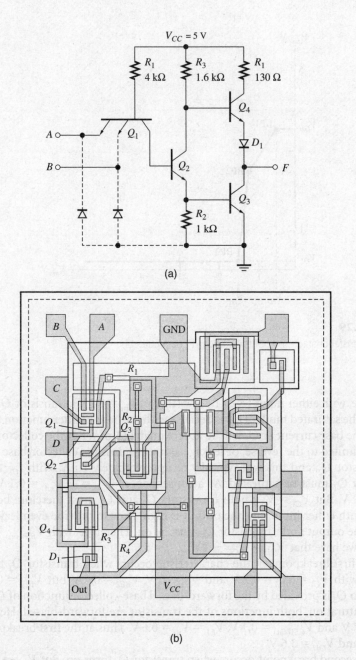

Figure 2.28
(a) Standard 2-input TTL NAND gate circuit. (b) Layout of a dual 4-input TTL NAND gate.

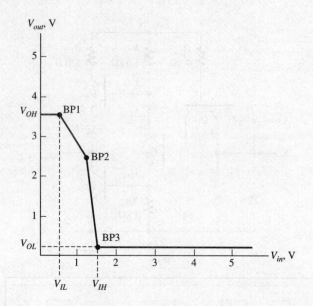

Figure 2.29
Voltage transfer characteristic of the standard TTL circuit.

First note, with either input (A or B) low (that is, $V_{in} = 0.1$ V), transistor Q_1 is operating in the saturated mode. This is because with the base-emitter junction forward-biased, the base current of Q_1 will be approximately 1 mA. But the collector current of Q_1 is limited to the reverse, or leakage, current across the collector-base junction of transistor Q_2, and this will typically be approximately 1 nA. With $I_{C1} \ll \beta_F I_{B1}$, transistor Q_1 must be saturated. As a consequence, $V_{CE1} = V_{CE(sat)} = 0.1$ V, and so $V_{C1} = 0.2$ V. But $V_{C1} = V_{B2}$; both transistors Q_2 and Q_3 must therefore be cut off. Hence, with either input low, the output is high. Now to provide even leakage current to the output node, transistor Q_4 must be on. Therefore, with $V_{BE4(on)} = V_{D1(on)} = 0.7$ V, we have that $V_{OH} = V_{CC} - 2V_{BE(on)} = 3.6$ V.

The first breakpoint in the characteristic occurs when transistor Q_2 turns on. That is, with $V_{C1} = V_{B2} = 0.7$ V and $V_{E2} = 0$ V, $V_{BE2} = 0.7$ V but $V_{BE3} = 0$ V. Base current to Q_2 is provided by the forward-biased base-collector junction of Q_1. Recall that in saturation, both junctions of the transistor are forward-biased. Hence with $V_{C1} = 0.7$ V and $V_{CE1(sat)} = 0.1$ V, $V_{E1} = V_{in} = 0.6$ V. Thus at the first breakpoint, $V_{IL} = 0.6$ V and $V_{OH} = 3.6$ V.

The second breakpoint occurs when transistor Q_3 turns on. But $V_{BE3} = V_{R2}$, and therefore $I_{E2} = V_{R2}/R_2$. Consequently, for $V_{BE3} = V_{BE(on)} = 0.7$ V, $I_{C2} = I_{E2} = 0.7$ V/1 $k\Omega = 0.7$ mA. The voltage at the collector of Q_2 is $V_{C2} = V_{CC} - I_{C2}R_3 = 5 - (0.7)(1.6)$ $= 3.9$ V. Note that with $V_{CE2} = V_{C2} - V_{E2} = 3.9 - 0.7 = 3.2$ V, Q_2 is operating in the forward-active mode. The gate output voltage is $2V_{BE(on)}$ below V_{C2}; therefore $V_{out} = 2.5$ V. To determine the input voltage, transistor Q_1 is still in the saturation mode, and $V_{C1} = V_{BE2} + V_{BE3}$; that is, $2V_{BE(on)} = 1.4$ V. Hence, $V_{in} = 1.3$ V. The coordinates of the second breakpoint are $V_{in} = 1.3$ V and $V_{out} = 2.5$ V.

The third, and final, breakpoint occurs when Q_3 saturates. The gate output voltage is then $V_{CE(sat)} = 0.1$ V. With transistor Q_2 also saturated, $V_{C1} = 2V_{BE(sat)} = 1.6$ V. Transistor Q_1 is still saturated, so that $V_{in} = 1.6 - 0.1 = 1.5$ V. The coordinates are $V_{in} = 1.5$ V and $V_{out} = 0.1$ V.

2.3.10 Propagation Delay Time

The use of a transistor at the input of the TTL circuit improves the propagation delay time, in particular t_{PLH}. Refer to Figure 2.28(a). For the output to go high, it is necessary to turn off base current to transistor Q_3. Therefore, we must quickly turn off transistor Q_2. Prior to the transition the input is at a high level and both transistors Q_2 and Q_3 are saturated, and $V_{C1} = 1.6$ V. With a high-to-low transition at the input, $V_{E1} = 0.1$ V. Therefore initially, $V_{CE1} = 1.5$ V and transistor Q_1 operates in the forward active mode. That is, until Q_1 saturates, the collector current is $I_{C1} = \beta_F I_{B1}$. This current, which can be appreciable, is the turn-off base current for transistor Q_2. Note that it is not until after Q_2 turns off that Q_1 saturates. Hence, because of the forward current gain β_F of transistor Q_1, transistor Q_2 quickly turns off. With Q_2 off, transistor Q_4 becomes a source of current to the output, causing the gate output to go high, provided that Q_3 is off. The turn-off base current for Q_3 is through R_2. The turn-off time for Q_3 is usually longer than that of Q_2. But transistor Q_1 does serve to decrease the propagation delay time t_{PLH}.

Later versions of TTL incorporated Schottky clamps to reduce propagation delays and additional devices to "square up" the voltage transfer characteristic by eliminating BP2 and moving BP1 to the right. They were known as Series 74S, 74LS, 74ALS, etc. For details on these circuits and on ECL, see the earlier edition of this text.

2.3.11 Input Clamp Diodes

Finally, in the description of the TTL circuit of Figure 2.28, the clamp diode from each input to ground should be noted. For the static conditions of a high or low level at the input, they are reverse-biased and play no part in the circuit. However, as the output changes state, the switching transition times of these circuits are very short. Any inductance associated with the load or power supply lines causes high-frequency oscillations ("ringing") to appear on the output lines. Hence the input to a gate can be greater than 5 V on the positive swing and less than 0 V on the negative swing. The positive swing reverse-biases the emitter-base junction of the input transistor, but the base resistor R_1 limits the current and no harm is done. On the negative swing, with transistor Q_1 saturated, the voltage at the collector will only be 0.1 V more positive than the emitter voltage. The result is that the collector-substrate isolation diode of Q_1 can be forward-biased. This can lead to undesired voltage spikes at other nodes in the circuit or possible fatal damage to the IC. The diodes at the input "clamp" the input voltage so that it cannot swing more negative than about -0.7 V. Later versions of TTL use Schottky diodes in the input clamp position.

The electrical characteristics for this standard TTL gate circuit are shown in Table 2.1. Note that the power-delay product, 100 pJ, of the original TTL circuit is much larger than that today's CMOS logic circuits. The most advanced TTL family, 74ALS, has typical propagation delay of 4 ns and typical power consumption of 1 mW, still far greater than for today's CMOS.

Table 2.1
Standard transistor-transistor logic (54/74 TTL): typical electrical characteristics at $T_A = 25°C$

V_{OH}/V_{OL}	3.5 V/0.2 V	Fan-out	10
V_{IH}/V_{IL}	1.5 V/0.5 V	Supply volts	+ 5.0 V
NM_H/V_L	2.0 V/0.3 V	Power dissipation per gate	10 mW
Logic swing	3.3 V	Propagation delay time	10 ns

REFERENCES

1. A. S. Grove, *Physics and Technology of Semiconductor Devices*, Wiley, New York, 1967.
2. R. S. Muller and T. Kamins, *Device Electronics for Integrated Circuits*, 2nd ed., Wiley, New York, 1986.
3. S. M. Sze, *Physics of Semiconductor Devices*, 2nd ed., Wiley-Interscience, 1981.
4. K-Y Toh, P-K Ko, and R. G. Meyer, "An Engineering Model for Short-Channel MOS Devices," *IEEE Journal of Solid-State Circuits*, vol. 23, no. 4, August 1988.
5. T. Sakurai and A. R. Newton, "Alpha-Power Law MOSFET Model and Its Applications to CMOS Inverter Delay and Other Formulas," *IEEE Journal of Solid-State Circuits*, vol. 25, no. 2, pp. 584–594, April 1990.
6. J. Meyer, "MOS Models for Circuit Simulation," *RCA Review*, vol. 32, pp. 42–63, 1971.
7. D. Ward and R. Dutton, "A Charge-Oriented Model for MOS Transistor Capacitances," *IEEE Journal of Solid-State Circuits*, vol. SC-13, pp. 703–708, 1978.
8. N. Arora, *MOSFET Models for VLSI Circuit Simulation*, Springer-Verlag, 1993.
9. V. H. Grinich and H. G. Jackson, *Introduction to Integrated Circuits*, McGraw-Hill, New York, 1975.
10. D. J. Hamilton and W. G. Howard, *Basic Integrated Circuit Engineering*, McGraw-Hill, New York, 1975.
11. H. Taub and D. Schilling, *Digital Integrated Electronics*, McGraw-Hill, New York, 1977.
12. D. A. Hodges and H. G. Jackson, Analysis and Design of Digital Integrated Circuits, 2nd ed., McGraw-Hill, New York, 1988, pp. 156–171.

PROBLEMS

P2.1 Below is a table of process parameters for a generic 0.13 μm technology.

Table P2.1

0.13 μm Process technology parameters

Typical Technology Parameters	Symbol	NMOS	PMOS
Gate thickness	t_{ox} [Å]	22	22
Poly doping level	N_D [cm^{-3}]	3×10^{20}	—
Poly doping level	N_A [cm^{-3}]	—	3×10^{20}
Substrate doping level	N_A [cm^{-3}]	3×10^{17}	—
N-well doping level	N_D [cm^{-3}]	—	3×10^{17}
Number of surface state charges	N_{SS} [cm^{-2}]	6×10^{11}	6×10^{11}

Using the data in Table P2.1, find the following threshold voltage values:

(a) Compute V_{T0}, the unimplanted, zero-bias threshold voltages for both NMOS and PMOS devices. Assume that there is no charge in the oxide itself, but there does exist a sheet charge at the Si-SiO$_2$ interface (computed as qN_{SS}).

(b) Normally, NMOS gates are doped with donors (n^+) while PMOS gates are doped with acceptors (p^+).

    (i)   How would V_{T0} be affected if we doped the PMOS poly gate with donors rather than acceptors?

    (ii) Calculate the new V_{T0}.

(c) We now want to adjust the threshold voltages of both the NMOS and PMOS devices so that we achieve the following threshold voltages: $V_{T0N} = 0.4$ V and $V_{T0P} = -0.4$ V. Calculate the threshold implant levels for the two cases in parts (a) and (b).

(d) Why do modern technologies have an n^+ poly gate for NMOS and a p^+ gate for PMOS devices?

P2.2 Find the effective mobility, (μ_e), of a PMOS transistor due to the vertical field if $t_{ox} = 22$ Å and $|V_{GS} - V_T| = 0.8$ V. Let $\theta = 4 \times 10^6$ V/cm and $\eta = 1.85$ in a 0.13 μm technology. Assume that $\mu_0 = 130$ cm^2/V-sec.

P2.3 This problem involves plotting several I-V characteristics of NMOS and PMOS transistors in a 0.13 μm technology. The 0.13 μm technology uses a 1.2 V power supply. The transistors are unit sized where $W = 100$ nm, $L = 100$ nm.

(a) Plot I_{DS} versus V_{DS} as a function of $V_{GS} = 0, 0.4, 0.8, 1.2$ V for both NMOS and PMOS devices.

(b) Plot I_{DS} versus V_{GS} with $V_{DS} = 1.2$ V for the NMOS device. Does the quadratic model hold for $0.13\ \mu m$ devices, or is it closer to linear with V_{GS}?

P2.4 Find the region of operation for each of the transistors in Figure P2.4. Assume $V_{T0} = 0.4$ V.

P2.5 In the circuits of Figure P2.5, determine the voltage across the capacitor after the circuit reaches steady state. Assume the capacitor is initially discharged ($V_x = 0$ V) and $V_{T0} = 0.4$ V.

P2.6 In the circuits of Figure P2.6, draw V_X versus V_{in} for $0 < V_{in} < 1.2$.

P2.7 Calculate the gate and junction capacitance of the transistor shown in Figure P2.7 if $L = 100$ nm, $W = 400$ nm, $Y = 300$ nm, $K_{eq} = 0.8$, $C_{jb} = 1.6$ fF/μm^2, $C_{ox} = 1.6 \times 10^{-6}$ F/cm^2, and $x_j = 65$ nm.

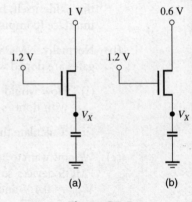

Figure P2.5

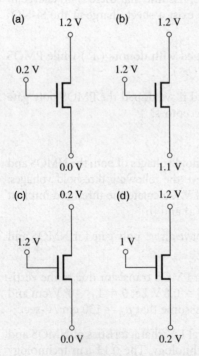

Figure P2.4

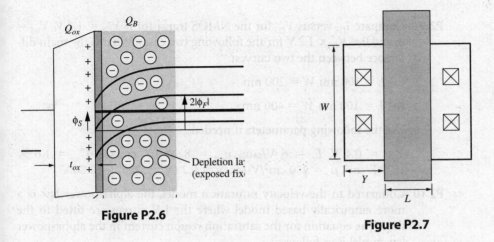

Figure P2.6

Figure P2.7

P2.8 Calculate the NMOS transistor current in each of the cases in Figure P2.8:

Use the following parameters if needed: $V_{T0} = 0.4$ V, $E_c = 6$ V/μm, $L = 100$ nm, $W = 400$ nm, $v_{sat} = 8 \times 10^6$ cm/sec, $C_{ox} = 1.6 \times 10^{-6}$ F/cm^2, $\mu_e = 270$ cm^2/V-sec, $\gamma = 0.2$ (V$^{1/2}$), $2|\phi_F| = 0.88$ V, $\lambda = 0.7$ V^{-1}.

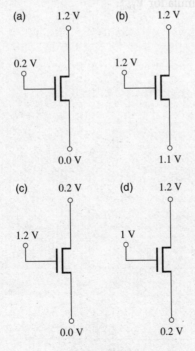

Figure P2.8

P2.9 Compare I_{DS} versus V_{DS} for the NMOS transistor if $V_{GS} = 1.2$ V, $V_{BS} = 0$, and $0 < V_{DS} < 1.2$ V for the following two cases. What is the main difference between the two curves?

(a) $L = 100$ nm $W = 200$ nm

(b) $L = 100$ nm $W = 400$ nm

Use the following parameters if needed:

$V_{T0} = 0.4$ V, $E_c = 6$ V/μm, $v_{sat} = 8 \times 10^6$ cm/sec, $C_{ox} = 1.6 \times 10^{-6}$ F/cm^2, $\mu_e = 270$ cm^2/V-sec, $\gamma = 0.2$ (V$^{1/2}$), $2|\phi_F| = 0.88$ V

P2.10 Compared to the velocity saturation model, the alpha-power law is a more empirically based model where the I-V curves are fitted to the data. The equation for the saturation region current in the alpha-power law model is as follows:

$$I_{DS} = K(W/L)(V_{GS} - V_T)^\alpha$$

(a) For the plots in Problem P2.3, compute the values for K and α for the NMOS and PMOS devices.

(b) For the linear region, develop a model where the current is linearly proportional to V_{DS} until the saturation region is reached. Derive a formula for V_{Dsat}.

Fabrication, Layout, and Simulation

3.1   Introduction

In this chapter we describe the close relationship between fabrication, layout, and simulation of integrated circuits. We begin by describing the CMOS fabrication process. The purpose is to give the reader some insight into the steps and issues associated with the manufacture of integrated circuits. Over the years, IC fabrication has become more and more complex. For each technology node, there are multiple processes available to the designer, depending on the target application of the chip. For example, there may be different processes for digital, memory, mixed-signal, low power, and so on. It is not possible to describe all of the pertinent issues in advanced CMOS processes in one chapter. The objective here is to present a generic process to provide an overview of the key steps of the fabrication process.

With this knowledge, the issues surrounding IC layout can be described. A layout is the physical description of the transistors and their connections in the IC design. The layout precisely defines the chip that will ultimately be fabricated. Every transistor and wire in the circuit must be specified in a geometric format in the layout. To ensure that the chip is properly fabricated, the final layout must conform to a set of design rules that are based on the resolution limits of the manufacturing equipment. The section on IC layout describes transistor layout considerations and some of the basic guidelines for digital CMOS layout, including design rules and their meaning. Full-chip layout issues are not addressed here.

Following the overview of layout, the simulation tool SPICE[1] is described along with the device parameters associated with the LEVEL 1 and BSIM3v3 MOS models. SPICE is the most widely used simulation tool in the industry for detailed circuit analysis. When a circuit is described for SPICE simulation, each MOS transistor requires two pieces of information: geometric and parametric. The geometric information is obtained directly from the layout. This includes the length, width, area, and perimeter information for each transistor. The parametric information is captured in the device models that are extracted from the fabrication process. The simplest device model is the LEVEL 1 model which is described in detail in this chapter. However, the most popular model in use today is BSIM3v3. The key parameters of this model are also described in this chapter. Advanced MOS transistor issues are presented in the context of the BSIM3 model.

The chapter concludes with a brief look at an emerging technology known as silicon-on-insulator (SOI).

For those who are relatively new to silicon integrated circuit technology and device modeling, the contents of this chapter may not be fully appreciated or understood until later chapters are covered. We recommend that this chapter and Chapter 2 be reviewed frequently as they contain the fundamental equations and concepts used throughout the rest of the book.

3.2   IC Fabrication Technology

3.2.1   Overview of IC Fabrication Process

Silicon transistors and integrated circuits are manufactured on wafers of single-crystal silicon, 200 to 300 millimeters (mm) in diameter and about 0.35 mm to 1.25 mm thick. This thickness is determined by the need to provide enough mechanical strength so that the wafer is not easily broken. The wafers are first polished to a mirror finish by abrasive lapping with finer and finer gritty material, followed by a chemical etch that leaves the surface virtually free of scratches and imperfections. Any defects on the wafer may cause a particular chip to fail and render it useless. This is very important in terms of the overall yield of the wafer. The chips that do not work to specifications are thrown out or must be repaired in some way, and this increases the per unit cost of the chips that actually work.

The fabrication process that forms the devices and circuits involves a sequence of pattern definition steps interspersed with other processes such as oxidation, etching, diffusion or ion implantation (*doping*), and material deposition. A variety of chemical agents and materials are used in this process. There may be 20 to 30 major steps in the fabrication process, each one requiring five or more operations. Approximately 100 to 200 distinct operations are required to produce complete

---

[1] For those readers not familiar with this simulation tool, a short tutorial on running SPICE is provided in Appendix A.

integrated circuits. After the processing is complete, each wafer is sawed into hundreds or thousands of identical rectangular chips. Today, a complex IC chip may be up to 30 mm on each edge and contain 100 million devices (transistors, resistors, diodes, etc.) or more.

Brief descriptions of some of the nomenclature in processing are as follows:

Oxidation: High-temperature exposure of silicon to oxygen to form SiO_2 (silicon dioxide).

Etching: Removal of undesired material from the surface with the use of a liquid or ionized gas etchant.

Diffusion: Doping process to form n-type or p-type material by high-temperature exposure to donor or acceptor impurities.

Ion Implantation: High-energy bombardment of silicon with donor or acceptor ions from particle accelerators followed by an annealing step to activate implants and repair any damage.

Chemical Vapor Deposition (CVD): Materials such as metal or oxide are deposited out of a gaseous mixture. Metals can also be deposited using sputtering.

The basic flow in the IC fabrication process is shown in Figure 3.1. Designers convert the circuit schematic into a layout consisting of geometric patterns that implement the transistors and interconnections. This geometric information is divided into *layers* such as n^+, p^+, p-well, n-well, poly, metal 1, metal 2, etc. Each

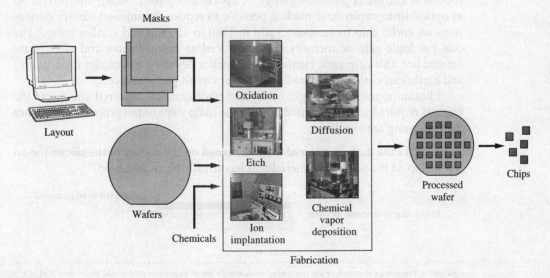

Figure 3.1
Overview of chip-making process.

layer corresponds to a major step in the fabrication process. The patterns, which convey precisely what designers want to build, are converted to a set of masks, one for each major step in the fabrication process. The masks are glass plates with patterns that specify the information that will be printed on the integrated circuit in a given step. They have transparent and opaque areas that match the geometric layout data for each separate layer.

The images on the masks are transferred to silicon wafers using an *optical lithography* process to simultaneously produce a large number of chips. The masks are aligned and exposed separately at each die site (or clusters of 2–8 die sites) across the wafer. This is similar to the use of a negative in photography. Many pictures can be produced from one negative. In chip fabrication, a 200 mm wafer may produce 1000 chips that are 5 mm × 5 mm in size. It is this parallel manufacturing of all chips on a wafer that keeps the cost of an integrated circuit relatively low.[2]

3.2.2 IC Photolithographic Process

The process of pattern transfer and pattern definition is repeated many times during the fabrication of an IC wafer. Each of these *masking steps* requires that the wafer be coated with a photosensitive emulsion known as *photoresist,* and then optically exposed in desired geometric patterns using a mask: a previously prepared photographic plate. This glass plate with an image of the pattern etched in chrome is generated from the design database. The image is optically projected onto the wafer using a projection aligner which is very much like an enlarger in photography. It projects the image of the mask onto the photoresist on the silicon wafer to *develop* it, that is, make it soluble.

After developing the photoresist, a specific process such as etching or doping is carried out in the exposed areas of the patterned wafer. This entire pattern transfer process is known as *photolithography,* or *optical lithography.* Steady improvements in optical lithography have made it possible to reduce the smallest surface dimensions on an IC chip from about 5 μm in 1980 to 130 nm and smaller today.[3] The cost per logic gate or memory cell is reduced as more devices and circuits are formed per unit chip area. Furthermore, smaller devices have smaller capacitances and hence can switch faster, leading to better circuit performance.

Photolithography uses light to develop photosensitive material and create the features required in an integrated circuit. The main steps of the processing sequence for patterning are as follows:

1. Place the desired material to be patterned on the surface of the silicon (or on top of the previous material that has already been processed):

Step 1: Apply material to wafer
Material to be patterned
Wafer

---

[2] However, the masks themselves are becoming increasingly more expensive and could easily run >$1M US in advanced deep submicron technologies.
[3] As a reference point, a hair from your head is about 50 μm in diameter!

2. Spin photoresistive material on top of the first material. Positive photoresist is a material that is difficult to remove unless it is *exposed* to ultraviolet (UV) light, and negative photoresist is difficult to remove unless it is *not exposed* to ultraviolet light. Typically positive photoresist is in use today:

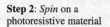 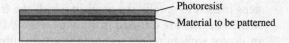

Step 2: *Spin* on a photoresistive material

3. Place a glass mask over the wafer and expose the resist material to UV light (positive photoresist assumed). The exposed areas are now soluble in a chemical agent:

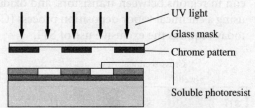

Step 3: Pattern photoresist with UV light through glass mask

4. Using the appropriate solvent, remove the resist and expose areas of the underlying material to be patterned. Etch away the underlying material to form the desired pattern:

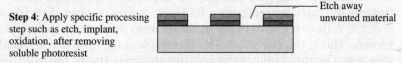

Step 4: Apply specific processing step such as etch, implant, oxidation, after removing soluble photoresist

5. After the previous step is completed, remove the rest of the photoresist:

Step 5: Wash off resist

The steps just described are used repeatedly for every major processing step whether it is oxidation, ion implantation, or deposition. However, due to the fine resolutions needed today, photolithography is reaching certain physical limits. Minimum feature sizes less than 0.35 μm are feasible from the standpoint of device operation but cannot be achieved with standard optical lithography because the wavelength of light is about 0.4 μm. To overcome this limitation of optical lithography, optical proximity correction (OPC) and phase-shift masks (PSMs) are in common use. These operations either pre-correct the masks to provide the desired final image on the chip, or use masks that phase shift the light to avoid unwanted interference patterns. Such advanced techniques have been used at 130 nm and below.

3.2.3   Making Transistors

Now that the basic photolithographic step has been illustrated, the manner in which transistors are made can be described. Deep submicron transistors are fabricated using a number of complex steps. Since our objective here is to highlight the main steps in the process, we will only present an overview of transistor fabrication. The major steps of a CMOS process are as follows.

1. Define well areas and transistor regions. The first set of photolithographic steps is used to specify the areas in which the transistors will be fabricated. NMOS devices are diffused in a *p*-type well. PMOS devices are diffused into an *n*-type well. In recent technologies, twin tubs are used, meaning that an *n*-well and a *p*-well are separately diffused into a common substrate. The transistor areas defined within the well areas are separated from one another using shallow trench isolation (STI). The "trenches" are dug out of the silicon in regions between transistors, and oxide is deposited in these trenches using a chemical vapor deposition process (CVD). The density of transistors today requires the exclusive use of STI.

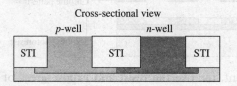
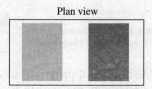

2. Define gate region. The second set of lithographic steps defines the desired patterns for gate electrodes. In a 0.13 μm process, a clean thermal oxide about 22 Å thick is grown in the transistor areas by exposure to oxygen in a furnace. This is the *gate oxide*. This thin oxide is the insulator in the MOS structure. Threshold adjustment implants are applied to the two gate regions to achieve the desired V_T values for PMOS and NMOS devices, respectively.

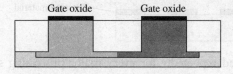

3. Define poly gate. Another CVD process deposits a layer of polycrystalline silicon (*poly*) over the entire wafer. Undesired poly and the underlying thin oxide are removed by chemical or plasma (reactive gas) etching thus producing a self-aligned[4] gate node. The term "self-aligned" refers to the fact that the source and drain regions will automatically align with the poly gate f the gate is placed down first.

---

[4] When metal gates were first used, it was difficult to align the gate over the channel region precisely. The use of polysilicon as the gate material eliminated this problem since it would be placed down first and the source and drain regions created afterwards. The chip yields increased dramatically and led to the exclusive use of this approach in MOS technology.

Polysilicon gate   Polysilicon gate

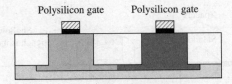

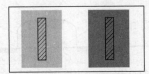

4. Form source/drain regions. A p^+ dopant (boron) is introduced into the n-well to form the p-channel transistor source and drain. Ion implantation is used for each doping step. Then an n^+ dopant (phosphorus or arsenic) is introduced into the p-well that will become the n-channel transistor source and drain. The poly gate requires a doping level that is n^+ for NMOS devices and p^+ for PMOS devices. This can be performed at the same time as the respective source/drain implants. During a subsequent annealing step, the final junction depth and undesired lateral diffusion under the gate are established.

n^+ implant p^+ implant

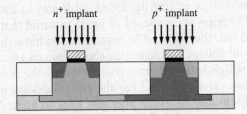

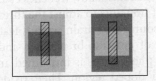

5. Deposit silicide material. The source, drain, and gate materials have relatively high resistance that may slow down the operation of the transistor. To reduce the resistance, a silicide material is deposited onto the source, drain, and poly regions. The masking step also defines the areas in which contacts to the transistors are to be made. Chemical or plasma etching selectively exposes bare silicon or poly in the contact areas.

Polycide

Salicide

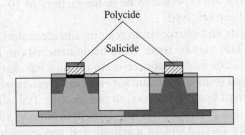

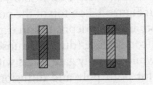

Now that the basic processing sequence for transistors has been described, we provide a few more details. Relative to early generations of MOS fabrication, the major changes are shallow trench isolation (STI), extensive channel region engineering, and the use of silicide materials to lower resistance. In Figure 3.2, the final

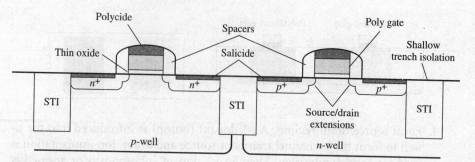

Figure 3.2
Deep submicron CMOS transistor structure.

structure of the NMOS and PMOS devices is shown. The n-channel and p-channel devices are placed in separate wells that sit in heavily doped substrates to avoid *latch-up*, as described later. The STI region is composed of oxide material that is deposited in shallow trenches etched into the silicon. The channel region has a variety of implants to adjust the threshold voltage and to reduce short-channel effects. The source and drain regions feature lightly doped extensions to reduce the possibility of junction breakdown and hot-carrier effects.[5] For the NMOS device, initially phosphorus is implanted and self-aligned to the poly gate edge to form the lightly doped region. Then, oxide is grown and etched to form the "spacers." An arsenic implant follows to create the heavily doped regions. A similar process is used for the PMOS device with boron.

In Figure 3.2, the self-aligned polysilicon gates and their thin oxide are directly above the channel with spacers on either side. Today the dielectric constant, or k, of a silicon dioxide gate, is roughly 4. As technology scales, the oxide is so thin that current tunneling through the gate node is likely to occur. To avoid this, thicker materials with higher k values are being pursued, the so-called *high-k* gate dielectrics. Target values of k for the gate material are expected to be in the vicinity of 10–12 once the process quality issues have been resolved.

To reduce the resistance of the gate and source/drain regions, silicide materials such as $TiSi_2$, WSi_2, $PtSi_2$, $CoSi_2$, or $TaSi$ may be used. The silicide material can be seen in Figure 3.2 on top of the polysilicon and the source/drain regions. For example, if titanium is deposited on exposed source/drain and gate regions, it reacts with the silicon surface (during a subsequent heating process) to produce the $TiSi_2$ silicide, while the poly gate reacts with it to produce *polycide*.[6] The application of silicides for both poly and diffusion are carried out in a self-aligned process using

---

[5] Hot carriers are electrons or holes created through impact ionization with enough energy to surmount the energy barrier between silicon and silicon-dioxide. This topic is discussed in more detail in a later section in this chapter.

[6] When a silicide is used on top of a polysilicon gate, it is referred to as *polycide*.

spacers that are the materials shown on either side of the poly gate. Self-aligned silicides are often called *salicides*. One thing to note in the diagram is that the poly gates are tall and thin; they may be 2000 Å high and 1000 Å wide. This gives rise to a fringing capacitance from the side of the poly gate to the surface of the silicon source/ drain region. This contributes to the overlap capacitance which is a combination of fringing capacitance and lateral diffusion underneath the gate.

3.2.4 Making Wires

Now that the transistor fabrication has been described, the next step in the process is to make the wires that connect the transistors. These connections, primarily done using a metal such as Al or Cu, are commonly known as *interconnect*. In the early generations of MOS technology, only one or two metal layers were available to wire up the devices. Since there were only a few thousands devices to connect, the wiring process was rather straightforward. With technology scaling, the transistor density has increased tremendously following Moore's Law. As the routing capacity of each layer was exhausted, additional levels of interconnect were required to complete the routing. The number of layers of interconnect has grown over the past 25 years from one layer to over eight layers.

The fabrication of interconnect begins with the first metal layer that is used to make contact with transistor source, drain, and gate terminals, and to connect them to nearby V_{DD}, Gnd, and inputs/outputs of other transistors. The starting point for wire fabrication is the structure after transistor fabrication.

1. Initially, a layer of insulating material is applied and then polished to a flat surface.

Insulating material

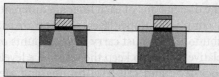
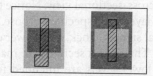

2. Next, contact holes are etched into the insulator and filled with a conducting material such as tungsten.

Contact cuts filled with tungsten   Contact cuts

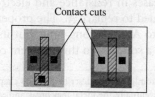

3. The metal material (either aluminum or copper) is then applied to the surface and patterned to form the desired wires.

Deposited and patterned metal 1

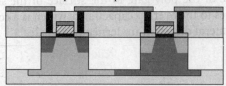
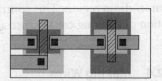

4. Next, another passivation layer is applied and polished to a flat surface. Another set of holes are cut into this layer for *vias*. This is the name used to describe material that forms connections between adjacent layers. Then another layer of metal is deposited and patterned. The final structure, including the second layer of metal, is shown below.

Deposited and patterned metal 2

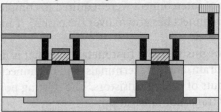

Metal 1   Metal 2

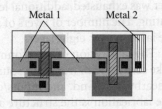

Similar steps are used to create the remaining metal layers that form a multi-level metal structure.

Figure 3.3 shows a representative interconnect structure with six layers of metal in a cross-sectional view. Notice that the dimensions of each layer are different since each layer has a specific purpose. For example, the upper layers of metal are used for global signals, clock, and power distribution, and must carry large amounts of current. Their cross sections are made relatively large to keep the resistance levels low. The lower levels are intended for block-level and cell-level routing and are kept small for high density.

The different levels are connected to each other using contacts or vias. Generally speaking, contacts are used to connect wires to transistors, while vias are used to connect one metal layer to another. In the past, aluminum (Al) was used for the metal layers and tungsten (W) was used to implement vias. However, due to increases in resistance and electromigration[7] problems, other materials have been pursued to replace Al. The properties of copper (Cu) have been known to be superior to Al for a long time, but its incompatibility with Si and SiO_2 limited its use until a solution to this problem could be developed. Unfortunately, copper diffuses

---

[7] Electromigration is described in later chapters as the movement of metal material over time due to current flow. Eventually, the metal may break and cause an open circuit (or a short circuit to a neighboring line) that leads to failure of the circuit.

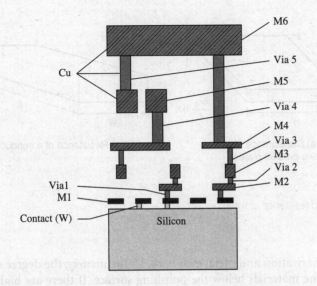

Figure 3.3
Multilevel metal interconnect.

very rapidly in silicon, and so great care must be taken to prevent contamination. Typically, a thin copper-cladding material such as TiN is used to surround it to prevent Cu from diffusing into SiO_2. This innovation has propelled copper into mainstream usage. Recently, Cu has been used for both wires and vias using a *dual Damascene* process, as depicted in Figure 3.3. Contacts to the poly gate and the source/drain regions are performed using tungsten since it has better adhesion properties than Cu.

Note that vias have resistance associated with them and should be kept as short as possible. This limits the vertical height between metal layers. Often, an array of vias is used to reduce the resistance when connecting between the upper layers of interconnect. Also, to connect from metal 2 to metal 5 requires a sequence of metal 2, via, metal 3, via, metal 4, via, and finally metal 5. Since a direct connect is not possible, the vias are often stacked on top of one another with metal in between. This is referred to as a *stacked via*. Rules exist on the number of vias that can be stacked.

One problem in fabricating deep submicron interconnect is that, as layers are placed on one another, the surface becomes uneven and this may create stresses and strains on the materials in each subsequent layer. Before a new layer of metal is placed on the chip, the surface must be planarized to assist in the photolithographic process of subwavelength geometries, and to avoid problems in the upper layers due to the unevenness of the previous layers. For this purpose, a procedure called chemical mechanical polishing (CMP) is employed whereby a chemical agent and a polishing mechanism are used to remove unwanted material until the surface is highly planar.

Chemical mechanical polishing is used in the front-end process for the planarization of the oxide material in shallow trench isolation, and in the back-end, for

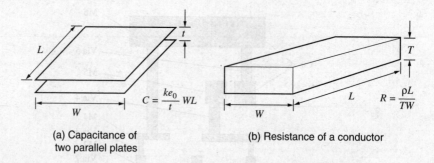

(a) Capacitance of
two parallel plates

(b) Resistance of a conductor

Figure 3.4
Capacitance and resistance of interconnect.

dielectric planarization and metal etch back. Unfortunately, the degree of planarity is related to the materials below the polishing surface. If there are high- and low-density areas of metal, the results in the two areas will not be uniform as *dishing* may occur. Dishing refers to a sagging of the material in certain areas during the CMP process. To enhance the performance of CMP, some amount of *metal fill* (or *poly fill* for the polysilicon layer) must be specified by the chip designer in the vacant areas to produce more planar surfaces. They are implemented as parallel metal lines during chip layout but are not part of the actual circuit. The natural consequences of introducing metal fill are to increase coupling capacitances of nearby signal lines on the same layer, and on adjacent layers above and below the fills; so it must be used carefully.

3.2.5 Wire Capacitance and Resistance

The two most important characteristics of the interconnect today are the capacitance and resistance. We first examine the capacitance of the wires in the interconnect structure. Consider a parallel plate capacitor shown in Figure 3.4a, with length L, a width W, and a separation of t between the plates.[8]

The basic formulation for a parallel-plate capacitance is given by

$$C = \frac{k\varepsilon_0}{t}WL \qquad (3.1)$$

where ε_0 is the permittivity of free space, k is the relative dielectric constant of the insulator, and t is the thickness of the insulating material. Although Equation (3.1) is only suitable for an isolated parallel-plate capacitor, it can give us some insight into the issues associated with deep submicron interconnect.

Consider the configuration of metal 1 and metal 2 wires shown in Figure 3.5. Three metal 1 wires are running adjacent to each other and going into the page. They are situated above a ground plane, which is the substrate. A metal 2 wire runs

---

[8] Note that these dimensions are *not* the channel length, channel width, and thin-oxide thickness. We have switched to the study of interconnect rather than devices.

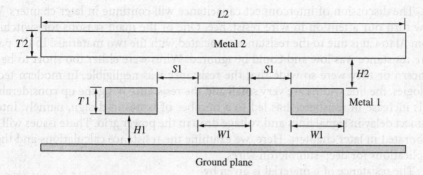

Figure 3.5
Wire dimensions for capacitance calculations.

on top of these wires. All the dimensions in the vertical direction are established during the fabrication process. That is, the height above the substrate and between different layers, H, and the thickness of the wires, T, are fixed values that cannot be modified by the designer. On the other hand, the horizontal dimensions are under the designers' control. Specifically, the width, W, spacing between wires, S, and the wire length, L, are all design variables.

If we focus on the center wire on metal 1 for a moment, there are many sources of capacitance. First, there are two *area* capacitances between it and the substrate below and the metal 2 above that depend on H1 and H2, respectively. Second, there is *lateral* capacitance between adjacent wires on the same level that is dependent on the spacing, S1. Finally, there are *fringing* capacitances between the conductor sidewalls and the upper conductor and lower substrate. Extracting the value of all of these capacitances would require three-dimensional analysis of the structure, and the total capacitance on the middle wire would be the sum of all the capacitances. Since capacitance controls the delay in our signals and determines the power dissipation, we seek to minimize the total capacitance seen by any wire.

There are many ways we can reduce the capacitance from a design perspective. The primary method is to space out the wires by making S as large as possible. From a fabrication perspective, Equation (3.1) tells us that the thickness, t, should be made as large as possible and the dielectric constant, k, should be made as small as possible. Here, the thickness is the height of the insulator between two metal lines on different layers, called the interlayer dielectric (ILD). It is important in determining the capacitive coupling between wires on adjacent layers. Of course, if H is too large, the overall height of the vias would increase. This tends to increase resistance and reduce reliability. The dielectric constant, k, of the insulating material is also important in determining the degree of capacitive coupling. The material between the metal lines is an insulator, typically silicon dioxide. The k for silicon dioxide is approximately 4. Recently, process engineers have developed dielectrics with lower values of k and these are referred to as *low-k* dielectrics. Values of $k \approx 3$ are in production use today. The goal is to reach a k of roughly 2 within the next few years, if possible.

The discussion of interconnect capacitance will continue in later chapters. We now turn our attention to wire resistance. One of the main reasons for switching from Al to Cu is due to the resistance associated with the two materials. In the past, wire resistance was low and could be ignored. Wires were either too short to be of concern or they were so wide that the resistance was negligible. In modern technologies, the line widths are very small and the resistance has gone up considerably. This increase in resistance has led to a number of issues in design, namely, interconnect delay in signal lines and voltage drop in the power grid. These issues will be elaborated in later chapters. Here, we examine the resistance calculations and their implications for deep submicron wires.

The resistance of a material is given by

$$R = \frac{\rho L}{A} = \frac{\rho L}{TW}$$

where ρ is the resistivity of the material in Ω-cm, L is the length of the wire, T is the thickness of the wire, and W is the wire width. This is illustrated in Figure 3.4b.

The leading term is an important one:

$$R_{sq} = \frac{\rho}{T}$$

where R_{sq} is termed the *sheet resistance* and has the units of *ohms per square* ($\Omega/\square$). The sheet resistance of any metal layer can readily be computed from the resistivity and the thickness, T. The two most common materials for metal are aluminum, with $\rho = 2.7\ \mu\Omega$-cm, and copper,[9] with $\rho = 1.7\ \mu\Omega$-cm. As a point of comparison, tungsten has a much higher resistivity of $5.5\ \mu\Omega$-cm.

The resistance of a segment of wire is

$$R = R_{sq}\frac{L}{W}$$

The ratio of L/W is referred to as the *number of squares* of wire. It is the aspect ratio of the wire in terms of length and width. Over the years, wires have been getting longer and narrower which increases the resistance since the number of squares increases. To keep resistance relatively low, the value of T has not been scaled at the same rate as the minimum line width.

In Figure 3.6, the cross-sectional views of the wires are shown as we scale technology. In the 1970s, the line width was fairly large with 5 μm being a typical value. Today, minimum line widths are below 0.13 μm and the resistance per square has increased significantly. On the other hand, the thickness of the wire has not scaled as quickly as compared to the width to keep sheet resistivity low. The more important fact is that the number of squares is significantly larger, partially due to the narrower widths but also due to the fact that wires are continuing to get longer.

---

[9] In practice, the ρ for copper is closer to 2.0 $\mu\Omega$-cm due to the cladding material needed to avoid diffusion into any neighboring oxide.

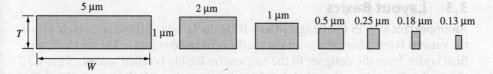

Figure 3.6
Interconnect cross-sections as technology scales.

Comparison of Al and Cu Wire Resistance   **Example 3.1**

Problem:

Compute the resistance for an aluminum wire in a 1980s 5 μm technology and a
0.18 μm technology of the year 2000. Compare this with a copper wire in the year
2002. First assume that the aluminum wire is 35 μm with a resistivity of 2.7 Ω-cm
and thickness of 1 μm. Then switch to a copper wire with a resistivity of 1.7 Ω-cm
and thickness of 0.4 μm that is also 35 μm long.

Solution:

Each wire is shown in plan view below. To determine the number of squares of
resistance, we divide the length of the wire, L, by the width, W, for both cases. We
can use Figure 3.6 to estimate the thickness. In the first case, the wire is 5 μm wide,
1 μm thick, and 35 μm long. In the second case, the wire is 0.18 μm wide and
0.5 μm thick. From these values, we can compute the resistance. Note that even for
these short wires the ratio of the resistance values is 50X.

1980: | | | | | | | = 7 squares

2000: ▭   = 194 squares

$R_{5\ \mu m\text{-wire}} = 2.7\ \mu\Omega\text{-cm}/1\ \mu m \times 7 \approx 0.2\ \Omega$ (1980)

$R_{0.18\ \mu m\text{-wire}} = 2.7\ \mu\Omega\text{-cm}/0.5\ \mu m \times 194 \approx 10\ \Omega$ (2000)

For the same wire in a 0.13 μm process, we have

$R_{0.13\ \mu m\text{-wire}} = 1.7\ \mu\Omega\text{-cm}/0.4\ \mu m \times 269 \approx 11\ \Omega$ (2002)

Note that the resistance for the wire in a 0.13 μm technology has been held to
roughly the same value as in the 0.18 μm technology due to the switch to copper.

3.3   Layout Basics

An important step in the design of any IC is the layout of the chip, which defines the various layers associated with the masks used in fabrication. The handoff of the final layout from the designer to the fabrication facility is called *tapeout*. Figure 3.7 shows the tapeout process that involves the flow of mask data from the design house, which is the company designing the chip, to the foundry, which is the company that fabricates the chip. The chip design information is usually represented by the designer in graphical form using a layout tool, and then converted into a binary output format called *GDS-II stream format*.[10] This format describes the polygons and their (x,y) positions in the layout that comprise each of the layers in the design. The geometric information must comply with a set of design rules that the foundry has painstakingly developed for a specific technology, such as 0.13 μm. The foundry also provides process parameters that are used for simulation purposes.

The goal of the layout process is to implement the design in a compact area while satisfying the *design rules* set by the foundry. Layout design is as much an art as it is a science, but there are some fundamental guidelines that must be adhered to if a chip is to be fabricated successfully. These guidelines, when violated, are flagged by modern CAD tools, called *design rule checkers* (DRCs), that can handle the billions of geometries needed to represent complex layouts. The design rules are

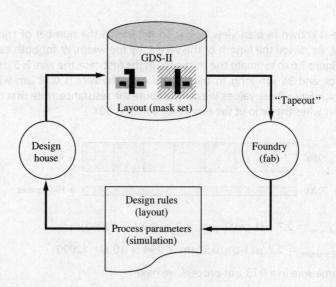

Figure 3.7
The flow of data between the design house and the foundry.

---

[10] GDS is a layout specification format originally developed by the Calma Corporation in the 1980s and later used as an industry standard.

a set of tolerances based on the minimum feature size imposed by a given technology. These tolerances are due to registration error in mask alignment going from one pattern to another, process control due to variation in exposure and etching, and overlap requirements to ensure low ohmic contact where necessary.

The minimum feature size for the layout varies according to the technology node chosen by the design house. Today, new designs are being implemented in 0.13 μm technology so the design rules are based on this minimum dimension. Since the minimum dimension may change from one technology to another, a technology-independent term, λ, was introduced in the 1980s. The minimum gate length was taken as 2λ and all design rules were based on this definition (note: this is not the channel length modulation parameter). As an example, if the minimum gate length is 200 nm, then $\lambda = 100$ nm. Similarly, for $L = 100$ nm, we set $\lambda = 50$ nm. While the notion of a linear scaling factor λ is not used in advanced technologies, it is still instructive when describing design rules and it will be used frequently in this book.

In general there are two types of design rules. One set is associated with the resolution possible in a particular layer and the second set is used for alignment constraints between two different layers. These two types are illustrated in Figure 3.8.

In the case of rules concerning resolution, the minimum line width and spacing are defined. In Figure 3.8a, the minimum line width is 3λ and the minimum spacing is 3λ. This is a typical pair of rules for the upper layers of metal.

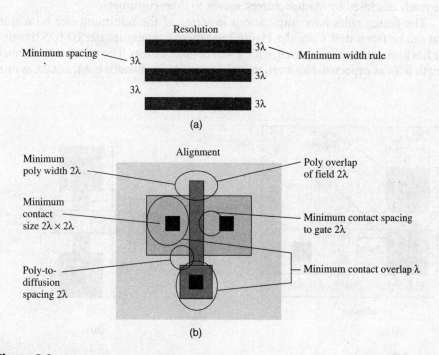

Figure 3.8
Two types of design rules: resolution and alignment.

The alignment rules are associated with two different layers, as shown in Figure 3.8b. For example, the poly overlap of field is set to 2λ. This rule is required so that the gate will completely cover the diffusion region. Otherwise, the transistor would become a resistor since the diffusion region would extend from source to drain. Another set of alignment rules are associated with contacts. The contacts are used to connect metal to diffusion or metal to poly. The minimum size contact is $2\lambda \times 2\lambda$. However, to ensure good contact, the two materials must overlap the contact by a minimum amount and, at the same time, must be a safe distance from other layers. In this example, the overlap of the contact by diffusion and metal is set to λ while the poly-to-contact spacing is set to 2λ. These rules ensure that good contact is made between the two desired materials (diffusion and metal) but not between two undesired materials (poly and diffusion). Similar rules hold for poly-to-metal contacts.

More specific layout rules, including minimum (and sometimes maximum) sizes of features on all mask layers, accompany every IC manufacturing process. There are over one hundred such rules that must be followed to satisfy the fabrication requirements. These rules are checked by DRC programs and must pass cleanly before a design is accepted by the foundry service. For actual chip layout, the precise information should be obtained from the foundry service. Typically, these rules are specified in absolute dimensions rather than in terms of λ. The details of new fabrication technologies, including the layout rules, are generally proprietary and are rarely disclosed by manufacturers, except to their customers.

The design rules have implications in terms of the minimum-size transistor that can be fabricated. Consider Figure 3.9a where a minimum size NMOS transistor has been laid out in a p-well, with a well contact shown. The minimum channel length is 2λ as expected. However, the minimum channel width is 4λ, not 2λ as one

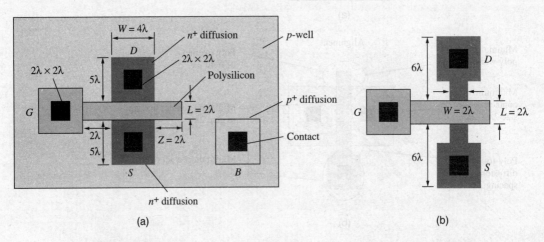

(a)   (b)

Figure 3.9
Alternative layouts of a minimum-size transistor.

might expect. This is due to the fact that the contact is $2\lambda \times 2\lambda$ and the diffusion must overlap it by 1λ on all sides. This adds 2λ to the width, which makes the minimum width equal to 4λ. The diffusion regions must extend out a minimum of 5λ since the contact-to-diffusion edge is λ, and the contact-to-poly spacing is 2λ. Therefore, the minimum diffusion area is $4\lambda \times 5\lambda$.

In order to create a transistor with $W = 2\lambda$, it will cost some extra area as shown in Figure 3.9b. The contacts must be pushed out and a narrow diffusion region created for the desired transistor width. The p-well edges (not shown) would also have to be pushed out due to design rules, and this may affect the spacing rules for nearby n-wells. While it is possible to create a minimum-size transistor when needed, it is more convenient to create a device with $W = 4\lambda$. It also has twice as much drive capability. The diffusion area is about the same in both cases.

The other interesting feature shown in Figure 3.9a is the well contact which is composed of a p^+ diffusion contact that will eventually connect to a metal line (not shown) that is attached to Gnd. This is the layout view of the bulk terminal of the transistor. The metal line, if added, would run across the well contact and also connect to the source of the NMOS transistor. This would ensure that the pn junctions were properly reverse-biased. Of course, the PMOS device has similar minimum size and well contact considerations that were just described for the NMOS device, with the polarities and materials of the opposite type.

3.4   Modeling the MOS Transistor for Circuit Simulation

Computer circuit simulators are essential tools in the analysis and design of MOS circuits. The computer program SPICE and its commercial derivatives, such as HSPICE™ and SmartSPICE™, are widely used for such tasks and are used for examples in this text. Other circuit simulators such as Spectre™ require similar modeling considerations.[11] One key point to stress is that a circuit simulator is not a circuit design tool but rather a circuit analysis tool. Novice designers have been known to use SPICE in a circuit design role, but it is not a replacement for thinking about how a circuit should work or how to design a circuit. The role of SPICE is to validate your design and its proper operation. It allows the designer to try various optimization techniques and carry out simulations that include process variations. In this mode, SPICE is one of the most useful tools in the integrated circuits industry.

3.4.1   MOS Models in SPICE

The SPICE tool simulates a user-specified circuit description with built-in models for each type of circuit element. The circuit description must include layout dimensions for each device to produce accurate results. The MOS transistor models are based on device physics and empirical equations derived from measurements of

---

[11] HSPICE is a trademark of Synopsys. SmartSPICE is a trademark of Silvaco. Spectre is a trademark of Cadence.

fabricated devices. The *device models* are developed by a group whose main responsibility is to accurately capture the behavior of semiconductor devices in the form of equations such as those described in Chapter 2 for V_T, I_{DS}, and capacitance. Once the *model developers* complete the device models, they are coded into a program such as SPICE and given a specific name. For example, LEVEL 1 (quadratic model), LEVEL 2, LEVEL 3, LEVEL 4 or 13 (BSIM1), LEVEL 39 (BSIM2), LEVEL 28, and LEVEL 49 (BSIM3) are well-recognized names within the industry for the different built-in models incorporated into SPICE over the past 25 years. Only one such model is invoked during any given run of SPICE.

Each of these models has a number of *model parameters* associated with them. The number of parameters can vary depending on the complexity of the model. Some of the parameters are related to the *physical* process technology, such as t_{ox}, x_j, N_A, N_D, μ_0, and so on. Other *electrical* parameters are associated with the transistor current equations or capacitance equations such as V_T, γ, λ, and C_{jo}. Yet another set are used to capture certain advanced features of the devices such as short-channel effects, narrow-channel effects, and device resistances. Using these parameters, SPICE computes the currents and capacitances of the devices during model evaluation, using the device voltages V_{GS}, V_{DS}, and V_{BS}. If some parameters are not specified, they are computed internally by the program. As an example, if γ is not specified, it will be computed using N_A.

The actual values assigned to the SPICE model parameters are generated through a process called *parameter extraction*. The group responsible for this activity is associated with the fabrication service, as shown in Figure 3.7, which in this case is the foundry. In parameter extraction, actual devices are measured in a variety of configurations. The measured data is fed to software programs that produce the parameter values. Some of the parameters have a physical meaning, so their values are known in advance, while others are empirical in nature and are only used to fit the equations to the measured data.

Once these parameters are extracted, they are placed in a file called a *model library*. There are many such MOS models in the model library. First, there are different sets of parameters for NMOS and PMOS devices. There are also different parameter sets for ranges of *W* and *L* values (called model *binning*) and for process variations. To fully capture all possible realistic scenarios, there may be dozens of different parameter sets in a model library.

After the models have been placed in the library, they are delivered to the design house for use in chip design. These model libraries should be "checked-out" thoroughly for accuracy and consistency using the SPICE program. This is done by running SPICE on a variety of different device sizes and operating conditions. Once they are approved for use, they are made available to the chip designers for actual simulations.

3.4.2 Specifying MOS Transistors

In Figure 3.10, an NMOS transistor layout is shown along with its corresponding symbol. The source and drain region extensions are specified by Y_S and Y_D. We will assume that $Y_S = Y_D = Y$ for our purposes, but they may differ from device to

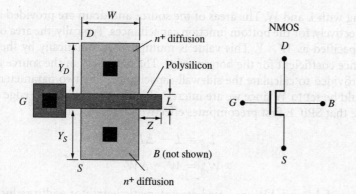

Figure 3.10
MOS layout and schematic for SPICE modeling.

device. There is a small poly gate overlap of the field given by $Z \times L$, which is usually small.

In the SPICE program, the user may specify the transistors and their connection with the format given below:

MOSFET

Mxxx D G S B mname $L =$ value $W =$ value AD $=$ value PD $=$ value AS $=$ value PS $=$ value

Mxxx	The instance name of the MOSFET.
D	The drain node.
G	The gate node.
S	The source node.
B	The bulk node.
mname	The name of the model to be used. This is also where you distinguish between a PMOS and NMOS.
L	The length of the transistor.
W	The width of the transistor.
AD	The area of drain diffusion bottom region.
PD	The drain edges to be used for sidewall capacitance.
AS	The area of the source diffusion bottom region.
PS	The source edges to be used for sidewall capacitance.

The specification begins with an "M" and a sequence of letters to form the instance name. This is followed by the drain, gate, source, and bulk connections. Next, the model name is specified. After the model, the dimensions of the device are provided beginning with L and W. The areas of the source and drain are provided as AS and AD, respectively, for the bottom junction capacitances. Typically, the area of the bottom is specified as $W \times Y$. This value is multiplied automatically by the junction capacitance coefficient for the bottom edge. The periphery of the source and drain is also provided to calculate the sidewall capacitance. The two parameters, PS and PD, should be set to W since we are interested in the channel facing edge only.

Note that SPICE first precomputes effective values of L and W:

$$L_{eff} = L - \Delta L$$
$$W_{eff} = W - \Delta W$$

(3.2)

The values of ΔL and ΔW are based on systematic length or width reductions and process-related variations. We will use W_{eff} and L_{eff} below to conform to these precomputed values.

Example 3.2   **SPICE MOS Transistor Specification**

To illustrate how a MOS transistor is specified to SPICE, we assume that $L = 0.2\ \mu$m, $W = 0.4\ \mu$m, and $Y = 0.5\ \mu$m. Then, AS = AD = $W \times Y$ = (0.4 μm) (0.5 μm) and PS = PD = 0.4 μm. If the drain node is `drainn`, and the gate node is `gaten`, while the source and bulk are grounded, we would specify the transistor instance as

```
M1 drainn gaten Gnd Gnd NMOS1 l=0.2u w=0.4u ad=0.2p pd=0.4u as=0.2p ps=0.4u
```

Here, the model invoked from the library is called NMOS1. The length, width, areas, and perimeters are all specified in absolute units of meters. Another alternative is to define a scale factor $\lambda = 0.1\ \mu$m (note this is not the channel length modulation parameter). Then all the transistor dimensions can be scaled relative to this value. This greatly improves the readability of the transistor description. It is specified using the .opt directive. For the same specifications, the device could be re-written as

```
.opt scale=0.1u     * Set scale factor=lambda
M1 drainn gaten Gnd Gnd NMOS1 l=2 w=4 ad=20 pd=4 as=20  ps=4
```

The model used by the simulator is given as NMOS1 in the above input specification. This would be retrieved from the model library and invokes one of the built-in device models. The LEVEL 1 and BSIM3 are the two device models considered in this book. The LEVEL 1 model employs the equations derived in Section 2.4. Today, BSIM3v3 is the workhorse model in industry and is adequate for most deep submicron MOS digital circuit analysis and design, provided parameters are extracted from measured data. This model is based on the description in Section 2.5. We now describe these two models in more detail.

3.5   SPICE MOS LEVEL 1 Device Model

The dc characteristics of the MOS LEVEL 1 model are defined by the device electrical parameters[12] VTO, KP, LAMBDA, PHI, and GAMMA. These parameters are directly associated with the model developed in Section 2.4. Ideally, the user should specify these parameters after measuring actual devices and extracting the corresponding values. However, these electrical parameters are computed by SPICE if process parameters, such as NSUB, TOX, and UO, are given; user-specified values always override internal calculation.

To illustrate one flow in SPICE, assume that VTO, NSUB, LAMBDA, TOX, and UO are specified by the library model. The computation of the threshold voltage begins with the calculation of the surface potential, PHI, based on the substrate doping level, NSUB:

$$\text{PHI} = 2 \times \frac{kT}{q} \ln\left(\frac{\text{NSUB}}{n_i}\right) \tag{3.3}$$

The oxide capacitance is computed using TOX:

$$C_{ox} = \frac{\varepsilon_{ox}}{\text{TOX}} \tag{3.4}$$

The body-effect parameter is then computed using NSUB and C_{ox}:

$$\text{GAMMA} = \frac{\sqrt{2\varepsilon_{si}q \times \text{NSUB}}}{C_{ox}} \tag{3.5}$$

Finally, the threshold voltage is computed using the following equation:

$$V_T = \text{VTO} + \text{GAMMA}(\sqrt{\text{PHI} - V_{BS}} - \sqrt{\text{PHI}}) \tag{3.6}$$

VTO is positive for enhancement-mode n-channel devices and negative for p-channel devices.

Next, the current equations are computed using the threshold voltage. If KP is specified, it is used directly in the current expression. If not, the mobility, UO, is used to compute it:

$$\text{KP} = \text{UO} \times C_{ox} \tag{3.7}$$

For the linear region, the current expression is

$$I_{DS} = \frac{W_{eff}}{L_{eff}} \frac{\text{KP}}{2} [2(V_{GS} - V_T)V_{DS} - V_{DS}^2](1 + \text{LAMBDA} \times V_{DS}) \tag{3.8}$$

$$V_{GS} \geq V_T \quad V_{DS} \leq V_{GS} - V_T$$

---

[12] SPICE parameters will be indicated with capitalization of all text when referring to the parameter.

For the saturation region, the current expression is

$$I_{DS} = \frac{W_{eff}}{L_{eff}} \frac{\text{KP}}{2} (V_{GS} - V_T)^2 (1 + \text{LAMBDA} \times V_{DS})$$

$$V_{GS} \geq V_T \quad V_{DS} \geq V_{GS} - V_T$$

(3.9)

Note that the channel length modulation parameter, LAMBDA, is used in both linear and saturation expressions for continuity of the current. It is important in SPICE that the equations be continuous from one region to another. Otherwise, the numerical methods used in the program have some difficulty converging to a solution. For this reason, the linear and saturation regions both require a term, $(1 + \text{LAMBDA} \times V_{DS})$, even though its effect is most prominent in the saturation region. As mentioned before, if any of the values of GAMMA, KP, or PHI are specified in the model library it would override the calculations given above.

The capacitances of MOS devices, modeled in several parts, are defined so they may be calculated easily from actual circuit layouts. Three constant capacitors, CGSO, CGDO, and CGBO, represent gate-source, gate-drain, and gate-body overlap capacitances. The CGBO term is due to the gate extension into the field region, defined by the region $Z \times L$ in Figure 3.10. The thin-oxide gate capacitance is calculated by the program as a function of applied voltages and distributed among the gate, source, drain, and body regions. The charge storage effects are included only if TOX is specified in the input description. There are two built-in models of the gate capacitances. LEVEL 1 uses the piecewise-linear voltage-dependent capacitance model proposed by Meyer. This model does not necessarily conserve charge and therefore must be used with care. It is not suitable for many circuits that rely on charge conservation of the model for proper operation. A more advanced model is available in higher-level MOS models such as BSIM3, as discussed in the next section.

The junction capacitances, for both source-body and drain-body *pn* junctions, are divided into bottom and periphery components. The junction capacitances are determined by the parameters CJ, CJSW, MJ, MJSW, and PB. Note that CJ is specified in F/m^2 and must be multiplied by the area of the source or drain, whereas CJSW is specified in F/m and must be multiplied by the perimeter of the source or drain. CJSW is premultiplied with the junction depth, XJ. The following equations are used to compute the capacitances:

$$C_{JD} = \frac{\text{CJ} \times \text{AD}}{\left(1 - \dfrac{V_J}{\text{PB}}\right)^{\text{MJ}}} + \frac{\text{CJSW} \times \text{PD}}{\left(1 - \dfrac{V_J}{\text{PB}}\right)^{\text{MJSW}}} \quad \text{drain junction}$$

$$C_{JS} = \frac{\text{CJ} \times \text{AS}}{\left(1 - \dfrac{V_J}{\text{PB}}\right)^{\text{MJ}}} + \frac{\text{CJSW} \times \text{PS}}{\left(1 - \dfrac{V_J}{\text{PB}}\right)^{\text{MJSW}}} \quad \text{source junction} \quad (3.10)$$

When specifying the information for a given transistor, it is important to include AS, AD, PS, and PD so that the correct calculations for junction capacitance can be performed.

There is some overlap among the parameters describing the junction current; for example, the reverse current can be input either as IS (in A) or as JS (in A/m^2). Whereas the first is an absolute value, the second is multiplied by AD and AS to give the reverse current of the drain and source junctions, respectively. This flexibility has been provided so that junction characteristics can either be entered as absolute values on model statements or related to areas AD and AS entered on device statements.

The MOS transistor has series resistances associated with the source and drain regions. If needed, these parasitic resistances can be expressed as either RD and RS (in Ω) or RSH (in Ω per square), the latter being multiplied by the number of squares NRD and NRS specified on the device instance line.

The reader should not be overwhelmed by the number of parameters and their detailed meanings. This is intended to give you the background needed when using SPICE. In fact, the LEVEL 1 device model has more parameters than the ones mentioned above. The complete list of SPICE parameters used in LEVEL 1 is given in Table 3.1 at the end of this chapter together with the corresponding symbols used in this text.

3.5.1   Extraction of Parameters for MOS LEVEL 1

To obtain satisfactory results for the LEVEL 1 model in circuit analysis and design, measured data on samples of MOS transistors must be obtained. The parameters may be extracted by fitting measured data to the device equations over the intended operating range of voltages and currents. These are, of course, the first-order equations associated with long-channel devices, so their use should be restricted to these types of devices. Similar steps for fitting parameters to measured data are used for the short-channel devices.

Methods of taking and reducing data to determine VTO, GAMMA, KP, and LAMBDA are illustrated in Figure 3.11. If the gate is connected to the drain, the device will be in the saturation region of operation, since $V_{DS} > V_{GS} - V_T$. In this condition, the long-channel saturation region equation can be rewritten as

$$\sqrt{2I_D} = \sqrt{\frac{W_{eff}\text{KP}}{L_{eff}}}\,(V_{GS} - V_T) \qquad (3.11)$$

By plotting $\sqrt{2I_D}$ versus V_{GS} as in Figure 3.11a, the x-intercept can be extracted as V_T and the slope of the line is $\sqrt{\dfrac{W_{eff}\text{KP}}{L_{eff}}}$. A number of measurements of the current can be made with $V_{BS} = 0$. This will produce the zero-bias threshold voltage, VTO. The value of KP can be extracted from the slope. By adjusting V_{BS}, repeating the measurements will produce additional values of the threshold voltage. Using these V_T values, the body-effect coefficient, GAMMA, can be obtained.

A second set of measurements is used to determine the channel-length modulation parameter LAMBDA, if needed. As seen in Figure 3.11b, the device can be disconnected at the gate and drain and two separate voltages applied. Keeping the device in saturation, two values of V_{DS} can be applied and the corresponding currents measured. From these two measurements, the value of LAMBDA can be extracted.

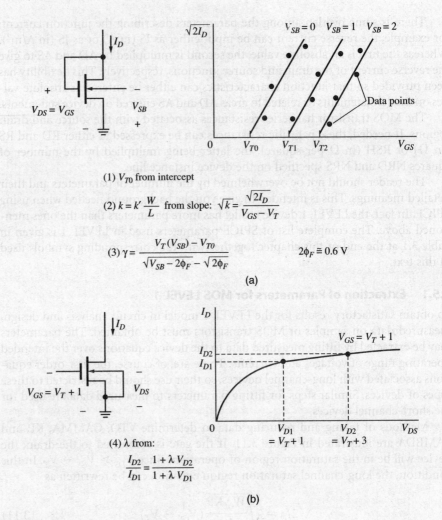

(1) V_{T0} from intercept

(2) $k = k' \dfrac{W}{L}$ from slope: $\sqrt{k} = \dfrac{\sqrt{2I_D}}{V_{GS} - V_T}$

(3) $\gamma = \dfrac{V_T(V_{SB}) - V_{T0}}{\sqrt{V_{SB} - 2\phi_F} - \sqrt{2\phi_F}}$ $2\phi_F \cong 0.6$ V

(a)

(4) λ from:

$$\dfrac{I_{D2}}{I_{D1}} = \dfrac{1 + \lambda \, V_{D2}}{1 + \lambda \, V_{D1}}$$

(b)

Figure 3.11

MOS transistor parameter extraction.

Example 3.3   **SPICE LEVEL 1 Model Specification**

Assume that after parameter extraction, the following values are determined:

$V_{T0} = 0.5$ V, $k' = \mu_0 C_{ox} = 300$ μA/V^2, $|2\phi_F| = 0.8$ V, $\gamma = 0.4$ V$^{1/2}$ and $\lambda = 0$

Then the corresponding SPICE parameters are

VTO = 0.5 V, KP = 300(10^{-6}), PHI = 0.8, GAMMA = 0.4, and LAMBDA = 0.

The library model would be specified as follows:

```
.model NMOS1 nmos level=1 vto=0.5 kp=300u phi=0.8 gamma=0.4 lambda=0
```

In a complete LEVEL 1 specification, many more parameters would be extracted and specified in the model line, but this example is only intended to show the process involved.

After specifying the circuit description and connecting it to the appropriate model library, the user provides a series of control statements to direct the analysis, and plot or print results. The details of this aspect of SPICE are program-specific. Tutorial information of this nature is provided in Appendix A. More complete user guides are available from the CAD vendors, and in the references listed at the end of this chapter.

While these examples illustrate the extraction of specific model parameters for LEVEL 1, the same basic concepts can be used to extract all of the needed parameters for the advanced models in SPICE. These models are kept in library files that are associated with a particular technology and invoked by the user when simulating a given circuit. Normally, the user should not modify the parameters in these files, although the models should be validated using SPICE. Since the models will not be generally viewed by users, those who are new to the field may choose to skip the next section without any loss to continuity.

*3.6   BSIM3 Model

Over the past 30 years much effort has gone into modeling the MOS transistor. Scaling has made what were previously second- and third-order effects into first-order effects. Analytical equations much more sophisticated than those presented thus far have been developed. More advanced SPICE models are available, such as LEVEL 2 and 3 models, and more recently, BSIM1, BSIM2, BSIM3, and BSIM4.

BSIM (Berkeley Short-channel IGFET Model) was developed at the University of California at Berkeley in the 1980s and 1990s, and work on the latest model continues today. BSIM3v3 is currently the most popular model for deep submicron devices. It is based on a quasi-two-dimensional model of the MOS device, with both physics-based and empirically-based equations. There are over 300 parameters in the complete model so the details of BSIM3v3 are beyond the scope of this book. However, the parameters for the BSIM3v3 are listed in Table 3.2 together with the corresponding symbols at the end of this chapter.

The goal of BSIM3 is to capture the key features of the dc and ac behavior of the deep submicron MOS transistor. Conceptually, the equations of Section 2.5 with velocity saturation form the basis of the model. The model in BSIM3v3 is much more elaborate and considers detailed physical effects as well as measured performance of fabricated devices in its implementation. We first describe the binning feature of BSIM3. Next, the threshold voltage equation, the mobility modeling, and current voltage expressions are presented. Finally, the capacitance modeling is described.

3.6.1   Binning Process in BSIM3

One of the limitations of any device model is that it is only as good as the parameter extraction that is carried out during the characterization process. Unfortunately, even careful parameter extraction for one device does not track across all the W and L sizes encountered in a design. As a result, a number of models are prepared for one technology as illustrated in Figure 3.12. Minimum and maximum widths and lengths are selected and a number of bins are defined. Typically, measured devices lie at the center of the bins (roughly where the numbers are placed) and are used to characterize the entire bin. A large number of parameters are dedicated to the binning process in BSIM, so it is important to understand this concept.

As an example, a total of nine bins are shown in the figure. The number and ranges for the bins will vary from foundry to foundry. Fortunately, in digital design, the minimum length is used for most devices, so the bins labeled 1, 4, and 7 are of most interest. However, the user should realize that different models may be invoked as the width is modified. Certain boundaries of the bins may have discontinuities that produce "interesting" results in the circuit simulator. As a side effect of this *binning process,* two devices near a boundary may have different drive capability if the threshold voltage has a sharp discontinuity across the boundary. It is worthwhile to plot, for example, V_T versus L and V_T versus W in SPICE to identify any possible issues in the models before using them in a design, especially when a new set of models first arrives from the foundry. Otherwise, the fabricated design may not match the expected performance from simulations.

3.6.2 Short-Channel Threshold Voltage

The threshold voltage expression was derived earlier in Section 2.3 as

$$V_T = V_{T0} + \gamma(\sqrt{2|\phi_F| + V_{SB}} - \sqrt{2|\phi_F|})$$

There are a number of effects that change the threshold voltage relative to the first-order equation, which we now explore. In BSIM3, the V_T formula starts with the same equation:

$$V_T = \text{VTHO} + \gamma(\sqrt{\text{PHI} - V_{BS}} - \sqrt{\text{PHI}}) \qquad (3.12)$$

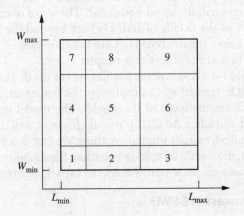

Figure 3.12
Model binning process.

Here, the value of VTHO is usually specified or computed using the flat-band voltage, VFB. However, this formulation does not accurately capture the vertical doping profile in the channel region. The γ term is actually dependent on the different doping levels in the channel *and* substrate regions. The surface doping is due to the threshold implant, NCH, while the doping in the substrate is NSUB, a much lower value. This variation in the doping profile must be modeled for accuracy.

In BSIM3, the term $2|\phi_F|$ is called PHI and is given by

$$\text{PHI} = 2\frac{kT}{q}\ln\left(\frac{\text{NCH}}{n_i}\right) \tag{3.13}$$

where NCH is the doping of the channel region.

To properly capture the effects of the two doping levels, the threshold voltage equation is modified as follows. First, two γ parameters are defined as

$$\gamma_1 = \frac{\sqrt{2\varepsilon_{si}q \times \text{NCH}}}{C_{ox}}$$

$$\gamma_2 = \frac{\sqrt{2\varepsilon_{si}q \times \text{NSUB}}}{C_{ox}} \tag{3.14}$$

The oxide capacitance is computed as usual using

$$C_{ox} = \frac{\varepsilon_{ox}}{\text{TOX}} \tag{3.15}$$

Then, the two new parameters, K1 and K2, are defined using γ_1 and γ_2:

$$\text{K1} = f(\gamma_2, \text{PHI})$$
$$\text{K2} = f(\gamma_1, \gamma_2, \text{PHI}) \tag{3.16}$$

Effectively, the K1 and K2 terms model the vertical profile in the channel region as an abrupt transition from NCH to NSUB at some depth x_t. Then, V_T is determined by

$$V_T = \text{VTHO} + \text{K1}\left(\sqrt{\text{PHI} - V_{BS}} - \sqrt{\text{PHI}}\right) - \text{K2} \times V_{BS} \tag{3.17}$$

There are two additional V_T effects that are worth noting. Both L_{eff} and W_{eff} have an impact on the threshold voltage. The effect of reducing L_{eff} is to reduce the threshold voltage. As the channel length decreases, the depletion regions of the source and drain move closer together and actually aid in the depletion process of the channel region. The effect of this charge sharing is shown in Figure 3.13a. This is referred to as the classical short-channel effect (SCE). However, there is another effect that tends to increase the threshold voltage as L_{eff} is reduced, as shown in Figure 3.13b. Due to oxidation-enhanced diffusion, a process whereby impurities gather at point defects at the two gate edges during oxidation, the surface doping levels in the channel region in short channels may be much higher than in long channels. This so-called reverse short-channel effect (RSCE), or threshold voltage roll-up, causes

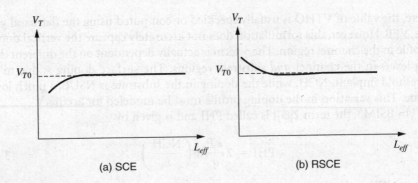

Figure 3.13

SCE and RSCE characteristics.

V_T to increase due to the lateral nonuniformity of the doping across the channel. Since SCE and RSCE act in opposite directions, the precise doping profile determines the dominance of one effect over the other as the channel length is reduced. Typically, the V_T "rolls up" as L_{eff} is decreased due to RSCE and then drops off in value as the classical SCE takes over. Both can be incorporated in a short-channel effect (SCE) term ΔV_{SCE}. It is useful to plot V_T versus L_{eff} for a model to observe these effects and also to examine any issues surrounding the binning process.

In some devices, the width can also play a role in determining the threshold voltage. If the channel width is close to the minimum width, the threshold voltage can actually increase in value. This is due to the fact that the poly gate overlap of the field (in Figure 3.10, the area defined by $Z \times L$) induces depletion-layer charge in the field region and this must be compensated for by an additional gate voltage. Its relative importance is reduced as the channel width increases, but it must be accounted for in narrow devices to derive accurate thresholds. This is called the *narrow-channel effect* (NCE). A term can be added to the threshold voltage, ΔV_{NCE}, to account for this effect. It is also useful to plot V_T versus W_{eff} to observe this effect and also to examine any issues surrounding the binning process.

Yet another factor to be included in the V_T calculation is the effect the drain-source voltage has on lowering the barrier for current flow. Normally, the gate-source voltage is responsible for inverting the surface by $2|\phi_F|$. In short-channel devices, the depletion region around the drain increases as V_{DS} increases, and it extends into the channel region. Conceptually, the drain-source voltage is assisting the gate voltage in the depletion process. It is referred to as drain-induced barrier lowering (DIBL). As the channel length is reduced, the potential barrier between the source and drain is reduced even without the application of a drain-source voltage due to the SCE described above. However, the potential barrier is reduced even further by applying V_{DS} because it enhances the depletion region in the channel.

Figure 3.14 illustrates this effect. At low values of V_{DS}, the threshold voltage is the same as the long-channel case. However, as V_{DS} increases, a decrease in V_{T0} is

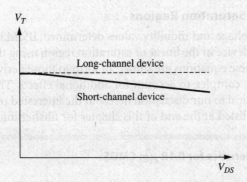

Figure 3.14
Drain-induced barrier lowering (DIBL).

observed that is almost linear with V_{DS}. An adjustment of the threshold voltage can accommodate the DIBL effect. We can subtract a term ηV_{DS} from the threshold voltage expression to account for the V_{DS} dependence.

The final form of the threshold voltage expression including all effects mentioned here is given by

$$V_T = \text{VTHO} + \text{K1}(\sqrt{\text{PHI} - V_{BS}} - \sqrt{\text{PHI}})$$

$$- \text{K2} \times V_{BS} - \eta V_{DS} - \Delta V_{\text{SCE}} + \Delta V_{\text{NCE}} \quad (3.18)$$

3.6.3   Mobility Model

A variety of mobility models are available in BSIM3 to capture the vertical and horizontal field effects. In all these models, the nominal mobility value is UO, and the parameters that modify this nominal value are UA, UB, and UC. One particular model for the vertical field effect is given in the equation below. It includes the effect of the vertical field and the substrate bias voltage, V_{BS}:

$$\mu_v = \frac{\text{UO}}{1 + (\text{UA} + \text{UC} + V_{BS})\left(\dfrac{V_{GS} - V_T}{t_{ox}}\right) + \text{UB}\left(\dfrac{V_{GS} - V_T}{t_{ox}}\right)^2} \quad (3.19)$$

The horizontal field component is based on the piecewise-continuous modeling of mobility as a function of the field, as described in Chapter 2. The parameter VSAT is the saturation velocity that is provided to BSIM3 and is used to compute the critical field

$$E_c = \frac{2\text{VSAT}}{\mu_v} \quad (3.20)$$

This relationship is used to guarantee continuity in the velocity versus electric field characteristic.

3.6.4 Linear and Saturation Regions

With the threshold voltage and mobility values determined, BSIM3 can compute the current through the device in the linear or saturation region using the operating voltages of the device. These equations are similar in form to those derived in Section 2.5, although much more complex to account for additional effects. The details of these equations are not critical to our discussion here, but the interested reader may consult any of the references listed at the end of this chapter for further information.

Example 3.4   **BSIM3 I-V Characteristics for 0.18 μm CMOS**

Problem:

Using a BSIM3 model for a 0.18 μm technology, plot I_{DS} versus V_{DS} for both PMOS and NMOS by sweeping V_{DS} from 0 to $V_{DD} = 1.8$ V at intervals of $V_{GS} = 1/2$ V_{DD}, 3/4 V_{DD} and V_{DD}. For convenience, let $W = 0.4$ μm and $L = 0.2$ μm, and set $\lambda = 0.1$ μm. What is the ratio of saturation currents between PMOS and NMOS at $|V_{GS}| = |V_{DS}| = V_{DD}$?

Solution:

```
*SPICE Input File
.param      Supply=1.8              * Set value of Vdd
.lib        'bsim3v3.cmos.18um'     * Set 0.18um library
.opt        scale=0.1u              * Set lambda
mp     drainp gatep Vdd   Vdd PMOS l=2 w=4 ad=20 pd=4 as=20 ps=4
mn     drainn gaten Gnd   Gnd NMOS l=2 w=4 ad=20 pd=4 as=20 ps=4
Vdd    Vdd    0 'Supply'
Vgsp   Vdd    gatep        dc
Vgsn   gaten  0            dc
Vdsp   Vdd    drainp       dc
Vdsn   drainn 0            dc
.dc    Vdsp   0 'Supply' 'Supply/20' Vgsp 0 'Supply' 'Supply/4'
.dc    Vdsn   0 'Supply' 'Supply/20' Vgsn 0 'Supply' 'Supply/4'
.plot dc      I1(mp)
.plot dc      I1(mn)
.end
```

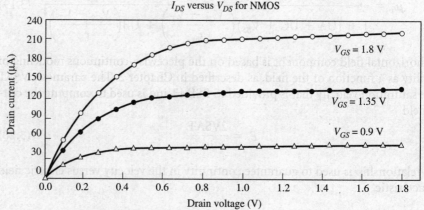

I_{DS} versus V_{DS} for NMOS

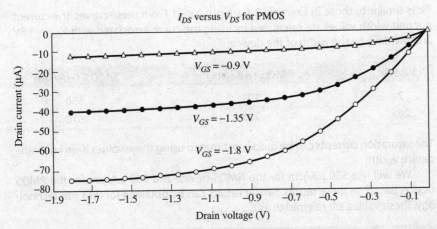

I_{DS} versus V_{DS} for PMOS

The ratio of the currents in saturation is obtained by using the topmost curve in each plot and computing the currents at $V_{DS} = 1.8$ V.

$$\text{Ratio} = \frac{I_{DS,N}(V_{GS} = V_{DD}, V_{DS} = V_{DD})}{I_{DS,P}(V_{GS} = V_{DD}, V_{DS} = V_{DD})} = \frac{220\ \mu A}{78\ \mu A} \approx 2.8$$

This is close to the ratio of 2.4 obtained in the previous chapter from the velocity saturation model.

SPICE Plots to Compute I_{on}

Example 3.5

Problem:

Calculate the current per unit of width in $\mu A/\mu m$ in the saturation region for both PMOS and NMOS at $V_{GS} = V_{DD}$ for a 2 × minimum width transistor and a 20 × minimum width transistor. Use the 0.18 μm technology data of Example 3.4.

Solution:

```
*SPICE Input File
.param                                Supply=1.8   * Set value of Vdd
.lib          'bsim3v3.cmos.18um'     * Set 0.18um library
.opt  scale=0.1u                      * Set lambda
mp    Gnd    gatep Vdd   Vdd    PMOS l=2 w=40 ad=200 pd=40 as=200 ps=40
mn    Vdd    gaten Gnd   Gnd    NMOS l=2 w=40 ad=200 pd=40 as=200 ps=40
Vdd   Vdd    0     'Supply'
Vgsp  Vdd          gatep 'Supply'
Vgsn  gaten Gnd          'Supply'
.dc   Vgsp   0     'Supply'     'Supply'
.dc   Vgsn   0     'Supply'     'Supply'
.plot dc     I1(mp)
.plot dc     I1(mn)
.end
```

Plots similar to those in Example 3.4 are produced. From these curves, the current per unit width values are calculated by using the curve associated with $V_{GS} = 1.8V$ and dividing by the width of the device:

Width	PMOS (μA/μm)	NMOS (μA/μm)
2×	195	550
20×	225	570

The saturation currents can be quickly estimated using these values if we know the device width.

We will use 550 μA/μm for the NMOS device and 200 μA/μm for the PMOS device, based on these results. Similar results can be obtained for 0.13 μm technology. These values are referred to as I_{on}.

3.6.5 Subthreshold Current

The subthreshold conduction region, where $V_{GS} < V_T$, is an important consideration in a multi-million transistor deep submicron design. The key issue is that the number of devices that are leaking current is so large that it consumes appreciable power. Furthermore, any dynamic logic circuits[13] are prone to charge leakage since devices are not fully turned off. A number of models exist in BSIM3 to model this region of operation. One such model is

$$I_{sub} = \beta_{sub} V_{th}^2 e^{(V_{GS} - V_T - V_{offset})/nV_{th}} \left(1 - e^{-V_{DS}/V_{th}}\right)$$

$$\beta_{sub} = UO \times C_d W_{eff}/L_{eff} \qquad C_d = \sqrt{\frac{q\varepsilon_{si} NCH}{PHI}} \qquad (3.21)$$

This model is similar in form to that described in Chapter 2. Note that the low-field mobility is used here since the gate voltage is rather small.

Example 3.6

SPICE Plots of BSIM3 Model in Subthreshold Region

Problem:

Plot $\log(I_{DS})$ versus V_{GS} for both PMOS and NMOS by sweeping V_{GS} from 0 to V_{DD} with $V_{DS} = V_{DD}$. Compute the current per unit width in the subthreshold region, called I_{off}, for each device.

---

[13] Dynamic circuits are the topic of Chapter 7.

Solution:

```
*SPICE Input File
.param                          Supply=1.8  * Set value of Vdd
.lib         'bsim3v3.cmos.18um'      * Set 0.18um library
.opt  scale=0.1u       * Set lambda
mp    Gnd   gatep Vdd   Vdd   PMOS l=2 w=4 ad=20 pd=4 as=20 ps=4
mn    Vdd   gaten Gnd   Gnd   NMOS l=2 w=4 ad=20 pd=4 as=20 ps=4
Vdd   Vdd   0     'Supply'
Vgsp  Vdd   gatep 'Supply'
Vgsn  gaten Gnd         'Supply'
.dc   Vgsp  0     'Supply'   'Supply/20'
.dc   Vgsn  0     'Supply'   'Supply/20'
.plot dc    I1(mp)
.plot dc    I1(mn)
.end
```

When $V_{GS} = 0.0$ V, the I_{off} for the NMOS device is 0.01 nA/0.4 μm = 25 pA/μm. For the PMOS device, $I_{off} = 0.008$ nA/0.4 μm = 20 pA/μm. These levels are relatively small compared to I_{on}.

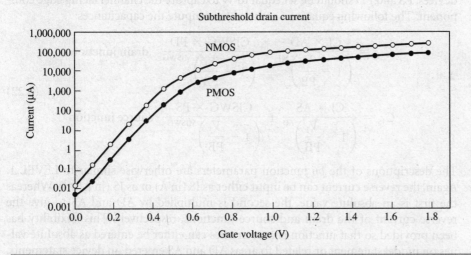

3.6.6 Capacitance Models

Many of the comments made earlier about the capacitance models for LEVEL 1 also apply to advanced models. However, in the advanced models, charge storage effects are much more accurately represented. Internal to the SPICE program, the capacitances are formulated using charge-conserving equations. From a user's perspective, the information provided to the program is essentially the same. The main difference between LEVEL 1 and BSIM3 is that SPICE will produce much more accurate results, especially for circuits that rely on charge conservation for proper operation.

The nonlinear thin-oxide capacitance due to TOX is calculated by the program as a function of applied voltages and distributed among the gate, source, drain, and body regions. The three capacitances, C_{gs}, C_{gd}, and C_{gb}, are computed based on the region of operation. It is important to point out that *charges* associated with the gate, drain, source, and bulk terminals are computed first, and then capacitances are derived from these terms. In this manner, the total charge in the system can be conserved, thereby producing much more accurate results than LEVEL 1. In addition, three constant capacitors, CGSO, CGDO, and CGBO, represent gate-source, gate-drain, and gate-body overlap capacitances. Today, CGSO and CGDO are due to a combination of fringing capacitances from the edge of the poly to the surface of the silicon and lateral diffusion. The CGBO term is due to the gate extension into the field region and is relatively small.

The nonlinear depletion-layer capacitances, for both source-body and drain-body *pn* junctions, is divided into bottom and periphery parameters, CJ and CJSWG, which vary as the MJ and MJSWG power of junction voltage, respectively. The sidewall capacitance is primarily due to the channel facing edge since the other three edges interface to STI oxide and are therefore small. When specifying the information for a given transistor, it is important to include AS, AD, PS, and PD so that the correct calculations for junction capacitance can be performed. For deep submicron devices, PS and PD should be set equal to W to capture the channel facing edge component. The following equations are used to compute the capacitances:

$$C_{JD} = \frac{CJ \times AD}{\left(1 - \dfrac{V_J}{PB}\right)^{MJ}} + \frac{CJSWG \times PD}{\left(1 - \dfrac{V_J}{PB}\right)^{MJSWG}} \quad \text{drain junction}$$

$$C_{JS} = \frac{CJ \times AS}{\left(1 - \dfrac{V_J}{PB}\right)^{MJ}} + \frac{CJSWG \times PS}{\left(1 - \dfrac{V_J}{PB}\right)^{MJSWG}} \quad \text{source junction}$$

(3.22)

The descriptions of the *pn* junction parameters are otherwise similar to LEVEL 1. Again, the reverse current can be input either as IS (in A) or as JS (in A/m²). Whereas the first is an absolute value, the second is multiplied by AD and AS to give the reverse current of the drain and source junctions, respectively. This flexibility has been provided so that junction characteristics can either be entered as absolute values on model statement or related to areas AD and AS entered on device statements.

3.6.7   Source/Drain Resistance

The parasitic drain and source series resistance is expressed as either RD and RS (in Ω) or RSH (in Ω per square), the latter being multiplied by the number of squares, NRD and NRS, input on the device instance line. In addition, an alternative method is available in BSIM3v3 that allows the specification of RSDW, in units of Ω-um, and $R_D + R_S$ is computed using the width. In its basic form,

$$R_{DS} = R_D + R_S = \frac{RDSW}{W_{eff}}$$

(3.23)

*3.7 Additional Effects in MOS Transistors

In this section, we describe some of the additional features and certain limitations on electrical characteristics of integrated circuit MOS devices.

3.7.1 Parameter Variations in Production

MOS transistors have always exhibited broad variations in major device parameters among production lots. As a result, a wide range of devices are measured and parameters are extracted to characterize the statistical variations. Particularly notable are variations in channel length, threshold voltage, and gate-oxide thickness. Additional models are added to the model library based on the extremes of the key parameters. These models are called *process corners* in that they capture parameters that would make the circuit unusually fast or unusually slow. Each corner represents different settings of the parameters that represent typical, fast, and slow situations. Designers perform SPICE simulations at a number of process corners during design. While these matters are progressively coming under better control, it is still quite common to find circuits with a 2 to 1 (or larger) unit-to-unit variation in dc power consumption and speed in a single production facility. A common response to this situation in industry is to use testing to sort the circuits according to speed and/or power consumption. Typically the fastest circuits are sold at a higher price.

3.7.2 Temperature Effects

MOS transistors display a temperature dependence that must be considered in circuit design. For example, an increase in temperature slows down the circuits and increases the subthreshold current. Parameters such as mobility and threshold voltage are temperature-dependent. Testing circuits at high temperature is very costly, so means are usually sought to predict high-temperature performance from room temperature tests. The process corners for SPICE simulations mentioned above are used to capture variations in operating temperature on the chip. In this mode, one temperature is specified for the entire design being analyzed. The corners may be defined as typical (room temperature), hot, and cold.

Mobility of carriers in the channel of a MOS transistor is an inverse function of absolute temperature according to the following empirical expression:

$$\mu(T) = \mu_0 \left(\frac{T}{300°\text{K}} \right)^{-1.5} \tag{3.24}$$

where μ_0 is the low-field mobility, and the temperature T is in kelvins (absolute). Thus, for a $100°\text{K}$ temperature increase, mobility may decrease by as much as 40%. Consider the current when the transistor V_{GS} is above the threshold voltage. In the saturation or linear region, the drain-source current is controlled by the carrier mobility. Therefore, the drive current will decrease as we increase the temperature.

The threshold voltage of both NMOS and PMOS enhancement-mode transistors is also affected by temperature variations. The V_T decreases in magnitude by 1.5 to 2 mV/°C with increasing temperature due to changes in ϕ_{GC} and $2\phi_F$. Usually the mobility variations are more significant for digital circuit performance.

It is also interesting to observe the effects of temperature variations on the subthreshold current. In the subthreshold region, the current is controlled by the minority carrier concentration which is dependent on n_i as follows:

$$n_i = 1.45 \times 10^{10} \left(\frac{T}{300°K} \right)^{1.5} e^{(1.12/0.0516 - E_g(T)/2V_{th})} \tag{3.25}$$

where E_g is the bandgap (1.12 eV for silicon). At room temperature, we know that $n_i = 1.45 \times 10^{10}/\text{cm}^3$. Therefore, the subthreshold current will increase as the temperature increases.

From the results above, it is clear that the temperature should be as low as possible for high drive current and low subthreshold current.

Example 3.7   **SPICE Temperature Variations**

Problem:

Plot I_{DS} versus temperature for both PMOS and NMOS transistors by sweeping temperature from $-40°$ C to $100°$ C with $V_{GS} = 0, V_{DD}$, and $V_{DS} = V_{DD}$. Explain the results. Use the values given in Example 3.4 for a 0.18 μm technology.

Solution:

The following input is used to obtain subthreshold results ($V_{GS} = 0$). A similar file can be used to obtain saturation results ($V_{GS} = V_{DD}$).

```
*SPICE Input File
.param      Supply=1.8          * Set value of Vdd
.lib        'cmos.18um'  * Set 0.18um library
.opt        scale=0.1u          * Set lambda
mp      Gnd     gatep Vdd    Vdd     PMOS l=2 w=4 ad=8 pd=4 as=8 ps=4
mn      Vdd     gaten Gnd    Gnd     NMOS l=2 w=4 ad=8 pd=4 as=8 ps=4
Vdd     Vdd     0       'Supply'
Vgsp    Vdd             gatep 0
Vgsn    gaten Gnd             0
.dc     TEMP    0       100    5
.plot dc    I1(mp)
.plot dc    I1(mn)
.end
```

The results are shown in the following figures. For the subthreshold region, the current increases as temperature increases. This is due to an increase in the minority carrier concentration, according to Equation (3.25), which controls current flow in this region of operation. In the case of the saturation region, the majority carrier current is controlled by the mobility. As temperature is increased, the mobility is reduced as indicated by Equation (3.24), and therefore the current is reduced.

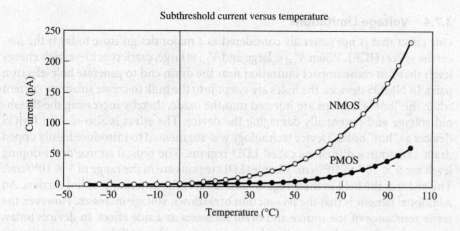

Subthreshold current versus temperature

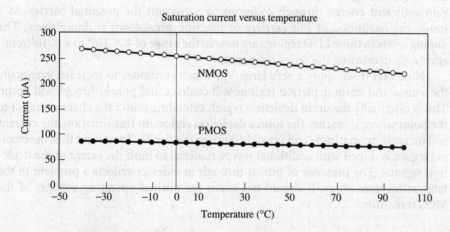

Saturation current versus temperature

3.7.3   Supply Variations

In addition to the process and temperature variations, there are also variations in the supply voltage from one region of the chip to another, depending on the current flow in the power grid. The voltage changes are due to resistance and inductance of the metal lines that comprise the power grid. These voltage changes are referred to as IR drops and Ldi/dt variations. If the voltage on the supply drops, the circuit slows down. If the drop is significant, the circuit may not function properly. Typically, designers account for this variation using process corners. The supply is reduced by 10% uniformly across the whole design during simulation. Even though this is not accurate, the circuits that are simulated are rather small and the simulations will provide useful results for these blocks.

3.7.4 Voltage Limitations

One effect that is not generally considered as a major design issue today is the *hot-carrier effect* (HCE). When V_{GS} is large and V_{DS} is large, carriers achieve high energy levels that can cause impact ionization near the drain end to generate hole-electron pairs. In NMOS devices, the holes are swept into the bulk to create substrate current while the "hot" electrons are injected into the oxide, thereby increasing the threshold voltage and potentially damaging the device. The effect is also seen in PMOS devices as "hot" holes. Device technology was augmented to introduce lightly doped drain and source diffusions called LDD regions. The typical source/drain doping levels are 5×10^{19} to $10^{20}/cm^3$ whereas LDD regions are in the range of $5 \times 10^{17}/cm^3$. This reduces the field in these regions and reduces the generation of hot carriers. An additional benefit is that the *pn* junction breakdown voltage increases. However, the series resistance of the source and drain increases as a side effect. In devices today, the supply voltage is being reduced as technology scales, and the carriers no longer gain sufficient energy through collisions to surmount the potential barrier. As a result, the likelihood of hot carriers or junction breakdown is diminishing. The doping levels in these LDD regions are now in the range of 4×10^{18} to $8 \times 10^{18}/cm^3$, effectively decreasing the series resistance.

Note that if we apply a very large V_{DS} which continues to increase, eventually the source and drain depletion regions will coalesce and *punch-through* will occur. This is essentially the drain depletion region extending under the channel region to the point where it reaches the source depletion region. In this situation, the current will increase dramatically and possibly damage the device. To prevent this, the channel region is doped with additional *p*-type material to limit the extent of the depletion regions. The presence of punch-through in a device reflects a problem in the fabrication technology. It should not occur for normal operating voltages of the MOS transistor.

3.7.5 CMOS Latch-up

All MOS transistor integrated circuits have undesired and potentially troublesome parasitic bipolar transistors that will conduct if one or more *pn* junctions become forward-biased. The potential consequences of bipolar transistor actions are much more serious in CMOS circuits. Figure 3.15 illustrates that a *pnp* transistor is possible with the *n*-type body as its base, while an *npn* transistor is possible with an n^+ source or drain electrode as its emitter, the *p*-well as its base, and the *n*-body as a collector.

In older technologies, the undesired parasitic circuit, shown schematically in Figure 3.15a, was present. The bipolar transistors originate as just described. The resistors R_1 and R_2 (also parasitic elements in the sense that they make no contribution to the desired MOS circuit function) originate in the bulk semiconductor material of the body and the *p*-type well. The other two resistors, R_3 and R_4, play a minor role in this scenario. Consider the extracted circuit in Figure 3.15b. If any appreciable current flows through R_1 raising the voltage at node A, the base-emitter junction of the bipolar transistor Q_1 will become forward-biased and turn on. This will reduce the voltage at node B, which will cause current to flow in R_2. This, in

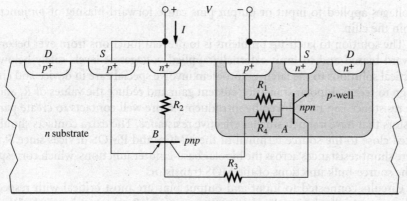

(a) Origin of parasitic elements

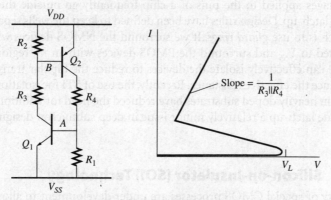

(b) *IV* characteristic of *pnp – npn* structure

Figure 3.15
Latch-up in CMOS circuits.

turn, will eventually turn on Q_2, which acts to pull node A even higher. More current will flow in Q_1 with the appropriate current gain, and this positive feedback action will increase the currents around the loop until breakdown occurs. Clearly, low values of resistance are desirable in order to make it more difficult to forward-bias the junctions.

Another way to view the behavior of the circuit is to look at the two-terminal current-voltage characteristics of this parasitic circuit, also depicted in Figure 3.15b. This type of device is referred to as a *thyristor* or *silicon-controlled rectifier* (SCR). As the voltage across the device increases, the current initially increases slowly. Above some critical voltage, V_L, both bipolar transistors begin to conduct and the current rises sharply from leakage levels to a value limited by resistors R_3 and R_4, often many milliamperes. This phenomenon is known as CMOS *latch-up*. In a sense, the high current state is latched and will not change until the power is turned off or one of the devices is permanently damaged. It can occur even at normal operating voltages if voltages applied to input or output pins cause forward-biasing of *pn* junctions within the chip.

The solution to latch-up problems is to prevent junctions from ever becoming forward-biased and to limit externally applied voltages at levels safely below V_L. Practical solutions to the latch-up problem involve special care in device and circuit design to reduce bipolar transistor current gain and reduce the values of R_1 and R_2. The resistance can be reduced by introducing more well contacts to create parallel resistors that have a much smaller effective resistance. The extra contacts should be placed close to the source terminal of the NMOS and PMOS devices since R_1 and R_2 are shunt resistances across the bipolar base-emitter junctions, which correspond to the source-bulk junctions of the MOS transistor.

Circuits connected to input and output pins are most critical with respect to latch-up, especially during the chip-testing process. When power is switched on and off, voltages applied to the pins of a chip frequently go outside the normal range causing latch-up. Design rules have been defined to keep the wells separated. Another approach is to use *guard rings*. If we surround the NMOS devices with a p^+ region connected to V_{SS} and surround the PMOS devices with an n^+ region connected to V_{DD}, we can effectively isolate the devices to reduce the bipolar transistor gain, and also reduce the effective resistance. Recently, the use of STI for isolation and twin-tub CMOS in heavily doped substrates have reduced the need for additional guard rings, and made latch-up a relatively minor issue in deep submicron design.

*3.8   Silicon-on-Insulator (SOI) Technology

A variety of special CMOS processes are under development to allow Moore's Law to continue well into the next decade. One of the more promising technologies is silicon-on-insulator (SOI), which gained popularity in the mid-1990s at a number of leading semiconductor companies.

Early attempts at SOI involved the use of silicon-on-sapphire (SOS) technology in the 1970s. The technology was effective, although costly as its name implies. Today, the insulating substrate is created by a high-energy ion-implantation of oxygen atoms well below the surface of a lightly doped silicon wafer. Then the wafer is annealed at a high temperature to produce a buried oxide layer. This process is referred to as Separation by Implanted Oxygen (SIMOX). Next, the *n*-wells and *p*-wells are formed in the substrate and separated by the STI process. Finally, the NMOS and PMOS devices are formed in the wells.

The basic structure of the CMOS-SOI technology is shown in Figure 3.16. This profile is the same as the standard bulk CMOS process except that a buried oxide has been introduced in place of the substrate. The SiO_2 layer is between 300–400 nm thick, while the silicon surface region is 100–200 nm thick. As a result of the insulating layer, all sides of the diffusion region have a greatly reduced capacitance. In fact, there is no longer a bottom edge junction capacitance; only a channel-edge capacitance remains relative to standard CMOS. The advantage of this structure is that the SOI circuits are much faster, dissipate less power, and are not susceptible to

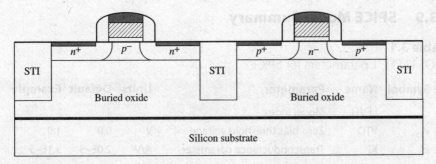

Figure 3.16
Structure of CMOS-SOI technology.

latch-up. This makes it a promising technology for high-speed and low-power design. Furthermore, there is reduced concern about substrate currents or the interaction of mixed-signal designs through the substrate. When technology scales below 65 nm, the doping levels required in bulk CMOS may be too high to be practical. At this point, SOI may be an attractive alternative.

Of course, like all technologies, there are a host of disadvantages or limitations. In SOI, the bulk is floating, which leads to a number of issues with the threshold voltage. The body-bias shifts around depending on the switching characteristics of the MOS device. As a result, the V_T shifts dynamically and this changes the transient characteristics of the circuit. The substrate region can be tied to the appropriate supply to remove this "history-dependent" feature, but this requires additional area. Another issue is related to a *kink* that exists in the *I-V* characteristics of the device around $V_{DS} = V_{DD}/2$. The V_T reduces in value and the current increases relative to the expected level and this has a noticeable effect on the transient operation. Self-heating is yet another concern since the devices are encased in oxides in all directions and it is difficult to transfer the heat generated by the devices. There is also a larger effect of DIBL on these types of devices. If these and other issues can be resolved, SOI is a strong contender for next generation CMOS technology.

Two main forms of SOI exist. The first type is the partially depleted (PD) SOI in which the depletion regions of the source/drain extend into the body but do not completely deplete all the charge in that region. In PD-SOI, the same bulk CMOS fabrication process can be used, with the addition of the SIMOX formation. It can be viewed as an evolutionary step. In fully depleted (FD) SOI, a much thinner silicon surface region and lower well doping levels are used, and the entire body of the transistor is depleted. The thickness of the silicon layer controls the threshold voltage. The development of the thinner silicon layer presents a processing challenge. However, this technology may be important to limit subthreshold current levels in sub-90 nm devices. As a result, many foundries are projecting that they will introduce PD-SOI at the 90 nm technology node, and fully depleted (FD) SOI at the 65 nm node.

*3.9   SPICE Model Summary

Table 3.1
MOS LEVEL 1 parameters for SPICE

Symbol	Name	Parameter	Units	Default	Example
	LEVEL	Model Index		1	
V_{T0}	VTO	Zero-bias threshold voltage	V	0.0	1.0
k'	KP	Transconductance parameter	A/V^2	2.0E−5	3.1E−5
γ	GAMMA	Bulk threshold parameter	V$^{1/2}$	0.0	0.37
$2\lvert\phi_F\rvert$	PHI	Surface potential	V	0.6	0.65
λ	LAMBDA	Channel-length modulation	V^{-1}	0.0	0.02
r_d	RD	Drain ohmic resistance	Ω	0.0	1.0
r_s	RS	Source ohmic resistance	Ω	0.0	1.0
	IS	Bulk junction saturation current	A	1.0E−14	1.0E−15
ϕ_B	PB	Bulk junction potential	V	0.8	0.87
	CGSO	Gate-source overlap capacitance per meter channel width	F/m	0.0	4.0E−11
	CGDO	Gate-drain overlap capacitance per meter channel width	F/m	0.0	4.0E−11
	CGBO	Gate-bulk overlap capacitance per meter channel length	F/m	0.0	2.0E−10
	RSH	Drain and source diffusion sheet resistance	Ω/square	0.0	10.0
C_{j0}	CJ	Zero-bias bulk junction bottom capacitance per square meter of junction area	F/m^2	0.0	2.0E−4
mj	MJ	Bulk junction bottom grading coefficient		0.5	0.5
	CJSW	Zero-bias bulk junction sidewall capacitance per meter of junction parameter	F/m	0.0	1.0E−9
$mjsw$	MJSW	Bulk junction sidewall grading coefficient		0.33	
	JS	Bulk junction saturation current per square meter of junction area	A/m^2		1.0E−8
t_{ox}	TOX	Oxide thickness	m	1.0E−7	1.0E−7
N_A or N_D	NSUB	Substrate doping	cm^{-3}	0.0	4.0E15

(continued)

Table 3.1
(Continued)

Symbol	Name	Parameter	Units	Default	Example
Q_{ss}/q	NSS	Surface state density	cm^{-2}	0.0	1.0E10
	NFS	Fast surface state density	cm^{-2}	0.0	1.0E10
	TPG	Type of gate material:		1.0	
		+ 1 opposite to substrate			
		−1 same as substrate			
		0 Al gate			
x_j	XJ	Metallurgical junction depth	m	0.0	1.0E−6
L_D	LD	Lateral diffusion	m	0.0	0.8E−6
μ_0	UO	Surface mobility	$cm^2/V\cdot s$	600	700

Table 3.2
BSIM3v3 model parameters for SPICE

Name	General, *W, L*, TOX Parameters	Units
LEVEL	MOSFET model selector	—
BINUNIT	Binning unit selector	—
DWB	Coefficient of the substrate bias' dependence of the width offset	$m/V^{1/2}$
DWG	Coefficient of the gate-voltage dependence of the width offset	m/V
LINT	Channel-length offset for dc I-V characteristics without bias	m
LL	Coefficient of length dependence for channel-length offset in I-V calculations	m
LLN	Power exponent of the length dependence in the calculation of the I-V and C-V channel-length offsets	—
LMAX	Maximum channel length	m
LMIN	Minimum channel length	m
LW	Coefficient of width dependence in the calculation of the dc channel-length offset	m
LWL	Coefficient of length and width dependence in the calculation of the dc channel-length offset	m
LWN	Power exponent of the width dependence in the calculation of the I-V and C-V channel-length offsets	—
MOBMOD	Mobility model selector	—

(*continued*)

Table 3.2

(Continued)

Name	General, *W*, *L*, TOX Parameters	Units
NCH	Channel doping concentration	cm^{-3}
TNOM	Device temperature	°C
TOX	Gate-oxide thickness	m
TOXM	Gate-oxide thickness at which the parameter set was extracted	m
VERSION	Establishes the version of the BSIM3 model to be used in simulation	—
WINT	Channel-width offset for dc I-V characteristics	m
WL	Coefficient of width dependence for channel-width offset in I-V calculation	m
WLN	Power exponent of the length dependence in the calculation of the I-V and C-V channel-width offsets	—
WMAX	Maximum channel width	m
WMIN	Minimum channel width	m
WW	Coefficient of width dependence in the calculation of the C-V channel width offset	m
WWL	Coefficient of length and width dependence in the calculation of the dc channel-width offset	m
VTH0	Threshold voltage of long-channel device at zero V_{BS}	V
W0	Channel-width offset to calculate narrow width's effect on the threshold voltage	m
WK1	Width sensitivity	$V^{1/2}\mu m$

Name	Mobility Parameters	Units
A0	Bulk charge effect coefficient for channel length	—
A1	First nonsaturation factor	V^{-1}
A2	Second nonsaturation factor	V^{-1}
AGS	Gate-bias coefficient of the body-charge coefficient, A_{bulk}	V^{-1}
B0	Channel-width coefficient for the calculation of the body-charge coefficient, A_{bulk}	m
	Channel-width offset for the calculation of the body-charge coefficient, A_{bulk}	M
KETA	Body-bias coefficient of the bulk charge coefficient	V^{-1}
LU0	Length sensitivity	$\mu m/V$

(continued)

Table 3.2
(Continued)

Name	Mobility Parameters	Units
LUA	Binning parameter for UA	
LUB	U0 sensitivity to effective channel length	$cm^2\mu m/(Vsec)$
LUC	Binning parameter for UC	
LVSAT	Binning parameter for VSAT	
PRWB	Body-effect coefficient of RDSW	$V^{-1/2}$
PRWG	Gate-bias effect coefficient of RDSW	V^{-1}
PU0	Binning parameter for U0	
PUB	Binning parameter for UB	
RDSW	Parasitic drain/source resistance per unit width	$\Omega\text{-}\mu m$
U0	Zero-field mobility at TNOM	$cm^2/V\text{-}sec$
UA	First-order mobility degradation coefficient	M/V
UB	Second-order mobility degradation coefficient	m^2/V^2
UC	Body-effect of mobility degradation coefficient	V^{-1}
VSAT	Carrier saturation velocity at TNOM	m/s
WA0	Binning parameter for A0	
WR	Exponent of the effective device width for the calculation of RDSW	—
WU0	Width sensitivity	$\mu m/V$
WUA	Binning parameter for UA	

Name	Subthreshold, Substrate, DIBL Parameters	Units
CDSC	Drain/Source to channel coupling capacitance	F/m^2
CDSCB	Body-bias sensitivity of CDSC	$F/m^2\text{-}V$
CDSCD	Drain-bias sensitivity of CDSC	$F/m^2\text{-}V$
CIT	Interface state capacitance	F/m^2
DSUB	L_{eff}-dependence exponent of the DIBL effects on the threshold voltage	—
ETA0	Sub-threshold region drain-induced barrier-lowering (DIBL) coefficient for V_{th}	—
ETAB	Bulk-bias coefficient of the DIBL effects	V^{-1}
LNFACTOR	Binning parameter for NFACTOR	
NFACTOR	Subthreshold turn-on swing factor	—
PETA0	Binning parameter for ETA0	
VOFF	Offset voltage in sub-threshold region	V
ALPHA0	First parameter of impact ionization current	m/V

(continued)

Table 3.2

(Continued)

Name	Subthreshold, Substrate, DIBL Parameters	Units
ALPHA1	Substrate current parameter	V^{-1}
BETA0	The second parameter of the substrate current due to impact ionization	V^{-1}
DELTA	Effective V_{DS} smoothing parameter	V
DROUT	L_{eff} dependence exponent in the DIBL correction on the Early voltage	—
PCLM	Channel-length modulation parameter for I_d	—
PDIBLC1	First coefficient of DIBL's correction on the Early voltage	—
PDIBLC2	Second coefficient of DIBL's correction on the Early voltage	—
PDIBLCB	Body-effect coefficient to the DIBL's correction on the Early voltage	—
PSCBE1	Substrate current induced body effect exponent 1	V/m
PSCBE2	Substrate current induced body effect exponent 2	m/V
PVAG	Gate-bias dependence of Early voltage	—
Name	**Temperature Parameters**	**Units**
AT	Temperature coefficient for saturation velocity	m/sec
KT1	Temperature coefficient for V_{th}	V
KT1L	Channel-length coefficient of the threshold voltage's temperature dependence	Vm
KT2	Body bias coefficient of V_{th} temperature effect	Vm
PKT1	Binning parameter for KT1	
PRT	Temperature coefficient of RDSW	$\Omega\,\mu m^{WR}$
PUA1	Binning parameter for UA1	
UA1	Temperature coefficient for UA	m/V
UB1	Temperature coefficient for UB	m^2/V^2
UC1	Temperature coefficient for UC	m/V^2
UTE	Temperature coefficient for the zero-field universal mobility U0	—
WUA1	Binning parameter for UA1	
Name	**Capacitance Parameters**	**Units**
CAPMOD	Capacitance model selector	—
CF	Fringing-field capacitance per side	F/m

(continued)

Table 3.2
(Continued)

Name	Capacitance Parameters	Units
CGDO	Voltage-independent gate-drain overlap capacitance per unit gate width	F/m
CGSO	Voltage-independent gate-source overlap capacitance per unit gate width	F/m
CJ	Source/Drain bottom junction capacitance	F/m²
CJSWG	Zero-bias gate-edge sidewall bulk junction capacitance	F/m
CJSW	Source/drain sidewall junction capacitance per unit length at the isolation sidewall, when the device temperature is equal to TNOM	F/m
CTA	Junction capacitance CJ temperature coefficient	1/°K
CTP	Junction sidewall capacitance CJSW temperature coefficient	1/°K
DLC	Effective channel-length offset for capacitance calculations	m
ELM	Elmore constant of the channel, used in BSIM3's non-quasi-static (NQS) model	—
JS	Source-bulk and drain-bulk junction saturation current per unit area when the device temperature (T_{device}) is equal to TNOM	A/m²
JSW	Sidewall bulk junction saturation current	A/m
MJ	Grading coefficient of the bottom-wall junction capacitance	—
MJSWG	Grading coefficient of the gate-edge sidewall junction capacitance	—
MJSW	Grading coefficient of the isolation-side sidewall junction capacitance	—
NQSMOD	A flag for the non-quasi-static model	—
PB	Built-in potential of the bottom-wall junction capacitance	V
PTP	Junction potential PHP temperature coefficient	V/°K
PTA	Junction potential PB temperature coefficient	V/°K
TLEVC	Temperature equation level selector for junction capacitances and potentials	—
XPART	Charge partition flag	—
XTI	Junction saturation current densities' temperature exponent	—

REFERENCES

1. R. C. Jaeger, *Introduction to Microelectronic Fabrication*, 2nd ed. Prentice-Hall, Upper Saddle River, NJ, 2002.

2. H. Veendrick, *Deep-Submicron CMOS ICs*, 2nd ed. Kluwer Academic Publishers, Boston, MA, 2000.

3. D. Foty, *MOSFET Modeling with SPICE: Principles and Practice*, Prentice-Hall PTR, 1997.

4. N. Arora, *MOSFET Models for VLSI Circuit Simulation*, Springer-Verlag, 1993.

5. L. W. Nagel, "SPICE2, A Computer Program to Simulate Semiconductor Circuits," *ERL Memorandum ERL-M520*, University of California, Berkeley, May 1975.

6. G. Massobrio and P. Antognetti, *Semiconductor Device Modeling with SPICE*, McGraw-Hill, 1993.

7. W. Liu, *MOSFET Models with SPICE Simulation including BSIM3v3 and BSIM4*, Wiley-Interscience, New York, 2001.

8. A. Vladimirescu, *The SPICE Book*, John Wiley and Sons, 1994.

9. HSPICE User's Manual, Synopsys Inc., Sunnyvale, CA, 1999.

10. K. Bernstein and N. Rohrer, *SOI Circuit Design Concepts*, Kluwer Academic Publishers, Boston, MA, 2000.

11. J. Plummer, M. Deal, P. Griffen, *Silicon VLSI Technology*, Prentice-Hall, Upper Saddle River, NJ, 2000.

12. J. E. Meyer, "MOS Models and Circuit Simulation," *RCA Review*, Vol. 32, March 1971, pp. 42–63.

PROBLEMS

For the SPICE problems below, use either 0.18 μm or 0.13 μm process technology with BSIM3 model library files, depending on what is available at your site. For convenience, we use $L = 200$ nm for a 0.18 μm technology and $L = 100$ nm for a 0.13 μm process.

P3.1. Figure P3.1 shows a setup used to perform parameter extraction of a LEVEL 1 model on a long-channel NMOS transistor at room temperature.

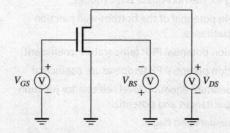

Figure P3.1

Experimental setup to measure I-V characteristics of an NMOS transistor.

From this setup, the current is measured for a number of different operating conditions as listed in Table P3.1.

Table P3.1

I-V characteristics for a long-channel NMOS transistor

V_{GS} [V]	V_{DS} [V]	V_{SB} [V]	I_D [μA]
1.2	1.2	0	1000
0.8	1.2	0	280
0.8	0.8	0	276
1.2	1.2	0.4	741

Using the data in Table P3.1, along with $W/L = 4.75$, $t_{ox} = 22$ Å and $2|\phi_F| = 0.88$ V find:

(a) the threshold voltage, V_{T0}

(b) the channel modulation parameter, λ

(c) the electron mobility, μ_n

(d) the body effect coefficient gamma, γ

P3.2. Consider the long-channel MOS device shown in Figure P3.2. At $t = 0$, the drain and source are at an initial voltage of 3.3 V. At $t = 0^+$, the current source turns on with a value of 10 μA. On the graph, sketch the voltage at the source and drain nodes as a function of time until a steady-state behavior is reached. Estimate the voltages for the end points of every region of operation on the graph. Also, calculate the slope in every region. The key to this problem is to include the proper capacitances in each region of operation.

For this problem, assume that $k' = \mu_n C_{ox} = 180$ μA/V², $V_{T0} = 0.6$ V, $V_T = 1.1$ V (Assume this is the correct threshold voltage when V_{BS} is not 0 V), and $W = 1.5$ μm, $L = 1$ μm (so the quadratic model can be used here). Use $t_{ox} = 100$ Å to compute the gate capacitances. Assume $C_{SB} = C_{DB} = 15$ fF are fixed junction capacitances.

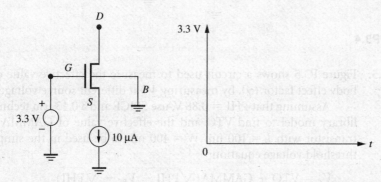

Figure P3.2

Check your results in SPICE. You will need to initialize the source and drain nodes to 3.3 V, and use a Level 1 MOS model to obtain the results.

P3.3. Figure P3.3 shows a circuit used to measure V_{T0}. First describe why gate and drain are connected together for the purposes of this measurement. Then using SPICE simulation, estimate V_{T0} for a transistor with $L =$ 100 nm, $W = 400$ nm. You do not need to specify the capacitance information for this measurement. Why? Where should the bulk terminal be connected? Why?

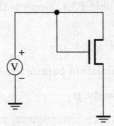

Figure P3.3

P3.4. Figure P3.4 shows a circuit that can be used to investigate the degree of channel-length modulation in short-channel transistors. Using SPICE simulation, determine whether a transistor with $L = 100$ nm, $W =$ 400 nm exhibits channel-length modulation. What is the range of voltage that should be applied to drain for the purposes of this measurement? Estimate the value of λ from the results of simulation.

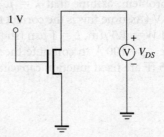

Figure P3.4

P3.5. Figure P3.5 shows a circuit used to measure the effective value of the body effect factor (γ), by measuring V_T at different source voltages.

Assuming that PHI = 0.88 V, use SPICE and a 0.13 μm technology library model to find VTO and the effective value of GAMMA for a transistor with $L = 100$ nm $W = 400$ nm to be used in the simplified threshold voltage equation:

$$V_T = \text{VTO} + \text{GAMMA}(\sqrt{\text{PHI} - V_{BS}} - \sqrt{\text{PHI}})$$

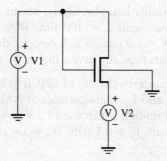

Figure P3.5

P3.6. Using SPICE simulation find the value of γ for a transistor with $L = 100$ nm and $W = 400$ nm. Use the circuit shown in Figure P3.6 to measure the body effect. What is the range of the voltage that can be applied to bulk (V_B)? Compute the current (I_{DS}) with $V_B = -1$ V and $V_B = 0$ V when $V_G = 1.2$ V. What is the effect on current as V_T increases?

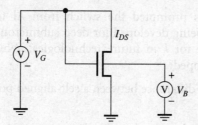

Figure P3.6

P3.7. Using SPICE and a 0.18 μm model, plot the subthreshold current versus V_{BS}, and saturation current versus V_{BS} for an NMOS device with $W = 400$ nm and $L = 200$ nm. Specify the range for V_{BS} as 0 to -2.0 V. Explain the results.

P3.8. Determine which of the following p-channel transistors have the highest and lowest magnitude of threshold voltage and describe why. Assume a 0.13 μm technology.

- A transistor with: $L = 0.1\ \mu$m, $W = 0.8\ \mu$m, $V_{SB} = 0.0$ V, $V_{DS} = -1.2$ V
- A transistor with: $L = 0.1\ \mu$m, $W = 0.4\ \mu$m, $V_{SB} = -0.5$ V, $V_{DS} = -1$ V
- A transistor with: $L = 0.1\ \mu$m, $W = 0.1\ \mu$m, $V_{SB} = -0.5$ V, $V_{DS} = -1$ V
- A transistor with: $L = 0.2\ \mu$m, $W = 0.4\ \mu$m, $V_{SB} = 0.0$ V, $V_{DS} = -1.2$ V
- A transistor with: $L = 0.2\ \mu$m, $W = 0.8\ \mu$m, $V_{SB} = 0.0$ V, $V_{DS} = -1.2$ V
- A transistor with: $L = 0.2\ \mu$m, $W = 0.1\ \mu$m, $V_{SB} = -0.5$ V, $V_{DS} = -1$ V

P3.9. Using SPICE simulation, plot $\log I_{DS}$ versus V_{GS} while varying V_{DS} for an NMOS device with $L = 100$ nm, $W = 400$ nm and PMOS with $L = 100$ nm, $W = 1.0$ μm. Which device exhibits more DIBL? Why do PMOS transistors typically have a higher V_T than NMOS transistors?

P3.10. This problem concerns the use of SPICE to examine effect of temperature on the I_{on} and I_{off} characteristics of NMOS and PMOS transistors in 0.13 μm technology, which use a 1.2 V power supply. The device sizes are $W_n = 0.8$ μm, $L_n = 0.1$ μm, $W_p = 1.6$ μm, $L_p = 0.1$ μm. Plot the following:

(a) Subthreshold region current for V_{GS} from 0 to 0.4 V for temperatures $T = -60, 25$, and 125°C.

(b) Above threshold region current for V_{GS} from 0.4 to 1.2 V for temperatures $T = -60, 25$, and 125°C.

(c) Explain the relationship between current and temperature for the two regions, above threshold and subthreshold, and explain the trends using equations involving temperature.

P3.11. What issues prompted the switch from Al to Cu? Why are low-k dielectrics being developed for deep submicron processes? What is the target value for k in future technologies? Why are high-k dielectrics being developed?

P3.12. What is the difference between a self-aligned poly gate and self-aligned silicide?

P3.13. Compute the length of an aluminum wire and a copper wire that has a resistance of 100 Ω. You can assume that the wire thickness is 0.8 μm and the wire width is 1 μm in both cases.

P3.14. Assume that two metal conductors with thickness 1 μm and length 100 μm are spaced apart by a distance S by silicon dioxide. Assuming that the k for SiO_2 is roughly 4, plot the capacitance as S is increased from 0.5 μm to 5 μm. On the same graph, plot the capacitance for a material with a $k = 2$. Explain both results.

MOS Inverter Circuits

4.1   Introduction

Digital MOS circuits are broadly categorized into two groups: static and dynamic. All nodes of a static of gate will have resistive paths to V_{DD} or ground. In dynamic circuits, the value of one or more nodes is based on stored charge on a capacitor. Another distinction between the two is based on whether periodic *clock signals* are necessary to achieve combinational logic functions. *Static circuits* require no clock or other periodic signals for their operation in combinational logic networks. Of course, clocks are required for sequential logic circuits, but they are usually applied only to normal logic gate inputs. *Dynamic circuits* require periodic clock signals synchronized with data signals for proper operation, even in combinational logic applications. In dynamic circuits, clock signals are applied to load elements, and so-called *transmission gates,* or *transfer gates.*

In this chapter, we study static inverters with emphasis on voltage transfer characteristics, noise margins, inverter configurations, and delay models. Analytical expressions will be developed for the design and analysis of various inverters using the equations and models described in Chapters 2 and 3. In subsequent chapters, we will follow up with gate circuits, sequential circuits, and dynamic logic circuits.

4.2 Voltage Transfer Characteristics

As we already know, a digital logic inverter takes an input and produces its complement at the output. The two possible binary output levels are 0 and 1. If the input is a logical "0," the output is a logical "1," and vice versa. In an ideal implementation of an inverter circuit, the two binary output levels are typically at ground[1] (zero volts) and the supply voltage, V_{DD}. The output transition between the 1 and 0 states should occur when the input is exactly equal to one-half the supply voltage (i.e., at $V_{DD}/2$). Realistic inverters have analog voltages that are discretized into one of the two logic states. To capture the features of ideal and practical inverters more formally, a plot of the output voltage, V_{out}, as a function of the input voltage, V_{in}, can be constructed. This plot, called a dc voltage transfer characteristic (VTC), can tell us much about the inherent properties of an inverter and other gates. It is also a useful way to compare various inverter configurations. It is produced by increasing the input voltage very slowly and plotting the resulting output voltage, as shown in Figure 4.1a.

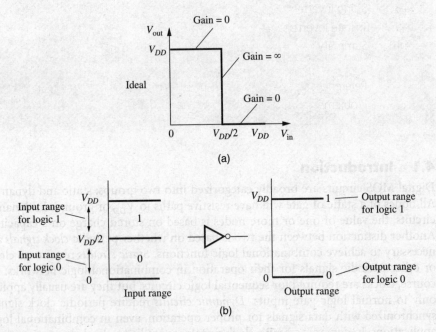

(a)

(b)

Figure 4.1
Ideal VTC of an inverter.

---

[1] We will also use Gnd and V_{SS} to refer to the ground terminal throughout the book.

The VTC in Figure 4.1a illustrates the desired features of an ideal inverter. The first thing to notice is that the switching point occurs at $V_{DD}/2$. At this point, the output switches from V_{DD} to Gnd. The slope of the VTC, referred to as the *gain*, is obtained by taking the derivative of V_{out} with respect to V_{in}:

$$\text{gain} = \frac{\partial V_{out}}{\partial V_{in}} \tag{4.1}$$

The gain can be computed at any point along the VTC. By examining the characteristic in Figure 4.1a, it is clear that there are three gain regions in the ideal inverter: two zero gain regions and one infinite gain region. The high gain region, separating the high output from the low output, is a feature required by all useful logic gates to regenerate high and low logic values if there is noise in the system. We will consider this property more carefully in the next section.

Another feature of the VTC is that the input range is very large while the output range is small for the ideal inverter. The *range* refers to the voltage interval over which a signal is considered to be a logic 0 or logic 1. Having a large input range and small output range is a desirable characteristic of a logic gate for noise immunity. It implies that there are low gain regions such that the input can vary significantly with little or no effect on the output. That is, the gate is able to reject noise at the input. The input range is $V_{DD}/2$ for both logic 0 and logic 1, as shown in Figure 4.1b; the output range is essentially zero for both logic 0 and logic 1. This is the ideal condition: the input can swing anywhere between 0 and $V_{DD}/2$ and the output will stay at 1; or, it can swing between $V_{DD}/2$ to V_{DD} and the output will stay at 0.

All practical logic gates fall short of the ideal performance, but depending upon the application, some are better than others. A more realistic VTC for the inverter is shown in Figure 4.2a. In practical inverters, the low output voltage, V_{OL}, may not reach Gnd, and the high output voltage, V_{OH}, may not reach V_{DD}. The output does not abruptly switch from V_{DD} to Gnd at $V_{DD}/2$. Instead, the concept of a switching point, V_S, is defined as the point where $V_{out} = V_{in}$. Rather than two zero gain regions and an infinite gain region, there is a region of low gain, followed by high gain, followed again by low gain as the input increases from 0 to V_{DD}. For a valid gate, the gain must be larger than one in the high gain region and less than one in the low gain region.

The input and output ranges for the nonideal inverter are provided in Figure 4.2b. The two input ranges that define 0 and 1 are smaller than the ideal case, while the two output ranges are larger than the ideal case. The input range for logic 0 is from 0 V to a point called V_{IL} where the input is still considered to be low. The input range for logic 1 is the interval from V_{OH} to V_{IH}, where the input is still considered to be high. Since $V_{IL} \neq V_{IH}$, a new interval exists between 0 and 1, defined as the *unknown* (X) or uncertain region. The output ranges are from V_{OL} to V_{OUL} for logic 0 and V_{OH} to V_{OUH} for logic 1. The values V_{OUL} and V_{OUH} define the edges of the two output ranges, and since they are not equal, an uncertain region (X) also exists in the output. Perhaps more importantly, the nonideal inverter retains the desirable noise rejection property if the input range is larger than the output range. This

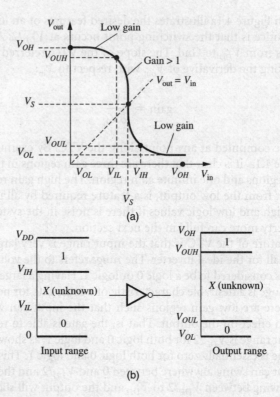

Figure 4.2
Practical VTC of an inverter.

implies that output fluctuations are small even with large input fluctuations due to noise.

To study this concept further, consider the effect of noise at the input of the inverter shown in Figure 4.3. In this example, the input varies considerably but remains within the valid logic 0 range for the input. The output varies by a smaller amount but remains in the range considered to be a valid logic 1. In terms of the voltage transfer characteristics, the input is varying in the range where the logic gate acts as a low-gain amplifier, from V_{OL} to V_{IL}. This attenuates the noise since the gain is less than one in this range. As a result, the output remains in the range V_{OUH} to V_{OH}. The next few inverters in the chain will attenuate the noise even further and eventually the noise is damped out of the system. If the output range were larger than the input range, a small fluctuation of the input voltage would produce a larger fluctuation at the output voltage. As the signal propagated through subsequent inverter stages, it would be corrupted and eventually the wrong answer would be produced. However, if the noise takes the input signal outside the proper range, the high gain of the inverter can still force subsequent stages to their correct values,

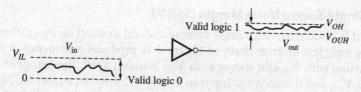

Figure 4.3
Effect of noise at logic gate input on the output.

assuming that the noise does not exceed a predefined threshold. This is the key (desirable) property of logic gates called the *regenerative* property.

4.3 Noise Margin Definitions

The word *noise* in the context of digital circuits and systems means unwanted variations of voltages or currents at logic nodes. If the magnitude of noise is too great, it will cause logic errors. However, if the noise amplitude at the input of any logic circuit is smaller than a specified critical magnitude known as the *noise margin* of that circuit, the noise will be attenuated as it passes from input to output. In properly functioning digital systems, the desired logic signals are restored to full amplitude without error, and noise does not accumulate from one logic stage to the next (as it does in analog systems).

Digital circuits typically exhibit variations in logic levels due to circuit manufacturing tolerances, temperature changes, power supply variations, and electrical loading at the output node. For example, noise may be transferred to logic nodes or interconnecting lines by unwanted capacitive or inductive coupling. Series inductance and resistance in ground and power supply lines shared by many logic elements are also a common source of noise problems. The worst combinations of all these effects are used to define the worst-case output voltage range. It is desirable to minimize these variations so that output logic levels are held within two narrow voltage ranges around V_{OH} and V_{OL}.

Noise margins are used to specify the range over which the circuits will function properly. A variety of noise metrics have been defined to characterize the noise performance of logic gates using the VTC. We will examine the single-source noise margin (SSNM) and the multiple-source noise margin (MSNM).[2] The robustness of a gate, that is, its ability to operate properly in the presence of noise, depends on how much noise can be applied before the gate fails and how much noise actually couples into the gate. The first factor is a function of the gate itself while the second factor is a function of the environment of the gate. We study the first factor in the next section and the second factor in Chapters 10 and 11. Both are important in the performance of a logic gate in an actual circuit.

In the literature, these are also referred to as single-stage and multi-stage noise margins, respectively.

4.3.1 Single-Source Noise Margin (SSNM)

The SSNM is associated with a *single noise source* and its effect on downstream logic gates. The noiseless inverter chain of Figure 4.4a produces a sequence of inverted values starting with V_{OL} and ending with V_{OL}. Without noise, the output of the first inverter is V_{OH} and this serves as input to the second inverter, and so on. As long as there is no noise in the system, the output of each inverter will remain at the values shown in the figure. When noise events occur, the outputs deviate from their steady-state values. We seek to find how much noise the inverter chain can tolerate before it fails.

The SSNM metric is defined as the largest noise level in a single stage that allows subsequent stages to recover to their proper value (the regenerative property). To illustrate this metric using Figure 4.4b, let us arbitrarily insert a noise source of magnitude v_n at the output of the first inverter. This noise will change the input to the second inverter to $V_{OH} - v_n$ and this, in turn, will affect its output value. The question is, how much noise can be tolerated at the input of the second inverter before its output and all subsequent outputs flip their logic values?

Figure 4.5 provides some insight into how the VTC can be used to determine the SSNM. Note that we have plotted the second inverter VTC in the normal orientation, but the third inverter has the input and output axes swapped for convenience. If V_{OH} is the output of the first inverter, we know that the output of the second inverter should be at V_{OL}. However, if a noise level of v_n is applied, the input of the second inverter will drop to $V_{OH} - v_n$ and its output will rise to a value well above V_{OL}, as shown in the figure (second inverter). This new output is the input to the third stage. To determine the value at the output of the third inverter, we transfer the second stage output value to the adjacent VTC (mirror image of the first one), and then read the new value directly from this VTC. This is depicted on the graph using arrows. Of course, to obtain the output of the fourth inverter, we now have to transfer this new value back to the first graph. This is a very cumbersome process given that we have so many stages in the inverter chain.

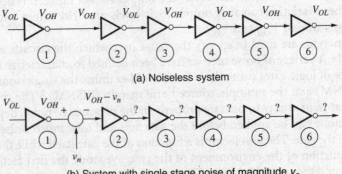

(a) Noiseless system

(b) System with single stage noise of magnitude v_n

Figure 4.4

Single-source noise analysis for inverter chain.

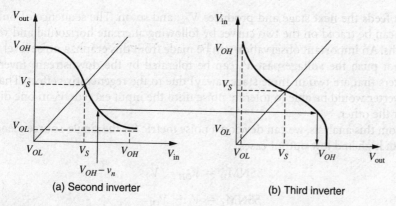

(a) Second inverter (b) Third inverter

Figure 4.5

Noise propagation in an inverter chain.

A more convenient way of obtaining the output values is shown in Figure 4.6. Since we are interested in the input and output conditions of the second inverter and beyond, we can plot the VTC of the even and odd inverters on the same graph. The normal orientation is used for all even inverters, while the swapped axes (V_{in} versus V_{out}) are used for odd inverters. This configuration allows us to switch back and forth between the two curves very quickly to determine the outputs of the subsequent stages. With this efficient method in hand, we can now go back to the question of determining the SSNM.

Consider Figure 4.6 in the context of the maximum possible noise that can be tolerated. When the input with noise v_n is applied to the second inverter, the output is V_{O2}. This is the input to the next stage which produces an output of V_{O3}. This

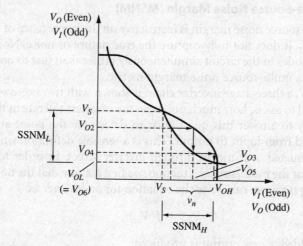

Figure 4.6

Graphical approach to SSNM calculation.

output feeds the next stage and produces V_{O4}, and so on. The sequence of output values can be traced on the two curves by following alternate horizontal and vertical paths. An important observation can be made from this graph: a noise level that does not push the voltage past V_S can be tolerated by the downstream inverters (inverters that are two or three stages away) due to the regenerative effect. That is, the inverter would be able to tolerate noise until the input exceeds V_S in one direction or the other.

From this analysis, we can develop a noise metric for the single-source scenario for both high and low output cases:

$$\text{SSNM}_H = V_{OH} - V_S$$
$$\text{SSNM}_L = V_S - V_{OL}$$

$$(4.2)$$

Any noise above these levels will cause the output to flip to the opposite value and recovery to the original value will not be possible. The importance of the switching threshold in the noise metric is clear. If an input is high, then noise will not adversely affect the chain until it reaches the switching threshold. Similarly, if the input is low, noise will not greatly affect the outputs until it reaches the switching threshold. An interesting side note is that if we want the inverter to switch, the input must be taken past V_S; hence, the name *switching threshold*.

Exercise 4.1   Using the graph of Figure 4.6, plot the trajectory of the outputs of a six-stage inverter chain when the noise level is greater than V_S at the input of the second inverter.

4.3.2   Multiple-Source Noise Margin (MSNM)

While the single-source noise margin is instructive on the importance of the switching threshold, V_S, it does not fully capture the true nature of noise. Noise tends to be added to all nodes in the circuit simultaneously rather than just to one node. We need to develop a multi-source noise margin metric.

In Figure 4.7, a three-stage inverter chain is shown with two noise sources. The question we need to ask is, how much noise can the inverters tolerate in this new situation? One way to answer this question is to determine the point at which the noise is amplified from input to output. This is a sensible definition since we want noise to be attenuated as it moves through inverter stages. In order to develop a metric suitable for the multi-source situation, we first assume that the noise is small. For a noiseless system, we can write the equation for an inverter as

$$V_{\text{out}} = f(V_{\text{in}})$$

With noise v_n added, a new output is produced:

$$V'_{\text{out}} = f(V_{\text{in}} + v_n)$$

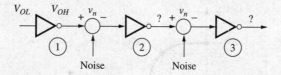

Figure 4.7
Multistage noise margin.

A Taylor series expansion[3] of the output function allows us to examine the important factors determining V_{out} in the presence of noise:

$$V'_{\text{out}} = f(V_{\text{in}}) + v_n \frac{\partial V_{\text{out}}}{\partial V_{\text{in}}} + (v_n)^2 \frac{\partial^2 V_{\text{out}}}{\partial V_{\text{in}}^2} + (v_n)^3 \frac{\partial^3 V_{\text{out}}}{\partial V_{\text{in}}^3} + \cdots$$

A simple interpretation of this equation is that the

noisy_output_voltage = noiseless_output + noise × gain + higher_order_terms

If we ignore the higher-order terms, then the output is simply the noiseless value plus the noise multiplied by the gain of the inverter. Given this result, we can develop a metric that is based on the gain of the inverter since it controls how the noise is amplified as it passes through the inverter.

Specifically, if the inverter is operating in a region where the gain $|\partial V_{\text{out}}/\partial V_{\text{in}}| > 1$, then the noise is amplified and added to the output. This is not a desirable situation. However, if we operate in the region where $|\partial V_{\text{out}}/\partial V_{\text{in}}| < 1$, then the circuit will attenuate the noise and faithfully try to hold the output in the desired range.

Based on the above analysis, we can now define more useful noise margins by using the VTC points where the gain is 1 to establish important transition points. In Figure 4.8, the VTC of the inverter is shown with the unity gain points identified. There are two unity gain points, with the slope of the line equal to -1 in both cases. The first unity gain point occurs where $V_{\text{in}} = V_{IL}$ and $V_{\text{out}} = V_{OUH}$. When $V_{\text{in}} < V_{IL}$, the output is still considered to be high. If $V_{\text{in}} > V_{IL}$, the gain exceeds unity and the output begins to drop significantly. Therefore, the input can safely swing from V_{OL} to V_{IL} without a significant drop in V_{out} or a significant gain in the noise. Likewise, the second unity gain point occurs at $V_{\text{in}} = V_{IH}$ and $V_{\text{out}} = V_{OUL}$. When $V_{\text{in}} > V_{IH}$, the output is considered to be a valid low. However, if $V_{\text{in}} < V_{IH}$, then the output passes the unity gain point and begins to rise in value. Therefore, the input can safely swing from V_{OH} to V_{IH} without a significant rise in V_{out}.

---

[3] A Taylor series expansion of a function $f(x)$ is a polynomial expansion of the function about a given operating point. We can write $f(x) = f(x_0) + (x - x_0)(\partial f/\partial x) + (x - x_0)^2(\partial^2 f/\partial x^2) + \cdots$. In our case, $x = V_{\text{in}} + v_n$, $x_0 = V_{\text{in}}$ and therefore $(x - x_0)$ is v_n.

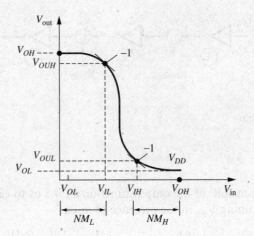

Figure 4.8

Unity gain noise margin definitions.

These two unity gain points and the output high and low values can be used to define the noise margins as follows:

$$NM_H = V_{OH} - V_{IH}$$
$$NM_L = V_{IL} - V_{OL} \tag{4.3}$$

As long as the inputs stay within these ranges, the gate will operate properly. In general, noise margins are different in high and low logic states so both must be calculated. There are a number of tradeoffs between the noise margins and other characteristics of circuit performance, as we will discover in the following sections. We will use the equations in (4.3) to compare a number of different inverter configurations in the rest of this chapter.

Example 4.1   **VTC for a Buffer**

Problem:

Sketch the VTC for a noninverting (buffer) gate. Identify the noise margins and any other important features on the VTC.

Solution:

The VTC for buffer is shown in the following diagram. In the noninverting case, the logic output value is equal to the logic input value so the buffer VTC is the mirror image of the inverter VTC. The two unity gain points have a positive slope and are given by V_{IL} and V_{IH}. The output high and low values are V_{OH} and V_{OL}, respectively. If we now place these values along the V_{in} axis, we can see from the figure that the input range of V_{OL} to V_{IL} and V_{IH} to V_{OH} are the intervals over which the output remains approximately constant. Beyond these ranges, the output enters the high gain region and amplifies the noise. It is clear that the noise margin definitions given above are meaningful metrics for inverters and buffers.

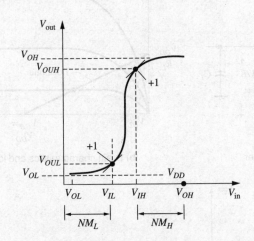

4.4 Resistive-Load Inverter Design

We begin our study of inverters with a configuration that uses a resistor attached to the drain of a MOS transistor, as in Figure 4.9. The resistive-load MOS inverter exhibits all of the essential features of MOS logic gates and is therefore a useful starting point. Subsequent extension of these concepts to CMOS inverter, NOR and NAND gates is very simple. In the rest of this chapter we will spend a good deal of time establishing analysis techniques to obtain the dc voltage transfer characteristics, noise margins, and propagation delays for inverters. Both NMOS and CMOS circuits are considered. Alternative load elements are compared, considering noise margin, power consumption, circuit density, transfer characteristics, and transient performance.

Figure 4.9a shows a single NMOS transistor connected with a resistor load to form an inverter. When the NMOS device is off, the resistor pulls the output high to V_{OH}. When the NMOS device is on, it forms a resistive divider with the pull-up device and produces a low output, V_{OL}. The design parameters are the values of R_L and W/L of the NMOS device. The supply voltage is also a design parameter, but it is usually specified by the technology chosen by the designer, or by system-level specifications. The quantitative design of such an inverter is guided by several considerations such as timing, power, and area, in addition to specifications for voltage levels and noise margins. By choosing the appropriate tradeoffs, values of R_L and W/L are selected that satisfy the design specifications across a wide range of process variations and operating conditions.

A new perspective on the VTC can be gained by plotting I versus V for the resistor and transistor on the same graph. Such a plot for the resistive-load inverter is

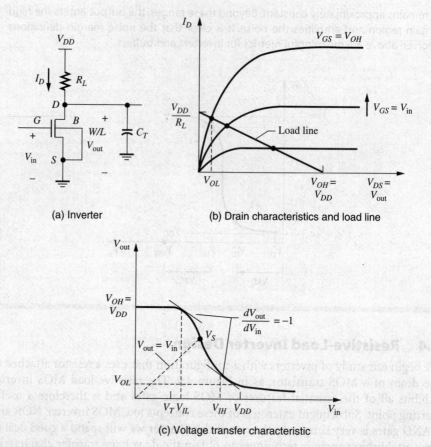

(a) Inverter

(b) Drain characteristics and load line

(c) Voltage transfer characteristic

Figure 4.9
NMOS inverter, resistor load.

called a load line characteristic, as shown in Figure 4.9b. It shows the current through the resistor superimposed with the current through the MOS device. At one extreme, the current through the resistor is V_{DD}/R_L and at the other extreme it is zero. Since the current is linearly related to voltage, the load characteristic is linear from $V_{DS} = 0$ to V_{DD}. From a dc perspective, the inverter current will always lie on the load line. When the output is V_{OH}, there is no current flowing through the two devices. When the output is V_{OL}, the current through both devices is equal

$$I_{DS} = I_R = \frac{V_{DD} - V_{OL}}{R_L} \quad (4.4)$$

The VTC can be found from the load line construction by noting that each value of $V_{in} = V_{GS}$ for the transistor gives a different drain current curve in Figure 4.9b. The intersection of the transistor drain characteristic curve with the resistor load line gives a value of $V_{\text{out}} = V_{DS}$. The plot of V_{out} versus V_{in} is the desired VTC as seen in Figure 4.9c.

While this graphical load line representation is instructive, we will generally not use this approach to determine the voltage transfer characteristics. Instead, we will formulate explicit solutions for each of the five critical points on the VTC of Figure 4.9c. Specifically, we will seek to find V_{OH}, V_{OL}, V_{IH}, V_{IL}, and V_S. This information is all that is required to sketch the VTC and determine the noise margins. To simplify the equations in the following sections, we assume that channel-length modulation factor, λ, is too small to have a significant effect on voltage transfer characteristics, although strictly speaking this is not true.

The value of V_{OH} can be obtained by setting the input voltage below the transistor threshold voltage V_T. Then no current flows, and the inverter output voltage V_{out} remains at V_{DD}. The nominal voltage representing a logic high level is

$$V_{OH} = V_{DD} \tag{4.5}$$

When a logic value of 1, represented by V_{OH}, is applied at the input of this inverter, the transistor is driven into the linear region of operation.[4] The output low level, V_{OL}, is found by equating the currents in the transistor and load, assuming the input of this inverter is driven by V_{OH}:

$$I_R = I_{DS} \text{ (lin)} \tag{4.6a}$$

Substituting in the expressions for the resistor current and NMOS current:

$$\frac{V_{DD} - V_{OL}}{R_L} = \frac{W_N}{L_N} \frac{\mu_n C_{ox}}{\left(1 + \dfrac{V_{OL}}{E_C L}\right)} [2(V_{OH} - V_T)V_{OL} - V_{OL}^2] \tag{4.6b}$$

The term in the denominator $V_{OL}/E_C L$ is small since V_{OL} is small. It can be neglected to first order to avoid iteration.[5] Then, setting $k = (W/L)\,\mu_n C_{ox}$:

$$\frac{V_{DD} - V_{OL}}{R_L} = \frac{k}{2}[2(V_{OH} - V_T)V_{OL} - V_{OL}^2]$$

Restating this in terms of V_{OL},

$$V_{OL}^2 - 2\left(\frac{1}{kR_L} + V_{DD} - V_T\right)V_{OL} + \frac{2V_{DD}}{kR_L} = 0 \tag{4.6c}$$

---

[4] When such an assumption is made about the operating region of a device, it must always be checked at the end of the calculation to make sure that the assumption is correct.

[5] It is important to be able to apply this type of engineering judgment to simplify potentially complicated equations.

This quadratic equation may be solved for V_{OL}. Only the positive root has physical significance. If V_{OL} is sufficiently small, the squared term may also be neglected to further simplify the solution. Using this approximation,

$$V_{OL} \approx \frac{V_{DD}}{1 + kR_L(V_{DD} - V_T)} \tag{4.6d}$$

Equation (4.6d) is instructive from a design perspective. Since we want to make V_{OL} small, we can accomplish this by increasing k (i.e., W/L), or increasing the resistance, R_L. In both cases, the decrease in V_{OL} is at the expense of area. Also, increasing R_L will make the rise time slower, while increasing k will make the fall time faster. As V_{OL} decreases with increasing k, we would also find that the power increases. The power, when the output is low, is given by

$$P = IV = \left(\frac{V_{DD} - V_{OL}}{R_L} \right) V_{DD} \tag{4.7}$$

The equation indicates that power will increase but only marginally. However, an increase in R_L will act to reduce the power consumption. The complex tradeoffs just described appear throughout the design process with timing, power, area, noise margins, etc. being traded-off against one another to achieve a given set of design specifications. Ultimately, the noise margins will dictate the choice of k and R_L for this type of inverter.

The noise margin voltages V_{IL} and V_{IH} are defined as the points at which

$$\frac{\partial V_{\text{out}}}{\partial V_{\text{in}}} = -1.0$$

The minus sign in this equation arises because V_{out} decreases as V_{in} increases for inverters. The VTC requires equal current in both devices. At $V_{\text{in}} = V_{IL}$, the output voltage is near V_{DD} and the transistor is operating in the saturation region. Thus,

$$I_R = I_{DS}\,(\text{sat}) \tag{4.8a}$$

By substituting the saturation current equation, we obtain

$$\frac{V_{DD} - V_{\text{out}}}{R_L} = \frac{Wv_{\text{sat}}C_{ox}(V_{\text{in}} - V_T)^2}{(V_{\text{in}} - V_T) + E_C L}$$

Since V_{in} is typically close to V_T when computing V_{IL}, we can simplify the saturation current expression by removing this term in the denominator:

$$\frac{V_{DD} - V_{\text{out}}}{R_L} \approx \frac{Wv_{\text{sat}}C_{ox}(V_{\text{in}} - V_T)^2}{E_C L}$$

Recalling that $v_{sat} = \mu E_C/2$, a substitution into the above results in

$$\frac{V_{DD} - V_{out}}{R_L} = \frac{W \mu_n C_{ox}(V_{in} - V_T)^2}{2L}$$

Setting $k = (W/L)\mu_n C_{OX}$ and differentiating with respect to V_{in},

$$-\frac{1}{R_L}\left(\frac{\partial V_{out}}{\partial V_{in}}\right) = k(V_{in} - V_T)$$

Setting $V_{in} = V_{IL}$ and the gain term to -1, we arrive at

$$k(V_{IL} - V_T)R_L = 1$$

This is easily solved for V_{IL}:

$$V_{IL} = V_T + \frac{1}{kR_L} \tag{4.8b}$$

It is interesting to note that V_{IL} is slightly above the threshold voltage, which makes sense from an intuitive standpoint. The n-channel device turns on at V_T and, at a slightly higher V_{GS}, the gain is equal to 1 in magnitude. To increase V_{IL} thereby increasing NM_L, we need to decrease k and R_L. This also increases V_{OL}, which is not desirable. Since both V_{IL} and V_{OL} shift in the same direction, it is difficult to affect NM_L significantly. Again, the two design parameters, R_L and W/L, will most likely be controlled by V_{OL}.

The value of V_{OUL} can be determined by substituting $V_{in} = V_{IL}$ into Equation (4.6b) and solving for V_{out}, if needed.

At the other unity gain point, where $V_{in} = V_{IH}$, the output voltage is near 0 V and the transistor is operating in the linear region. Therefore,

$$\frac{W}{L}\frac{\mu_n C_{ox}}{\left(1 + \dfrac{V_{out}}{E_C L}\right)}\left[(V_{in} - V_T)V_{out} - \frac{V_{out}^2}{2}\right] = \frac{V_{DD} - V_{out}}{R_L}$$

The denominator of the current expression has a term $V_{out}/E_C L$ that will be small in the computation of V_{IH} so it can be neglected. We use this simplification and write

$$k\left[(V_{in} - V_T)V_{out} - \frac{V_{out}^2}{2}\right] \approx \frac{V_{DD} - V_{out}}{R_L} \tag{4.8c}$$

Taking the partial derivative of this equation:

$$k\left[(V_{in} - V_T)\frac{\partial V_{out}}{\partial V_{in}} + V_{out} - V_{out}\frac{\partial V_{out}}{\partial V_{in}}\right] = -\frac{1}{R_L}\frac{\partial V_{out}}{\partial V_{in}}$$

Since $V_{in} \doteq V_{IH}$ and the gain term is -1, we obtain

$$V_{IH} = V_T + 2V_{out} - \frac{1}{kR_L} \tag{4.8d}$$

The explicit value of $V_{in} = V_{IH}$ and the corresponding value of V_{out} are found by substituting Equation (4.8d) into Equation (4.8c), namely,

$$\frac{k}{2}[2(V_{IH} - V_T)V_{out} - V_{out}^2] = \frac{V_{DD} - V_{out}}{R_L} \tag{4.8e}$$

Solving these two equations together produces:

$$V_{IH} = V_T + \sqrt{\frac{8V_{DD}}{3kR_L}} - \frac{1}{kR_L} \tag{4.8f}$$

By increasing kR_L, we can reduce V_{IH} and increase NM_H. However, this increases the rising delay and increases power slightly. Note that changes in k and R_L have no effect on V_{OH}, so it is possible to increase NM_H, if desired.

The value of V_{OUL} can be determined by substituting V_{IH} into Equation (4.8e) and solving for V_{out}, if needed.

An additional point on the VTC that is important is where $V_{in} = V_{out} = V_S$. At this operating point, the NMOS transistor is in saturation since $V_{DS} = V_{GS}$, which implies that $V_{DS} > V_{Dsat}$. The switching voltage is found by equating currents

$$\frac{Wv_{sat}C_{ox}(V_S - V_T)^2}{(V_S - V_T) + E_C L} = \frac{V_{DD} - V_S}{R_L} \tag{4.9}$$

Since V_S is typically in the midpoint of the voltage swing, it is possible to set up an iterative equation with an initial guess of $V_{DD}/2$ to obtain V_S. Alternatively, Equation (4.9) can be written as a quadratic equation and solved directly.

Once all five points have been computed, the VTC of the inverter can be quickly sketched.

Example 4.2

Noise Margins for R-Load Inverter

Problem:

Given the following data for an inverter like the one shown in Figure 4.9a, find the multi-source noise margins.

$$k' = \mu_n C_{ox} = 430 \ \mu A/V^2, \quad V_T = 0.4 \ V, \quad \frac{W}{L} = 2.0$$

$$V_{DD} \doteq 1.2 \ V, \quad R_L = 20 \ k\Omega$$

Solution:

$$V_{OH} = V_{DD} = 1.2 \ V \quad and \quad k = k'\left(\frac{W}{L}\right) = 430 \ \frac{\mu A}{V^2} \times 2.$$

Find V_{OL} by solving (4.6d) with the given data (assuming transistor is linear):

$$V_{OL} \approx \frac{V_{DD}}{1 + kR_L(V_{DD} - V_T)} = \frac{1.2}{1 + (430 \times 10^{-6})(2)(20 \times 10^3)(1.2 - 0.4)} \approx 0.08 \text{ V}$$

Note that V_{OL} is safely below V_T. Also, the assumption that the transistor is in the linear region is valid.

Find V_{IL} using (4.8b):

$$V_{IL} = \frac{1}{kR_L} + V_T = 0.46 \text{ V}$$

A check confirms that the transistor is in the saturation region, as assumed.

Find V_{IH} from (4.8f):

$$V_{IH} = V_T + \sqrt{\frac{8V_{DD}}{3\,kR_L}} - \frac{1}{kR_L} = 0.4 + \sqrt{\frac{8}{3}\frac{1.2}{(2)430(10^{-6})20(10^3)}} - \frac{1}{(2)430(10^{-6})20(10^3)} \approx 0.77 \text{ V}$$

Again, the transistor is in the linear region, as assumed. The noise margins are then

$$NM_L = V_{IL} - V_{OL} = 0.46 - 0.08 = 0.38 \text{ V}$$

$$NM_H = V_{OH} - V_{IH} = 1.2 - 0.77 = 0.43 \text{ V}$$

SPICE Comparison to Hand Analysis in 0.18 μm CMOS   **Example 4.3**

Problem:

Compare SPICE VTC results to hand calculations for a resistive-load NMOS inverter with $R_L = 30$ kΩ, $W = 400$ nm, $L = 200$ nm (i.e., $W/L = 2$). That is, find V_{OH}, V_{OL}, V_{IH}, V_{IL}, and V_S. Useful parameters for 0.18 μm CMOS are as follows:

$$k' = \mu_n C_{ox} = 270 \text{ }\mu\text{A/V}^2, \quad C_{ox} = 1 \text{ }\mu\text{F/cm}^2, \quad V_T = 0.5 \text{ V}$$

$$E_c L = 1.2 \text{ V}, \quad V_{DD} = 1.8 \text{ V}, \quad v_{sat} = 8 \times 10^6 \text{ cm/s}$$

Solution:

The SPICE file would be as follows:

```
*Resistive-load inverter example
*Set supply and library
.param Supply=1.8                    *for 0.18 technology
.include 'bsim3v3.cmosp18.lib'
.opt scale=0.1u                      *Set lambda
*Power supply
.global Vdd Gnd
```

```
Vdd        Vdd Gnd  'Supply'          *Supply is set by .lib call
*Top level simulation netlist
Rup        Vdd out  30k
mn         out in   Gnd   Gnd  NMOS1  l=2 w=4 ad=0 pd=0 as=0 ps=0
Vin        in  Gnd  'Supply'
*Simulation
.dc        Vin 0    'Supply'          'Supply/50'
.plot      dc  V(out)
.end
```

The SPICE file produces the following VTC. The graph is annotated with the key points. Using these values, the noise margins and switching threshold are

$$NM_L = V_{IL} - V_{OL} = 0.558 - 0.085 = 0.473 \text{ V}$$

$$NM_H = V_{OH} - V_{IH} = 1.8 - 0.972 = 0.828 \text{ V}$$

$$V_S = 0.78 \text{ V}$$

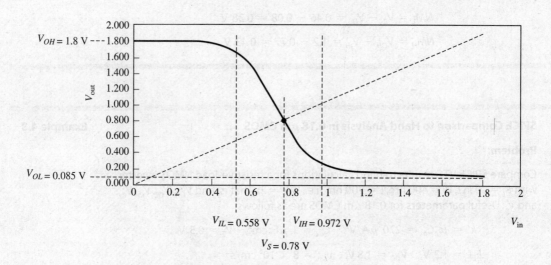

To compare against hand calculation, we first find $V_{OH} = V_{DD} = 1.8 \text{ V}$. Next find V_{OL}:

$$V_{OL} \approx \frac{V_{DD}}{1 + kR_L(V_{DD} - V_T)} = \frac{1.8}{1 + (2)\left(270 \frac{\mu A}{V^2}\right)(30 \text{ k}\Omega)(1.8 - 0.5)} \approx 0.082 \text{ V}$$

Then find V_{IL}:

$$V_{IL} = \frac{1}{kR_L} + V_T = 0.06 + 0.5 = 0.56 \text{ V}$$

Find V_{IH} as follows:

$$V_{IH} = V_T + \sqrt{\frac{8V_{DD}}{3\,kR_L}} - \frac{1}{kR_L} = 0.5 + 0.54 - 0.06 = 0.98 \text{ V}$$

The noise margins are

$$N_{ML} = V_{IL} - V_{OL} = 0.478 \text{ V}$$

$$N_{MH} = V_{OH} - V_{IH} = 0.817 \text{ V}$$

These are quite close to the SPICE results.

The last step is to compute the switching threshold using Equation (4.9):

$$\frac{W\upsilon_{sat}C_{ox}(V_S - V_T)^2}{(V_S - V_T) + E_C L} = \frac{V_{DD} - V_S}{R_L}$$

$$\frac{0.4(10^{-4})(8 \times 10^6)(10^{-6})(V_S - 0.5)^2}{(V_S - 0.5) + 1.2} = \frac{1.8 - V_S}{30\ k\Omega}$$

This equation can be rearranged and solved to produce

$$V_S = 0.89 \text{ V}$$

However, this value is about 15% higher than the SPICE result. Part of the reason is that the channel-length modulation parameter has been neglected in this calculation. Recall that the transistor is in saturation when computing V_S. By examining the SPICE curve shown below for $V_{GS} = 0.9$ V, there is a noticeable increase in the current in saturation due to channel-length modulation and DIBL. If we included a term $(1 + \lambda V_S)$ in the current equation and decreased V_T due to DIBL, the actual saturation current would be larger. This would reduce the switching threshold to 0.78 V rather than the value of 0.89 V computed by hand.

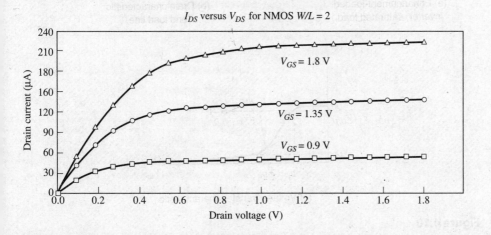

I_{DS} versus V_{DS} for NMOS $W/L = 2$

4.5 NMOS Transistors as Load Devices

The resistor loads require a large amount of chip area if realized in a standard MOS process. In fact, the area would be more than 100 times that of the transistor. It would also produce a large rise time. For these reasons, conventional resistors are rarely used as loads in MOS digital circuits. The following section describes several alternative ways of using NMOS transistors to perform the function of a pull-up resistor.

4.5.1 Saturated Enhancement Load

A single NMOS transistor with the gate connected to the drain can be used as a load device, as shown in Figure 4.10a. The purpose of this device is to pull up the output node to V_{OH}, so it is referred to as the pull-up (or load) device. This configuration is called a saturated enhancement load inverter since $V_{GS} = V_{DS}$. As a result, this load transistor can operate only in saturation or cutoff. Note that the body is

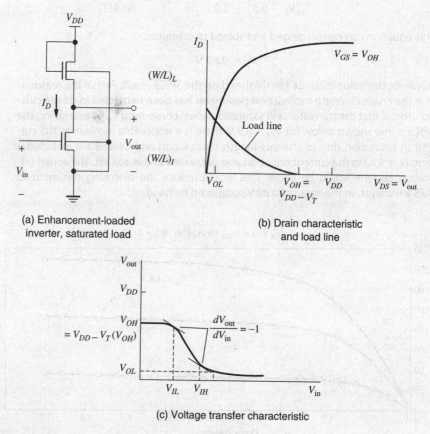

(a) Enhancement-loaded
inverter, saturated load

(b) Drain characteristic
and load line

(c) Voltage transfer characteristic

Figure 4.10
NMOS inverter, saturated enhancement load.

grounded because it is usually common to all transistors in a single well. Therefore, this transistor will experience body effect.

The other NMOS device pulls down on the output node to try to discharge it and, therefore, is referred to as the pull-down (or inverting) device. The relative sizes of the two transistors determine the output voltages, and so it is called a *ratioed* inverter. The importance of the device ratio is that it determines whether or not the inverter will function properly. If, for example, the sizes are chosen such that V_{OL} is much higher than the threshold voltage, then it will not operate as an inverter. In this sense, a ratioed inverter requires careful sizing of the pull-up and pull-down devices for proper operation. Conversely, a *ratioless* inverter does not require a specific ratio between the pull-up and pull-down devices to operate properly.

The ratio K_R for a MOS inverter[6] is defined as

$$K_R = \frac{k_{\text{invert}}}{k_{\text{load}}} = \frac{k'(W/L)_I}{k'(W/L)_L} = \frac{(W/L)_I}{(W/L)_L} \tag{4.10}$$

Subscripts I and L are added to distinguish between inverting (I) and load (L) devices. The value of K_R in ratioed inverters determines the value of V_{OL}. In a well-designed inverter, V_{OL} will about 5% of V_{DD}. If the value of K_R is large, V_{OL} is small. It should also be clear that increasing the value of K_R increases the circuit area.

The load line construction and the VTC for the inverter with the saturated load are shown in Figure 4.10b and c. A careful examination of the VTC curve reveals a serious deficiency of the saturated enhancement load that has been overlooked so far. The output high level V_{OH} is not equal to V_{DD} as it was for the resistor load. The pull-up transistor ceases to conduct after its gate-source voltage decreases to the threshold voltage. The result is that the output node does not rise above $V_{DD} - V_{TL}$. The threshold voltage of the load device, V_{TL}, is no longer V_{T0} as it is for the pull-down device, because the full output voltage appears as a body bias between source and body of the load device. The threshold voltage is given by the equation derived in Chapter 2:

$$V_{TL} = V_{T0} + \gamma(\sqrt{V_{SB} + 2|\phi_F|} - \sqrt{2|\phi_F|}) \tag{4.11}$$

where $V_{SB} = V_{OH}$. The resulting value of V_{OH} is one threshold voltage below the supply voltage. If $V_{DD} = 1.2$ V and $V_{TL} = 0.45$ V (including body-bias), then $V_{OH} = 1.2 - 0.45 = 0.75$ V. This may be too small to be acceptable as a high input to the next gate, making it difficult to design circuits that will operate with safe noise margins on a low supply voltage. In fact, this is one reason why early MOS circuits required higher voltage supplies.

Show that the pull-up device of Figure 4.10a is indeed in saturation or cutoff during normal operation. **Exercise 4.2**

---

[6] Some books use the term *beta ratio* (β_R) in place of the K_R. We avoid this terminology to avoid confusion with the current gain *beta* of a bipolar transistor.

The VTC for the saturated load inverter is computed as before. Here we will illustrate the approach to obtain only V_{OH} and V_{OL}. First, to find V_{OH} recall that the output node can only rise to a threshold drop below V_{DD} before the load device ceases to conduct. Therefore, we can write

$$V_{OH} = V_{DD} - V_T(V_{OH})$$

$$= V_{DD} - [V_{T0} + \gamma(\sqrt{V_{OH} + 2|\phi_F|} - \sqrt{2|\phi_F|})] \qquad (4.12)$$

To obtain the solution, use a substitute variable, $x = \sqrt{V_{OH} + 2|\phi_F|}$, and solve the quadratic equation in x. Only the positive root is meaningful from a physical standpoint. The fact that the output voltage cannot rise above $V_{DD} - V_{TL}$ adversely affects the NM_H value. The reduction is so severe that it is not a suitable load for most logic gates in a CMOS design. However, we may occasionally encounter this type of load due to the operating voltages of a given circuit.

Example 4.4

Computation of V_{OH} for a Saturated Enhancement Load Inverter

Problem:

Calculate the V_{OH} of the NMOS inverter shown in Figure 4.10a. Assume the following parameters for a 0.13 μm technology. Comment on the magnitude of the result:

$$2|\phi_F| = 0.88 \text{ V}, \quad \gamma = 0.2 \text{ V}^{1/2}, \quad V_T = 0.4 \text{ V}, \quad V_{DD} = 1.2 \text{ V}$$

Solution:

$$V_{OH} = V_{DD} - V_{TL} = V_{DD} - V_{TL}(V_{SB})$$

$$= V_{DD} - [V_{T0} + \gamma(\sqrt{V_{SB} + 2|\phi_F|} - \sqrt{2|\phi_F|})]$$

$$= 1.2 - [0.4 + 0.2(\sqrt{V_{OH} + 2|-0.44|} - \sqrt{2|-0.44|})]$$

$$= 0.8 - 0.2\sqrt{V_{OH} + 0.88} + 0.2\sqrt{0.88}$$

$$= 0.99 - 0.2\sqrt{V_{OH} + 0.88}$$

Solve by iteration, starting at the (optimistic) value $V_{OH} = 1.2$ V.

Old V_{OH}	New V_{OH}
1.20	0.70
0.70	0.74
0.74	0.73
0.73	0.73

$$\therefore V_{OH} = 0.73 \text{ V}$$

Clearly, a V_{OH} of 0.73 V from a 1.2 V supply is not acceptable as input to the next gate. Also, note that faster convergence would have been obtained had we started with $V_{OH} = 1.2 - 0.4 = 0.8$ V.

To find V_{OL}, we equate the currents in the two transistors. V_{OL} is the output voltage from this inverter when its input voltage is V_{OH}, the output high level of another identical inverter. For correct results, we need to know which form of the drain current equation (e.g., linear or saturated) to use for each transistor.

When conducting, the load transistor in this circuit is always saturated since $V_{DS} = V_{GS}$. As for the inverting transistor, with $V_{GS} = V_{OH}$, the output voltage should be lower than V_{T0} if there is to be any noise margin. Therefore, our assumption is that the pull-down transistor is in the linear region. Now equate the drain currents, using the appropriate equations:

$$I_{DI}(\text{lin}) = I_{DL}(\text{sat})$$

We can substitute in the current equations to obtain

$$\frac{W_I}{L_I} \frac{\mu_n C_{ox}}{\left(1 + \dfrac{V_{out}}{E_{CN}L_I}\right)} \left[(V_{in} - V_{TI})V_{out} - \frac{V_{out}^2}{2} \right] = \frac{W_L v_{sat} C_{ox}(V_{DD} - V_{out} - V_{TL})^2}{(V_{DD} - V_{out} - V_{TL}) + E_{CN}L_L}$$

This expression is used whenever the pull-up is saturated and the pull-down is in the linear region. But note that the load transistor threshold voltage V_{TL} is modified by the body effect, due to the voltage V_{out}, which appears between its source and the (grounded) substrate. When Equation (4.11) is used to evaluate V_{TL} (V_{out}) in the above, the resulting expression is a high-order polynomial. Direct solution by hand to find V_{OL} is tedious and susceptible to error. Simulation using SPICE or an equivalent computer program is a desirable alternative. If hand analysis is necessary, choose several values of V_{out}, substitute in the above equation, and solve the resulting linear first-order equation in V_{in}. Fortunately, V_{out} is small and will not have a significant effect on V_{TL}.

One other shortcoming of this type of inverter is similar to the resistive-load inverter: there is dc power dissipation when the output is low. Since current flowing directly from V_{DD} to Gnd when the output is at V_{OL}, the power dissipation is significant, especially if many such gates exist in the logic design. This is another reason why this type of inverter is rarely used.

Design of Saturated Load Inverter   Example 4.5

Problem:

Design the saturated enhancement load inverter of Figure 4.10a such that it delivers a low output voltage of $V_{OL} = 0.1$ V when the input is V_{DD}. Assume a 0.13 μm technology, with $L = 100$ nm and let the pull-up device be of unit size. Use the parameters

$\mu_n = 270$ cm^2/V-s, $C_{ox} = 1.6$ μF/cm^2, $V_{T0} = 0.4$ V, $V_{DD} = 1.2$ V

$E_{CN}L = 0.6$ V, $v_{sat} = 8 \times 10^6$ cm/s, $\gamma = 0.2$ V$^{1/2}$

Solution:

Use the current equation for the pull-down in the linear region and the pull-up in the saturation region.

$$\frac{W_I}{L_I} \frac{\mu_n C_{ox}}{\left(1 + \frac{V_{out}}{E_{CN}L_I}\right)} \left[(V_{in} - V_{TI})V_{out} - \frac{V_{out}^2}{2}\right] = \frac{W_L v_{sat} C_{ox}(V_{DD} - V_{out} - V_{TL})^2}{(V_{DD} - V_{out} - V_{TL}) + E_{CN}L_L}$$

We can eliminate C_{ox} and then set $V_{in} = V_{DD}$ (we should really set it to V_{OH} but we keep things simple in this problem) and $V_{out} = V_{OL}$:

$$\therefore \frac{W_I}{L_I} \frac{\mu_n}{\left(1 + \frac{V_{OL}}{E_{CN}L_I}\right)} \left[(V_{DD} - V_{TI})V_{OL} - \frac{V_{OL}^2}{2}\right] = \frac{W_L v_{sat}(V_{DD} - V_{OL} - V_{TL})^2}{(V_{DD} - V_{OL} - V_{TL}) + E_{CN}L_L}$$

Since we know that the output voltage is $V_{OL} = 0.1$ V, we can compute the correct V_{TL}:

$$V_T = [V_{T0} + \gamma(\sqrt{V_{SB} + 2|\phi_F|} - \sqrt{2|\phi_F|})]$$
$$= [0.4 + 0.2(\sqrt{0.1 + 2|-0.44|} - \sqrt{2|-0.44|})]$$
$$= 0.4 + 0.2(\sqrt{0.1 + 0.88} - \sqrt{0.88})$$
$$= 0.41 \text{ V}$$

The degree of body effect is small, as one would expect with a body-bias of 0.1 V. We can substitute the known quantities and solve for the transistor sizes:

$$\therefore \frac{W_I}{0.1(10^{-4})\text{cm}} \frac{(270 \text{ cm}^2/\text{V-s})}{(1 + (0.1/0.6))} \left[(1.2 - 0.4)0.1 - \frac{0.1^2}{2}\right]$$

$$= \frac{W_L(8 \times 10^6 \text{ cm/s})(1.2 - 0.1 - 0.41)^2}{(1.2 - 0.1 - 0.41) + 0.6}$$

$$\therefore K_R = \frac{W_I}{W_L} = \frac{2.95}{1.75} = 1.7$$

If $W_L = 100$ nm, then $W_I = 170$ nm.

4.5.2   Linear Enhancement Load

The output high level V_{OH} of the previous example can be increased simply by connecting the gate of the load transistor to a dc voltage of V_{GG}, which is sufficiently greater than V_{DD}. This is shown in Figure 4.11a. The desirable value for V_{GG} is given by

$$V_{GG} > V_{DD} + V_{TL}(V_{DD}) \tag{4.13}$$

where the last term is simply the value of V_{TL} with a body bias of V_{DD}. When this condition is met, the load device can pull the output all the way to V_{DD}. The pull-up device, when considering the quadratic model equations, operates in the linear

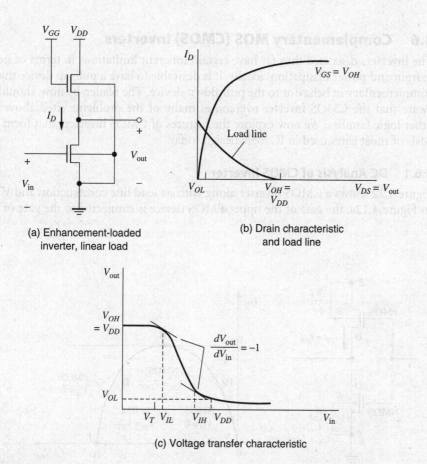

(a) Enhancement-loaded
inverter, linear load

(b) Drain characteristic
and load line

(c) Voltage transfer characteristic

Figure 4.11
NMOS inverter, *linear* enhancement load.

region over the entire range of V_{out}, since throughout this range the load device is operating with $V_{DS} < V_{GS} - V_{TL}$. For this reason, the names *linear load, nonsaturated load,* or *triode load* were applied to this mode of operation. With the velocity saturation model, this name no longer applies. The device can be in the linear region or the saturation region, depending on the output voltage; in fact, when the output is low, it is saturated. However, we will use the term *linear* to reflect its original name, even though this name is a misnomer for short-channel devices.

Figure 4.11b shows the load line construction for this type of inverter. The linear enhancement load has several disadvantages when used in static inverters and gates. More chip area is required, since an extra voltage source V_{GG} with associated additional interconnections on the chip is needed. The required value of K_R is even larger than for a saturated enhancement load. Furthermore, there is dc power dissipation in the output low state. These types of inverters are rarely, if ever, used as stand-alone gates. However, the operating conditions of the circuit may occasionally create this type of situation.

4.6 Complementary MOS (CMOS) Inverters

The inverters discussed thus far have certain inherent limitations in terms of noise margin and power dissipation. Ideally, it is desirable to have a pull-up device that is complementary in behavior to the pull-down device. The reader, by now, should be aware that the CMOS inverter overcomes many of the problems cited above for other logic families. We now explore the features of CMOS inverters that form the basis of most gates used in IC logic design today.

4.6.1 DC Analysis of CMOS Inverter

Figure 4.12 shows a CMOS inverter along with its load line construction and VTC. In Figure 4.12a, the gate of the upper PMOS device is connected to the gate of the

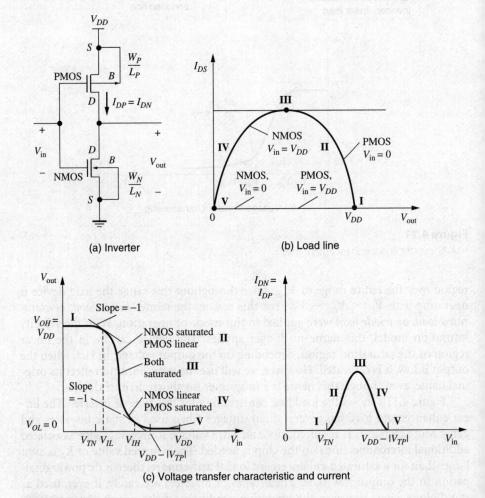

(a) Inverter (b) Load line

(c) Voltage transfer characteristic and current

Figure 4.12
CMOS inverter characteristics.

lower NMOS device. The PMOS device has a substrate connection to V_{DD} while the NMOS body is connected to Gnd. This is required to keep the source/drain junctions reverse-biased.

The operation of the CMOS inverter is as follows. When the input is at V_{DD}, the NMOS device is conducting while the PMOS device (which has $V_{GS} = 0$ V) is cut off. The result is that V_{out} is 0 V. Hence the drain current of the NMOS is limited to the very small leakage current of the PMOS, even though a highly conductive channel is present in the NMOS device. When the input is at ground, the NMOS device is cut off while the PMOS device is conducting. Only the small leakage current of the NMOS device can flow, so V_{out} is equal to V_{DD}. Therefore, we find that $V_{OH} = V_{DD}$ and $V_{OL} = 0$ V, which implies large noise margins for CMOS inverters. A completely symmetrical VTC is obtained if $V_{TP} = -V_{TN}$ and $k_P = k_N$.

The gate is static in that there is always a conducting path from the output to V_{DD} or Gnd. The only currents that flow in steady state are the subthreshold currents of the nominally off device and leakage currents of reverse-biased *pn* junctions. Quiescent power dissipation is in the nanowatt range. Although no steady-state current flows, the *on* transistor supplies current to drive any load resistance or capacitance whenever the output voltage differs from 0 V or V_{DD}. The tiny steady-state power consumption of CMOS in either logic state is its most attractive feature. The resistive-load and NMOS-only circuits all suffer from power dissipation in the output low state and therefore are inappropriate for use in high-density deep submicron designs.

The load line construction for the CMOS inverter requires some explanation. Shown in Figure 4.12b are I_{DS} versus V_{out} curves for each transistor. When V_{GS} is equal in magnitude to V_{DD} for either device, the drain current curves are given by the curves on Figure 4.12b. When gate-source voltage is zero for either device, drain current is zero. Thus, the two devices behave almost as ideal loads for each other. The two logic states lie at $V_{out} = 0$ and $V_{out} = V_{DD}$ along the horizontal V_{out} axis, both at $I_{DS} = 0$.

The drain current of an *n*-channel device can be computed if the polarities in Figure 4.12a are observed. In normal operation of a *p*-channel device, V_{GS}, V_{DS}, and V_{TP} all have negative values. Drain current I_{DS}, defined as flowing *out* of the drain for PMOS, has a positive value. Another way to handle the change of signs for PMOS analysis is simply to use absolute values of all voltages in the drain current equations. If you use this approach, check to be sure that the PMOS devices are properly biased for normal operation. The gate must be negative with respect to source by more than a threshold voltage if current is to flow.

The complete VTC and noise margins can now be determined. The form of the VTC is shown in Figure 4.12c. It is useful to divide the curve into five regions as shown in the figure. Sequencing from region I to region V is carried out by starting with the input voltage V_{in} at 0 V and increasing its value until V_{DD} is reached.

Region I: *n*-off, *p*-lin. The NMOS device is off while the PMOS device is linear, although it has a $V_{DS} = 0$. The output remains at $V_{OH} = V_{DD}$ up to the point when $V_{in} = V_{TN}$.

Region II: *n*-sat, *p*-lin.   The NMOS device is on and in saturation, while the PMOS device is still in the linear region since its V_{DS} is relatively small. The current equation in this region is given by

$$I_{DN}(\text{sat}) = I_{DP}(\text{lin})$$

Therefore,

$$\frac{W_N v_{\text{sat}} C_{ox} (V_{\text{in}} - V_{TN})^2}{(V_{\text{in}} - V_{TN}) + E_{CN} L_N}$$

$$= \frac{W_P}{L_P} \frac{\mu_p C_{ox}}{\left(1 + \dfrac{V_{DD} - V_{\text{out}}}{E_{CP} L_P}\right)} \left[(V_{DD} - V_{\text{in}} - |V_{TP}|)(V_{DD} - V_{\text{out}}) - \frac{(V_{DD} - V_{\text{out}})^2}{2} \right]$$

The VTC in this region is computed by setting V_{in} and solving for V_{out}.

Region III: *n*-sat, *p*-sat.   This involves the nearly vertical segment of the VTC where both transistors are saturated. By equating the saturated drain current equations for the two transistors, we obtain

$$I_{DN}(\text{sat}) = I_{DP}(\text{sat})$$

Therefore,

$$\frac{W_N v_{\text{sat}} C_{ox} (V_{\text{in}} - V_{TN})^2}{(V_{\text{in}} - V_{TN}) + E_{CN} L_N} = \frac{W_P v_{\text{sat}} C_{ox} (V_{DD} - V_{\text{in}} - |V_{TP}|)^2}{(V_{DD} - V_{\text{in}} - |V_{TP}|) + E_{CP} L_P}$$

Note that V_{out} is not present in this expression since the gain is (ideally) infinite due to modeling limitations of the current equations. The voltage V_S at which $V_{\text{in}} = V_{\text{out}}$ falls within this segment of the VTC. The value can be determined by setting V_{in} to V_S in the above expression:

$$\frac{W_N v_{\text{sat}} C_{ox} (V_S - V_{TN})^2}{(V_S - V_{TN}) + E_{CN} L_N} = \frac{W_P v_{\text{sat}} C_{ox} (V_{DD} - V_S - |V_{TP}|)^2}{(V_{DD} - V_S - |V_{TP}|) + E_{CP} L_P}$$

To solve for V_S is not straightforward, so a few simplifications are needed. Since V_S is expected to be approximately $V_{DD}/2$, the leading term in the denominator of both sides of the equation is smaller than the $E_C L$ term. To greatly simplify the equation, we remove these terms from both sides and cancel out $v_{\text{sat}} C_{ox}$ to obtain

$$\frac{W_N (V_S - V_{TN})^2}{E_{CN} L_N} = \frac{W_P (V_{DD} - V_S - |V_{TP}|)^2}{E_{CP} L_P}$$

Taking the square root of both sides, we solve for V_S:

$$V_S = \frac{V_{DD} - |V_{TP}| + \chi V_{TN}}{1 + \chi} \tag{4.14}$$

where

$$\chi = \sqrt{\dfrac{\dfrac{W_N}{E_{CN}L_N}}{\dfrac{W_P}{E_{CP}L_P}}} = \sqrt{\dfrac{\mu_n W_N}{\mu_p W_P}} \qquad (4.15)$$

The switching threshold is very useful when sketching the VTC. As we increase χ, the switching threshold shifts left while decreasing the value shifts the switching threshold to the right. We can shift the VTC to the left by increasing the size of the NMOS device, or shift it to the right by increasing the size of the PMOS device. This shift in VTC produces a *skewed* inverter.

Computation of V_S for CMOS Inverter in 0.13 μm Technology   Example 4.6

Problem:

Calculate the switching voltage of a CMOS inverter with each the following PMOS sizes: $W_P = 400$ nm and $W_P = 100$ nm. W_N is the same size of 100 nm for both cases. How does change in W_P affect the switching voltage?

Solution:

Compute V_S using Equations (4.14) and (4.15):

$$W_N = 0.1\ \mu\text{m} \qquad W_P = 0.4\ \mu\text{m}$$

$$\chi = \sqrt{\dfrac{\dfrac{W_N}{E_{CN}L_N}}{\dfrac{W_P}{E_{CP}L_P}}} = \sqrt{\dfrac{W_N E_{CP}}{W_P E_{CN}}} = \sqrt{\dfrac{(0.1)(24)}{(0.4)(6)}} = 1.0$$

$$V_S = \dfrac{0.8 + (0.4)1.0}{1 + 1.0} = 0.6\ \text{V}$$

Re-computing for the second case:

$$W_N = 0.1\ \mu\text{m} \qquad W_P = 0.1\ \mu\text{m}$$

$$\chi = \sqrt{\dfrac{\dfrac{W_N}{E_{CN}L_N}}{\dfrac{W_P}{E_{CP}L_P}}} = \sqrt{\dfrac{W_N E_{CP}}{W_P E_{CN}}} = \sqrt{\dfrac{(0.1)(24)}{(0.1)(6)}} = 2.0$$

$$V_S = \dfrac{0.8 + (0.4)2.0}{1 + 2.0} = 0.53\ \text{V}$$

We find that lowering W_P decreases V_S which shifts the VTC to the left.

We now continue on with the region-wise analysis.

Region IV: *n*-lin, *p*-sat. The NMOS device is on and in the linear region since V_{DS} is small, while the PMOS device is still in saturation. The current equation in this region is given by

$$I_{DN}(\text{lin}) = I_{DP}(\text{sat})$$

Therefore,

$$\frac{W_N}{L_N} \frac{\mu_n C_{ox}}{\left(1 + \dfrac{V_{out}}{E_{CN}L_N}\right)} \left[(V_{in} - V_{TN})V_{out} - \frac{V_{out}^2}{2} \right]$$

$$= \frac{W_P \upsilon_{sat} C_{ox}(V_{DD} - V_{in} - |V_{TP}|)^2}{(V_{DD} - V_{in} - |V_{TP}|) + E_{CP}L_P}$$

The VTC in this region is computed by setting V_{in} and solving for V_{out}.

Region V: *n*-lin, *p*-off. The applied input voltage is above $V_{DD} - |V_{TP}|$, so the output is now 0 V and will remain that way up to and beyond $V_{in} = V_{DD}$.

It is instructive to examine the transfer characteristic of the dc current versus voltage, as shown in Figure 4.12c. Here, current does not flow except in the range $V_{TN} < V_{in} < V_{DD} - |V_{TP}|$, again reinforcing the advantage of the CMOS inverter in terms of power dissipation. The peak current occurs in region III with both devices in saturation.

The noise margin calculations begin with the observations that $V_{OH} = V_{DD}$ and $V_{OL} = 0$ V. Next, V_{IL} and V_{IH} are determined from the $\partial V_{out}/\partial V_{in} = -1$ condition. At $V_{in} = V_{IL}$, the inverter is in region II and so the NMOS device is saturated while the PMOS device is in the linear region:

$$I_{DN}(\text{sat}) = I_{DP}(\text{lin})$$

Applying the two current equations to the above, we obtain

$$\frac{W_N \upsilon_{sat} C_{ox}(V_{in} - V_{TN})^2}{(V_{in} - V_{TN}) + E_{CN}L_N} = \frac{W_P}{L_P} \frac{\mu_p C_{ox}}{\left(1 + \dfrac{V_{DD} - V_{out}}{E_{CP}L_P}\right)}$$

$$\times \left[(V_{DD} - V_{in} - |V_{TP}|)(V_{DD} - V_{out}) - \frac{(V_{DD} - V_{out})^2}{2} \right]$$

This equation looks somewhat cumbersome but can be greatly simplified. First, note that the term $(V_{in} - V_{TN})$ in the denominator of the *n*-channel device is small relative to $E_{CN}L_N$ since the input voltage is slightly above V_{TN}. Second, the expression $(V_{DD} - V_{out})/E_{CP}L_P$ in the denominator of the p-channel device is also small, since V_{out} is around V_{DD}. These two terms are negligible when the inverter operating point is in region II around V_{IL}. This results in the following equation:

$$\frac{W_N v_{sat} C_{ox} (V_{in} - V_{TN})^2}{E_{CN}L_N} = \frac{W_P}{L_P} \mu_p C_{ox}$$

$$\times \left[(V_{DD} - V_{in} - |V_{TP}|)(V_{DD} - V_{out}) - \frac{(V_{DD} - V_{out})^2}{2} \right]$$

Recalling that $v_{sat} = \mu_n E_{CN}/2$ and substituting into the above produces

$$\frac{W_N}{L_N} \frac{\mu_n C_{ox}}{2} (V_{in} - V_{TN})^2 = \frac{W_P}{L_P} \mu_p C_{ox}$$

$$\times \left[(V_{DD} - V_{in} - |V_{TP}|)(V_{DD} - V_{out}) - \frac{(V_{DD} - V_{out})^2}{2} \right] \qquad (4.16)$$

Essentially, we are back to the first-order MOS model equations for this calculation. To solve for V_{IL}, the equation above must be differentiated with respect to V_{in}:

$$\frac{W_N}{L_N} \mu_n (V_{in} - V_{TN}) = \frac{W_P}{L_P} \mu_p \left[(V_{DD} - V_{in} - |V_{TP}|) \left(-\frac{\partial V_{out}}{\partial V_{in}} \right) \right.$$

$$\left. + (V_{DD} - V_{out})(-1) - (V_{DD} - V_{out}) \left(-\frac{\partial V_{out}}{\partial V_{in}} \right) \right]$$

After substituting in k_N and k_P, and setting $\partial V_{out}/\partial V_{in} = -1$ and $V_{in} = V_{IL}$, the result is

$$V_{IL} = \frac{2V_{out} - V_{DD} - |V_{TP}| + (k_N/k_P)(V_{TN})}{1 + (k_N/k_P)} \qquad (4.17)$$

This equation is dependent on V_{out}, which is still unknown. The next step is to solve Equations (4.16) and (4.17) together to obtain V_{IL} and the corresponding $V_{out} = V_{OUH}$.

A similar process is used to obtain the equations for V_{IH}. At $V_{in} = V_{IH}$, the inverter is most likely in region IV and, therefore, the NMOS device is linear while the PMOS device is saturated.

$$I_{DN}(\text{lin}) = I_{DP}(\text{sat})$$

Applying the two current equations, we obtain:

$$\frac{W_N}{L_N} \frac{\mu_n C_{ox}}{\left(1 + \dfrac{V_{out}}{E_{CN}L_N}\right)} \left[(V_{in} - V_{TN})V_{out} - \frac{V_{out}^2}{2} \right] = \frac{W_P \upsilon_{sat} C_{ox}(V_{DD} - V_{in} - |V_{TP}|)^2}{(V_{DD} - V_{in} - |V_{TP}|) + E_{CP}L_P}$$

This equation can also be greatly simplified. Again, note that the term $V_{out}/E_{CN}L_N$ in the denominator of the n-channel device is small and the expression $(V_{DD} - V_{in} - |V_{TP}|)$ in the denominator of the p-channel device is also small relative to $E_{CP}L_P$. These two terms are negligible when the inverter operating point is in region IV around V_{IH}. This results in the following equation:

$$\frac{W_N}{L_N} \mu_n C_{ox} \left[(V_{in} - V_{TN})(V_{out}) - \frac{(V_{out})^2}{2} \right] = \frac{W_P \upsilon_{sat} C_{ox}(V_{DD} - V_{in} - |V_{TP}|)^2}{E_{CP}L_P}$$

Noting that $\upsilon_{sat} = \mu_p E_{CP}/2$ and substituting into the above produces

$$\frac{W_N}{L_N} \mu_n C_{ox} \left[(V_{in} - V_{TN})(V_{out}) - \frac{(V_{out})^2}{2} \right] = \frac{W_P}{L_P} \frac{\mu_p C_{ox}}{2} (V_{DD} - V_{in} - |V_{TP}|)^2$$

(4.18)

Again, we are back to the first-order MOS model equations. To solve for V_{IH}, the equation above must be differentiated with respect to V_{in}:

$$\frac{W_N}{L_N} \mu_n C_{ox} \left[(V_{in} - V_{TN})\frac{\partial V_{out}}{\partial V_{in}} + (V_{out}) - V_{out}\frac{\partial V_{out}}{\partial V_{in}} \right]$$

$$= \frac{W_P}{L_P} \mu_p C_{ox}(V_{DD} - V_{in} - |V_{TP}|)(-1)$$

After substituting in k_N and k_P, and setting $\partial V_{out}/\partial V_{in} = -1$ and $V_{in} = V_{IH}$, this yields

$$V_{IH} = \frac{2V_{out} + V_{TN} + (k_P/k_N)(V_{DD} - |V_{TP}|)}{1 + (k_P/k_N)}$$

(4.19)

This expression is substituted in the above drain current equation to obtain explicit solutions for V_{IH} and the corresponding value of $V_{out} = V_{OUL}$.

Example 4.7

SPICE Analysis and Hand Calculation of CMOS Inverter in 0.18 μm Technology

Problem:

Compare SPICE analysis and hand analysis for a CMOS inverter of Figure 4.12a, with $W_N = 400$ nm and $W_P = 800$ nm, for the VTC parameters. Use 0.18 μm technology parameters as follows:

$$\mu_n = 270 \text{ cm}^2/\text{V-s}, \quad \mu_p = 70 \text{ cm}^2/\text{V-s},$$

$$C_{ox} = 1.0 \ \mu\text{F/cm}^2, \quad V_{TN} = 0.5 \text{ V}, \quad V_{TP} = -0.5 \text{ V}$$

$$E_{CN}L = 1.2 \text{ V}, \quad E_{Cp}L = 4.8 \text{ V}, \quad \upsilon_{sat} = 8 \times 10^6 \text{ cm/s},$$

$$V_{DD} = 1.8 \text{ V}, \quad L = 200 \text{ nm}$$

Solution:

```
*CMOS Inverter Example
*Set supply and library          *
.param Supply=1.8                *for 0.18 technology
.include 'bsim3v3.cmosp18.lib'
.opt scale=0.1u                  *Set lambda
.global  Vdd  Gnd
Vdd       Vdd  Gnd  'Supply'      *Supply is set by .lib call
*Top level simulation netlist
mp        out  in    Vdd    Vdd PMOS1 l=2 w=8 ad=0 pd=0 as=0 ps=0
mn        out  in    Gnd    Gnd NMOS1 l=2 w=4 ad=0 pd=0 as=0 ps=0
*Top level simulation netlist
Vin       in   Gnd   'Supply'
*Simulation
.dc       Vin  0     'Supply'  'Supply/50'
.plot     dc   V(out)
.end
```

From the SPICE simulation using the above input, the plot shown below is produced.

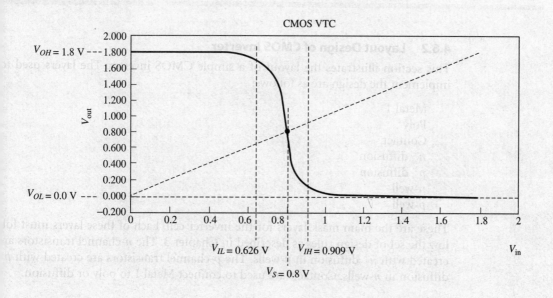

The VTC parameters from SPICE are $V_{OH} = 1.8\,V, V_{OL} = 0\,V, V_{IL} = 0.626\,V, V_{IH} = 0.909\,V,$ $V_S = 0.8\,V.$ Therefore, the noise margins are

$$NM_H = 1.8 - 0.909 = 0.891\ V$$

$$NM_L = 0.626 - 0 = 0.626\ V$$

For hand analysis, we already know that $V_{OH} = 1.8\,V$, and $V_{OL} = 0\,V.$
The computation of V_S can be carried out as before, with $0.18\ \mu m$ parameters:

$$W_N = 0.4\ \mu m \qquad W_P = 0.8\ \mu m$$

$$X = \sqrt{\dfrac{\dfrac{W_N}{E_{CN}L_N}}{\dfrac{W_P}{E_{Cp}L_P}}} = \sqrt{\dfrac{W_N E_{CP}}{W_P E_{CN}}} = \sqrt{\dfrac{(0.4)(24)}{(0.8)(6)}} = 1.41$$

$$V_S = \dfrac{1.8 - 0.5 + (0.5)1.41}{1 + 1.41} = 0.83\ V$$

This value is quite accurate relative to the SPICE results. The values for V_{IL} and V_{IH} require some effort but eventually produce $V_{IL} \approx 0.7\ V$ and $V_{IH} \approx 1.0\ V.$ Therefore,

$$NM_H = 1.8 - 1.0 = 0.8\ V$$

$$NM_L = 0.7 - 0 = 0.7\ V$$

While these are not accurate results, they are within 15% of SPICE and are good enough for hand analysis.

4.6.2 Layout Design of CMOS Inverter

This section illustrates the layout of a simple CMOS inverter. The layers used to implement the design are as follows:

Metal 1
Poly
Contact
n^+ diffusion
p^+ diffusion
n-well
p-well

These are the main mask layers for the inverter cell. Each of these layers must fol-low the set of design rules as described in Chapter 3. The n-channel transistors ar-created with n^+ diffusion in p-wells. The p-channel transistors are created with p^- diffusion in n-wells. Contacts are used to connect Metal 1 to poly or diffusion.

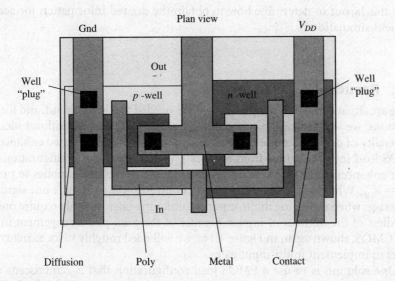

Figure 4.13
Layout of CMOS inverter.

A plan view of a CMOS inverter layout is shown in Figure 4.13. In the plan view, there are two wells, separated by a safe distance, that contain the n and p devices. The n-devices are in the p-well and the p-devices are in the n-well. The inputs for the two devices are formed on the poly layer. When poly crosses diffusion, a transistor is formed. In this case, poly crossings over the n^+ and p^+ regions form the two transistors. The input signal is on poly since it will be driving the gates of the two transistors. All input signals must eventually be connected to the poly layer since all transistor gates are poly gates.

The n-channel transistor has its source connected to Gnd while its drain is connected to the output. The p-channel device has its source connected to V_{DD} and its drain connected to the output. The output is taken on the Metal 1 layer since metal can be connected directly to the diffusion regions. This output will drive another gate so it must switch to poly at some point using a metal-to-poly contact, not shown in the figure.

There are a total of four contacts associated with the inverter itself: two for the n-device and two for the p-device. There are also two other contacts that are shown here. These contacts connect the wells to Gnd and V_{DD}, respectively, to keep the pn junctions reverse-biased. They are often referred to as "well plugs."

The layout is important in that the dimensions and areas needed for simulation are extracted from them. Specifically, SPICE simulations require L, W, AS, AD, PS, and PD, as illustrated earlier. The area and perimeter data are primarily for the transient analysis so they have not been used in the SPICE input examples in this chapter. We will be specifying this information in later chapters. Therefore, it is useful to study this layout to determine how to obtain the desired information for accurate transient simulation.

4.7 Pseudo-NMOS Inverters

There are situations where a high fanin gate is needed in a logic circuit, and for these situations, we would like to use the advantage of NMOS loads, without incurring the penalty of degraded noise margins or two supplies. The saturated enhancement NMOS load inverter suffers from a lower V_{OH} than the other configurations. The linear enhancement NMOS load inverter requires two voltage supplies to produce $V_{OH} = V_{DD}$. While we rarely see these types of inverters, they do have one significant advantage: when designing multi-input (multifanin) gates, we only require one load regardless of the number of inputs. Because of the *push-pull* arrangement in standard CMOS, shown again in Figure 4.14a, we will need roughly twice as many transistors to implement multi-input gates.

One solution is to use a PMOS load configuration that is reminiscent of the NMOS load, as shown in Figure 4.14b. We call this a *pseudo-NMOS* configuration as a reminder of its relation to the NMOS-style loads. The gate of the PMOS device is connected to ground so that the transistor is always on. This device is able to pull the output to V_{DD} when the NMOS device is off without the need for additional supplies. However, it will fight the NMOS transistor when it is on. Therefore, it must be sized along with the NMOS device to deliver the desired V_{OL}. This makes it a ratioed inverter, whereas the standard CMOS inverter is ratioless. When the output is low, power is dissipated in the pseudo-NMOS inverter just as in the other NMOS inverter configurations. This limitation directs us to use this approach sparingly to minimize overall chip power. However, the real value of the pseudo-NMOS configuration will be clear when we examine multi-input gates: it will have a much smaller area than the standard CMOS gate.

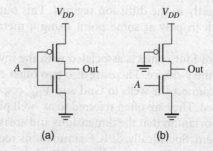

Figure 4.14
(a) CMOS. (b) Pseudo-NMOS inverters.

The voltage transfer characteristics of the pseudo-NMOS inverter can be computed in the usual way and will not be described here. However, V_{OH} and V_{OL} calculations are illustrated. From our discussion above, we already know that

$$V_{OH} = V_{DD} \tag{4.20}$$

The derivation of V_{OL} is as follows:

$$I_{DP}(\text{sat}) = I_{DN}(\text{lin})$$

$$\frac{W_P v_{sat} C_{ox}(V_{DD} - |V_{TP}|)^2}{(V_{DD} - |V_{TP}|) + E_{CP}L_P} = \frac{W_N}{L_N} \frac{\mu_n C_{ox}}{\left(1 + \dfrac{V_{OL}}{E_{CN}L_N}\right)} \left[(V_{DD} - V_{TN})(V_{OL}) - \frac{(V_{OL})^2}{2} \right] \tag{4.21}$$

Since V_{OL} is small, this equation can be simplified to

$$V_{OL} \cong \frac{I_{DP}(\text{sat})}{k_N(V_{DD} - V_{TN})}$$

The sizes of the two devices can be computed based on the desired V_{OL}.

Design of a Pseudo-NMOS Inverter in 0.18 μm with SPICE Comparison   **Example 4.8**

Problem:

Design a pseudo-NMOS inverter of Figure 4.14b, to deliver $V_{OH} = V_{DD} = 1.8$ V, and $V_{OL} = 0.065$ V. Plot the VTC using SPICE to confirm your results. Use the following 0.18 μm technology parameters:

$$\mu_n = 270 \text{ cm}^2/\text{V-s}, \quad \mu_p = 70 \text{ cm}^2/\text{V-s}, \quad C_{ox} = 1.0 \ \mu\text{F/cm}^2,$$

$$V_{TN} = 0.5 \text{ V}, \quad V_{TP} = -0.5 \text{ V}, \quad E_{CN}L = 1.2 \text{ V}, \quad E_{CP}L = 4.8 \text{ V},$$

$$v_{sat} = 8 \times 10^6 \text{ cm/s}, \quad V_{DD} = 1.8 \text{ V}, \quad L = 200 \text{ nm}$$

Solution:

To design the inverter of Figure 4.14b with the proper V_{OH}, we set $V_{DD} = 1.8$ V. To compute the transistor widths to deliver $V_{OL} = 0.065$ V, use Equation (4.21). The required value of W_N/W_P can be obtained as follows:

$$\frac{W_P v_{sat} C_{ox}(V_{DD} - |V_{TP}|)^2}{(V_{DD} - |V_{TP}|) + E_{CP}L_P} = \frac{W_N}{L_N} \frac{\mu_n C_{ox}}{\left(1 + \dfrac{V_{OL}}{E_{CN}L_N}\right)} \left[(V_{DD} - V_{TN})(V_{OL}) - \frac{(V_{OL})^2}{2} \right]$$

$$\therefore \frac{W_P(8 \times 10^6)(1.8 - 0.5)^2}{(1.8 - 0.5) + 4.8} = \frac{W_N}{0.2(10^{-4})} \frac{270}{\left(1 + (0.065/1.2)\right)} \left[(1.8 - 0.5)(0.065) - \frac{(0.065)^2}{2}\right]$$

$$\therefore \frac{W_N}{W_P} \cong 2.0$$

If we set $W_P = 400$ nm, then $W_N = 800$ nm. This should produce the desired $V_{OL} = 0.065$ V.

Now check the results with SPICE.

```
*Pseudo-NMOS Inverter Example
*Set supply and library
.param Supply = 1.8          *for 0.18 technology
.include 'bsim3v3.cmosp18.lib'
.opt scale = 0.1u            *Set lambda
.global Vdd   Gnd
Vdd       Vdd   Gnd  'Supply'   *Supply is set by .lib call
*Top level simulation netlist
mp        out   Gnd  Vdd    Vdd PMOS1 l=2 w=4 ad=0 pd=0 as=0 ps=0
mn        out   in   Gnd    Gnd NMOS1 l=2 w=8 ad=0 pd=0 as=0 ps=0
*Top level simulation netlist
Vin       in    Gnd  'Supply'
*Simulation
.dc       Vin   0    'Supply' 'Supply/50'
.plot     dc    V(out)
.end
```

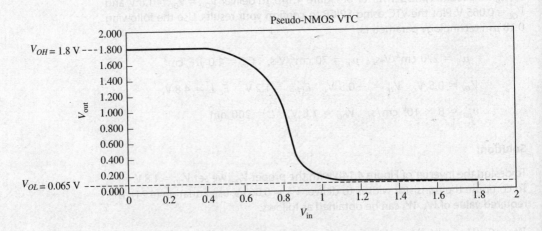

The SPICE results show that $V_{OH} = 1.8$ V and $V_{OL} = 0.065$ V.

4.8   Sizing Inverters

Inverter sizing is the problem of selecting the W/L values for the pull-up and pull-down transistors to satisfy a set of design specifications. The proper selection of device sizes for the basic inverters discussed thus far involves a tradeoff between timing, power, area, and noise margins. Usually one or two of these factors controls the ultimate device sizes.

For the CMOS inverter, we usually focus on the timing to determine the device sizes, since the inverter is ratioless and standby power is small. For the pseudo-NMOS inverter, the sizes depend primarily on the desired V_{OL} (noise margin parameter) and timing.

It is useful to compare the sizing problem for the CMOS inverter and the pseudo-NMOS inverter. In order to do so, we must first develop a simple timing model. More advanced timing models will be the subject of Chapter 6. Here we seek to introduce a simple approach that is extremely valuable for hand calculations.

Figure 4.15a illustrates two important timing specifications: t_{PHL} and t_{PLH}. These are the high-to-low and low-to-high propagation delays, as shown using the waveforms for the input and output voltages of an inverter. A step input is applied to the inverter and the output propagation time is measured at the 50% point. To make the delay calculation simple, we assume that the inverter can be modeled with an effective on-resistance, R_{eff}, driving a load capacitance, C_L.

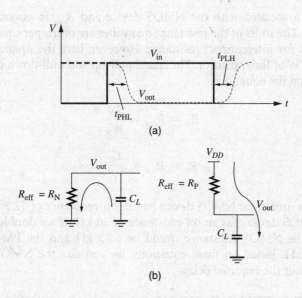

(a)

(b)

Figure 4.15
Simple timing model for inverter sizing.

The output response to a step input is an exponential waveform. For the falling case, a pull-down resistance, $R_{eff} = R_N$, is connected to the capacitive load and the output response is given by

$$V_{out}(t) = V_{DD}\, e^{-t/R_N C_L} \qquad (4.22a)$$

For the rising case, the on-resistance is $R_{eff} = R_P$ and the output is given by

$$V_{out}(t) = V_{DD}(1 - e^{-t/R_P C_L}) \qquad (4.22b)$$

In both cases, the 50% point occurs at

$$\tau = 0.69 R_{eff} C_L \qquad (4.22c)$$

The two values of R_{eff} are defined as the average on-resistances in the pull-up and pull-down cases, respectively. These values are both inversely proportional to W/L since the resistance decreases as we increase W/L. The NMOS and PMOS devices have different on-resistances that we can compute using SPICE simulations on unit-sized devices when driving a known capacitance. If we measure t_{PHL} and t_{PLH}, we can extract the equivalent on-resistances. From such SPICE measurements, we find that:[7]

$$R_{eqn} = 12.5 \text{ k}\Omega/\square \qquad (4.23a)$$

$$R_{eqp} = 30 \text{ k}\Omega/\square \qquad (4.23b)$$

where R_{eqn} is associated with the NMOS device and R_{eqp} is associated with the PMOS device. The units of the resistance quantities are ohms per square, similar to the units used for interconnect resistance. However, here the *square* refers to the aspect ratio L/W of the transistor. The actual pull-up and pull-down resistances are computed using the equations:

$$R_N = R_{eqn} \times \frac{L_N}{W_N} \qquad (4.24a)$$

$$R_P = R_{eqp} \times \frac{L_P}{W_P} \qquad (4.24b)$$

For example, a unit-sized NMOS device has an on-resistance of 12.5 kΩ whereas a unit-sized PMOS device has an on-resistance of 30 kΩ. If we double the width of each device, the NMOS resistance would be 6.25 kΩ and the PMOS resistance would be 15 kΩ. Based on these equations, we can size the NMOS and PMOS devices to deliver the required delay.

---

[7] These values are approximately correct for a number of different technologies including 0.35 μm, 0.18 μm, and 0.13 μm.

Comparison of CMOS and Pseudo-NMOS Inverters

Example 4.9

Problem:

Given the CMOS and pseudo-NMOS inverters of Figure 4.14, size the two inverters to achieve the following specifications, assuming that the output loading is 50 fF. Use 0.13 μm technology parameters:

$$\mu_n = 270 \text{ cm}^2/\text{V-s}, \quad \mu_p = 70 \text{ cm}^2/\text{V-s}, \quad C_{ox} = 1.6 \ \mu\text{F}/\text{cm}^2,$$

$$V_{TN} = 0.4 \text{ V}, \quad V_{TP} = -0.4 \text{ V}$$

$$E_{CN}L = 0.6 \text{ V}, \quad E_{CP}L = 2.4 \text{ V}, \quad v_{sat} = 8 \times 10^6 \text{ cm/s},$$

$$V_{DD} = 1.2 \text{ V}, \quad L = 100 \text{ nm}$$

CMOS Inverter: $t_{PHL} = t_{PLH} < 50$ ps; $V_{OH} = 1.2$ V and $V_{OL} = 0$ V; low dc power; minimum area

Pseudo-NMOS Inverter: $t_{PHL} < 50$ ps; $V_{OH} = 1.2$ V and $V_{OL} = 0.1$ V; minimum dc power; minimum area

Solution:

For the CMOS inverter, timing is the highest priority. The noise margin parameters of V_{OH} and V_{OL} are satisfied by choosing $V_{DD} = 1.2$ V. The power requirement is satisfied since it is a standard CMOS gate. The area requirement can be satisfied by meeting but not exceeding the timing specification. That is, we do not size the devices any larger than needed. For the timing requirement, we make use of (4.22c):

$$t = 0.7 R_{eff} C_L = 0.7 R_{eff} \times 50 \text{ fF} = 50 \text{ ps} \Rightarrow R_{eff} = 1.4 \text{ k}\Omega$$

Using (4.24a), we can determine the NMOS (W/L) value:

$$R_N = R_{eqn} \times \frac{L}{W} = 12.5 \text{ k}\Omega \times \frac{L}{W} = 1.4 \text{ k}\Omega \Rightarrow \frac{W_N}{L_N} = 8.75$$

Now, (4.24b) can be used to obtain the value of the PMOS device sizes:

$$R_P = R_{eqp} \times \frac{L}{W} = 30 \text{ k}\Omega \times \frac{L}{W} = 1.4 \text{ k}\Omega \Rightarrow \frac{W_P}{L_P} = 21$$

Since $L = 0.1 \ \mu$m, we now have the sizes that satisfy the design specifications:

$$\frac{W_N}{L_N} = \frac{0.875 \ \mu\text{m}}{0.1 \ \mu\text{m}} \qquad \frac{W_P}{L_P} = \frac{2.1 \ \mu\text{m}}{0.1 \ \mu\text{m}}$$

For the pseudo-NMOS gate, we prioritize V_{OL} in the sizing process since it is a ratioed circuit. We can satisfy the V_{OH} requirement by choosing $V_{DD} = 1.2$ V. The sizing of the NMOS device should be the same as in the CMOS case since its timing requirement is the same. We can satisfy the power and area requirements by meeting but not exceeding the V_{OL} and t_{PHL} requirements. To compute the PMOS device size, use (4.21):

$$\frac{W_P v_{sat} C_{ox}(V_{DD} - |V_{TP}|)^2}{(V_{DD} - |V_{TP}|) + E_{CP}L_P} = \frac{W_N}{L_N} \frac{\mu_n C_{ox}}{\left(1 + \frac{V_{OL}}{E_{CN}L_N}\right)}\left[(V_{DD} - V_{TN})(V_{OL}) - \frac{(V_{OL})^2}{2}\right]$$

Using this equation, we apply the known values and solve for W_P:

$$\frac{W_P 8(10^6)(1.6)(10^{-6})(1.2 - 0.4)^2}{(1.2 - 0.4) + 2.4}$$

$$= 8.75 \times \frac{430 \ \mu A/V^2}{\left(1 + (0.065/0.6)\right)}\left[(1.2 - 0.4)(0.065) - \frac{(0.065)^2}{2}\right]$$

$$\therefore W_P = 0.665 \ \mu m$$

Based on this result, we can specify the device sizes:

$$\frac{W_N}{L_N} = \frac{0.875 \ \mu m}{0.1 \ \mu m} \qquad \frac{W_P}{L_P} = \frac{0.665 \ \mu m}{0.1 \ \mu m}$$

For the pseudo-NMOS case, the two device sizes are about the same. This implies that t_{PLH} will be well above 100 ps (i.e., more than twice as large as t_{PHL}). This is the price that must be paid for using this type of load. There will also be more power dissipated with the output low as in the NMOS load cases. However, the area is far less than CMOS for high-fanin gate circuits, as will be seen later.

4.9 Tristate Inverters

To close out this chapter, we introduce a special type of inverter or buffer used in situations where a bus is to be driven by multiple drivers. In addition to driving the bus high or low, the inverter must be able to assume a high-impedance state at the output so that it is effectively disconnected from the bus. This can be achieved with the inverter configuration shown in Figure 4.16. In this circuit, there are two additional transistors that can be enabled or disabled with the *EN* signal and its complement. When *EN* is high, both the *p*-channel and *n*-channel devices are *on*. The inverter operates as a regular inverter except that there are two transistors in the signal path.

When the *EN* signal is low, both the *p*-channel and *n*-channel devices are turned off and the output enters a high-impedance condition (sometimes called a *high-Z* state). The inverter no longer controls the output voltage. Rather, some other bus driver can set the value of the bus. Typically, only one set of drivers should be driving a bus at a given point in time. Otherwise, conflicts would arise if multiple drivers try to gain control of the bus at the same time. If no other driver is controlling the bus, the previous value is stored at the output. Therefore, the *EN* signal is critical in determining when a given driver exercises control or relinquishes control of the bus. Other forms of tristate drivers exist and will be described later in the book.

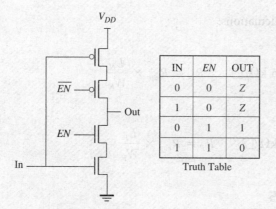

IN	EN	OUT
0	0	Z
1	0	Z
0	1	1
1	1	0

Truth Table

Figure 4.16
Tristate buffer.

4.10   Summary

Useful technology parameters for 0.18 μm CMOS:

$$\mu_n = 270 \text{ cm}^2/\text{V-s}, \quad \mu_p = 70 \text{ cm}^2/\text{V-s}, \quad t_{ox} = 35 \text{ Å},$$

$$C_{ox} = 1.0 \ \mu\text{F/cm}^2, \quad V_{TN} = 0.5 \text{ V}, \quad V_{TP} = -0.5 \text{ V}$$

$$E_{CN}L = 1.2 \text{ V}, \quad E_{CP}L = 4.8 \text{ V}, \quad v_{sat} = 8 \times 10^6 \text{ cm/s},$$

$$V_{DD} = 1.8 \text{ V}, \quad 2|\phi_F| = 0.85 \text{ V}, \quad \gamma = 0.3 V^{1/2}, L = 2\lambda = 200 \text{ nm}$$

Useful technology parameters for 0.13 μm CMOS:

$$\mu_n = 270 \text{ cm}^2/\text{V-s}, \quad \mu_p = 70 \text{ cm}^2/\text{V-s}, \quad t_{ox} = 22 \text{ Å},$$

$$C_{ox} = 1.6 \ \mu\text{F/cm}^2, \quad V_{TN} = 0.4 \text{ V}, \quad V_{TP} = -0.4 \text{ V}$$

$$E_{CN}L = 0.6 \text{ V}, \quad E_{CP}L = 2.4 \text{ V}, \quad v_{sat} = 8 \times 10^6 \text{ cm/s},$$

$$V_{DD} = 1.2 \text{ V}, \quad 2|\phi_F| = 0.88 \text{ V}, \quad \gamma = 0.2 V^{1/2}, L = 2\lambda = 100 \text{ nm}$$

CMOS noise margins:

• Single-Source Noise Margins

$$\begin{aligned} SSNM_H &= V_{OH} - V_S \\ SSNM_L &= V_S - V_{OL} \end{aligned} \quad V_S \cong \frac{V_{DD} - |V_{TP}| + \chi V_{TN}}{1 + \chi} \quad \chi = \sqrt{\frac{W_N/E_{CN}L_N}{W_P/E_{CP}L_P}}$$

• Multiple-Source Noise Margins

$$NM_H = V_{OH} - V_{IH}$$
$$NM_L = V_{IL} - V_{OL}$$

On resistance calculations:

- NMOS

$$R_{eqn} = 12.5 \text{ k}\Omega/\square \qquad R_N = R_{eqn} \times \frac{L_N}{W_N}$$

- PMOS

$$R_{eqp} = 30 \text{ k}\Omega/\square \qquad R_P = R_{eqp} \times \frac{L_P}{W_P}$$

REFERENCES

A long list of references exists for this material. Here are a few recent ones.

1. S. M. Kang and Y. Leblebici, *CMOS Digital Integrated Circuits, Analysis and Design*, 3rd ed., McGraw-Hill, New York, NY, 2003.

2. J. Rabaey, *Digital Integrated Circuits: A Designer Perspective*, 2nd ed., Prentice-Hall, Upper Saddle River, NJ, 2003.

3. H. Veendrick, *Deep-Submicron CMOS ICs*, 2nd ed., Kluwer Academic Publishers, Boston, MA, 2000.

4. J. P. Uyemura, *CMOS Logic Circuit Design*, Kluwer Academic Publishers, Boston, MA, 1999.

PROBLEMS

All problems assume 0.13 μm technology parameters, although 0.18 μm technology may be used with the appropriate modifications.

P4.1. The circuits of Figure P4.1 show different implementations of an inverter whose output is connected to a capacitor.

(a) Which one of the circuits consumes static power when the input is high?

(b) Which one of the above circuits consumes static power when the input is low?

(c) V_{OH} of which circuit(s) is 1.2 V?

(d) V_{OL} of which circuit(s) is 0 V?

(e) The proper functionality of which circuit(s) depends on the size of the devices?

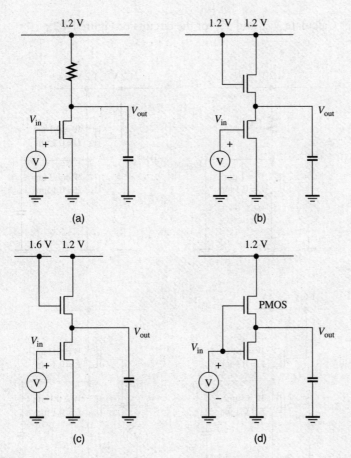

Figure P4.1

P4.2. Calculate V_{OH} and V_{OL} of the circuits of Figure P4.2.

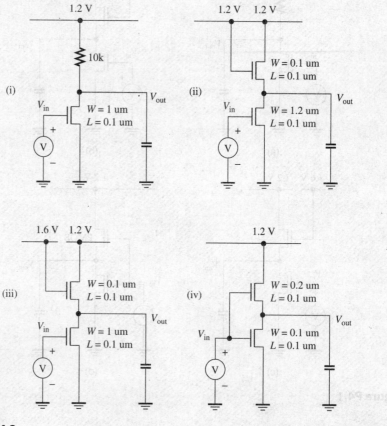

Figure P4.2

P4.3. Compute V_{IL} and V_{IH} of a CMOS inverter with device sizes $W_P = 16\lambda$ and $W_N = 4\lambda$, and one with $W_P = 8\lambda$ and $W_N = 4\lambda$. Compare the resulting multistage noise margins, NM_H and NM_L.

P4.4. A saturated enhancement load inverter has a pull-up and pull-down size of $W = 4\lambda$. Calculate V_{OH}, V_{OL}, V_{IH}, and V_{IL}. Compare your results with SPICE. Which values are not as accurate in relation to the SPICE results and why?

P4.5. Design a CMOS inverter with a switching voltage V_S of $\frac{2}{3}V_{DD}$. What is the resulting ratio of W_P/W_N?

P4.6. The circuit of Figure P4.6a has eight inverters in series:

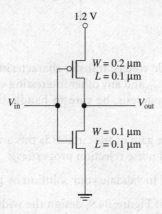

Figure P4.6a

Each inverter is designed as in Figure P4.6b:

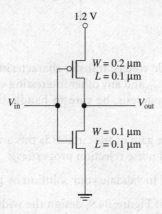

Figure P4.6b

If the input voltage is zero, the output of the first inverter will be 1.2 V. However, if the input is 0.45 V because of noise, the output deviates from 1.2 V. Using SPICE simulation, determine after how many stages of inverters, the deviation of the output signal is less than 2%. At what value of input does the inverter chain flip its output values?

P4.7. A new logic family is proposed whereby the NMOS device acts as a load device and the PMOS device acts as the inverting device, as shown in Figure P4.7. What are the advantages and disadvantages of this *pseudo-PMOS* architecture over the pseudo-NMOS architecture?

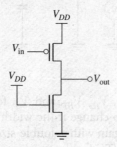

Figure P4.7
A pseudo-PMOS device.

P4.8. (a) What is the intended function of the circuit shown in Figure P4.8? What is the output swing?

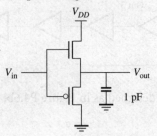

Figure P4.8

(b) Draw the dc voltage transfer characteristic of the above gate. Label V_{OL} and V_{OH}, and any other interesting values in the VTC. Since the gate has hysteresis, be sure to handle both the rising and falling cases.

(c) What is the gain of the circuit? Is this a valid gate (i.e., does it have the needed noise rejection properties)?

(d) Use SPICE to validate your solution by plotting the VTC.

P4.9. In the circuits of Figure P4.9, design the widths of the pull-down transistors so that $V_{OL} = 0.1$ V. (All transistors are minimum size, $L = 0.1$ μm.) Explain the results.

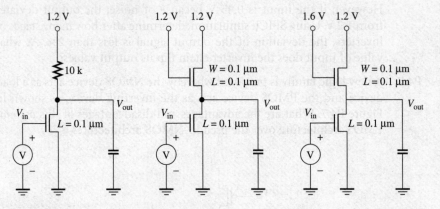

Figure P4.9

P4.10. Calculate V_{OH}, V_{OL}, V_{IL}, V_{IH}, and V_S, for Figure P4.10. How do you expect each value to change if the width of the PMOS transistor doubles? Calculate V_S again with a double-sized PMOS device to verify your answer. Sketch the VTC for the two cases.

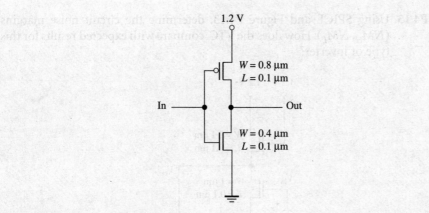

Figure P4.10

P4.11. Compute the peak dc current of the inverter of Figure P4.10. At what voltage does this occur?

P4.12. For the circuits of Figure P4.12, compute the ratio of W_D/W_L for the following cases, given that $V_{in} = 1.2$ V:

(a) $V_{out} = V_{OL} = 0.1$ V

(b) $V_{out} = V_{TN} = 0.4$ V

(c) $V_{out} = V_S \cong 0.6$ V

What happens to the ratio as the desired output voltage increases?

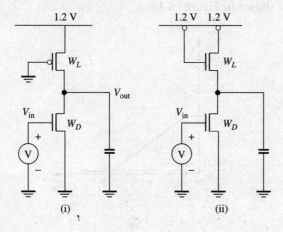

Figure P4.12

P4.13. Using SPICE and Figure P4.13, determine the circuit noise margins (NM_H, NM_L). How does the VTC compare with expected results for this type of inverter?

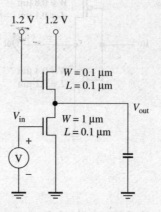

Figure P4.13

P4.14. Design a static CMOS inverter with

(a) $V_S = 0.6 \, V_{DD}$

(b) $V_S = 0.4 \, V_{DD}$

(c) What happens to the propagation delays in these two cases? Compute t_{PHL} and t_{PLH}. Explain the tradeoffs.

P4.15. A new type of logic gate is designed with the voltage transfer characteristics shown in Figure P4.15.

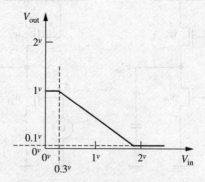

Figure P4.15

(a) Does this inverter have the regenerative property. Why or why not?

(b) Consider a chain of such gates with 100 stages. For an input of 0^v, what is the output of the last inverter?

(c) How much noise can the inverter tolerate? Is it possible to define the noise margin for this gate?

P4.16. The two CMOS circuits of Figure P4.16 are intended to be tristate buffers. Do both of these gates work as tristate buffers? Is one better than the other? Explain.

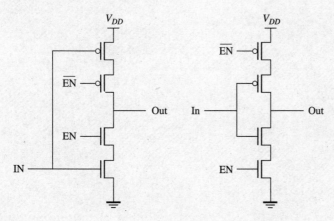

Figure P4.16

CHAPTER

5

Static MOS Gate Circuits

5.1   Introduction

This chapter addresses the design of combinational and sequential CMOS static logic gates. The material is built upon the foundations established in Chapter 4. In this chapter, we will continue to view the transistor as a logic switch with series resistance. For a unit-sized NMOS device, the series resistance is approximately 12.5 kΩ, whereas a unit-sized PMOS device is approximately 30 kΩ. These large-signal resistance values represent the average on-resistances when switching from high to low or low to high. Using the concepts of switch-based logic design, we can construct combinational logic gates such as NANDs, NORs, XORs, and multiplexers. We will examine the operation of these gates in detail and then study the voltage transfer characteristics (VTC), transistor sizing, first-order timing characteristics, and power. Extensions of switch-based networks can be used to implement complex logic functions in a single CMOS stage through the application of the duality principle and DeMorgan's Laws.

Sequential logic elements have the ability to store information. The outputs of a sequential block are functions of both input and output values. As such, they are characterized by positive feedback loops between the outputs and inputs. In this chapter, the definitions and distinctions between two types of sequential elements, flip-flops and latches, are reviewed. Sequential circuits are constructed using conventional CMOS or pseudo-NMOS logic. In later chapters, we use clever techniques to reduce the number of transistors needed to implement these functions. The basic operation, limitations, and timing constraints for a variety of sequential elements are examined, including SR latches, JK flip-flops, D flip-flops, and D latches. We also describe certain timing constraints, the so-called set-up and hold times, for D-type flip-flops and latches.

Power and timing are the two main design specifications for digital integrated circuits. In this chapter, we explore the relationships between these two factors. We seek to minimize power and reduce delay as much as possible, but usually one is traded off against the other. Circuit activity is a key factor in the total power dissipation. Reducing the activity of a chip is the best way of reducing dynamic (or switching) power in CMOS circuits. This can be accomplished most effectively by choosing logic architectures that exhibit low activity. In addition, the arrival times of signals at gate inputs should be made equal to minimize glitches that unnecessarily contribute to power consumption. Further, the rise and fall times of all signals should be equalized, wherever possible, to limit power due to short-circuit current flow during switching. Power consumption of most circuits can also be decreased by reducing the operating voltage. This is the main reason why the supply voltage is reduced in each technology generation.[1] However, the threshold voltage has not been scaling as rapidly in order to control subthreshold leakage. When many millions of transistors are sitting idle but leaking current, it contributes significantly to the static (or standby) power consumption.

Since power and timing are usually traded off when designing circuits, a metric is needed to establish the goodness of a design relative to these two factors. To improve a design, we should try to reduce both power and delay. Therefore, a useful metric can be devised by multiplying the power by the delay to obtain a power-delay product, which is a measure of the energy needed to perform a given logic operation. This metric is most valuable when comparing single gate configurations that use the same supply voltage and drive the same load. However, it suffers from some limitations if used to compare the power of two different designs that perform the same function. A more effective metric when comparing two designs is the energy-delay product. This metric is obtained by multiplying the energy (i.e., power-delay product) by delay.

---

[1] Roughly speaking, the power supply voltage (in volts) is 10 times the technology generation (given in microns). For example, a 3.3 V supply is used in a 0.35 μm technology, a 1.8 V supply in a 0.18 μm technology, and a 1.2 V supply in a 0.13 μm technology.

In this chapter, basic static NAND and NOR gate circuits are described in Section 5.2 with emphasis on gate sizing, voltage transfer characteristics, and fanin/fanout considerations. Section 5.3 illustrates how complex functions can be implemented in a single CMOS stage using duality and DeMorgan's Law. The other useful logic functions such as XOR, XNOR, and multiplexers are described in Sections 5.4 and 5.5, respectively. Basic sequential circuit elements are explored in Sections 5.6 and 5.7. To conclude the chapter, we examine the important components of power dissipation in Section 5.8, and power-delay tradeoffs in Section 5.9.

5.2   CMOS Gate Circuits

To build NOR and NAND gates in CMOS is rather straightforward. We use the switch-level concepts that two NMOS transistors in series perform a logical AND function and two NMOS transistors in parallel perform a logical OR function. Similarly, two PMOS transistors in parallel perform an AND function and two PMOS transistors in series perform an OR function. The resulting circuits for the 2-input NOR and 2-input NAND gates are illustrated in Figure 5.1. For the 2-input NOR gate of Figure 5.1a, the output is pulled low if either A or B is high. This requires two pull-down devices in parallel. However, both inputs must be low to produce a high output. This requires two series p-channel devices connected from the output to V_{DD}. All NMOS devices have their bulk terminals connected to Gnd, while the PMOS devices have their bulk nodes connected to V_{DD}.

For the 2-input NAND gate of Figure 5.1b, the output is low only if both A and B are high. This implies two series-connected n-channel devices from the output to ground. On the other hand, if either input is low, then the output will go high. This can be implemented with two parallel p-channel devices connected from V_{DD} to the output. The extension to multiple input gates follows along the same lines. Specifically, for a multiple *fanin* NOR gate, we would have many parallel NMOS devices

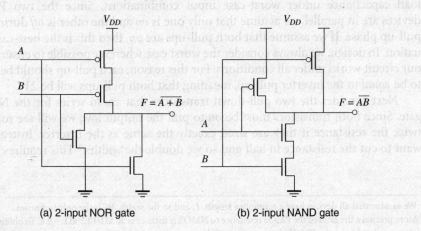

(a) 2-input NOR gate   (b) 2-input NAND gate

Figure 5.1
CMOS NOR and NAND gates.

and a *stack* of series-connected PMOS devices. For the NAND gate with multiple inputs, we would have a *stack* of NMOS devices connected to the output, and an equal number of parallel PMOS devices connected to the output.

Exercise 5.1	Draw 3-input and 4-input NOR and NAND gates. We often refer to these gates with names such as NAND3, NOR3, NAND4, and NOR4 for convenience. Explain how they each work. Do you see any problems arising as you increase the number of fanins (inputs) to 10?

5.2.1 Basic CMOS Gate Sizing

Now consider transistor sizing of CMOS logic gates, specifically NANDs and NORs. As mentioned before, transistor sizing is the process of specifying the widths of the transistors in the logic gates.[2] When we studied the inverter in the previous chapter, it was clear that device sizes control the rise and fall propagation delays in static CMOS. This is the primary reason why we specify the sizes of the transistors. To obtain approximately equal rise/fall delays, we found that the PMOS device must be roughly twice the size of the NMOS device. This is because its on-resistance for PMOS is roughly double that of the NMOS device.[3] For the time being, we will use the 2:1 ratio. Later, we will elaborate on the best ratio for the pull-up and pull-down transistors.

Given the 2:1 device sizes for the inverter of Figure 5.2a, we can now determine the transistor sizes in multifanin gates. Assume for the moment that all gates drive a single load capacitance, C_L and that we want to obtain the same delay as the inverter for the rise/fall cases. First, consider the NAND gate in Figure 5.2b. There are two parallel PMOS devices and two series NMOS devices. Sizing the four transistors is based on achieving the same delay as the inverter when driving the same load capacitance under worst-case input combinations. Since the two PMOS devices are in parallel, we assume that only one is *on* and the other is *off* during the pull-up phase. If we assume that both pull-ups are *on*, then this is the best-case situation. In design, we always consider the worst case wherever possible to ensure that our circuit works under all conditions. For this reason, each pull-up should be sized to be *equal* to the inverter pull-up, meaning that both pull-ups will be $2W$.

Next consider the two pull-down transistors that are in series for the NAND gate. Since both transistors must be *on* to pull the output low, we will see roughly twice the resistance if they are sized exactly the same as the inverter. Instead, we want to cut the resistance in half and so we double the widths.[4] This requires a size

---

[2] We assume that all devices have a minimum length, L, and so the width, W, is the only unknown.

[3] More precisely, the ratio of the PMOS resistance to NMOS resistance is 30 kΩ/12.5 kΩ = 2.4. To obtain equal delays we should size the PMOS device to be 2.4X larger than the NMOS device. However, we will find that there are a number of factors that make a 2:1 ratio a better choice. In fact, this 2:1 ratio was also the preferred ratio in the past due to mobility considerations.

[4] Recall that resistance is inversely proportional to the width.

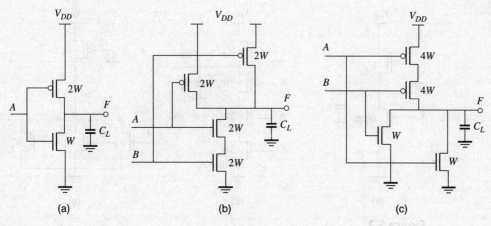

Figure 5.2
Device sizes for CMOS (a) inverter, (b) NAND, and (c) NOR gates.

of $2W$ for both pull-down devices.[5] As a result, all four devices in the NAND gate are $2W$ devices.

Similar considerations apply to the NOR gate of Figure 5.2c. Here the PMOS devices are in series and the NMOS devices are in parallel. Using the same arguments, both NMOS devices should be set to W to match the pull-down delay of the inverter in the worst case. The PMOS devices need to be doubled relative to the inverter case since they are in series. This leads to two $4W$ devices in series for the pull-up case to effectively cut the resistance in half for each device.

The same approach would be used to size multi-input pseudo-NMOS gates. The pseudo-NMOS inverter was covered in Chapter 4 and is shown again in Figure 5.3a. The size of the pull-up device is set to W_p and the pull-down device to W_n. The ratio of W_n/W_p depends primarily on the desired V_{OL}. For pseudo-NMOS gates, only the NMOS devices need to be sized since there is one PMOS pull-up and its size would remain the same as in the pseudo-NMOS inverter[6] of Figure 5.3a.

Consider sizing 3-input pseudo-NMOS NAND and NOR gates. For the NAND gate of Figure 5.3b, we would use devices with size $3W_n$; that is, use devices that are three times larger than its inverter counterpart. The reason is that there are three resistors in series and we must increase the size of the transistors by three to reduce the effective resistance of the pull-down path to that of the inverter. For the NOR gate of Figure 5.3c, the pull-down devices would all be the same size as the pseudo-NMOS inverter case since they are in parallel. Again, the worst-case condition has only one transistor pulling down, not all three. Therefore, the size must be set with this in mind.

The sizing of the NAND gate of Figure 5.3b can be understood from two other perspectives. First, it can be viewed from a layout perspective, as shown in Figure 5.4.

---

[5] This is true for long channel devices. More accurate device sizes would include velocity saturation effects but they are not considered until Chapter 6.

[6] There is an assumption here that the only capacitance is a single output loading C_L.

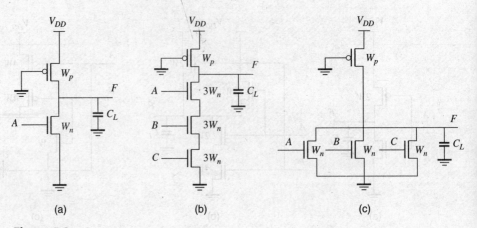

(a) **(b)** **(c)**

Figure 5.3
Device sizing for pseudo-NMOS (a) inverter, (b) NAND, and (c) NOR gates.

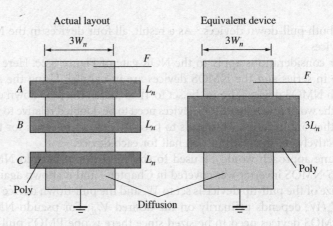

Figure 5.4
Layout and equivalent size of 3X device.

The layout of the NMOS series stack is given on the left, with three inputs, A, B, and C, on the poly layer. One diffusion region is defined with a width of $3W_n$, and three transistors with length L_n are created. The output F is identified at the top of the stack. When the inputs are connected together, the three devices in series can be merged to produce one "super" device with a size of $3W_n/3L_n$. This produces an effective size of W_n/L_n, which is equivalent to the size for the pseudo-NMOS pull-down of the inverter. Note that the sizing achieves the same delay characteristics as the inverter but also produces the same V_{OL}. In other words, we size pseudo-NMOS gates for both V_{OL} and timing when we choose the W/L ratios for the individual devices.

Another way to view the sizing of series stacks is to recall that the transistor on-resistance is inversely proportional to W. Larger values of W decrease the series resistance of the transistor. What if we had three different W values in the series stack? When determining an equivalent W_{eq}, one can use the fact that the W values would combine as if we had parallel resistance.[7] For example, if we have three transistors in series with widths W_1, W_2, and W_3, we would combine them together to form an equivalent device with a width

$$W_{eq} = \frac{W_1 W_2 W_3}{W_1 W_2 + W_2 W_3 + W_3 W_1} \qquad \text{(series stack, all devices on)} \qquad (5.1)$$

This value can be used to determine on-resistance of the combined devices. For the case when all W's are equal to $3W_n$, this reduces to W_n, as expected.

In the case of a NOR gate, if all parallel pull-down devices are on simultaneously, the W values would combine as if we had series resistance to produce the equivalent value, W_{eq}:

$$W_{eq} = W_1 + W_2 + W_3 \qquad \text{(parallel devices, all devices on)} \qquad (5.2)$$

Of course, we design the NOR gate assuming that only one pull-down device is *on* at a time, since this is the worst case.

3-Input NAND and NOR Gate Sizing

Example 5.1

Problem:

Determine the device sizes for 3-input NAND and NOR gates in conventional CMOS. Assume that the basic inverter is sized according to Figure 5.2a and that the goal of the design is to have NAND3 and NOR3 gates with the same delay characteristics as the inverter.

Solution:

Applying the considerations given in the above section, we derive the following sizes for the NAND3 and NOR3, respectively.

---

[7] Here we make use of the inverse relationship between R and W. The series stack produces series resistance, not parallel resistance!

Exercise 5.2   Determine the device sizes for NAND4 and NOR4 gates (i.e., 4-input versions of each type of gate). When you draw the two circuits, notice how high the series stacks are getting. We usually do not see 5-input gates because of the height of the series stacks and the corresponding resistances and layout areas.

5.2.2 Fanin and Fanout Considerations

When designing standard CMOS logic gates, it should be noted that there is a significant penalty for gates with a large number of inputs, so-called high *fanin* gates. This is due to the resistance of series stacks. Beyond 3 or 4 inputs, the resistance will be too high or the area will be too large. Consider the case of an 8-input AND gate. What is the best way to implement such a gate? It is certainly not as a single NAND with eight inputs followed by an inverter. The eight series NMOS devices would have to be very large to lower the resistance, as shown in Figure 5.5. However, the delay would still be unacceptable since the series stack would behave as an RC ladder circuit, due to the resistance and self-capacitance[8] of each transistor.

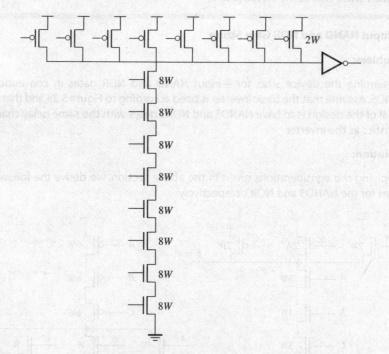

Figure 5.5
Eight-input AND gate.

---

[8] Self-capacitance effects would introduce a capacitor at each internal node of the series stack. These issues will be described in Chapter 6.

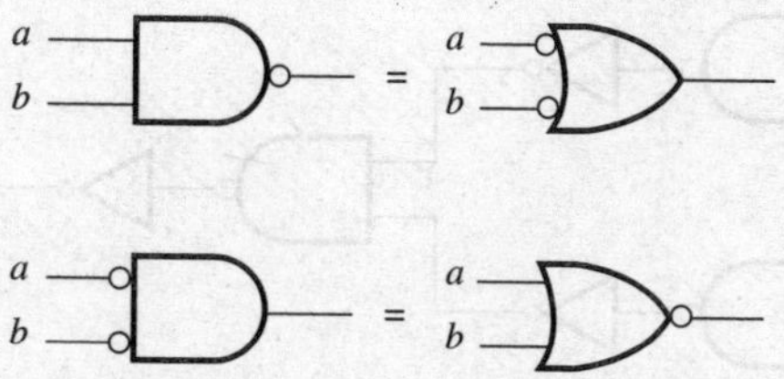

Figure 5.6

Schematic rendition of DeMorgan's Law.

One alternative is to use DeMorgan's Laws and a pseudo-NMOS NOR gate to replace the AND gate. DeMorgan's Laws, in the most basic form, can be stated as

$$\overline{(a + b)} = \bar{a} \cdot \bar{b}$$

$$\overline{(a \cdot b)} = \bar{a} + \bar{b} \qquad\qquad (5.3)$$

Graphically, we can represent the two equations as shown in Figure 5.6.

The application of DeMorgan's Law for the AND8 is shown in Figure 5.7a. Here the inputs to the AND gate are all inverted. We will need additional inverters at each input but they are not shown. The AND gate is converted to an 8-input NOR. The pseudo-NMOS implementation is shown in Figure 5.7b. This gate dissipates more power than the static implementation and exhibits a larger t_{PLH}. But the area is greatly reduced relative to the 8-input CMOS NAND because we only have one pull-up device, the pull-downs are much smaller, and the t_{PHL} is significantly lower.

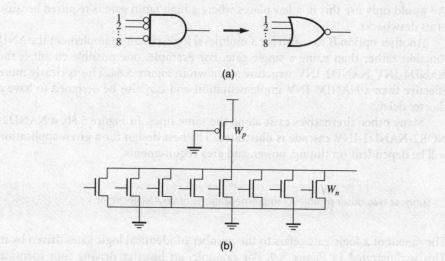

(a)

(b)

Figure 5.7

Using DeMorgan's Law to convert AND to NOR.

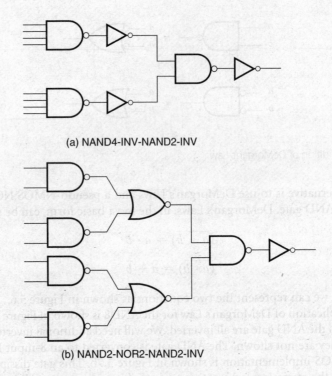

(a) NAND4-INV-NAND2-INV

(b) NAND2-NOR2-NAND2-INV

Figure 5.8
Multilevel logic implementation of an AND8 function.

We would only use this in a few places where a high fanin gate is required because of its drawbacks.

Another option is to construct a multilevel logic circuit to implement the AND function rather than using a single gate. For example, one possible circuit is the NAND4-INV-NAND2-INV structure as shown in Figure 5.8a. This is clearly more effective than a NAND8-INV implementation and can also be designed to have a shorter delay.

Many other alternatives exist along the same lines. In Figure 5.8b, a NAND2-NOR2-NAND2-INV cascade is illustrated. The best design for a given application will be dependent on timing, power, and area requirements.

Exercise 5.3   Suggest two other multilevel implementations of an AND8 circuit.

The *fanout* of a logic gate refers to the number of identical logic gates driven by it. This is illustrated in Figure 5.9. For example, an inverter driving four identical inverters is called a fanout-of-four (FO4) inverter. The fanout ratio is obtained by taking the total capacitance driven by the gate and dividing it by the input capacitance of the gate. When *cell libraries* are designed, the sizes of the devices must be

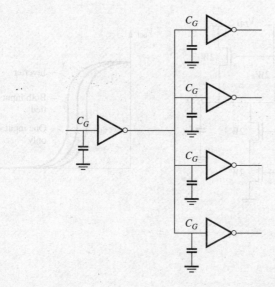

Figure 5.9
An inverter driving four identical fanouts.

specified without knowing the actual load being driven. Typically, gates are designed to drive a specific number of fanouts to deliver a specific target delay. In fact, different cells are designed to drive a different number of loads. Ultimately, the choice of the width, W, is based on this fanout ratio, as will be seen in Chapter 6.

5.2.3 Voltage Transfer Characteristics (VTC) of CMOS Gates

The VTC of CMOS gates are very similar to that of the CMOS inverter. Since there are multiple inputs, the actual characteristics depend on how the inputs are switched. For the 2-input NAND gate, shown in Figure 5.10, we first consider the case when one input is held high while the other is switched from low to high. In this case, one p-channel device can be removed from consideration (open circuit) while one n-channel device can be handled as a short-circuit since it behaves like a small resistor. If input A is held high while input B is switched from low to high, the gate is equivalent to an inverter with a $2W$ pull-up device and a $2W$ pull-down device. The resulting transfer characteristic would shift to the left of the standard inverter. If both inputs were switched together, we would have a $4W$ pull-up device and a W pull-down device, so the VTC would shift to the right of the standard inverter. These two curves are shown in Figure 5.10 relative to the standard inverter.

For the 2-input NOR gate, shown again in Figure 5.11, we would obtain similar results. Assume that input $B = 0$, while the A input is switched from low to high. In this case, one n-channel device can be removed from consideration (open circuit) while one p-channel device can be treated as a short-circuit. This implies that we have an equivalent inverter with a $4W$ pull-up device and a W pull-down device.

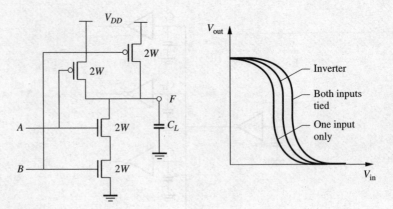

Figure 5.10
VTC for NAND2 gate.

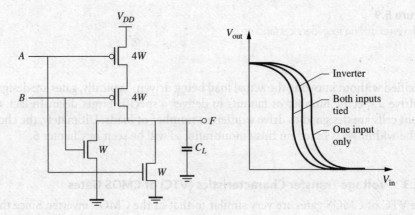

Figure 5.11
VTC for NOR gate.

Therefore, the V_S should shift to the right of a standard 1X inverter VTC. A second case exists when both inputs are connected together and switched from low to high. We have effectively a $2W$ pull-up and a $2W$ pull-down, which would produce a switching threshold, V_S, that is shifted to the left of the standard inverter. These results are illustrated in Figure 5.11.

Similar considerations would apply to multiple input NAND and NOR gates. Each individual input, if applied separately, produces a slightly different VTC (but not significantly different). In any case, the single-input switching case is usually taken as the VTC of the gate. From inspection of Figures 5.10 and 5.11, the NOR gate has a higher switching threshold than the NAND gate, and therefore NM_L is higher and NM_H is lower for the NOR gate as compared to the NAND gate.

SPICE Example of VTC for NAND Gate in 0.18 μm Technology　　　　　**Example 5.2**

Problem:

(a) Compute the switching threshold, V_S, of a 2-input NAND gate shown in Figure 5.10 under two conditions: with one input tied to V_{DD} while the other input is swept from 0 to V_{DD} and a second case where both inputs are tied together. Assume 0.18 μm technology parameters with all transistor widths set to 400 nm.

(b) Using SPICE, compare the VTC curves of a 2-input NAND for the two cases above and compare the switching threshold results. Also include the two inputs, A and B, switching separately. Why are the results slightly different for each input?

Solution:

(a) When one input is high and the other is varied from 0 to V_{DD}, it is equivalent to having a pull-up with $W_P = 400$ nm and a pull-down of $W_N = 400$ nm (treat the other one as a very small resistor):

$W_N = 400$ nm, $\quad W_P = 400$ nm:

$$X = \sqrt{\frac{W_N/E_{CN}L_N}{W_P/E_{Cp}L_P}} = \sqrt{\frac{W_N E_{CP}}{W_P E_{CN}}} = \sqrt{\frac{(400)(24)}{(400)(6)}} = 2.0$$

$$V_S = \frac{1.8 - 0.5 + (0.5)2.0}{1 + 2.0} = 0.77 \text{ V}$$

When both inputs are varied from 0 to V_{DD}, it is equivalent to having a pull-up with $W_P = 800$ nm and a pull-down of 200 nm:

$W_P = 800$ nm, $\quad W_P = 200$ nm:

$$X = \sqrt{\frac{W_N/E_{CN}L_N}{W_P/E_{Cp}L_P}} = \sqrt{\frac{W_N E_{CP}}{W_P E_{CN}}} = \sqrt{\frac{(200)(24)}{(800)(6)}} = 1.0$$

$$V_S = \frac{1.8 - 0.5 + (0.5)1.0}{1 + 1.0} = 0.9 \text{ V}$$

(b) To compare the results against SPICE, use the following descriptions:

```
*NAND Gate with one input B tied to Vdd, input A switching
*Set supply and library
.param Supply=1.8                      *for 0.18 technology
.lib    'bsim3v3.cmosp18.lib'
.opt scale=0.1u                        *Set lambda
*Power supply
.global         Vdd     Gnd
Vdd             Vdd     Gnd     'Supply' *Supply is set by .lib call
```

```
*Top level simulation netlist
mpa     out  A      Vdd      Vdd      PMOS1  l=2  w=4  ad=20  pd=4  as=20  ps=4
mpb     out  Vdd    Vdd      Vdd      PMOS1  l=2  w=4  ad=20  pd=4  as=20  ps=4
mna     out  A      x        Gnd      NMOS1  l=2  w=4  ad=20  pd=4  as=20  ps=4
mnb     x    Vdd    Gnd      Gnd      NMOS1  l=2  w=4  ad=20  pd=4  as=20  ps=4
Vin     A    Gnd    'Supply'
* Simulation
.dc     Vin  0      'Supply'          'Supply/50'
.plot   dc   V(out)
.end


*NAND Gate with input A tied to Vdd, input B switching
*Set supply and library
.param Supply=1.8              *for 0.18 technology
.lib    'bsim3v3.cmosp18.lib'
.opt scale=0.1u               *Set lambda
*Power supply
.global               Vdd     Gnd
Vdd             Vdd  Gnd      'Supply' *Supply is set by .lib call
*Top level simulation netlist
mpa     out  Vdd    Vdd      Vdd      PMOS1  l=2  w=4  ad=20  pd=4  as=20  ps=4
mpb     out  B      Vdd      Vdd      PMOS1  l=2  w=4  ad=20  pd=4  as=20  ps=4
mna     out  Vdd    x        Gnd      NMOS1  l=2  w=4  ad=20  pd=4  as=20  ps=4
mnb     x    B      Gnd      Gnd      NMOS1  l=2  w=4  ad=20  pd=4  as=20  ps=4
Vin     B    Gnd    'Supply'
*Simulation
.dc     Vin  0      'Supply'          'Supply/50'
.plot   dc   V(out)
.end


*NAND Gate with both inputs tied together
*Set supply and library
.param Supply=1.8              *for 0.18 technology
.lib    'bsim3v3.cmosp18.lib'
.opt scale=0.1u               *Set lambda
*Power supply
.global Vdd    Gnd
Vdd             Vdd  Gnd      'Supply'       *Supply is set by .lib call
*Top level simulation netlist
mpa     out  in     Vdd      Vdd      PMOS1  l=2  w=4  ad=20  pd=4  as=20  ps=4
mpb     out  in     Vdd      Vdd      PMOS1  l=2  w=4  ad=20  pd=4  as=20  ps=4
mna     out  in     x        Gnd      NMOS1  l=2  w=4  ad=20  pd=4  as=20  ps=4
mnb     x    in     Gnd      Gnd      NMOS1  l=2  w=4  ad=20  pd=4  as=20  ps=4
```

```
Vin     in     Gnd     'Supply'
*Simulation
.dc     Vin     0       'Supply'        'Supply/50'
.plot   dc      V(out)
.end
```

The following results are produced by SPICE:

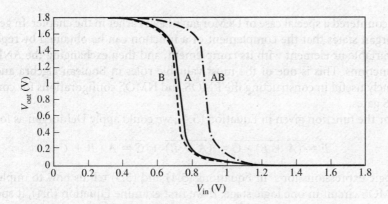

As expected, the curve with both inputs tied is to the right of the curve for single inputs. From SPICE, $V_S = 0.745$ V for input A switching, $V_S = 0.721$ V for input B switching, and $V_S = 0.883$ V for the case where the two inputs are tied together. These are close to the hand calculated values. The hand calculations tend to produce slightly higher values due to the approximations made to simplify the expression for V_S. The reason why input A produces a slightly higher value of V_S is that the corresponding transistor experiences body effect during the switching process.

5.3   Complex CMOS Gates

There are many situations where we would like to implement more complicated functions than just NANDs and NORs. For example, if we wanted to realize the logic for

$$F = \overline{(A + B) \cdot C} \tag{5.4}$$

we could implement it as a series of multilevel logic gates consisting of ANDs, ORs, and inverters. However, CMOS lends itself to efficient implementation of such functions through the use of *duality* and *DeMorgan's Laws*. Implementations of this variety are referred to as AND-OR-INVERT (AOI) and OR-AND-INVERT (OAI) gates. Consider the fact that in a NAND gate, we have parallel PMOS devices and series NMOS devices. These are duals of each other. Similarly, NOR gates have parallel NMOS devices and series PMOS devices. Again, these are duals of each other.

The dual of any logic function can be obtained by exchanging the AND and OR operations. For example, the following functions are duals:

$$ab \Leftrightarrow a + b$$

$$(a + b)c \Leftrightarrow ab + c$$

We encountered a special case of DeMorgan's Laws earlier in the chapter. In general, DeMorgan states that the complement of a function can be obtained by replacing each variable or element with its complement, and then exchanging the AND and OR functions. This is one of the most valuable rules in Boolean algebra and it is extremely useful in constructing the PMOS and NMOS configurations for complex CMOS gates.

For the function given in Equation (5.4), we could apply DeMorgan as follows:

$$F = \overline{(A + B) \cdot C} = \overline{(A + B)} + \overline{C} = \overline{A} \cdot \overline{B} + \overline{C} \qquad (5.5)$$

The logic expressions for F in Equations (5.4) and (5.5) tell us how to implement the CMOS circuit in one logic stage. If we first examine Equation (5.4), it specifies how the NMOS devices should be configured. Since the NMOS transistors act to pull the output low, we should complement F to obtain its implementation. The NMOS function is $\overline{F} = (A + B) \cdot C$. The NMOS implementation requires two parallel transistors with inputs A and B in series with a third transistor with input C.

Equation (5.5) reveals how we should implement the PMOS function. Since the PMOS function pulls the output high and the devices effectively complement each term, we should implement the function after a term-by-term complement. That is, we should implement $F = AB + C$ using the PMOS devices. This requires two series PMOS devices to implement AB and one parallel transistor with the input C. The resulting function is an OAI function, as shown in Figure 5.12.

To generalize the example shown above, we need to combine duality and DeMorgan to produce a desired function in a single stage. In fact, we need to construct two switch networks to implement a function in CMOS: a pull-down network (n-complex) and a pull-up network (p-complex), as shown Figure 5.13. The n-complex is defined as the complement of the function that sets the output to 0 due to an active path to Gnd. The p-complex is defined as the function of complemented variables that sets the output to 1 creating a path to V_{DD}. The two functions should be duals of one another (after each literal is complemented).

Algorithmically, we should take the given function F and produce the complement to obtain the function that we implement in the n-complex. The dual network should be used for the p-complex. This is obtained by exchanging AND and OR operations. A visual inspection of the two networks for the duality property can be carried out to check for correctness at the end of the process. Sizing the transistors follows the same steps as described for the basic NAND and NOR gates.

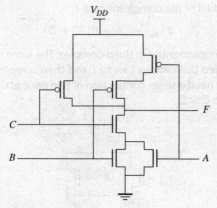

Figure 5.12

Complex CMOS gate implementation of $\overline{(A + B) \cdot C}$.

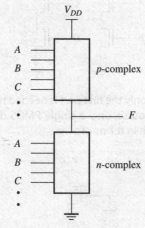

Figure 5.13

Generalized complex gate representation.

Complex CMOS Gate Circuits   **Example 5.3**

Problem:

Implement $F = \overline{AB + CD}$ as a single-stage complex CMOS gate and a pseudo-NMOS gate.

Solution:

For the CMOS gate: first complement F to obtain the n-complex function: $\overline{F} = AB + CD$. This implies that we need two series NMOS paths in parallel with one another. One series path implements AB while the other implements CD.

Next, take the dual of the complement of F:

$$\overline{F}|_{dual} = (A + B)(C + D)$$

This is the function implemented in the p-complex. The same expression would be obtained if we applied DeMorgan's Law to F and then complemented each literal. This implies that we need a series connection of two parallel devices, one with A or B and the other with C or D.

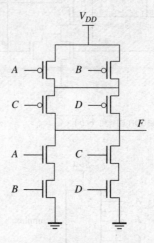

For the pseudo-NMOS gate, only the first part is needed to construct the n-complex. The pull-up network is, of course, only a single PMOS device. Clearly, this is more efficient than the CMOS case in terms of area.

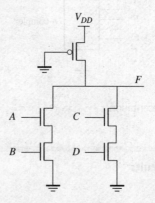

5.4 XOR and XNOR Gates

Two logic functions that are important in digital design are the XOR and the XNOR functions:

$$f_{XOR} = \overline{a}b + a\overline{b} = (XOR)$$

$$f_{XNOR} = \overline{a}\,\overline{b} + ab = (XNOR)$$

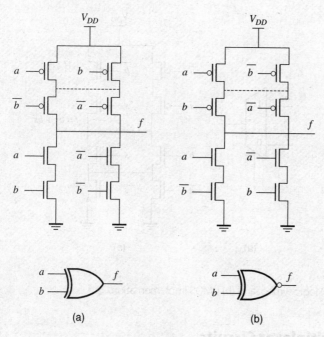

Figure 5.14

Static implementation of (a) XOR and (b) XNOR gates.

There are a variety of ways to implement these functions. A number of static versions of these gates will be presented here, while versions based on the CMOS transmission gate will be presented in later chapters.

The straightforward implementation assumes that we have access to a, $\bar{a}$, b, and $\bar{b}$. In that case, the implementations are simply based on the material in the above sections. The corresponding circuits are shown in Figure 5.14. For the XOR gate, we first complement the f_{XOR} function and use it to create the pull-down function. Therefore, two branches are needed, one for ab and the other for $\bar{a}\bar{b}$. The transistor configuration can be interpreted as follows: if both a and b are high, or a and b are low, the output is low. Otherwise, the output is high.

The pull-up branch implements the f_{XOR} function directly but replaces each term with its complement. The result is shown in Figure 5.14a. Note that the additional connection between the p-channel devices is unnecessary in this case (shown as a dotted line).

A similar process is used to obtain the XNOR gate of Figure 5.14b. In this case, the pull-down tree consists of the complement of f_{XNOR} with each branch implementing $\bar{a}b$ and $a\bar{b}$, respectively. This implies that if a and b are different, the output will be low. Otherwise it will be high. The pull-up network should implement the dual, with parallel connections in place of the series connections of the pull-down tree.

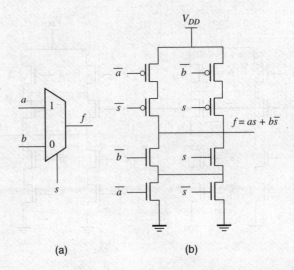

Figure 5.15
Multiplexer (a) logic symbol and (b) CMOS implementation.

5.5   Multiplexer Circuits

The multiplexer circuit produces an output by selecting one of N inputs. There are many ways to implement this type of circuit. We will examine transmission gate versions in Chapter 7. Here we examine the simplest possible multiplexer to select one out of two possible inputs. The function to be implemented is

$$f = as + b\bar{s} \quad (MUX)$$

where s is the selection signal and a and b are the two inputs. This function is reminiscent of the XOR and XNOR gates and can be implemented in a similar fashion as shown in Figure 5.15. The multiplexer is often referred to in its short form as the MUX.

5.6   Flip-Flops and Latches

In all logic circuits described so far, the output is directly related to the input by some logic combination. Typically, there are no feedback loops in these circuits, so the outputs are always a logical combination of the inputs. As a class, these circuits are known as *combinational logic circuits*.[9]

There is another class of circuits, known as *sequential logic circuits*, in which the new outputs also are dependent on the inputs and the preceding values of outputs. Examples are counters and data registers. A characteristic of static sequential circuits is that one or more output nodes are intentionally connected back to inputs to give *positive feedback*, or *regeneration*. This is the same type of regenerative property

---

[9] Some have been known to inadvertently use the term combinatorial circuits rather than the correct term: combinational circuits.

that was described for inverter chains, except that the signal propagates around feedback loops in sequential circuits.

Basic to sequential circuits is the *bistable circuit*. This type of circuit has two stable operating points. Prominent examples of the bistable circuit found in digital ICs are

1. Latches

2. Flip-flops

These two terms have been used interchangeably in the literature, but there is a fundamental difference between them. We will explore this difference in more detail throughout this section, but a brief explanation of the two types of elements is in order here. Latches propagate values from input to output continuously when enabled (typically by a clock signal) whereas flip-flops propagate values at discrete points in time (typically on the rising or falling edge of a clock). As such, latches are said to be *level-sensitive* or *transparent,* whereas flip-flops are said to be *edge-triggered.* This section will elaborate these concepts and include analysis and design of these circuits using CMOS technologies. The circuits can be implemented directly using the gates described above, although more efficient architectures are available as seen in later chapters.

5.6.1   Basic Bistable Circuit

We begin with a simple bistable circuit and progress to the elements that are used in mainstream chip design. Shown in Figure 5.16 are two cross-coupled logic inverters and a voltage transfer characteristic that is typical of such a circuit. The plotted VTC for Inverter 1, V_{out} versus V_{in}, and Inverter 2, V_{in} versus V_{out}, are shown on the same graph. Note that there are three possible operating points for the circuit: points A, B, and C. A and B are *stable operating points*, while C is an *unstable point* (sometimes referred to as a *metastable* point).

At point A, the low voltage level of V_{in} results in a high voltage level at V_{out}, which causes a low level at V_{in}. Similarly, the high voltage level of V_{in} at point B

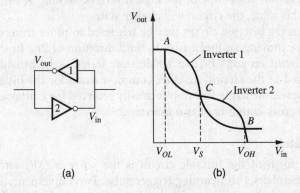

(a)   (b)

Figure 5.16

Cross-coupled inverters and corresponding VTC.

causes a low level at V_{out} which in turn reinforces the high level of V_{in}. Since these two operating conditions are self-consistent, A and B are considered to be stable points of operation. Alternatively, the gain of the two inverters at the two stable points is less than unity which keeps their outputs stable.

At point C, the slope is positive and greater than unity (in magnitude). Both Inverter 1 and 2 are conducting. As a result, point C is unstable since any small voltage change introduced into the circuit at, say, V_{in} will be amplified and *regenerated* around the circuit loop, causing the operating point to move to one of the two stable points. With V_{in} made positive with respect to V_{out} due to noise, stability is reached at point B. With the polarity of the noise source reversed, stability is realized at point A. Note that the cross-over point is the switching threshold, V_S, a value that was used to determine the single source noise margin. In essence, the cross-coupling of two inverter circuits results in a *bistable* circuit with two stable states. For stability it is necessary that the voltage gain around the loop be less than 1; otherwise, the positive gain will amplify the change and eventually force the outputs to switch to the opposite state due to the regenerative effect.

For a bistable circuit to change state it is necessary that the voltage gain of the circuit be made greater than 1. This can be accomplished by introducing a *trigger voltage pulse* at V_{in}. With the input of Inverter 1 in the low state, a positive trigger pulse is required at V_{in}. The voltage amplitude of the pulse should be sufficient to raise the voltage past V_S where the gain of the circuit is greater than unity; then, due to the cross-coupled circuit and resulting positive feedback, the trigger pulse will be regenerated and a change to the opposite state will be initiated.

The width of the trigger pulse need be only a little greater than the total propagation delay time around the circuit loop. The average propagation delay for a single gate is given by

$$t_P = \frac{t_{PHL} + t_{PLH}}{2} \tag{5.6}$$

where t_{PHL} is the high-to-low propagation delay, and t_{PLH} is the low-to-high propagation delay. The delay around the inverter loop is $t_{PHL} + t_{PLH}$; that is, twice the average propagation delay time of the logic inverters. So long as the trigger pulse is greater than this value, the circuit will change state.

In summary, a bistable circuit may be triggered to move from one stable state to the other by moving an input past V_S for a duration of $2t_P$. In the absence of a trigger, the circuit remains in that stable state indefinitely, provided that power remains applied to the circuit. Another common name for the bistable circuit is a *flip-flop*. However, the name flip-flop is usually reserved for a more complex circuit than a simple cross-coupling of two inverters.

5.6.2   SR Latch

The simplest form of the bistable circuit is the *set-reset (SR) latch*. This circuit latches, or remembers, the incoming trigger pulse. Two implementations of this circuit are described below. It is a useful circuit that forms the basis of the memory circuits, described in Chapter 8.

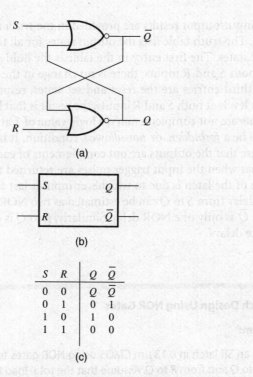

(a)

(b)

S	R	Q	$\overline{Q}$
0	0	Q	$\overline{Q}$
0	1	0	1
1	0	1	0
1	1	0	0

(c)

Figure 5.17
SR latch composed of cross-coupled NOR gates.

SR Latch with NOR Gates. In Figure 5.17a, the SR latch is implemented with two NOR2 gates. One of the inputs of each NOR gate is used to cross-couple to the output of the other NOR gate, while the second input provides a means of triggering the latch from one stable state to the other. This circuit is considered to be a latch since the output is a continuous function of the input values (i.e., it is transparent). The logic symbol for the latch is shown in Figure 5.17b. The two outputs Q and $\overline{Q}$ are complementary and, by definition, the latch is in the *set state* with a logic 1 at the Q output and logic 0 at the $\overline{Q}$ output. Conversely, with a logic 0 at the Q output and logic 1 at the $\overline{Q}$ output, the latch is in the *reset state*.

From Figure 5.17a, it can be seen that a logic 1 at the set (S) input will cause a logic 0 at the $\overline{Q}$ output and, with the reset (R) input at logic 0, it will result in a logic 1 at the Q output. That is, the latch is now set, and the S input can safely be returned to the 0 state. The trigger pulse at the S input of sufficient duration causes the latch to be set. Alternatively, a logic 1 at the R input will cause a logic 0 at the Q output and, with the S input now at a logic 0, the result is a logic 1 at the $\overline{Q}$ output. Since the latch responds to high voltage levels at the inputs, S and R are referred to as *active high inputs*. When the inputs are both returned to the 0 state, the flip-flop behaves as a cross-coupled pair of inverters, as shown in Figure 5.16a, that hold the value until further changes are experienced at the inputs.

The input/output results are provided in the *truth table* for the SR latch in Figure 5.17c. The truth table lists the output states for all the possible combinations of the input states. The first entry in the table is the hold state since, with low voltage levels at both S and R inputs, there is no change in the Q and $\overline{Q}$ outputs. The second and third entries are the reset and set states, respectively. In the fourth entry with high levels at both S and R inputs, the result is that both Q and $\overline{Q}$ are low. Since the outputs are not complementary, a logic value of 1 at both S and R inputs is considered to be a *forbidden*, or *not-allowed*, condition. It is only considered forbidden in the sense that the outputs are not complements of each other. Actually what happens is that when the input trigger pulses are returned to their quiescent levels, the final state of the latch is due to whichever input is last to go low.

The delay from S to Q can be estimated as two NOR gate delays, while the delay from S to $\overline{Q}$ is only one NOR delay. Similarly, R to Q is one gate delay while R to $\overline{Q}$ is two gate delays.

Example 5.4   **SR Latch Design Using NOR Gates**

Problem:

Design an SR latch in 0.13 μm CMOS using NOR gates to deliver a delay of 400 ps from S to Q and from R to $\overline{Q}$. Assume that the total load to be driven by Q and $\overline{Q}$ is 100 fF, and $L = 100$ nm.

Solution:

The following cross-coupled NOR configuration is used to implement the SR latch.

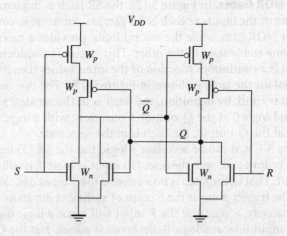

To obtain the desired propagation delays, we use the relationship $t_{PHL} = t_{PLH} = 0.7 R_{eff} C_L$. There are two propagation delays from S to Q and R to $\overline{Q}$, so we divide the two delays equally between the two NOR gates. For the NMOS devices, we know that $R_{eqn} = 12.5$ k$\Omega/\square$. Therefore,

$$t_{PHL} = 0.7(12.5 \text{ k}\Omega)\frac{L}{W}(100 \text{ fF}) = 200 \text{ ps}$$

$$\therefore \frac{W}{L} = 4.4$$

Set $W_n = 440$ nm for both NMOS devices.

For PMOS devices, we use our rule-of-thumb and simply quadruple the size of the NMOS devices to obtain $W_p = 1.76$ μm.

SR Latch with NAND Gates. The SR latch can also be designed with NAND gates, as in Figure 5.18a. Similar to the NOR circuit, the reset condition of the latch is with $Q = 0$ and $\bar{Q} = 1$. However, with the NAND circuit, the S and R inputs are normally at logic 1. The latch is set with $S = 0$, and reset with $R = 0$. Hence this latch responds to *active low inputs*, as is indicated by the small circles at the S and R inputs of the

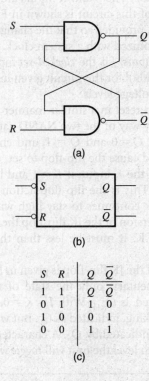

(a)

(b)

S	R	Q	$\bar{Q}$
1	1	Q	$\bar{Q}$
0	1	1	0
1	0	0	1
0	0	1	1

(c)

Figure 5.18
SR latch with NAND gates.

logic symbol shown in Figure 5.18b. It is also reflected in the characteristic table of Figure 5.18c. For the NAND configuration of the SR latch, the forbidden condition requires $S = R = 0$ since this leads to $Q = \overline{Q} = 1$.

The delay from S to Q can be estimated as one NAND gate delay, while the delay from S to $\overline{Q}$ is two NAND delays. Similarly, R to Q is two gate delays while R to $\overline{Q}$ is only one gate delay. The design of this circuit follows the design of the NAND gates described earlier. However, the problem of the forbidden state prevents this type of memory element from frequent use, as in the case of the NOR latch.

Exercise 5.4   Draw the transistor schematics for NAND-based SR latches using CMOS gates and pseudo-NMOS gates. Size the devices to deliver 400 ps propagation delays when driving 100 fF loads in 0.13 μm technology. Use the same solution process as shown for the NOR gates in Example 5.4.

5.6.3   JK Flip-Flop

By the addition of two feedback lines the ambiguity at the output of the SR latch, when both S and R inputs are activated at the same time, can be overcome. The device is known as a *JK flip-flop*. The S and R inputs are renamed J and K, respectively. An all-NAND version of this circuit is shown in Figure 5.19a. An important addition is a *clock* (CK) input, provided so that the change in the output logic states of the flip-flop can be synchronized with a system clock. Hence, the J and K inputs are termed the *synchronous inputs; J* is the *clocked-set* input and K the *clocked-reset* input. Note from the logic symbol for this circuit given in Figure 5.19b that all three inputs are activated by high voltage levels.

The JK flip-flop is set and reset in a similar manner to the SR latch, except for the synchronizing with CK, by way of the two NAND gates at the input of the flip-flop. With the flip-flop reset, $Q = 0$ and $\overline{Q} = 1$, and entry is only by way of the J input. A value of $J = 1$ would cause the flip-flop to set, making the Q output high and $\overline{Q}$ low. This now enables the K input; if $K = 1$ and if CK is still high, the flip-flop will again change state. This is the flip-flop action from which it derives its name.[10] Note that if the clock continues to stay high with $J = K = 1$, the flip-flop will oscillate. Hence for this version of the JK flip-flop there is a very definite restriction on the pulse width of CK. It must be less than the propagation delay time through the flip-flop.

The characteristic table of the JK flip-flop is given in Figure 5.19c. Since the two outputs are always complementary, only the state of the output following the $n + 1$st clock is given, indicated as Q_{n+1}. With $J = K = 0$, there is no change in the state of the flip-flop after clocking, indicated as Q_n. But with $J = K = 1$, the flip-flop changes state when clocked, indicated by $\overline{Q}_n$. A characteristic of all JK flip-flops is that with both J and K at a high level the unit will *toggle* when clocked; that is, it will

---

[10] Technically, the outputs are directly controlled by the inputs while the clock is high and therefore it should be referred to as a latch.

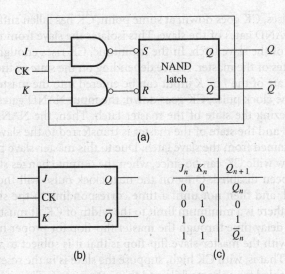

(a)

(b)

J_n	K_n	Q_{n+1}
0	0	Q_n
0	1	0
1	0	1
1	1	$\overline{Q_n}$

(c)

Figure 5.19
JK flip-flop.

change state irrespective of its original state. Again, if the clock is high for a long enough period, the flip-flop output will oscillate in this type of configuration. This undesirable limitation can be eliminated with the master-slave principle, described in the next section.

5.6.4 JK Master-Slave Flip-Flop

As shown in the logic diagram of Figure 5.20, the JK *master-slave* flip-flop is simply a cascade of two JK flip-flops, with the master driving the slave. An important point to notice is that the master is activated by CK, but the slave is activated by an inverted form of CK, namely, $\overline{\text{CK}}$. The operation of the master-slave principle is as

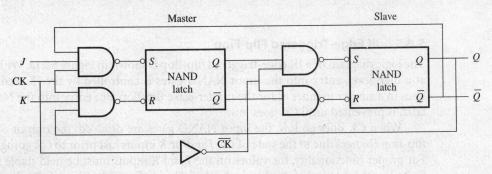

Figure 5.20
Master-slave flip-flop using JK flip-flop.

follows. As CK rises, $\overline{CK}$ goes down; at some point, $\overline{CK}$ has fallen sufficiently to disable the input NAND gates of the slave. This isolates the slave from the master and freezes the state of the slave latch. In the meantime, CK rises enough to enable the input NAND gates of the master. Hence depending on the state of the J and K feedback lines, the state of the J or K input can be entered into the master. Now on the falling edge of the clock pulse, CK goes down; the input NAND gates to the master are disabled, freezing the state of the master latch. Then, the NAND gates to the slave are enabled and the state of the master is transferred to the slave. The outputs Q and $\overline{Q}$ are obtained from the slave latch. Due to this master-slave principle, there is no limit to how wide CK can be since, when the output changes state, entry into the master has been disabled. Only on the next clock pulse will the master input gates be enabled, and then not until a time corresponding to the slave being disabled. Note that there is a minimum limit to the width of CK. It must be wider than the propagation delay time through the master flip-flop for proper functionality.

A problem with the master-slave flip-flop is that it is subject to what is known as *ones catching*. That is, with CK high, suppose the slave is in the reset state, and the J input gate is enabled for a short while and then returns to 0. This will inadvertently set the first latch. Since this is a level sensitive circuit, the high value on J will propagate into the master latch and lock in place. Thus, any "spike" or "glitch" on the J input line will cause the master latch to be set. It is impossible to reset this latch, since entry into the K input gates is disabled by the K feedback line. Thus, we say the J input has *caught a 1* that will subsequently be transferred to the slave when CK goes down. One way to prevent ones catching is to keep the duration of the l state for CK as short as possible. Another way is to make use of JK *edge-triggered* flip-flops, which is the preferred approach.

Exercise 5.5	Draw a timing diagram that illustrates the 1's catching drawback of the JK master-slave flop of Figure 5.20. Start by placing the JK in the reset state and apply a periodic clock signal. When the clock is high, introduce a short pulse on the J input. Draw the corresponding logic waveforms on the outputs of the NAND latches. When does the undesired 1 appear at the Q output?

5.6.5   JK Edge-Triggered Flip-Flop

The logic diagram of a JK edge-triggered flip-flop is shown in Figure 5.21a. With CK at a high level, entry into the input NAND gates is controlled by the JK feedback lines in a similar manner as for the master-slave flip-flop. But entry into the NAND latch is prevented until CK goes low.

When CK does go low, the input NAND gates are disabled; the output of the flip-flop changes due to the state of the J and/or K inputs just prior to CK going low. For proper functionality, the values on the J and K inputs must be held stable for a finite length of time before the clock edge. This is the *set-up time* of the flip-flop. The circuit is forgiving of any spikes or glitches on the J or K lines prior to this time as long as the set-up time is satisfied. Some flip-flop designs require the state of the

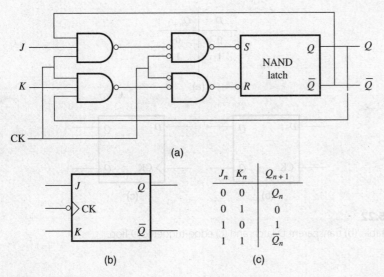

Figure 5.21
JK negative edge-triggered flip-flop.

J_n	K_n	Q_{n+1}
0	0	Q_n
0	1	0
1	0	1
1	1	$\overline{Q}_n$

J and K input lines to remain stable for a time even after the clock edge arrives. This is known as the *hold time*. Usually the minimum hold time is 0 ns.

As shown in Figure 5.21b, the logic symbol for an edge-triggered flip-flop is differentiated from the master-slave by a small $>$ sign at the CK input. The presence or absence of the inverting symbol is used to indicate whether the outputs Q and $\overline{Q}$ change on the falling or rising edge of the clock pulse. The logic symbol indicates a negative edge-triggered flip-flop. The corresponding truth table is shown in Figure 5.21c.

In summary of the JK flip-flops, we have noted that the device may be of the master-slave or edge-triggered type. The outputs may change following or on the rising or falling edge of the clock pulse. The device usually has additional inputs for direct set and reset so that the outputs can be initialized to the desired settings.

5.7 D Flip-Flops and Latches

Another very useful flip-flop, most widely used in CMOS digital circuits and systems for the storage of data, is the *D flip-flop*. The truth table of a D-type flip-flop is shown in Figure 5.22a. With clocking, the Q output simply follows the D input. The $\overline{Q}$ output is always complementary to the Q output.

The D-flop may be of two types. It may be *transparent*, as shown in the logic diagram (Figure 5.22b). The CK input is really an enable input that, when high, allows the Q output to follow the D input. The state of the element is frozen only when CK goes low. Or, it may be *edge-triggered*, as in Figure 5.22c. Similar to other edge-triggered flops, with CK either high or low the D input has no effect on the

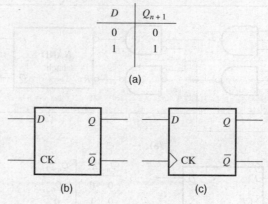

D	Q_{n+1}
0	0
1	1

(a)

(b)

(c)

Figure 5.22

(a) Truth table, (b) transparent D-latch, and (c) edge-triggered D-flop.

output. Data are transferred from the D input to the output only on the rising edge of the clock pulse.[11] At this point, it should be emphasized that the working definition of a latch is an element that is level-sensitive and transparent, whereas a flip-flop is edge-triggered and otherwise opaque.[12]

To further describe the difference between the two types of sequential elements, it is useful to examine the outputs, given the same input and clock signal. Consider Figure 5.23 where the D-latch is driven by IN and CLK. The output is a continuous function of the input while the clock is high. That is, the D-latch allows the input to propagate through the latch to the output when CLK is high and prevents its propagation when low. Initially, the output is unknown. When the clock goes high, the low input propagates to the output. When the input data goes high, it appears at the output after a short delay. When the clock goes low, the last value of the input is held. Note that the falling edge of CLK is the important one since this is when the data is latched at the output. Further changes in the input are not propagated to the output. Therefore, the small negative pulse in the input of Figure 5.23 is not seen at the output.

Now consider the D-flop in Figure 5.24. In this case, it is constructed using two D-latches in a master-slave configuration driven by CLK. For the positive edge-triggered D-flop, the important edge is the leading edge of the clock waveform. The leading edge captures and propagates the last value at the input just prior to the clock transition; the final state of the flip-flop is due to the state of the D input just before clocking occurs. In the waveform shown, there are two points sampled: in one case, the input is low and in the other case the input is high. As a result, we see a transition at the output corresponding to the second rising clock edge. The actions

---

[11] Since there is no bubble on the CK input, this is a positive edge-triggered flip-flop; a bubble would indicate a negative edge-triggered flop.

[12] Designers tend to use the terms flip-flop and latch interchangeably which is some cause for confusion. We will strictly use latch and flip-flop definitions from this point onward in this text to avoid such confusion.

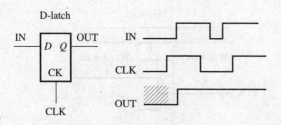

Figure 5.23
D-latch operation.

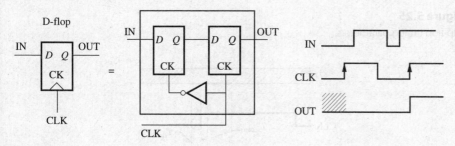

Figure 5.24
D-flop operation.

are equivalent to a sample-and-hold circuit, where the sampling is done when the clock edge hits the flop.

There are a number of important timing characteristics associated with flops and latches. The timing parameters for the flip-flop are illustrated in Figure 5.25. The clock edge is the reference point for these timing parameters. The setup time, T_{setup}, is the time that the incoming data must be stable before the clock arrives. The hold time, T_{hold}, is the length of time that the data remains stable after the clock arrives for proper operation. As shown in the figure, if the data is stable before the setup time and continues to be stable after the hold time, the flop will properly capture the data. However, if it settles after the hold time it is guaranteed to fail. A failure implies storage of the wrong data.

If the data arrives within the period designated by the setup and hold times, the flop may or may not capture the correct value. This is the uncertainty interval. However, the user of such a flop should not permit signals to stabilize in this range since proper performance is not guaranteed. Another parameter of importance is the clock-to-Q delay, $T_{clk\text{-}q}$. This is the delay from the time that the clock arrives to the point at which the Q output stabilizes. In reality, the incoming data must arrive at T_{setup} before the clock hits, and the output is valid at $T_{clk\text{-}q}$ after the clock edge. Viewed in this way, the "overhead" of the flop is $T_{setup} + T_{clk\text{-}q}$. When designing flops, we should try to minimize T_{setup}, T_{hold}, and $T_{clk\text{-}q}$.

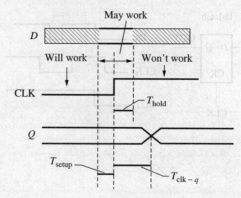

Figure 5.25
Flip-flop timing parameters.

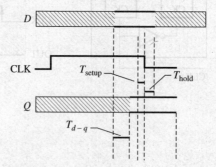

Figure 5.26
Latch timing parameters.

A similar set of parameters applies to the D-latch as shown in Figure 5.26. The interesting edge of the clock is the falling edge, so the corresponding setup and hold times are associated with this edge. However, data begins to flow after the positive going edge of the clock so the setup and hold times are not as critical, and are typically much smaller for the D-latch. The more important parameter is the "overhead" associated with the latch, which is referred to as the D-to-Q delay, $T_{d\text{-}q}$. This is the amount by which the data is delayed by the presence of the latch. Since the latch is transparent when the clock is high, we are more interested in reducing the delay between input and output as opposed to the setup and hold times. However, if there is a late arriving signal near the falling edge, it must satisfy the setup and hold constraints or the circuit will fail.

We now illustrate how a D-latch can be constructed using conventional CMOS logic. A logic diagram for the D-latch is given in Figure 5.27. This is suitable for implementation using AOI gates as shown in Figure 5.28. An edge-triggered D-type flip-flop may be constructed from two such transparent latches in cascade driven by complementary clocks. The number of transistors needed to realize a D-flop in this

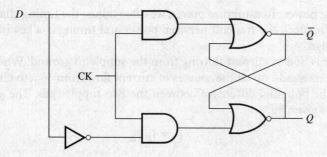

Figure 5.27
Gate level realization of D-latch.

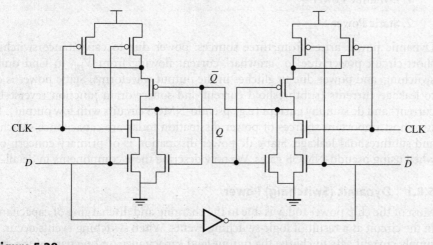

Figure 5.28
AOI implementation of D-latch.

manner is large. More efficient circuits for D-latches and D-flip-flops will be presented in Chapter 7.

5.8 Power Dissipation in CMOS Gates

Power consumption in CMOS digital designs has been increasing at an alarming rate over the past few technology generations. It has become perhaps the most important design specification in recent years since it affects power grid design, chip temperature, packaging decisions, and long-term reliability. If the trend for chip power continues, it will begin to dictate the logic/memory composition of future designs and force most of the chip to be dominated by memory, which consumes less power than logic circuits. In this section, we examine the sources of power dissipation in CMOS gates and describe circuit techniques to minimize power in CMOS designs. As we describe these techniques, take note of the role of timing in controlling power. To minimize power, we often adjust the timing characteristics of a design. In effect, the tradeoff between power and timing is a key issue in CMOS digital design.

Power is due to current flowing from the supply to ground. When computing power, we must add up all the sources of current flow from V_{DD} to Gnd and multiply it by the potential difference between the two supply rails. The general power equation is given by

$$P = I_D V_{DD} \tag{5.7}$$

where I_D is the current flowing from V_{DD} to Gnd.

In CMOS, the sources of power can be broadly categorized into two groups:

1. Dynamic Power

2. Static Power

Dynamic power arises from three sources: power due to capacitance switching, short-circuit power due to "crowbar" current flowing from V_{DD} to Gnd during switching, and power due to glitches in the output waveforms. Static power is due to leakage currents (subthreshold current and source/drain junction reverse-bias current) and dc standby current (e.g., pseudo-NMOS circuits with low output). The two most important sources of power dissipation today are capacitance switching and subthreshold leakage. Static dc power dissipation is of primary concern only when using pseudo-NMOS gates. We now describe these components in detail.

5.8.1 Dynamic (Switching) Power

Most of the chip power today is due to the charging and discharging of capacitances in the circuit as a result of logic switching events. When switching events occur, the supply current acts to charge the output load capacitance on one part of the cycle, and discharge the capacitance on the other half of the cycle. Effectively, we have current flowing from V_{DD} to Gnd (albeit on different parts of the cycle) and this leads to power dissipation. The frequency of switching, f, determines the actual power that is consumed.

To compute the average power dissipation due to switching, we need to determine I_D and multiply it with V_{DD}. The considerations are detailed for the CMOS inverter of Figure 5.29a. When the input switches from high to low, the PMOS device turns on, as shown in Figure 5.29b. It charges up the output to V_{DD}, thereby storing energy on the capacitor. When the input switches from low to high, the NMOS device turns on and discharges the capacitor as illustrated in Figure 5.29c. The average charging current is

$$I_{D,\text{avg}} = C \frac{dV}{dt} = \frac{C_L \Delta V_{\text{swing}}}{\Delta t} = C_L V_{DD} f_{\text{avg}} \tag{5.8}$$

Note that in the above equation, we assume that the average switching frequency of the inverter is f_{avg} and the voltage swing is V_{DD}.

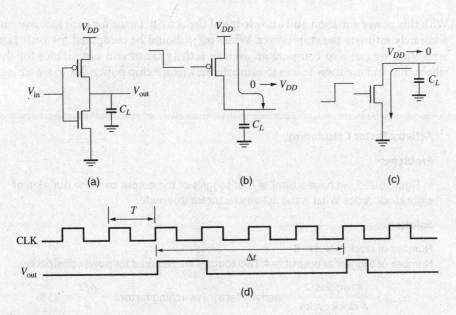

Figure 5.29
Dynamic power dissipation considerations.

The combination of these two processes results in power dissipation. Since the current is associated with a capacitor, we can write

$$P_{\text{switching}} = I_{D,\text{avg}} V_{DD} = C_L \Delta V_{\text{swing}} f_{\text{avg}} V_{DD} = C_L V_{DD}^2 f_{\text{avg}} \quad (5.9)$$

This equation tells us exactly what our options are to reduce power: keep C_L small, reduce the swing, reduce V_{DD}, or reduce the switching frequency, f_{avg}. The approach used to reduce power will be dependent on the design style used, timing constraints, area constraints, and other tradeoffs. Usually power reduction requires a combination of many methods.

One factor that we should examine more closely is the average switching frequency of the inverter, f_{avg}. The clock frequency is normally taken to be f_{clk} and clearly the clock switches on every cycle.[13] If we refer to a transition from high to low or low to high as a *toggle*, then it follows that we need two toggles to have power dissipation. On the other hand, most logic gates do not switch on every cycle as shown in Figure 5.29d. The average frequency of operation can be specified using an activity factor, $\alpha_{0 \to 1}$, that is multiplied by the clock frequency, f_{clk}. The power equation can be modified to include this activity factor as follows:

$$P_{\text{switching}} = \alpha_{0 \to 1} C_L V_{DD}^2 f_{\text{clk}} \quad (5.10)$$

---

[13] In fact, the clock circuit may consume up to 40% of the chip power due to its large capacitance and high frequency.

With this power equation and knowledge of the activity factor for each gate, we can accurately estimate the chip power. While $\alpha_{0 \to 1}$ should be computed for each gate separately, we can also compute an average activity factor and capacitance for the whole chip and use these values to estimate the average chip power due to switching.

Example 5.5   **Activity Factor Calculation**

Problem:

In Figure 5.29d, we have a total of four toggles of the output over the duration of eight clock cycles. What is the activity factor for this node?

Solution:

Number of clock cycles = 8
Number of toggles at output = 4. Two toggles are required for power dissipation.

$$\alpha_{0 \to 1} = \frac{\# \text{ toggles}/2}{\# \text{ clock cycles}} = \text{activity factor (switching factor)} = \frac{4/2}{8} = 25\%$$

Example 5.6   **Comparison of Hand Calculation of Power with SPICE**

Compute the power due to switching for an inverter with $W_p = 800$ nm and $W_n = 400$ nm driving a total load of 50 fF with an average switching frequency of 250 MHz. Compare the results with a transient simulation in SPICE. Which value is larger, the one obtained by hand calculation or by SPICE? Use 0.18 μm technology parameters for the analysis with $V_{DD} = 1.8$ V. Ignore parasitic capacitances and set input rise/fall times to 300 ps in SPICE.

Solution:

The dynamic power can be computed by hand as

$$P = CV^2 f = (50 \text{ fF})(1.8)^2(250 \text{ MHz}) = 40.5 \ \mu\text{W}$$

A SPICE simulation can be performed to confirm this result. A transient analysis is required, followed by an average power measurement over a 4 ns period. Note that the inverter must toggle high and low in order to create a "power event." The input file for SPICE is as follows:

```
*Power dissipated by inverter
*Set supply and library
.param Supply=1.8              *for 0.18 technology
.lib    'bsim3v3.cmosp18.lib'
.opt scale=0.1u                *Set lambda
```

```
* Power supply
.global            Vdd      Gnd
Vdd               Vdd      Gnd      'Supply' *Supply is set by .lib call
*Subcircuit
.subckt inv   in      out
mp       out       in      Vdd      Vdd      PMOS1 l=2 w=8 ad=0 pd=0 as=0 ps=0
mn       out       in      Gnd      Gnd      NMOS1 l=2 w=4 ad=0 pd=0 as=0 ps=0
Cload    out       Gnd     50fF
.ends
* Top level simulation netlist
Xinv     in        1       inv
Vin      in        Gnd     pulse    0    'Supply' 1ns 200ps 200ps 1.7ns
4ns
* Simulation
.tran              50ps    5ns
.measure           tran    avgpwr   avg      P(Xinv) from=1n to=5n
.end
```

From this simulation, the average power dissipated by the inverter during the interval is found to be 46.3 μW. This is approximately 14% higher than the hand calculation.

As seen in the above example, if we run SPICE on a single inverter and measure power, we will find that the measured value exceeds the hand-calculated value. That is, $P_{SPICE} > CV_{DD}^2 f$. Why would this be the case? The primary reason is due to short-circuit current or crowbar current (although a very small percentage of it is due to leakage current). The origin of the crowbar current, I_{SC}, is illustrated in Figure 5.30.

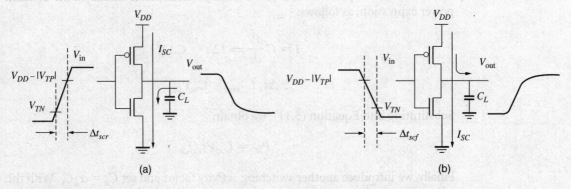

Figure 5.30
Short-circuit current flow during switching process.

Crowbar current is the current that flows directly from V_{DD} to Gnd during switching events. The reason why short-circuit flows is that for a certain period of time both transistors are *on* simultaneously; that is, $|V_{GS}| > |V_T|$ for both devices. If we apply a step input, only one device would be *on* at any given point in time, and we would not observe any short-circuit current. However, since all inputs have a finite slope, both devices are *on* when $V_{TN} < V_{in} < V_{DD} - |V_{TP}|$. Crowbar current flows in both charging and discharging conditions. The time period that short-circuit current flows depends on the rise/fall time of the input:

$$\Delta t_{sc} = \Delta t_{scr} + \Delta t_{scf}$$

where Δt_{scr} and Δt_{scf} are illustrated in Figure 5.30. When discharging, the sum of the supply current and the discharging current flows through the pull-down device. This is illustrated in Figure 5.30a. During the charging process, part of the supply current flows to the capacitor while the remainder flows to Gnd as shown in Figure 5.30b. The average power associated with this current is

$$P_{SC} = I_{SC} V_{DD}$$

Since crowbar current flows during all switching events, it is possible to rewrite the equation as follows. Taking $I_{SC,\text{avg}}$ as the average crowbar current during the two switching intervals, then

$$I_{SC} = \frac{\Delta t_{sc}}{T} I_{SC,\text{avg}}$$

This can be substituted into the previous equation to obtain

$$P_{SC} = \frac{\Delta t_{sc} I_{SC,\text{avg}}}{T} V_{DD} = \Delta t_{sc} I_{SC,\text{avg}} V_{DD} f_{\text{clk}} \qquad (5.11)$$

It is desirable to replace the first two terms by a term that is similar to the dynamic power expression, as follows:

$$I = C \frac{dV}{dt} \Rightarrow I \Delta t = C \Delta V$$

$$\therefore \Delta t_{sc} I_{SC,\text{avg}} = C_{sc} V_{DD}$$

Substituting into Equation (5.11), we obtain

$$\therefore P_{SC} = C_{sc} V_{DD}^2 f_{\text{clk}}$$

Finally, we introduce another switching activity factor and set $C_{sc} = \alpha_{sc} C_L$. With this adjustment, we have

$$P_{SC} = \alpha_{sc} C_L V_{DD}^2 f_{\text{clk}} \qquad (5.12)$$

In effect, we are incorporating all the effects of the short-circuit current into a factor α_{sc} that depends on the device threshold voltages and input rise and fall times. The total dynamic power can be written as

$$P_{\text{dynamic}} = \alpha_{0\rightarrow1}C_L V_{DD}^2 f_{\text{clk}} + \alpha_{sc}C_L V_{DD}^2 f_{\text{clk}} = \alpha C_L V_{DD}^2 f_{\text{clk}} \qquad (5.13)$$

The first term accounts for the power due to capacitance switching while the second term accounts for the short-circuit power. The new α incorporates both the activity factor and short-circuit current effects.

To reduce short-circuit power, we should set the rise and fall times, or *edge rates*, to be as short as possible. This will minimize Δt_{sc}, the time that both devices are on. However, this is a local optimization that may not be globally optimal. If we use large drivers at the input to reduce the rise/fall times, this increases the capacitance, thereby increasing the overall dynamic power. In effect, there is a tradeoff between dynamic power of the previous gate and short-circuit power of the next gate. We usually seek to minimize the total power due to the sum of these two components. One solution that has been found to be effective is to make the input and output edge rates sharp and about equal. This tends to minimize the overall power due to the two components of dynamic power. This is one example where, in order to minimize power, we must consider the timing characteristics of the signals. We will find many instances where the timing is an important factor in reducing the overall chip power.

There is one other source of dynamic power due to differences in the arrival times of signals at gate inputs. If a given input signal arrives first and forces the output to switch, and later another input signal arrives and causes the output to switch back to the original value, we have a *glitch* in the output. This type of undesired output pulse causes unnecessary power dissipation, which can be modeled in terms of switching power. It can be a major component of the total power if the designer is not careful. Glitches tend to propagate through the fanout gates and cause unintended transitions in subsequent stages, increasing the power dissipation even further. Depending on the number of glitches in the chip, it can quickly add up to a nonnegligible amount of power.

To reduce glitches, signals should be made to arrive at roughly the same time at all gate inputs. This requires a balancing of the path delays and gate delays in a combinational logic block. Whenever possible, the designer should select logic circuits that minimize the potential for glitches. This may also involve retiming a given circuit or selecting architectures that are glitch free, or exhibit fewer glitches than others. The key, as will be clear in many design guidelines throughout this book, is to keep things as balanced as possible.

Glitch Example Using NOR Gate   **Example 5.7**

Problem:

Using SPICE and a 0.18 μm technology, adjust the inputs of a 2-input NOR gate until a glitch appears at the output during a transient analysis. Under what conditions does a glitch occur? How should such a glitch be prevented?

Solution:

Create a SPICE file with a 2-input NOR gate. During the analysis, one input should be switching from low to high while the other is switching from high to low in the same interval to create a glitch. To prevent such a glitch, all the inputs should arrive at the same time.

```
*NOR Gate Glitching Example
*Set supply and library
.param Supply=1.8              *for 0.18 technology
.temp   25                     *Override temperature by setting it before
                                .lib
.lib    'bsim3v3.cmosp18.lib'
.opt scale = 0.1u              *Set lambda
*Power  supply
.global Vdd    Gnd
Vdd     Vdd    Gnd    'Supply' * Supply is set by .lib call
*Top level simulation netlist
mpa     out    ina    x      Vdd   PMOS l=2 w=16 ad=80 pd=16 as=80 ps=16
mpb     x      inb    Vdd    Vdd   PMOS l=2 w=16 ad=80 pd=16 as=80 ps=16
mna     out    ina    Gnd    Gnd   NMOS l=2 w=4 ad=20 pd=4 as=20 ps=4
mnb     out    inb    Gnd    Gnd   NMOS l=2 w=4 ad=20 pd=4 as=20 ps=4
Va      ina    Gnd    pulse  'Supply' 0 1ns 100ps 100ps 4.1ns 8ns
Vb      inb    Gnd    pulse  'Supply' 0 1ns 100ps 100ps 2ns    4ns
*Simulation
.tran   100ps 9ns
.plot   tran V(out)
.end
```

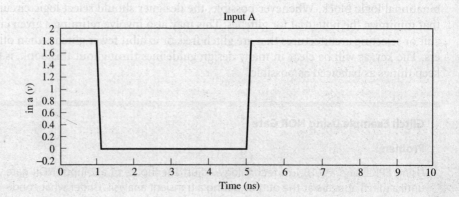

Input A

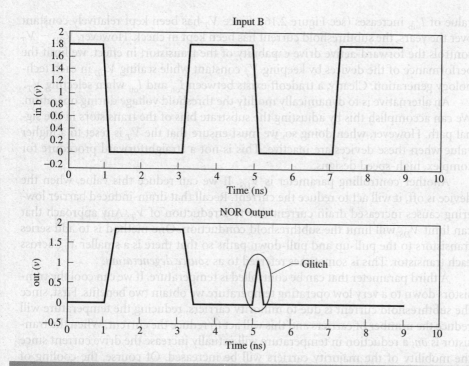

5.8.2   Static (Standby) Power

Standby power is an important design consideration for low-power battery-operated, or portable, devices. There are three basic sources of static power: subthreshold leakage, *pn* junction leakage, and dc current in the output low state. Today, leakage currents are beginning to control design decisions even for high-performance non-portable applications. As a result, this component of power is gaining more attention in the IC design industry from process engineers, circuit designers, and CAD engineers.

The most important issue is the subthreshold leakage. In recent years, it has grown significantly due to the close proximity of the source and drain. This results in a bipolar transistor action, where the substrate is the base of the bipolar transistor, and the source and drain act as the emitter and collector, respectively. Subthreshold current is due to diffusion current of minority carriers across the channel region. From earlier discussions in Chapter 2, we found that the subthreshold current equation has the form

$$I_{sub} = I_s e^{[q(V_{GS} - V_T - V_{offset})/nkT]} \left(1 - e^{(-qV_{DS}/kT)}\right)$$

When we examine this expression from a power perspective, we try to identify the controlling parameters to keep I_{sub} as low as possible. Specifically, if $V_{GS} = 0$, then V_T controls the magnitude of the subthreshold current. As V_T is reduced, the value of I_{sub} increases (see Figure 2.16). Since V_T has been kept relatively constant over the years, the subthreshold current has been kept in check. However, $V_{DD} - V_T$ controls the forward-active drive capability of the transistor; in effect, we limit the performance of the devices by keeping V_T constant while scaling V_{DD} in each technology generation. Clearly, a tradeoff exists between I_{on} and I_{off} when selecting V_T.

An alternative is to dynamically modify the threshold voltage during operation. We can accomplish this by adjusting the substrate bias of the transistors in the signal path. However, when doing so, we must ensure that the V_T is reset to a higher value when these devices are inactive. This is not a straightforward procedure for complex, high-speed designs.

Another controlling parameter is V_{DS}. If we can reduce this value, when the device is off, it will act to reduce the current. Recall that drain-induced barrier lowering causes increased drain current due to a reduction of V_T. Any approach that can limit V_{DS} will limit the subthreshold conduction. One method is to add series transistors to the pull-up and pull-down paths so that there is a smaller V_{DS} across each transistor. This is sometimes referred to as *source degeneration*.

A third parameter that can be controlled is temperature. If we can cool the transistors down to a very low operating temperature we obtain two benefits. First, since the subthreshold current is due to minority carriers, reducing the temperature will reduce the number of carriers and this will act to reduce the current. When the transistor is *on*, a reduction in temperature will actually increase the drive current since the mobility of the majority carriers will be increased. Of course, the cooling of chips requires a much more expensive package, which will increase the cost of the design.

Another source of leakage is due to the reverse-bias of source and drain junctions. The percentage of the overall power dissipation is rather small but we should still understand its origin. The basic diode equation is given by

$$I_{pn} = I_0 \left(e^{(q/kT)V_{SB}} - 1 \right) \qquad \text{where } I_0 = A \cdot J_s$$

In reverse-bias mode, the current is $I_{pn} = -A J_s$, where A is the area of the junction and J_s is the current density. The areas of interest are the bottom of the junction and the channel-facing sidewall. Therefore, we need to keep these areas as small as possible by minimizing the source and drain areas. The currents are typically in the pA to nA range and are negligible in most digital designs. The combination of subthreshold current and the pn junction current is referred to as leakage current:

$$I_{leak} = I_{sub} + I_{pn} \tag{5.14}$$

Since the NMOS and PMOS have different leakage currents, I_{leak} can be based on the average leakage of the pull-up and pull-down paths. The total static power dissipation due to these two components is

$$P_{static} = (I_{sub} + I_{pn}) V_{DD} \tag{5.15}$$

One final form of static power is found in the pseudo-NMOS gates when the output is low. In this case, the current, I_{DC}, through the gate is computed by setting the output to V_{OL} and determining the current flow through any device in the current path. This current is multiplied by V_{DD} to obtain the power

$$P_{DC} = I_{DC}V_{DD} \tag{5.16}$$

This power can be relatively large. If we design a circuit with exclusively pseudo-NMOS gates, the power budget would be exceeded very quickly, much like the NMOS technology on which it is based. Recall that NMOS technology gave way to CMOS technology due to the dc standby power when the output of a gate was low. Imagine that you have 2 million logic gates and half of them are dissipating power. You quickly realize that you will exceed your power budget no matter what you do since the mere existence of the gates implies power dissipation. Therefore, pseudo-NMOS should be used sparingly.

5.8.3 Complete Power Equation

For a standard CMOS gate, the power equation is given by

$$P = \alpha\, C\, V_{DD}^2 f_{clk} + I_{leak}V_{DD} \tag{5.17}$$

where the short-circuit current effects are included in the α term.

For a pseudo-NMOS gate, the complete power equation is given by

$$P = \alpha\, C\, V_{DD}^2 f_{clk} + I_{leak}V_{DD} + \frac{I_{DC}V_{DD}}{2} \tag{5.18}$$

where the last term considers the fact that the dc current is flowing only half the time.

DC Power Dissipation for Pseudo-NMOS Inverter in 0.13 μm Technology　　　　**Example 5.8**

Problem:

Compute the dc power dissipated by the pseudo-NMOS inverter when the output is low, given that $V_{OL} = 0.1$ V, $W_n/L_n = 9$. Use 0.13 μm technology parameters.

Solution:

The current flowing through the inverter can be computed using the current through the pull-down transistor that is in the linear region of operation:

$$I_{DC} = \frac{W_N}{L_N}\, \frac{\mu_n C_{ox}}{\left(1 + \dfrac{V_{OL}}{E_{CN}L_N}\right)} \left[(V_{DD} - V_{TN})(V_{OL}) - \frac{(V_{OL})^2}{2} \right]$$

Using the parameter values for 0.13 μm CMOS:

$$I_{DC} = 9 \times \frac{430\ \mu\text{A/V}^2}{(1 + (0.1/0.6))} \left[(1.2 - 0.4)(0.1) - \frac{(0.1)^2}{2} \right] = 250\ \mu\text{A}$$

$$\therefore P = I_{DC}V_{DD} = 250\ \mu\text{A} \times 1.2\ \text{V} = 300\ \mu\text{W}$$

5.9 Power and Delay Tradeoffs

In most designs today, the primary tradeoff is between power and delay. We have already seen that equalizing the input arrival times will reduce glitches and equalizing the edge rates will minimize short-circuit current. Clearly, it is not sufficient to optimize one without considering the other. If we improve a design relative to power but it slows down the circuit, the results may not be acceptable. Similarly, an improvement in speed may only be achieved at the expense of power. Therefore, a metric is needed that allows us to balance the two design objectives in a meaningful way.

One such metric that has been popular for many years is the *power-delay product (PDP)*. The rationale is that, if we are interested in reducing power and reducing delay, then why not take the product of the two and try to minimize them together? At an intuitive level, this makes sense. If we follow this thought process to establish a metric for gates, then:

$$PDP = P_{avg}t_P \qquad (5.19)$$

where P_{avg} is the average power and t_P is the average propagation delay of a gate. Considering only the dominant source of power for a gate, we have

$$P_{avg} = CV_{DD}^2 f$$

and the propagation delay is

$$t_P = \frac{1}{2f}$$

assuming that the switching period is twice the propagation delay. Combining these results, we obtain

$$PDP = CV_{DD}^2 f \frac{1}{2f} = \frac{CV_{DD}^2}{2} \qquad (5.20)$$

This is an energy quantity and, as such, the PDP represents the energy required to perform a specific operation. The reason why we view this as an energy quantity is that energy is the time integral of power. If we compute the energy stored in the capacitor after a charging operation, we obtain

$$E_C = \int_0^\infty i_c(t)v_{out}(t)dt = \int_0^\infty C\frac{dv_{out}}{dt}v_{out}(t)(dt) = \int_0^{V_{DD}} Cv_{out}(t)dv_{out} = \frac{1}{2}CV_{DD}^2$$

In this case, the operation is to switch from low to high. In a similar fashion, Equation (5.20) defines the PDP as the energy per toggle operation for a gate.

The PDP can be minimized by reducing the capacitance C, the voltage swing ΔV_{swing} or the power supply voltage, V_{DD}. However, the metric has some limitations. If the PDP of two designs performing the same operations are compared, it would still be difficult to tell which one is better. For example, if one used a lower supply voltage to reduce PDP, the metric would not capture the fact that the delay is also reduced. Also, using smaller transistors would reduce C, but may also slow down the circuit. Because of the cancellation of the delay term when deriving the PDP, we have lost valuable timing information.

A solution to this problem is to define another metric that multiplies the PDP by the delay. This is termed the *energy-delay product (EDP)*. It is given as follows:

$$\text{EDP} = \text{PDP} \times t_P \tag{5.21}$$

We already have the equation for PDP, but we need a new formulation for t_P:

$$I = C\frac{dV}{dt}$$

$$\therefore \Delta t = \frac{C\Delta V}{I} \tag{5.22}$$

$$\therefore t_P = \frac{C\Delta V}{I_{\text{sat}}} \approx \frac{CV_{DD}}{K_2(V_{DD} - V_T)}$$

where K_2 is a constant that depends on device sizes. Combining Equations (5.20) and (5.22), we obtain:

$$\text{EDP} = \frac{C^2 V_{DD}^3}{2K_2(V_{DD} - V_T)} \tag{5.23}$$

Now, whenever power supply values or device sizes are altered, they are captured in the EDP. This is a better metric for low-power design.

If the goal of the overall design is to reduce the EDP, then it is instructive to examine how a number of designs would compare using this metric. For this purpose, we plot the EDP of several designs (*a, b, c,* and *d*) on a qualitative graph of energy vs. 1/delay in Figure 5.31. The lines shown in the graph have equal EDP and are therefore equivalent in terms of this metric. Designs that lie closer to the *x*-axis

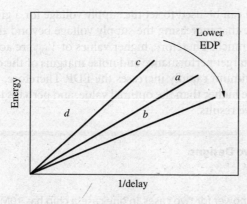

Figure 5.31
Energy versus 1/delay for four designs: *a, b, c, d.*

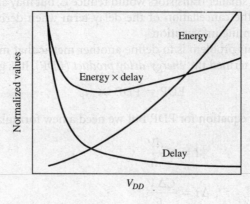

Figure 5.32
Energy-delay product versus supply voltage.

are better since their energy-delay product is lower. Surprisingly, for the four cases shown, design b is the best and design d is the worst in terms of EDP.

Another way to view this metric is to examine the energy, delay, and EDP on the same normalized graph as a function of the supply voltage, V_{DD}. This is shown in Figure 5.32. As the power supply voltage decreases, delay increases, but the energy per operation decreases. Therefore, an optimum EDP must exist and it can be obtained by differentiating Equation (5.23) with respect to V_{DD} and setting the result to zero:

$$\frac{\partial \text{EDP}}{\partial V_{DD}} = 0$$

$$\therefore V_{DD}^{*} = \frac{3}{2} V_T$$

This optimum value can be used to set the supply voltage for a given technology. It is interesting to note that increasing the supply voltage beyond the optimum does not affect EDP very much. Therefore, higher values of V_{DD} are acceptable and may be necessary for the target performance and noise margins of the design. A decrease in V_{DD} from the optimum rapidly increases the EDP. Therefore, it is important to keep the supply value higher than the optimal value, and perhaps this is the best way to interpret the above results.

Example 5.9   **Comparison of Two Designs**

Problem:

Compare the chip power for two cases. In one case, a chip has 10M gates, an activity factor of 10%, $V_{DD} = 1.8$ V, a clock frequency of 500 MHz and an average capacitance per node of 20 fF. In the second case, a chip has 50M gates, an activity factor of 5%, $V_{DD} = 1.2$ V, a clock frequency of 1 GHz and an average capacitance per node of 10 fF. Which design is better and why?

Solution:

Case 1: 10M gates, $\alpha = 0.1$, $C = 20$ fF, $V_{DD} = 1.8$ V, $f_{clk} = 500$ MHz $\rightarrow P = 32.4$ W

Case 2: 50M gates, $\alpha = 0.05$, $C = 10$ fF, $V_{DD} = 1.2$ V, $f_{clk} = 1$ GHz $\rightarrow P = 36$ W

The two power levels are about the same, so it appears that the two designs are about equivalent. Now compute the energy-delay product.

Case 1: EDP $= Pt_p^2 = 32.4 \,(2 \text{ ns})^2 = 130(10^{-18})$J-s

Case 2: EDP $= Pt_p^2 = 36 \,(1 \text{ ns})^2 = 36(10^{-18})$J-s

The second design has a smaller energy-delay product and therefore is superior.

5.10   Summary

For a series stack with three devices, the width of a single equivalent device is

$$W_{eq} = \frac{W_1 W_2 W_3}{W_1 W_2 + W_2 W_3 + W_3 W_1} \qquad \text{(series stack)}$$

For a parallel set of devices, the equivalent width with all devices turned on is

$$W_{eq} = W_1 + W_2 + W_3 \qquad \text{(parallel devices)}$$

Average propagation delay

$$t_P = \frac{t_{PHL} + t_{PLH}}{2}$$

Dynamic and static power:

$$P_{\text{dynamic}} = \alpha_{0 \to 1} C_L V_{DD}^2 f + \alpha_{sc} C_L V_{DD}^2 f = \alpha C_L V_{DD}^2 f$$

$$P_{\text{static}} = (I_{\text{sub}} + I_{pn}) V_{DD}$$

For a standard CMOS gate, the complete power equation is given by

$$P = \alpha C V_{DD}^2 f_{clk} + I_{\text{leak}} V_{DD}$$

For a pseudo-NMOS gate, the complete power equation is given by

$$P = \alpha C V_{DD}^2 f_{clk} + I_{\text{leak}} V_{DD} + \frac{I_{DC} V_{DD}}{2}$$

Energy-delay product:

$$\text{EDP} = \text{PDP} \times t_p = P \times t_p \times t_p$$

REFERENCES

A long list of references exists for this material. Here are a few recent ones.

1. S. M. Kang and Y. Leblebici, *CMOS Digital Integrated Circuits, Analysis and Design*, 3rd ed., McGraw-Hill, 2003.

2. J. Rabaey, *Digital Integrated Circuits: A Designer Perspective*, 2nd ed., Prentice-Hall, Upper Saddle River, NJ, 2003.

3. H. Veendrick, *Deep-Submicron CMOS ICs*, 2nd ed., Kluwer Academic Publishers, Boston, MA, 2000.

4. D. D. Gajski, *Principles of Digital Design*, Prentice-Hall, NJ, 1997.

5. J. P. Uyemura, *CMOS Logic Circuit Design*, Kluwer Academic Publishers, Boston, MA, 1999.

6. A. Bellaouar and M. Elmasry, *Low-Power Digital VLSI Design, Circuits and Systems*, Kluwer Academic Publishers, Boston, MA, 1995.

7. A. Chandrakasan, R. Brodersen, *Low Power Digital CMOS Design*, Kluwer Academic Publishers, Boston, MA, 1995.

8. T. Burd and R. Brodersen, *Energy Efficient Microprocessor Design*, Kluwer Academic Publishers, Boston, MA, 2002.

PROBLEMS

P5.1. Design static CMOS gates that have the following outputs. You may assume the availability of true and complement forms of each signal for the input. Note that you should be able to design each function as a single gate. Device sizing is not required for this problem.

$$(a) \ Out = ABC + BD$$
$$(b) \ Out = AB + \overline{A}C + BC$$
$$(c) \ Out = \overline{A + B + CD} + A$$

P5.2. Implement the functions associated with a full adder in static CMOS using the fact that these are majority functions. That is, if most of the inputs are high, the output will be high, and if most of the inputs are low, the output will be low. A useful property of majority functions is that they are self-duals. The full adder has three inputs, A, B, and C_{in}, and two outputs, Sum and C_{out}. The expressions for the outputs are as follows:

$$C_{out} = AB + C_{in}(A + B)$$
$$Sum = \overline{C_{out}}(A + B + C_{in}) + ABC_{in}$$

P5.3. Design a static CMOS gate that performs the Boolean function $F = (A \oplus B)C + BC$. You can use inverters to generate any complementary inputs needed. Sizing is not required here.

P5.4. Find the logic function for the circuit in Figure P5.4. What is the worst case V_{OH} and V_{OL}? (Note: this is a contrived circuit that would not be used in a real design.)

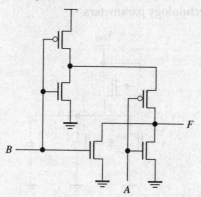

Figure P5.4

P5.5. The circuits of Figure P5.5 are pseudo-NMOS and pseudo-PMOS gates. What function is performed by each gate? Size the transistors so that the pseudo-NMOS gate has $V_{OL} = 0.1V_{DD}$ and the pseudo-PMOS gate has $V_{OH} = 0.9V_{DD}$. Can you suggest why pseudo-PMOS is not favorable (compared to pseudo-NMOS)? All transistors have a length of 2λ.

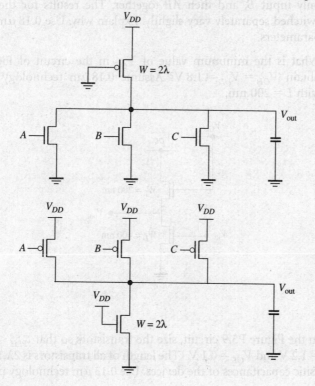

Figure P5.5

P5.6. The circuit of Figure P5.6 is a saturated-enhancement load NMOS NOR gate. Calculate V_{OL} and V_{OH}, and the dc current and power when the output is low. Assume that all the transistors are $2\lambda/2\lambda$ devices. Assume $0.13\ \mu m$ technology parameters.

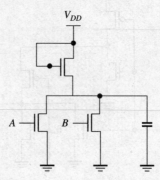

Figure P5.6

P5.7. Calculate V_S of a 2-input NOR gate when one input is switching and with both inputs tied together. The devices sizes are $W_p = 16\lambda$ and $W_n = 4\lambda$. Then use SPICE to find the VTC when switching only input A, only input B, and then AB together. The results for the two inputs switched separately vary slightly. Explain why. Use $0.18\ \mu m$ technology parameters.

P5.8. What is the minimum value of V_{GG} in the circuit of Figure P5.8 to obtain $V_{OH} = V_{DD} = 1.8\ V$? Assume $0.18\ \mu m$ technology parameters, with $L = 200\ nm$.

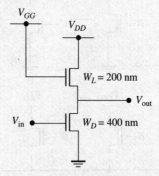

Figure P5.8

P5.9. In the Figure P5.9 circuit, size the transistors so that $t_{PLH} < 50\ ps$; $V_{OH} = 1.2\ V$ and $V_{OL} = 0.1\ V$. (The length of all transistors is 2λ.) Ignore parasitic capacitances of the devices. Use $0.13\ \mu m$ technology parameters.

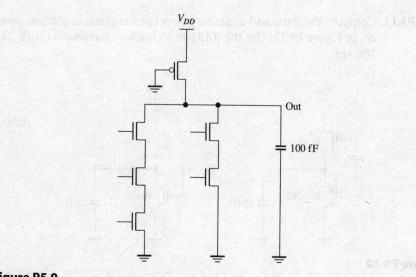

Figure P5.9

P5.10. Design a CMOS gate whose output is Out = $AB + \overline{A}\overline{B}C$. If the minimum length of the transistors is 0.1 μm and the gate is connected to 75 fF load, calculate the width of the transistors so that $t_{PHL} = t_{PLH} < 50$ ps.

P5.11. Calculate the dc static power and dynamic switching power in the circuit in Figure P5.11 if the average switching frequency is $f_{avg} = 100$ MHz. What is the combined average power due to these two components. Use the 0.13 μm technology parameters with $2\lambda = 100$ nm. Ignore device parasitic capacitances.

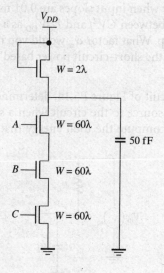

Figure P5.11

P5.12. Compute the static and dynamic power consumption of the two inverters in Figure P5.12. Use the $0.13\ \mu$m technology parameters with $2\lambda = 100$ nm.

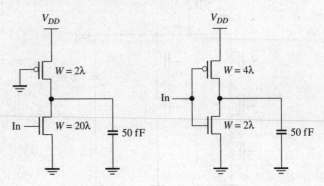

Figure P5.12

Sketch the VTC of the inverters and show on the graph in which region we have power due to dc current, subthreshold current, and short-circuit current.

P5.13. In this question, the idea is to develop a simple equation for the total switching power for $0.18\ \mu$m technology that also incorporates the short-circuit power. To do this, use HSPICE to compare the amount of power due to CV^2f versus power due to short-circuit current, $I_{SC}V_{DD}$ in a 4X inverter driving three different load capacitances: 20 fF, 40 fF, and 80 fF. For the same three load capacitances determine the two components of power when input slopes are 0.01 ns, 0.1 ns, and 0.2 ns. Build a table of ratios between CV^2f and $I_{SC}V_{DD}$ as a function of capacitive load and input ramp. What factor α_{sc} would you multiply the CV^2f power by to incorporate the short-circuit power based on this table? (Assume that $f = 200$ Mhz.)

P5.14. For the RC circuit of Figure P5.14, determine the total energy delivered by the voltage source to the circuit when a step input from 0 to V_{DD} is applied. Next compute the total energy that is stored by the capacitor.

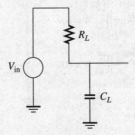

Figure P5.14

What happened to the rest of the energy that was delivered by the voltage source?

P5.15. Do you expect the overall power consumption of a synchronous digital system to increase or decrease when temperature increases (assume the clock frequency does not change)? Explain.

P5.16. Design an SR latch in $0.13\,\mu$m CMOS using NAND gates to deliver a delay of 400 ps from S to Q and from R to $\overline{Q}$. Assume that the total load to be driven by Q and $\overline{Q}$ is 100 fF.

P5.17. The voltage waveforms shown in Figure P5.17 are applied to the JK master-slave flip-flop illustrated in Figure 5.20. With the flip-flop initially reset, show the resulting waveform at the Q output of the master and slave latches.

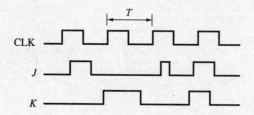

Figure P5.17

P5.18. Repeat the above problem for the JK edge-triggered flip-flop shown in Figure 5.21. Assume the flip-flop is initially set.

P5.19. Implement a positive-edge triggered D flip-flop with set and reset inputs using only NAND3 gates (i.e., no inverters). The inputs should be S, R, D, and CK, while the outputs are Q and $\overline{Q}$. Number the NAND gates 1 through 6. Then, answer the following questions:

(a) With CK = D = low and S = R = high, determine the output state of each gate (1 or 0). Assume the flip-flop is initially set.

(b) Repeat part (a) after CK = high.

High-Speed CMOS Logic Design

6.1   Introduction

This chapter addresses the issues of high-speed logic design in CMOS technology. When designing any logic circuit, we seek to find a combination of gates and gate sizes that perform the desired function and satisfy the timing requirements. The correct functionality is obtained by the proper selection of logic gates, while the timing requirements are satisfied by proper gate sizing. Often, we try to design a logic circuit to run as fast as possible so that the clock cycle can be minimized. In the process of optimizing the logic circuit, we will encounter logic paths that have the longest delays from input to output. These are the so-called *critical paths*. If we reduce the delays along the critical paths, the worst-case delay is reduced, and the speed of the circuit is increased. The delay of each gate is controlled by its driving resistance and the load capacitance. In this chapter, we first focus on detailed delay calculation for logic gates and then turn our attention to the optimization of critical paths. Our overall goal is to maximize the speed of a circuit, while minimizing the area and power dissipation.

In the last chapter, we used a simple switching delay model to compute device sizes for inverters. Here we examine detailed calculations for the switching delay of a logic gate driving a load capacitance, C_L. The currents available to charge and discharge C_L are the drain currents of the driver and load transistors. These drain currents are a function of both V_{in} and V_{out}. Accurate simulation results, in which V_{in} and V_{out} are both changing with time while satisfying the nonlinear dc device equations, can be obtained point by point in the time domain using SPICE or a similar program. However, we would like to be able to analyze circuits quickly using "back-of-the-envelope" hand calculations. With suitable simplifying approximations, a first-order hand analysis is possible. Simplified analyses of this sort are helpful in developing insight into circuit performance and in making the most effective use of subsequent computer simulations.

For hand analysis of a transient circuit response, we first approximate the input waveform by a step function. In this approximation, the input step is assumed to occur at the 50% point of the actual input waveform. Later we will remove this assumption and compute delays when the input is a ramp function. For now, assume an ideal step function as the input.

When we discuss the delay of a path through a logic circuit, we need to define the precise meaning of delay. In Figure 6.1a, a series of three gates are connected to form a logic path from input to output. The switching delay from input to output is referred to as the *propagation delay*. This notion of propagation delay can be defined in a variety of different ways. In all cases, we have to define reference points along the waveform transition from high to low or low to high at which the delay is measured.

One possible reference point is the switching threshold, V_S, from the voltage transfer characteristics, as shown in Figure 6.1b. This is the most sensible definition since the input and output are at the same voltage by the definition of V_S. However, the switching threshold varies from one gate to another and depends on which

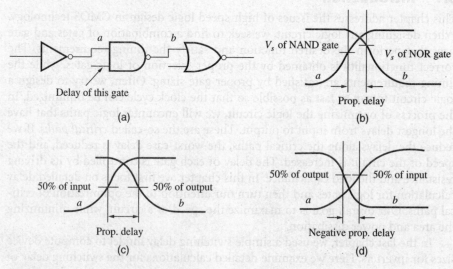

Figure 6.1
Definitions of propagation delay.

input switches. It would take some effort to compute this value for each gate in the logic path before we perform a delay calculation. Therefore, it is not a practical reference point for hand calculation.

Another approach is to use the 50% point of the input and output, as shown in Figure 6.1c. This is a reasonable definition for the propagation delay and is independent of the gate type. In fact, most signals have a switching threshold that is approximately equal to the 50% point. One problem is that it is possible for the 50% point of an output to occur before the 50% point of the input due to different rise and fall times, as shown in Figure 6.1d. Therefore, we have to be prepared to handle negative propagation delays if we use the 50% point as the switching point. Most signals have similar rise/fall times so we should not encounter negative delays very often. If a negative delay does arise, it indicates that we have a slow gate in the path and we may need to fix the design. Overall, this 50% definition is the most practical and intuitive reference point for propagation delay.

Occasionally, the rise and fall times of signals are of interest in delay calculation. This type of calculation also requires a consistent definition. If we simply use the time to transition from V_{OL} to V_{OH} or vice versa, we have a problem in defining exactly when the signal begins to switch and when it stops switching. For example, if we consider an exponent signal, such as

$$V_{out}(t) = V_{DD}\, e^{-t/RC}$$

we might be tempted to compute the value of t with $V_{out} = V_{OL}$. We would find that the value of t is infinite in this case—a rather impractical solution. Instead, designers use a 10% to 90% delay for rise times and 90% to 10% delay for fall times. This is shown in Figure 6.2a and Figure 6.2b for rise and fall times, respectively.

6.2   Switching Time Analysis

With these definitions in place, we now consider the switching characteristics of the CMOS inverter of Figure 6.3a. When the *input* makes a step change from V_{OH} to V_{OL}, the pull-down transistor turns off while the pull-up transistor turns on. The

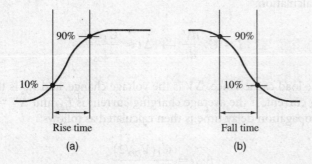

Figure 6.2
Rise and fall time definitions.

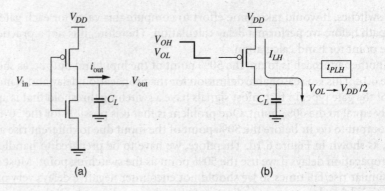

(a) (b)

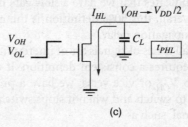

(c)

Figure 6.3
CMOS inverter delay calculation.

situation is illustrated by Figure 6.3b. The time required for V_{out} to charge from V_{OL} to the 50% point can be calculated by assuming that the lumped load capacitance is charged by the current through the pull-up device.

Similarly, when the *input* makes step transition from V_{OL} to V_{OH}, the pull-down transistor turns on while the pull-up transistor shuts off. The situation is illustrated by Figure 6.3c. The time required for V_{out} to discharge from V_{OH} to the 50% point can be calculated by assuming that the lumped load capacitance is discharged by the current through the pull-down device. In both cases, we can use the following formula for the calculation:

$$I = C_L \frac{dV}{dt} \rightarrow \Delta t \approx \frac{C_L \Delta V}{I_{DS}}$$

where C_L is the load capacitance, ΔV is the voltage change, and I_{DS} is the charging or discharging current. If the average charging current is I_{LH} and $\Delta V = V_{DD}/2$, the *low-to-high* propagation delay time is then calculated as follows:

$$t_{PLH} = \frac{C_L(V_{DD}/2)}{I_{LH}} \tag{6.1}$$

The propagation delay from *high to low* is calculated in the same manner as above with an average current of I_{HL}.

$$t_{PHL} = \frac{C_L(V_{DD}/2)}{I_{HL}} \tag{6.2}$$

The average propagation delay is defined as

$$t_P = \frac{t_{PLH} + t_{PHL}}{2} \tag{6.3}$$

We now compute expressions for the propagation delay for the CMOS inverter beginning with a step input from V_{OL} to V_{OH}. Using Figure 6.3 as a guide, we first compute t_{PHL} using Equation (6.2). The only unknown is I_{HL}.

To compute this value, we need to first determine the region of operation of the NMOS device, and this involves a calculation of V_{Dsat}. Since V_{Dsat} is technology-dependent, we will illustrate the steps with 0.13 μm technology parameters. Using $V_{DD} = 1.2$ V, $V_T = 0.4$ V, and $E_C L = 0.6$ V

$$V_{Dsat} = \frac{(V_{GS} - V_T)E_C L}{(V_{GS} - V_T) + E_C L} = \frac{(1.2 - 0.4)(0.6)}{(1.2 - 0.4) + (0.6)} \cong 0.34 \text{ V}$$

Since the output is making a transition from 1.2 V to 0.6 V, which implies that $V_{DS} > V_{Dsat}$ at all times, the NMOS device remains in saturation for the entire duration of interest for t_{PHL}. Therefore, the average current is simply the saturation current for the *n*-channel device, $(I_{Dsat})_n$.

$$t_{PHL} = \frac{C_L(V_{DD}/2)}{(I_{Dsat})_n} \tag{6.4a}$$

In the previous chapter, we found that $t_{PHL} = 0.7R_N C_L$. If we compare this formula to (6.4a), we see that

$$R_N = \frac{V_{DD}/2}{0.7(I_{Dsat})_n} \tag{6.4b}$$

Next, we compute t_{PLH} using Equation (6.1). The only unknown is I_{LH} due to the PMOS device. For the *p*-channel pull-up device, the saturation voltage is given by

$$V_{Dsat} = \frac{(1.2 - 0.4)2.4}{(1.2 - 0.4) + 2.4} = 0.6 \text{ V}$$

The PMOS device is also in saturation during the transition. Based on this, we can use the equation

$$t_{PLH} = \frac{C_L(V_{DD}/2)}{(I_{Dsat})_p} \tag{6.5a}$$

If we compare this formula to the one used in the previous chapter, we see that

$$R_P = \frac{V_{DD}/2}{0.7(I_{Dsat})_p} \qquad (6.5b)$$

By considering unit-size devices, we can compute R_{eqn} and R_{eqp} from Equations (6.4b) and (6.5b).

Example 6.1   **Hand Calculation of Effective Resistance**

Problem:

Using 0.13 μm technology parameters, compute R_{eqn} and R_{eqp} from the equations above for unit-sized devices.

Solution:

For the NMOS device,

$$
\begin{aligned}
I_{Dsat} &= \frac{W_N v_{sat} C_{ox} (V_{DD} - V_{TN})^2}{(V_{DD} - V_{TN}) + E_{CN} L_N} \\
&= \frac{(0.1)(10^{-4})8(10^6)1.6(10^{-6})(1.2 - 0.4)^2}{(1.2 - 0.4) + 0.6} \approx 60\ \mu A
\end{aligned}
$$

$$\therefore R_{eqn} = \frac{1.2/2}{0.7(60\ \mu A)} = 14.5\ k\Omega$$

For the PMOS device,

$$
\begin{aligned}
I_{Dsat} &= \frac{W_P v_{sat} C_{ox} (V_{DD} - |V_{TP}|)^2}{(V_{DD} - |V_{TP}|) + E_{CP} L_P} \\
&= \frac{(0.1)(10^{-4})8(10^6)1.6(10^{-6})(1.2 - 0.4)^2}{(1.2 - 0.4) + 2.4} \approx 25\ \mu A
\end{aligned}
$$

$$\therefore R_{eqp} = \frac{1.2/2}{0.7(25\ \mu A)} = 33.5\ k\Omega$$

It is interesting to compare the above results with SPICE simulations. In fact, we have been using the results from SPICE in all timing calculations thus far

$$R_{eqn} \approx 12.5\ k\Omega/\square$$

$$R_{eqp} \approx 30\ k\Omega/\square$$

The hand calculations and SPICE are in close agreement implying that our assumptions are all basically correct. The actual currents in SPICE are somewhat higher than our hand calculations producing smaller values of R_{eq}.

From these values, we can compute R_N and R_P by dividing them by the W/L of each device:

$$R_N = R_{eqn}\left(\frac{L}{W}\right)_n$$

$$R_P = R_{eqp}\left(\frac{L}{W}\right)_p$$

(6.6)

We will find that R_P and R_N work well for timing calculation, but these values *should not* be used for any other purpose. These values are obtained from the timing equations and therefore are only expected to work in the timing applications. In reality, the on-resistance is nonlinear and its value depends on the applied voltages.

6.2.1   Gate Sizing Revisited—Velocity Saturation Effects

Since we are already discussing the issues of proper sizing, we should go back and examine the CMOS NAND and NOR sizing operations. Consider the three standard gates shown in Figure 6.4. The inverter has a pull-up device of $2W$ and a pull-down device of W. The NAND gate has two pull-ups that are $2W$ each and two pull-downs that are $2W$ each. The NOR gate has two pull-ups that are $4W$ each and two pull-downs that are W each. These sizes are accurate for the quadratic device model, but do not incorporate the effects of velocity saturation. Some adjustments are now introduced to include velocity saturation.

To understand the effect, we compare a single device with a pair of stacked devices, as shown in Figure 6.5. Ignoring all capacitances except C_L for the moment, we would find that the single device of size W in Figure 6.5a takes longer to discharge the load capacitance than two series stacked $2W$ devices of Figure 6.5b. The reason for this can be explained based on the region of operation of the transistors in the two cases. The single M_0 device is in saturation for the entire transition of the output from V_{DD} to $V_{DD}/2$ and delivers a current of I_0. The two series devices, M_1 and M_2, each operate in different regions during the transition from V_{DD} to $V_{DD}/2$. We know that both conduct the same amount of current. To satisfy this requirement, M_1

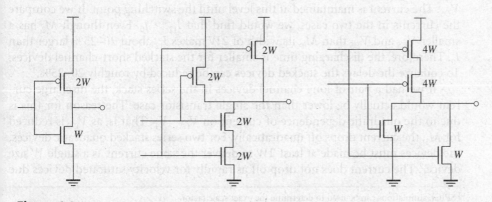

Figure 6.4
CMOS gate sizing without including velocity saturation.

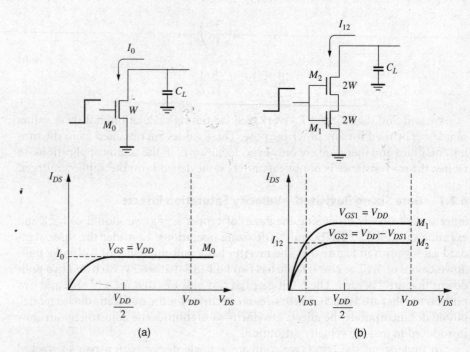

Figure 6.5

Stacked devices with velocity saturation.

is forced into the linear region with a smaller V_{DS1} while M_2 operates in the saturation region with a larger V_{DS2}.

When these operating conditions are established, the resulting current through both devices is equal to I_{12}, the saturation region current of M_2. This is illustrated in Figure 6.5b. The upper curve is for M_1 with $V_{GS1} = V_{DD}$, and the lower curve is for M_2 with $V_{GS2} = V_{DD} - V_{DS1}$. M_2 sets the current value based on its values of V_{GS} and V_{DS}. The current is maintained at this level until the switching point. If we compare the currents in the two cases, we would find that $I_{12} > I_0$. Even though M_2 has a smaller V_{GS} and V_{DS} than M_0, its width of $2W$ makes I_{12} about 20–25% larger than I_0. Therefore, the discharging time is smaller for the stacked short-channel devices. To equalize the delays the stacked devices can be reduced by roughly 20–25%.[1]

If we had a pair of long channel devices in the series stack, the discharge current would actually be lower than the single transistor case. The reason for this is due to the quadratic dependence of current on $V_{GS} - V_T$. That is, as V_{GS} is reduced for M_2, the current drops off quadratically. For two series stacked quadratic devices, the devices must be made at least $2W$ to deliver the same current as a single W size device.[2] The current does not drop off as rapidly for velocity saturated devices due

---

[1] SPICE simulations can be used to determine the exact scale factor.
[2] When body-effect is included, the size must be slightly larger than $2W$.

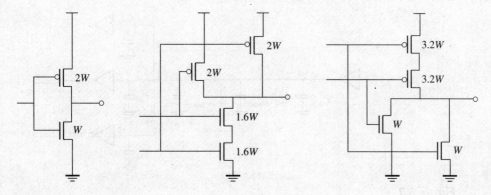

Figure 6.6
Transistor sizing for NAND and NOR including velocity saturation.

to a more linear dependence of current on $V_{GS} - V_T$. As a result, they are able to deliver a larger current.

The NAND2 and NOR2 gates can be resized including this effect, as shown in Figure 6.6. Here we have assumed that stacked devices must be scaled by 0.8 to produce the same current as a single device. The NAND gate pull-downs are resized to $1.6W$ to account for the velocity saturation effects. Similarly, the NOR gate pull-ups are resized to $3.2W$ to account for velocity saturation. These values will produce rise and fall delays that are equal to the reference inverter, assuming that the loading capacitance is a fixed value C_L. The correct values for a particular technology can be derived from SPICE simulation.

In general, there are many additional factors that control the final device sizes. For example, body-effect tends to reduce the current of the top device in the stack so a slightly larger device size is preferable as the number of transistors in the stack increases. There are also additional self-capacitances in NAND and NOR gates that must be charged and discharged. Furthermore, device sizes determine noise margins, and rise and fall times. When all factors are considered, the original sizes in Figure 6.4 provide satisfactory results. Therefore, we will continue to use the sizes shown in Figure 6.4 when sizing devices, although we now know how to compute more accurate values if needed.

6.3   Detailed Load Capacitance Calculation

So far, we have assumed a fixed external loading on the output of logic gates. The load capacitance is actually comprised of three components as shown in Figure 6.7: the self-loading capacitance, the interconnect or wire capacitance, and the fanout capacitance. For delay calculation, we sum these individual quantities to obtain a lumped capacitance:

$$C_{\text{load}} = C_{\text{self}} + C_{\text{wire}} + C_{\text{fanout}} \qquad (6.7)$$

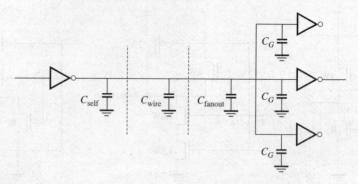

Figure 6.7
Components of the loading capacitance on a gate.

Although each of these components is somewhat complicated, our goal is to quickly compute the load capacitance using simplified equations.

6.3.1 Fanout Gate Capacitance

The first type of loading capacitance to consider is the fanout capacitance due to the inputs of subsequent gates, C_G. This capacitance can be large, depending on the number of fanouts being driven by the gate. The total fanout capacitance is the sum of each of the gate capacitances, as shown in Figure 6.7:

$$C_{\text{fanout}} = \Sigma C_G$$

The capacitances for each fanout, assuming that they are all inverters, are illustrated in Figure 6.8. We are interested in the specific terms associated with V_{in} since we are driving this input. Each transistor has a term due to the thin-oxide and two terms due to the overlap capacitance. The capacitances that must be taken into account are: C_{Gn}, C_{Gp}, and C_{OL}.

From Chapter 2, we know that the thin-oxide capacitance is voltage dependent, but since we are driving the transistor from the gate node, we can use $C_{ox}WL$ to compute its worst-case value. The total input capacitance for the inverter is the sum of all the components in Figure 6.8:

$$
\begin{aligned}
C_G &= C_{Gn} + 2C_{OL} + C_{Gp} + 2C_{OL} \\
&= C_{ox}LW_n + 2C_{ol}W_n + C_{ox}LW_p + 2C_{ol}W_p \\
&= (C_{ox}L + 2C_{ol})(W_n + W_p)
\end{aligned}
\tag{6.8}
$$

The leading term in this expression is technology dependent and can be pre-computed. For $0.13 \, \mu m$ technology, the value of $C_{ox}L = 1.6 \times 10^{-6}$ F/cm$^2 \times$

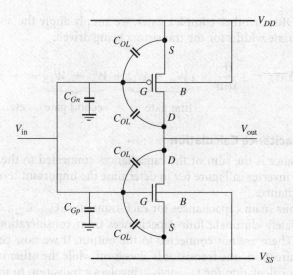

Figure 6.8
Input capacitance calculation.

$0.1\ \mu\text{m} = 1.6\ \text{fF}/\mu\text{m}$. In Chapter 2, we approximated the overlap capacitance as $C_{ol} = 0.25\ \text{fF}/\mu\text{m}$. Therefore, we now redefine C_g as

$$C_g = C_{ox}L + 2C_{ol} = 1.6\ \text{fF}/\mu\text{m} + 2(0.25\ \text{fF}/\mu\text{m}) \cong 2\ \text{fF}/\mu\text{m} \quad (6.9)$$

The total capacitance due to the thin-oxide and the overlap capacitance is roughly $2\ \text{fF}/\mu\text{m}$. This value has been almost constant for over 20 years. We will use $2\ \text{fF}/\mu\text{m}$ for the gate capacitance and multiply it by the width of the devices to obtain the total capacitance.

For an inverter

$$C_G = C_g W = 2\ \text{fF}/\mu\text{m} \times W_n + 2\ \text{fF}/\mu\text{m} \times W_p$$

$$= 2\ \text{fF}/\mu\text{m}(W_n + W_p)$$

If we are driving n identical gates with a capacitance of C_G each, then the total fanout capacitance is

$$C_{\text{fanout}} = \Sigma C_G = n \times C_G = n \times \Sigma C_g W$$

If we had n different inverters, then we could just add them up as follows:

$$\therefore \Sigma C_G = 2\,\frac{\text{fF}}{\mu\text{m}} \times (\underbrace{W_{p1} + W_{n1}}_{\text{first inverter}} + \underbrace{W_{p2} + W_{n2}}_{\text{second inverter}} + \cdots)$$

For NANDs, NORs, or other complex gates, we simply apply the above equation with the appropriate widths for the transistors being driven:

$$\therefore \Sigma C_G = 2\frac{\text{fF}}{\mu\text{m}} \times (\underbrace{W_{p1} + W_{n1}}_{\text{first gate}} + \underbrace{W_{p2} + W_{n2}}_{\text{second gate}} + \cdots)$$

etc.

6.3.2 Self-Capacitance Calculation

The self-capacitance is the sum of the capacitances connected to the output, V_{out}. We examine the inverter in Figure 6.9 to determine the important terms to include in the self-capacitance.

There are four main capacitances for each transistor: C_{GS}, C_{GD}, C_{DB}, and C_{SB}. We can immediately eliminate four capacitances from consideration: C_{GSn}, C_{GSp}, C_{SBn}, and C_{SBp}. These are not connected to the output. If we now consider a step input in either direction, one transistor is always off while the other one is in saturation. Since our calculation for t_{PHL} or t_{PLH} involves a transition to the 50% point, we can assume that the transistors are in saturation or cutoff. In either region, the gate-to-drain capacitance, C_{GD}, is negligible. This leaves only the overlap capacitances from gate-to-drain, and one junction capacitance per device, C_{DBn} and C_{DBp}.

The overlap capacitance must be handled in a special manner since it is connected from the input to output. When the input makes a transition from 0 to V_{DD}, the output makes a transition from V_{DD} to 0. As a result, the overlap capacitance experiences a voltage swing of $2V_{DD}$. We can model this by assuming that the swing is only V_{DD} and then doubling the size of the capacitance. This process of doubling

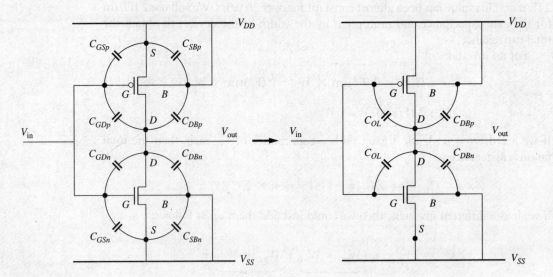

Figure 6.9

Output capacitance calculation.

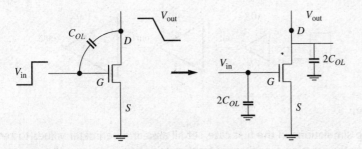

Figure 6.10
Handling the overlap capacitance using Miller Effect.

the capacitance value, commonly referred to as *Miller Effect* modeling, is shown in Figure 6.10. It implies that the output must deliver twice as much charge to the overlap capacitance to account for the fact that the input and output are switching by the same amount in opposite directions.

We can now compute the total self-capacitance of the inverter. It is simply the junction capacitances plus the overlap capacitances due to fringing and lateral diffusion (with the inclusion of Miller Effect):

$$C_{self} = C_{DBn} + C_{DBp} + 2C_{OL} + 2C_{OL}$$

$$\doteq C_{jn}W_n + C_{jp}W_p + 2C_{ol}(W_n + W_p) \qquad (6.10)$$

$$= C_{eff}(W_n + W_p)$$

Here, we relate the capacitance to an effective capacitance per width, C_{eff}. To simplify the calculations, we have combined C_{jn} and C_{jp} into one term. As we saw in Chapter 2, the junction capacitance depends on the doping levels, the type of junction, the voltage transition, and the areas of the source and drain regions. However, for hand calculation purposes, it is convenient to combine them. The average junction capacitance for the two junctions is approximately 0.5 fF/μm for 0.13 μm technology. The overlap capacitance is roughly 0.25 fF/μm. Therefore,

$$C_{eff} = C_j + 2C_{ol} \approx 0.5 \text{ fF}/\mu m + 2(0.25 \text{ fF}/\mu m) \approx 1 \text{ fF}/\mu m$$

The total self-capacitance is computed by multiplying C_{eff} by the device width, W.

Using SPICE to Determine C_g and C_{eff} in 0.18 μm Technology   **Example 6.2**

Problem:

Find C_g and C_{eff} for an 0.18 μm technology from SPICE using the following circuit. The 10X inverter drives a 40X inverter which drives a 160X inverter. Apply positive and negative step inputs and measure the propagation delays at node *out*. Devise a way of extracting the two desired capacitance parameters.

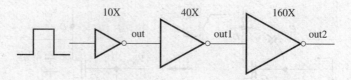

Solution:

Run two simulations. In the first case, set all area and perimeter values to zero to eliminate the junction capacitances from consideration. Measure the propagation delay for both the rising and falling cases and extract C_g. Next, set all the area and perimeter values to their proper quantities and measure the propagation delays again. The increase in delay is due to junction capacitances so the value of C_{eff} can be extracted.

```
*Cg Calculation (no area or perimeter specified)
.param      Supply=1.8                 *Set value of Vdd
.lib        'bsim3v3.cmosp18.lib'      *Set 0.18um library
.opt        scale=0.1u                 *Set lambda
.global vdd     gnd
vdd         vdd           gnd 1.8
m1      out in1 vdd vdd       pch    l=2 w=40  ad=0    as=0 pd=0    ps=0
m2      out in1 0 0           nch    l=2 w=20  ad=0    as=0 pd=0    ps=0
m3      out1 out vdd vdd      pch    l=2 w=160 ad=0    as=0 pd=0    ps=0
m4      out1 out 0 0          nch    l=2 w=80  ad=0    as=0 pd=0    ps=0
m5      out2 out1 vdd vdd     pch    l=2 w=640 ad=0    as=0 pd=0    ps=0
m6      out2 out1 0 0         nch    l=2 w=320 ad=0    as=0 pd=0    ps=0
vin1      in1       gnd  pwl (0 0 9ps 0 10ps 1.8 199ps 1.8 200ps 0)
.tran 5ps 350ps
.print tran v(in1) v(out)
.end
```

The propagation delay for the falling case is 40ps and the rising case is 55ps. We can use the delay equation to solve for C_g for these two cases.

$$t_{PHL} = 0.7\, R_N C_{fanout}$$

$$\therefore 40\ \text{ps} = 0.7\, \frac{(12.5\ \text{k}\Omega)}{10} C_g(8\ \mu m + 16\ \mu m)$$

$$\therefore C_g \cong 1.9\ \text{fF}/\mu m$$

$$t_{PLH} = 0.7\, R_P C_{fanout}$$

$$\therefore 55\ \text{ps} = 0.7\, \frac{(30\ \text{k}\Omega)}{20} C_g(8\ \mu m + 16\ \mu m)$$

$$\therefore C_g \cong 2.2\ \text{fF}/\mu m$$

The results show that the gate capacitance is slightly higher for the low to high transition. An average value of $C_g = 2$ fF/μm is obtained, as expected. Next we run a simulation with the areas and perimeters specified and compute the value of C_{eff} based on the increase in the propagation delays relative to the previous SPICE runs.

```
*Ceff Calculation (areas and perimeters specified)
.param      Supply=1.8          *Set value of Vdd
.lib        'bsim3v3.cmosp18.lib'    *Set 0.18um library
.opt        scale=0.1u          *Set lambda
.global vdd gnd
vdd       vdd  gnd 1.8
m1        out  in1 vdd vdd    pch  l=2 w=40 ad=200 as=200 pd=40 ps=40
m2        out  in1 0 0        nch  l=2 w=20 ad=100 as=100 pd=20 ps=20
m3        out1 out vdd vdd    pch  l=2 w=160 ad=800 as=800 pd=160 ps=160
m4        out1 out 0 0        nch  l=2 w=80 ad=200 as=200 pd=80 ps=80
m5        out2 out1 vdd vdd   pch  l=2 w=640 ad=3200 as=3200 pd=640 ps=640
m6        out2 out1 0 0       nch  l=2 w=320 ad=1600 as=1600 pd=320 ps=320
vin1      in1       gnd pwl (0 0 9ps 0 10ps 1.8 199ps 1.8 200ps 0)
.tran 5ps 350ps
.print tran v(in1) v(out)
.end
```

The propagation delay for the falling case is 44 ps and the rising case is 59 ps. We can use the same delay equations to solve for C_{eff} for these two cases.

$$t_{PHL} = 0.7\ R_N C_{fanout}$$

$$\therefore 44 \text{ ps} = 0.7\ \frac{(12.5 \text{ k}\Omega)}{10}\ (C_g(24\ \mu m) + C_{eff}\ (6\ \mu m))$$

$$\therefore C_{eff} \cong 0.8 \text{ fF}/\mu m$$

$$t_{PLH} = 0.7\ R_P C_{fanout}$$

$$\therefore 59 \text{ ps} = 0.7\ \frac{(30 \text{ k}\Omega)}{20}\ (C_g(24\ \mu m) + C_{eff}\ (6\ \mu m))$$

$$\therefore C_{eff} \cong 0.7 \text{ fF}/\mu m$$

The results are also close to the values computed by hand calculations. It is acceptable to use $C_{eff} = 1$ fF/μm for hand calculations since it slightly over-estimates the capacitance. In fact, when using ramp inputs, the output capacitance increases slightly due to a Miller Effect on C_{gd} of any device in the linear region of operation. We will find that 1 fF/μm is a more suitable value.

We now extend our analysis to CMOS NAND and NOR gates. Since the considerations for NANDs and NORs are similar in nature, we will illustrate the process with the NOR gate in Figure 6.11. A symbolic layout of the NOR gate is shown in

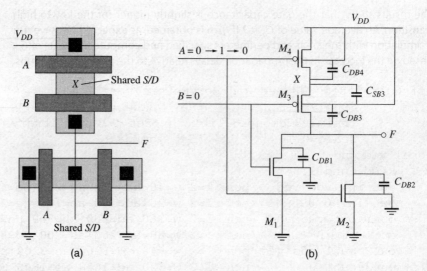

Figure 6.11
Self-capacitances for a NOR gate.

Figure 6.11a and the corresponding transistor schematic in Figure 6.11b. To compute the worst-case self-capacitance, consider the pull-down case first with a propagation delay of t_{PHL}. The output node must be discharged to Gnd by one of the pull-down devices. In the worst-case, input A switches from low to high while B remains low since the capacitances at both the output node and the internal node X must be discharged. Assuming a step change at input A, the capacitance at the output node is comprised of the indicated junction capacitances of the n-channel and p-channel devices. Therefore,

$$C_{\text{self}} = \underbrace{C_{DB1} + C_{DB2}}_{n^{+}\text{shared } S/D} + C_{DB3} + \underbrace{C_{SB3} + C_{DB4}}_{p^{+}\text{shared } S/D}$$

$$= C_{DB12} + C_{DB3} + C_{SDB34} \tag{6.11}$$

Note that the two n-channel devices have a single shared source/drain region at node F, which we have called C_{DB12}, and the two p-channel devices have a shared drain region at node X, referred to as C_{SDB34}. We should not "double count" these junction capacitances. The layout of a gate will dictate whether source/drain sharing must be incorporated into the calculations. Therefore, a sketch of the layout is useful when computing self-capacitance.

Note also that if input A stays low but B goes high, the only output capacitances to be charged are $C_{DB12} + C_{DB3}$. This will lead to a faster switching time. However, we are not interested in this case since it is not the worst case.

We now consider the analysis for the charging from low to high at the output. If we assume that input A switches from high to low while input B remains low, then the total capacitance to be charged is given by Equation (6.11). However, if B switches rather than A, only the capacitances connected to F are charged up. Therefore, this is the best-case situation and of less interest for delay calculation. A similar kind of analysis can be carried out for the NAND gate and is left as an exercise for the reader.

Draw a simplified layout of a 2-input NAND gate and determine the worst-case capacitance components at the output assuming a step input. Specify the input combinations that create the worst-case scenarios.

Exercise 6.1

Capacitance Calculation for 3-input NAND Gate

Example 6.3

Problem:

For the NAND3 gate below, determine the worst-case capacitance components at the input and output assuming a step input. Express the result in terms of W, C_g, and C_{eff}. Consider the source/drain sharing carefully.

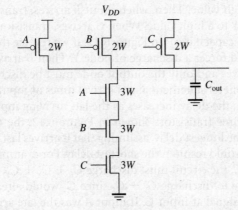

Solution:

The worst-case input capacitance is simply: $C_{in} = C_g(W_n + W_p) = C_g(3W + 2W) = C_g(5W)$.

The output capacitance is the self-capacitance. The n-channel transistors share source/drain regions at their intermediate nodes. Two of the three p-channel devices also share their source/drain region. Therefore,

$$C_{load} = C_{eff}(W_n + W_n + W_n) + C_{eff}(W_p + W_p)$$

$$= C_{eff}(3W + 3W + 3W) + C_{eff}(2W + 2W)$$

$$= C_{eff}(13W)$$

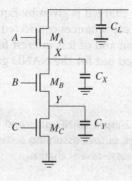

Figure 6.12
Propagation delay depends on arrival time of A, B, and C.

One aspect that is implicit in the descriptions above is that the actual delay depends on the order in which inputs switch. We illustrate the input-dependent delay concepts with the series stack of Figure 6.12. Assume that all inputs are low and the output node is high. If input A arrives first, transistor M_A will turn on and charge node X to a high value. Then, when input B arrives, transistor M_B turns on and charges up node Y to a high value. When C arrives, transistor M_C turns on and must discharge all the capacitances in Figure 6.12. If we reverse the order of arrival, then C arrives first and forces a discharge of node Y. Then B arrives and discharges node X. Finally A arrives and only the output node must be discharged.

We can make a general statement about arrival times of inputs and its effect on delay. In a series stack, the delay increases as the late arriving input is further from the output. For the three transistors shown in Figure 6.12, the C input closest to ground would cause the longest delay, assuming that it arrives last, while the A input closest to the output would result in the shortest delay. For example, if the late arriving signal is at input C, the circuit must discharge $C_L + C_X + C_Y$. If input B arrived late then it would have to discharge $C_L + C_X$ since C_Y would already be discharged by an earlier arriving signal at input C. If input A was the late arriving signal, then it would only need to discharge C_L, since C_Y and C_X would have already been discharged.

There are a number of ways to design around this delay difference. If we know which input is going to be delayed, we could make sure that it was closest to the output; that is, we would reorder the inputs such that the earliest signals arrive lower in the stack and the latest signals arrive near the top of the stack. In Figure 6.12, we hope that A arrives last and C arrives first.

Another approach is to resize the devices to accommodate the worst-case situation. To reduce delay, we should size $M_C > M_B > M_A$. Each device is progressively larger as we move from the output to ground since each one must discharge a progressively larger capacitance. The problem with this approach is that the device capacitances are increased as the device sizes are increased. The layout of each transistor requires more diffusion area due to the spacing requirements of design rules. The correspondingly larger capacitances act to offset the advantages of progressive sizing.

6.3.3 Wire Capacitance

A third component of load capacitance is wire capacitance, or interconnect capacitance. In the past, the interconnect capacitance was not a significant part of the overall capacitance calculation due to the fact that the wires were relatively short and the devices were very large. Today, wires are much longer and devices are much smaller so we need to include this component in the load capacitance calculation. For very short wires, such as those less than a few microns, we can ignore the capacitance. For wires that are greater than a few microns, we should include the lumped wire capacitance. For very long wires, we will have to deal with distributed RC effects and capacitive coupling effects, as described in Chapter 10. In the meantime, for hand calculations, the lumped wire capacitance can be computed as

$$C_{wire} = C_{int}L_W = 0.2 \text{ fF}/\mu\text{m} \times (\text{wirelength}) \tag{6.12}$$

Capacitance Calculation for Inverter　　　　　　　　　　　　　**Example 6.4**

Problem:

A CMOS inverter has a pull-up device that is $8\lambda:2\lambda$ and a pull-down device that is $4\lambda:2\lambda$. It drives four identical inverters. Compute the load capacitance using $0.18\ \mu\text{m}$ technology parameters. Assume that the wire capacitance is negligible.

Solution:

Fanout capacitance: inverter is driving four identical inverters:

$$C_{fanout} = 4 \times C_g(W_N + W_P) = 4(2 \text{ fF}/\mu\text{m})(0.4\ \mu\text{m} + 0.8\ \mu\text{m}) = 9.6 \text{ fF}$$

Self-capacitance:

$$C_{self} = C_{eff}(W_N + W_P) = (1 \text{ fF}/\mu\text{m})(0.4\ \mu\text{m} + 0.8\ \mu\text{m}) = 1.2 \text{ fF}$$

Total capacitance:

$$C_{load} = C_{fanout} + C_{self} + C_{wire} = 9.6 + 1.2 + 0 = 10.8 \text{ fF}$$

6.4 Improving Delay Calculation with Input Slope

So far we have assumed a step input at each gate when computing the delay. In reality, each input behaves more like a ramp with an exponential tail. This increases the delay relative to the step input case. In this section, we explore the effect of a finite input slope on the propagation delay.

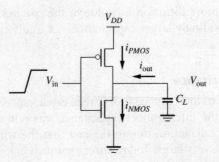

Figure 6.13
KCL at output of CMOS inverter.

Consider the inverter of Figure 6.13 where the input is switching as a ramp function with a given slope. We can apply KCL to the output node to obtain the relationship between the three currents:

$$i_{out} = C_L \frac{dV_{out}}{dt} = i_{NMOS} - i_{PMOS} \tag{6.13}$$

All three currents are a function of V_{in} and V_{out}. We are most interested in the charging and discharging current, i_{out}. It is possible to compute the output current using Equation (6.13) by selecting different values of V_{in} and V_{out}, calculating i_{NMOS} and i_{PMOS}, and then taking their difference. The results of such i_{out} computations are plotted in Figure 6.14 as a contour map on a two-dimensional plane of V_{out} versus V_{in}. Normally the voltage transfer characteristic is plotted in this plane. Here we plot the output current under all possible operating conditions. The regions with the same shading have i_{out} values that are in the same range.

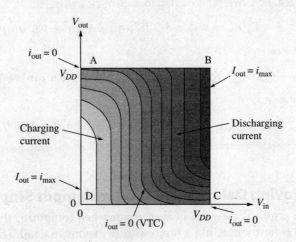

Figure 6.14
Inverter output current as a function of V_{out} and V_{in}.

Notice that the curve in the center of the plot (where $i_{out} = 0$) is exactly the voltage transfer characteristic (VTC). In fact, this line represents the dc operating point of the inverter as the input changes very slowly. However, when the input is varied rapidly, the operating points occur away from the VTC. If the input is increased rapidly, we move to the right of the VTC. There is more NMOS current than PMOS current, so the output capacitance is discharged. If the input is decreased rapidly, we move to the left of the VTC where the current through the PMOS device increases to charge the output capacitance. As we move to contours further away from the VTC in either direction, the current increases in magnitude (whether charging or discharging). Therefore, the VTC curve in the center represents a "valley" if the contour map is viewed as a three-dimensional diagram. As a result, the outermost edges are labeled as $i_{out} = i_{max}$ since these are the regions of highest current levels.

It is instructive to consider what happens on this contour map when a step input or a ramp input is applied. These two cases are shown in Figure 6.15. First consider the step input case of Figure 6.15a. If the input starts at 0 V and the output is at V_{DD}, we are at the top left corner of the plot labeled A. When a positive going step occurs, we move instantaneously to the opposite corner labeled B where $i_{out} = i_{max}$ (since the input is at V_{DD}). Then, the discharging current, due entirely to the NMOS device, follows along the right-most edge of the graph until point C is

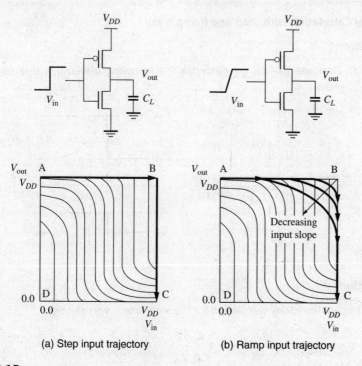

(a) Step input trajectory   (b) Ramp input trajectory

Figure 6.15
Simplified inverter output current as a function of V_{out} and V_{in}.

reached where $i_{out} = 0$. As the NMOS device moves from point B to point C, it switches from saturation to the linear region of operation. A negative going step would start at point C, switch immediately to point D and then eventually return to point A.

Next, examine the positive ramp input case in Figure 6.15b. In this case, the current trajectory depends on the slope of the input ramp. If the slope is high, it behaves similar to the step input case. As the slope is decreased, the trajectory "cuts the corner" as shown in the figure. This implies that the current gradually ramps up to i_{max} rather than instantaneously reaching this value. Therefore, the discharging process will take longer in the ramp case, since there is less current initially to discharge the capacitance.

A similar kind of result is obtained for the negative ramp case except that the "corner-cutting" will be in the vicinity of D on the graph. Again, the effect of the actual input/output trajectory is to decrease the current supplied initially to charge the output. Therefore, the delay increases when a ramp input is applied.

The exact increase in the delay depends on a number of factors, but is ultimately controlled by the output current waveform as a function of time. The example below illustrates how analytical expressions can be obtained for the delay with step and ramp inputs.

Example 6.5   **Delay Calculation with Step and Ramp Inputs**

Problem:

(a) Compute the $t_{PHL,step}$ delay for the following waveforms due to a step input.

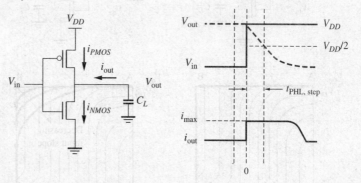

Solution:

The propagation delay calculation for the step case is very simple:

$$i_{out} = i_{max} = C_L \frac{dV_{out}}{dt} = C_L \frac{V_{DD}/2}{t_{PHL,step}}$$

$$\therefore t_{PHL,step} = C_L \frac{V_{DD}/2}{i_{max}}$$

(b) Compute the $t_{PHL,ramp}$ delay for the following waveforms for the input ramp using the corresponding output current. The rise time of the input voltage is t_r.

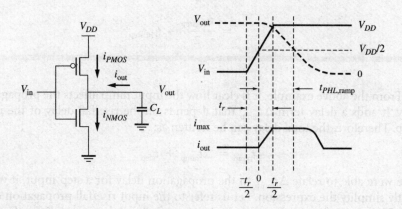

Solution:

The propagation delay for the ramp case can be derived as follows:

$$i_{out} = C_L \frac{dV_{out}}{dt}$$

$$\therefore \int i_{out} \, dt = \int C_L \, dV_{out}$$

$$\therefore \int_0^{t_r/2} i_{max} \frac{t}{t_r/2} \, dt + \int_{t_r/2}^{t_{PHL,ramp}} i_{max} \, dt = C_L \int_0^{V_{DD}/2} dV_{out}$$

$$\therefore \frac{i_{max}}{t_r/2} \frac{t^2}{2} \Big|_0^{t_r/2} + i_{max} \, t \Big|_{t_r/2}^{t_{PHL,ramp}} = C_L V_{DD}/2$$

$$\therefore i_{max} \frac{t_r}{4} + i_{max}(t_{PHL,ramp} - t_r/2) = C_L V_{DD}/2$$

$$\therefore t_{PHL,ramp} = \frac{t_r}{4} + \frac{C_L V_{DD}/2}{i_{max}}$$

(c) Write an expression for the ramp delay in terms of the step delay and the input rise time.

Solution:

By examining the results of the two solutions above, we find that:

$$t_{PHL,ramp} = \frac{t_r}{4} + t_{PHL,step}$$

If we use the approximation that $t_r \cong 2t_{PLH,step}$, then

$$t_{PHL,ramp} \approx \frac{2t_{PLH,step}}{4} + t_{PHL,step}$$

$$= \frac{t_{PHL,step}}{2} + t_{PHL,step}$$

From the above example, it is clear how the input ramp affects the propagation delay. It adds a delay term Δt_{ramp} that depends on the rise/fall delay of the input ramp. Therefore, the total delay can be written as:

$$t_{ramp} = \Delta t_{ramp} + t_{step}$$

If we were able to relate Δt_{ramp} to the propagation delay for a step input, it would greatly simplify the expression. Let us refer to the input rise/fall propagation delay as t_{in}. Then, according to the example above, we find that $\Delta t_{ramp} = t_{in}/2$ for the given output waveform. That is,

$$t_{ramp} \approx \frac{t_{in}}{2} + t_{step} \tag{6.14}$$

This is a very convenient result for the delay of an inverter chain with a ramp input as shown in Figure 6.16. The value of t_{step} for an inverter is given by 0.7RC and the value of Δt_{ramp} for the next stage can be approximated as 0.7RC/2, which we round down to 0.3RC for convenience. If we combine terms in the propagation delay as shown in Figure 6.16 and assume that the input propagation delay is roughly equal to the propagation delay of the last stage (a reasonable assumption if propagation delays are roughly equal in the circuit), then the total delay can be computed very simply as:

$$\text{Total\_delay} \approx \sum_i R_i C_i \tag{6.15}$$

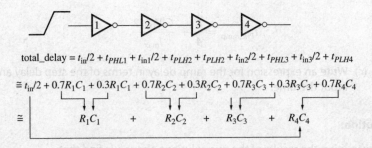

$$\text{total\_delay} = t_{in}/2 + t_{PHL1} + t_{in1}/2 + t_{PLH2} + t_{PLH2} + t_{in2}/2 + t_{PHL3} + t_{in3}/2 + t_{PLH4}$$

$$\cong t_{in}/2 + 0.7R_1C_1 + 0.3R_1C_1 + 0.7R_2C_2 + 0.3R_2C_2 + 0.7R_3C_3 + 0.3R_3C_3 + 0.7R_4C_4$$

$$\cong \qquad R_1C_1 \quad + \quad R_2C_2 \quad + \quad R_3C_3 \quad + \quad R_4C_4$$

Figure 6.16
Inverter chain delay for a ramp input.

That is, we no longer have to carry around a factor of 0.7 in the delay calculation if we are dealing with ramp inputs. Since most circuits that we will encounter have ramp inputs, we can safely use Equation (6.15) for delay calculation.

In summary, accurate propagation delay estimates are obtained for inputs with finite slopes by simply adding up the product of the on-resistance and the load capacitance for each stage of logic. The resulting delays are consistent with SPICE results if the on-resistances and capacitances are computed accurately.

Delay Calculation for Inverter Driving Four Fanout Inverters   **Example 6.6**

Problem:

(a) A CMOS inverter has a pull-up device that is 8λ:2λ and a pull-down device that is 4λ:2λ. It drives four identical inverters. Compute the inverter delay using 0.18 μm technology parameters. Assume a ramp input and negligible wire capacitance.

(b) Compute the delay for a chain of four inverters assuming a ramp input. Include the effect of differing rise and fall delays.

Solution:

(a) From a previous example, we obtained the values of the fanout and self capacitance. We will set the wire capacitance to zero for simplicity:

$$C_{load} = C_{fanout} + C_{self} + C_{wire} = 9.6 + 1.2 + 0 \approx 10.8 \text{ fF}$$

The t_{PHL} delay for an inverter driving four identical inverters is

$$t_{PHL} = R_{eff}C_{load} = (12.5 \text{ k}\Omega)\left(\frac{L}{W}\right)(10.8 \text{ fF})$$

$$= (12.5 \text{ k}\Omega)\left(\frac{1}{2}\right)(10.8 \text{ fF}) = (6.25 \text{ k}\Omega)(10.8 \text{ fF}) \approx 68 \text{ ps}$$

The t_{PLH} delay for an inverter driving four identical inverters is

$$t_{PHL} = R_{eff}C_{load} = (30 \text{ k}\Omega)\left(\frac{L}{W}\right)(10.8 \text{ fF})$$

$$= (30 \text{ k}\Omega)\left(\frac{1}{4}\right)(10.8 \text{ fF}) = 7.5 \text{ k}\Omega(10.8 \text{ fF}) \approx 81 \text{ ps}$$

$$\therefore t_p = \frac{t_{PHL} + t_{PLH}}{2} = \frac{68 + 81}{2} = 74.5 \text{ ps}$$

Therefore, the average fanout-of-four (FO4) delay of the inverter is roughly 75 ps.

(b) For a chain of four inverters, compute the FO1 rise and fall delays.

$$t_{PHL} = R_{eff}C_{load} = (6.35 \text{ k}\Omega)(2.4 + 1.2)\text{fF} = 22.5 \text{ ps}$$

$$t_{PLH} = R_{eff}C_{load} = (7.5\text{k}\Omega)(2.4 + 1.2)\text{fF} = 27 \text{ ps}$$

The total delay is twice the sum of each delay:

$$\tau_{total} = 2(t_{PHL} + t_{PLH}) = 2(22.5 \text{ ps} + 27 \text{ ps}) = 99 \text{ ps}$$

Example 6.7   **Optimal PMOS Device Size For Inverter Chain**

Problem:

Inverter sizing can be performed to equalize rise/fall delays or to minimize the propagation delay. Consider the four inverters in a chain shown below. Assuming that the NMOS devices are all 4λ, size the PMOS devices with the following objectives:

(a) equalize the rise/fall delays

(b) minimize the delay through the chain

What is the delay through four such inverters in the two cases?

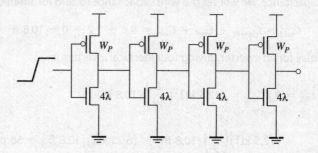

Solution:

(a) To equalize the delays, the PMOS devices would have to be approximately 2.4 times larger than the 4λ NMOS device. Therefore, the PMOS device size is approximately 10λ. The total capacitance at each output is 4.2 fF.

The delay of the chain is simply four times the delay of each stage:

$$\tau_{total} = 4t_{PHL} = 4R_{eff}C_{load} = 4(12.5 \text{ k}\Omega)\left(\frac{2}{4}\right)(4.2 \text{ fF}) \approx 105 \text{ ps}$$

This is a larger value than we obtained with a PMOS device of 8λ in the previous example.

(b) To minimize the delay, write the delay equation for the first two inverters:

$$D = \sum RC = (R_P)(C_g + C_{eff})(W_P + W_N) + (R_N)(C_g + C_{eff})(W_P + W_N)$$

$$= \left(\frac{30L_P}{W_P} + \frac{12.5L_N}{W_N}\right)(C_g + C_{eff})(W_P + W_N)$$

$$= \left(\frac{30(2\lambda)}{W_P} + \frac{12.5(2\lambda)}{4\lambda}\right)(2 + 1)(W_P + 4\lambda)$$

$$= \left(\frac{60\lambda}{W_P} + \frac{25\lambda}{4\lambda}\right)(2 + 1)(W_P + 4\lambda)$$

$$= \left(\frac{60\lambda(3)(W_P + 4\lambda)}{W_P} + \frac{25}{4}(3)(W_P + 4\lambda)\right) = \left(180\lambda + \frac{720\lambda^2}{W_P}\right) + \frac{75}{4}(W_P + 4\lambda)$$

To optimize the delay, take the derivative of this expression with respect to W_P.

$$\frac{\partial D}{\partial W_P} = -\frac{720\lambda^2}{W_P^2} + \frac{75}{4} = 0$$

$$\therefore W_P = \sqrt{\frac{720\lambda^2}{75/4}} = 2\lambda\sqrt{720/75} = 6.2\lambda$$

Based on the simple models for delay, the optimal ratio of the PMOS device to the NMOS device is approximately 6:4.

From the previous example, we can recalculate the delay for a chain of four inverters:

$$C_{load} = C_{fanout} + C_{self} + C_{wire} = 2 + 1 + 0 \approx 3\text{ fF}$$

The rise delay for an inverter driving another identical inverter is:

$$t_{PLH} = R_{eff}C_{load} = (30\text{ k}\Omega)\left(\frac{2}{6}\right)(3\text{ fF}) \approx 30\text{ ps}$$

The fall delay for an inverter driving another identical inverter is:

$$t_{PHL} = R_{eff}C_{load} = (12.5\text{ k}\Omega)\left(\frac{2}{4}\right)(3\text{ fF}) \approx 18.8\text{ ps}$$

The total delay is

$$\tau_{total} = 2(t_{PHL} + t_{PLH}) = 2(18.8\text{ ps} + 30\text{ ps}) = 97.6\text{ ps}$$

which is slightly faster than the inverters in the previous example.

Exercise 6.2   Use SPICE simulations to find the optimal sizing of the PMOS and NMOS devices that produce minimum delay through the inverter chain in the previous example. How do your results compare with the hand calculations?

Clearly the selection of the PMOS:NMOS ratio from a timing perspective is a function of many factors. We can equalize the rise and fall delays, or minimize the delay through a chain. A number of nonlinear effects, such as ramp inputs and oxide and junction capacitances will determine the actual delay. Designers typically use a 2:1 ratio since it is a reasonable compromise between minimum delay and equal rise/fall times.

6.5 Gate Sizing for Optimal Path Delay

6.5.1 Optimal Delay Problem

We now address the general design problem of *optimizing* gate sizes to minimize the delay of a logic path. In order to carry out circuit optimization, the problem must be specified carefully. Consider the circuit of Figure 6.17a where we are trying to drive a large load, C_{load}, with the objective of minimizing the delay. Without any other constraints, we would try to make the inverter as large as possible, as shown in Figure 6.17b, so that the $R_{eff}C_{load}$ is as small as possible. However, there is no gate driving this inverter and, in this unconstrained (and unrealistic) situation, it is difficult to produce a meaningful solution. Therefore, the optimization problem has not been specified properly.

Next, consider the inverter chain of Figure 6.18 driving the same capacitive load. If the problem is to minimize the delay through the chain, our first instinct would be to size the third inverter to be as large as possible. However, this time the third inverter places a load on the second inverter and its delay will increase as we increase the size of the third inverter. This is illustrated in Figure 6.19 along with a corresponding increase in its input capacitance. We have effectively shifted the delay problem to the previous gate.

If we make the second inverter large so that it can drive the third inverter, then the first inverter is heavily loaded. As a result, we are producing locally optimal

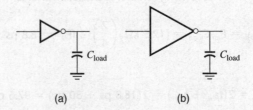

(a)   (b)

Figure 6.17
Sizing inverters to drive a large capacitive load.

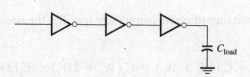

Figure 6.18
Optimal path delay problem.

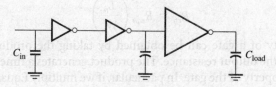

Figure 6.19
Input loading effects of large drivers.

solutions, but inadvertently passing the problem to the previous stage. Again, this problem is not properly constrained and does not have a meaningful solution. The proper specification of the optimal path delay problem involves the minimization of the path delay given both input *and* output loading constraints. In Figure 6.19, if we specify both C_{in} and C_{load} and ask for the optimal sizing to minimize the delay, the problem is properly specified, and we can focus on its solution.

Given the proper specification, what is the optimal sizing of the gates in the logic path? Actually, there are two unknowns in general: the number of logic gates needed in the path and their corresponding sizes. To carry out this optimization, we write the delay equation in the form that was derived earlier:

$$path\_delay = \sum R_i C_i$$

where R_i is the driving resistance of each gate and C_i is the output loading capacitance on the gate. Then, we select the transistor widths to minimize the delay.

6.5.2 Inverter Chain Delay Optimization—FO4 Delay

We now turn our attention to the problem of driving a large capacitive load starting with a small input capacitance. The assumption here is that we need several logic stages of increasing size to drive the load. How many stages do we need and how should they be scaled in size? In the previous section, we noticed that when we increased the inverter size, two things happened: We reduced the delay of the gate and increased the input capacitance seen by the previous gate. That is, changing the size of a gate affects both the input capacitance and the output resistance of a gate.

The input capacitance of a gate completely specifies the sizes of the devices and is given by

$$C_{in} = C_g(W_n + W_p) = C_g(W_n + 2W_n) = C_g(3W_n) \qquad (6.16)$$

If we know the total input capacitance of an inverter, we can assign the specific PMOS and NMOS device widths using Equation (6.16).

The effective output resistance for the NMOS device is given by

$$R_{eff} = R_{eqn}\left(\frac{L_n}{W_n}\right) \qquad (6.17)$$

A useful property of a gate can be obtained by taking the product of the input capacitance and the output resistance. The product generates a time constant which is an intrinsic property of the gate. In particular, if we multiply Equations (6.16) and (6.17) together, we obtain

$$\tau_{inv} = R_{eff}C_{in} = R_{eqn}\left(\frac{L_n}{W_n}\right)C_g(3W_n) = 3R_{eqn}C_gL_n \qquad (6.18)$$

The reason why this value is interesting is that it captures the input and output effects of sizing in one term. We want to know how effective a gate is at driving a load capacitance while minimizing its input capacitance. This single quantity tells us about these two aspects of the gate. Note that the size of the inverter can be doubled, tripled, or made any size, and the time constant will remain the same. Of course, the self-capacitance term increases when the size increases, but it is not part of this intrinsic time constant. However, it is part of another term associated with the parasitic capacitance of the gate, as we will find shortly.

Next, consider the delay of a single-stage inverter shown in Figure 6.20. If the input has a finite rise time, then we can write the delay as

$$t_{delay} = R_{eff}\left[C_{out} + C_{self}\right]$$

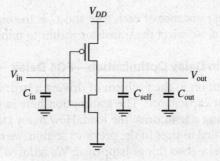

Figure 6.20
Delay for inverter driving a load.

In order to incorporate the intrinsic time constant term, τ_{inv}, into the formulation, we multiply and divide through by C_{in}:

$$t_{delay} = R_{eff}C_{in}\left[\frac{C_{out}}{C_{in}} + \frac{C_{self}}{C_{in}}\right] = \tau_{inv}\left[\frac{C_{out}}{C_{in}} + \gamma_{inv}\right] \quad (6.19)$$

where γ_{inv} is the ratio of self-capacitance to input capacitance for the inverter:

$$\gamma_{inv} = \frac{C_{self}}{C_{in}} \quad (6.20)$$

This value is highly dependent on the layout of the gate, since C_{self} depends on the layout. The ratio of C_{out}/C_{in} is called the fanout ratio, f, or the electrical effort.

Computation of τ_{inv} and γ_{inv} for 0.13 μm Technology   **Example 6.8**

Problem:

Compute τ_{inv} and γ_{inv} for an inverter in a 0.13 μm technology.

Solution:

$$\tau_{inv} = 3R_{eqn}C_gL_n = 3(12.5\ \text{k}\Omega)(2\ \text{fF}/\mu\text{m})(0.1\ \mu\text{m}) = 7.5\ \text{ps}$$

$$\gamma_{inv} = \frac{C_{self}}{C_{in}} = \frac{C_{eff}(3W)}{C_g(3W)} = \frac{1\ \text{fF}/\mu\text{m}}{2\ \text{fF}/\mu\text{m}} = 0.5$$

Compute τ_{inv} and γ_{inv} for a 0.18 μm technology.   **Exercise 6.3**

Returning to the inverter sizing problem, we want to optimize the delay of the chain in Figure 6.21.

The delay through the stages can be computed as:

$$\text{total\_delay} = \sum_{j=1}^{N} \tau_{inv}\left(\frac{C_{j+1}}{C_j} + \gamma_{inv}\right)$$

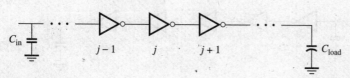

Figure 6.21

Optimal sizing of inverter chain.

By substituting in the widths to compute the capacitances, we obtain

$$\text{total\_delay} = \sum_j \tau_{\text{inv}}\left(\frac{C_g W_{j+1}}{C_g W_j} + \gamma_{\text{inv}}\right) = \sum_j \tau_{\text{inv}}\left(\frac{W_{j+1}}{W_j} + \gamma_{\text{inv}}\right)$$

We can gain some insight into what happens at the optimal solution by taking two consecutive delay terms that are dependent upon the size of inverter j:

$$D_j = \tau_{\text{inv}}\left(\frac{W_j}{W_{j-1}} + \gamma_{\text{inv}}\right) + \tau_{\text{inv}}\left(\frac{W_{j+1}}{W_j} + \gamma_{\text{inv}}\right)$$

To obtain the optimal delay for these two stages, we take the partial derivative of D_j with respect to W_j:

$$\frac{\partial D_j}{\partial W_j} = \tau_{\text{inv}}\frac{1}{W_{j-1}} - \tau_{\text{inv}}\frac{W_{j+1}}{W_j^2} = 0$$

$$\therefore \frac{W_j}{W_{j-1}} = \frac{W_{j+1}}{W_j}$$

$$\therefore W_j = \sqrt{W_{j+1} W_{j-1}}$$

An important result has been produced: to obtain the minimum delay, the size of the middle inverter should be the *geometric mean* of the size of the previous inverter and the next inverter. In this case, the geometric mean is simply the square root, since we are only considering two stages. In general, it is the Nth root if we were optimizing all N stages of inverters at once.

One way to achieve this geometric sizing is to increase each inverter by a fanout factor f which can be determined using the relationship between the input capacitance, the output capacitance, and the number of stages. The general case is shown in Figure 6.22. Each stage drives an inverter that is f times larger than itself. The size of each inverter is the geometric mean of the inverter before and after it, as required for optimality. It is interesting to note that the delay through each gate must be the

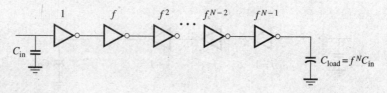

Figure 6.22
Series chain of inverters.

same since each one drives an inverter that is f times itself. The overall delay is simply N times the delay of one inverter.

Since both f and N are unknowns, we can use the relationship between them to determine their optimal values. Using Figure 6.22 we see that

$$f^N C_{in} = C_{load}$$

$$\therefore N = \frac{\ln(C_{load}/C_{in})}{\ln f} \tag{6.21}$$

From Equation (6.19), the gate delay and the total delay can be written as

$$gate\_delay = \tau_{inv}\left(\frac{C_j}{C_{j-1}} + \gamma_{inv}\right)$$

$$total\_delay = N \times \tau_{inv}\left(\frac{C_j}{C_{j-1}} + \gamma_{inv}\right) \tag{6.22}$$

Substituting in Equation (6.21), and setting $f = C_j/C_{j-1}$, we obtain:

$$total\_delay = \frac{\ln(C_{load}/C_{in})}{\ln f} \times \tau_{inv}(f + \gamma_{inv}) \tag{6.23}$$

The total delay is plotted as a function of f and γ in Figure 6.23. The curves indicate that the optimal value of f lies in the range of 2.5 to 4. The curves have a very shallow optimum so any value in this range may be appropriate, depending on γ. In prior textbooks, the optimal value of f was found to be e, the exponential value.

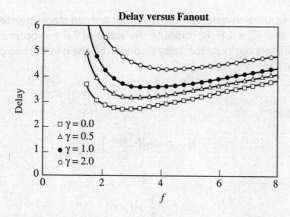

Figure 6.23
Delay versus fanout f for different γ values.

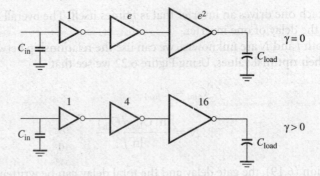

Figure 6.24

Inverter sizing for optimal delay.

From Equation (6.23), this value is obtained when $\gamma = 0$ which implies that the junction capacitance is ignored. From the curve for $\gamma = 0$ in Figure 6.23, the optimum value of e can also be extracted. This type of sizing is shown in Figure 6.24. Today the junction capacitance and interconnect capacitance can act to increase the needed drive of the inverter. In a $0.13~\mu$m technology, $\gamma = 0.5$. Therefore, the use of $f = 3$ or $f = 4$ is more suitable. Typically, we use the value $f = 4$ and give the associated delay a special name: the fanout of 4 delay, or FO4 delay. The sizing for a three-stage inverter chain under FO4 rules is given in Figure 6.24 where each successive inverter is 4 times larger than the previous one.

Example 6.9

Optimal Sizing for Inverter Chains

Problem:

Compute the optimal inverter fanout ratio f for a three-stage inverter chain with $C_{load} = 200$ fF and $C_{in} = 1$ fF. Recompute the value of f if the optimal number of stages is used. Then, compute the delay through the chain in the two cases, assuming $\tau_{inv} = 7.5$ ps and $\gamma = 0.5$.

Solution:

Use the fact that

$$N \ln f = \ln\left(\frac{C_{load}}{C_{in}}\right)$$

Therefore,

$$\ln f = \frac{1}{3}\ln(200)$$

$$\therefore f = 5.84$$

This is the optimal fanout if we are constrained to use three stages. If we want to improve the delay, we first remove the restriction of the number of stages. Then, we can compute the number of stages using the equation:

$$N = \ln\left(\frac{C_{load}}{C_{in}}\right)/\ln f$$

To solve for N, we need to estimate f. From Figure 6.23 $f \approx 3.6$. Therefore,

$$N = \ln(200)/\ln(3.6) = 4.1$$

Now try using four stages (since an integer must be used). Then, f can be recomputed as

$$\ln f = \frac{1}{4}\ln(200)$$

$$\therefore f = 3.8$$

The delays of the two solutions can be computed using Equation (6.22):

$$\text{total\_delay} = N \times \tau_{inv}\left(\frac{C_j}{C_{j-1}} + \gamma_{inv}\right)$$

For the three-stage case,

$$\text{total\_delay} = 3 \times (7.5 \text{ ps})(5.84 + 0.5) = 142.8 \text{ ps}$$

For the four-stage case,

$$\text{total\_delay} = 4 \times (7.5 \text{ ps})(3.8 + 0.5) = 128 \text{ ps}$$

Therefore, the best solution is to have four inverter stages with each inverter sized to be 3.8X larger than the previous inverter.

6.5.3 Optimizing Paths with NANDs and NORs

Chains of NAND or NOR gates can be handled in the same way as inverters with appropriate modifications. For the NAND chain of Figure 6.25, the total delay can be derived as

$$\text{total\_delay} = \sum_j \tau_{nand}\left(\frac{C_{j+1}}{C_j} + \gamma_{nand}\right)$$

where τ_{nand} is the intrinsic time constant for the NAND gate, and γ_{nand} is the ratio of the self-capacitance to the input gate capacitance. If the same curves of delay versus fanout are drawn for the NAND gates as we constructed for the inverters (see Figure 6.23), we would also find that $f \approx 4$. The optimal value of f would equalize the delays of all stages.

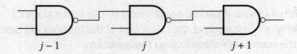

Figure 6.25
Series chain of NAND gates.

For a chain of consecutive NOR gates, we would produce a similar equation:

$$\text{total\_delay} = \sum_j \tau_{\text{nor}}\left(\frac{C_{j+1}}{C_j} + \gamma_{\text{nor}}\right)$$

where τ_{nor} is the intrinsic time constant for the NOR gate, and γ_{nor} is its ratio of the self-capacitance to the input gate capacitance. The fanout ratio $f \approx 4$ works well for this case. Again, the proper value of f would make the delays of all stages identical.

The intrinsic time constants for the NAND and NOR gates can be derived as follows. Considering the device sizes shown in Figure 6.4, we can compute the effective output resistance and the input capacitance, and then multiply the two together:

$$\tau_{\text{nand}} = R_{eff}C_{in} = R_{eqn}\left(\frac{L_n}{W_n}\right)4W_nC_g = 4R_{eqn}C_gL_n$$

$$\tau_{\text{nor}} = R_{eff}C_{in} = R_{eqn}\left(\frac{L_n}{W_n}\right)5W_nC_g = 5R_{eqn}C_gL_n \qquad (6.24)$$

Typical logic paths in a digital circuit may have a variety of gate types. Consider the optimal delay for the situation shown in Figure 6.26.

The total delay can be written as follows:

$$\text{total\_delay} = \tau_{\text{nand}}\left(\frac{C_{j+1}}{C_j} + \gamma_{\text{nand}}\right) + \tau_{\text{inv}}\left(\frac{C_{j+2}}{C_{j+1}} + \gamma_{\text{inv}}\right) + \tau_{\text{nor}}\left(\frac{C_{j+3}}{C_{j+2}} + \gamma_{\text{nor}}\right)$$

$$(6.25)$$

The delay through stages j and j + 1 is given by

$$D_{j+1} = \tau_{\text{nand}}\left(\frac{C_{j+1}}{C_j} + \gamma_{\text{nand}}\right) + \tau_{\text{inv}}\left(\frac{C_{j+2}}{C_{j+1}} + \gamma_{\text{inv}}\right)$$

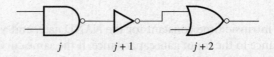

Figure 6.26
Series of mixed gates in a logic path.

For minimum delay, we take the derivative with respect to C_{j+1}:

$$\frac{\partial D_{j+1}}{\partial C_{j+1}} = \tau_{\text{nand}}\left(\frac{1}{C_j}\right) - \tau_{\text{inv}}\left(\frac{C_{j+2}}{C_{j+1}^2}\right) = 0$$

$$\therefore \tau_{\text{nand}}\left(\frac{C_{j+1}}{C_j}\right) = \tau_{\text{inv}}\left(\frac{C_{j+2}}{C_{j+1}}\right)$$

$$\therefore \tau_{\text{nand}}FO_j = \tau_{\text{inv}}FO_{j+1}$$

where $FO_j = C_{j+1}/C_j$ and $FO_{j+1} = C_{j+2}/C_{j+1}$. Another important result has been established. For this case, the delay is minimized when the $\tau \times FO$ of a given gate is equal to the $\tau \times FO$ of the next gate. That is, the gate delays do not have to be equal but rather the fanout portions of the delays must be equal to reach the optimal solution. To support this result, if we now apply the analysis to the next two stages we would obtain

$$D_{j+2} = \tau_{\text{inv}}\left(\frac{C_{j+2}}{C_{j+1}} + \gamma_{\text{inv}}\right) + \tau_{\text{nor}}\left(\frac{C_{j+3}}{C_{j+2}} + \gamma_{\text{nor}}\right)$$

$$\frac{\partial D_{j+2}}{\partial C_{j+2}} = \tau_{\text{inv}}\left(\frac{1}{C_{j+1}}\right) - \tau_{\text{nor}}\left(\frac{C_{j+3}}{C_{j+2}^2}\right) = 0$$

$$\therefore \tau_{\text{inv}}\left(\frac{C_{j+2}}{C_{j+1}}\right) = \tau_{\text{nor}}\left(\frac{C_{j+3}}{C_{j+2}}\right)$$

$$\therefore \tau_{\text{inv}}FO_{j+1} = \tau_{\text{nor}}FO_{j+2}$$

Again, the same result is obtained: to optimize the delay, we must set the fanout portion of the delay to be equal for all gates.

Computing Optimal Gate Sizes along a Critical Path   **Example 6.10**

Problem:

Find the device sizes that optimize the delay through the indicated path for the circuit below.

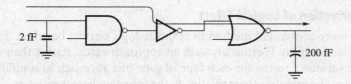

Solution:

We must equalize the fanout portion of the delay. Therefore,

$$\therefore \tau_{\text{nand}}\left(\frac{C_{j+1}}{C_{\text{in}}}\right) = \tau_{\text{inv}}\left(\frac{C_{j+2}}{C_{j+1}}\right) = \tau_{\text{nor}}\left(\frac{C_{\text{load}}}{C_{j+2}}\right)$$

We take the product of these three components and then obtain the geometric mean:

$$\text{Fanout\_delay} = \sqrt[3]{\tau_{\text{nand}}\left(\frac{C_{j+1}}{C_{\text{in}}}\right) \times \tau_{\text{inv}}\left(\frac{C_{j+2}}{C_{j+1}}\right) \times \tau_{\text{nor}}\left(\frac{C_{\text{load}}}{C_{j+2}}\right)}$$

$$= \sqrt[3]{\tau_{\text{nand}} \times \tau_{\text{inv}} \times \tau_{\text{nor}}\left(\frac{C_{\text{load}}}{C_{\text{in}}}\right)} = \sqrt[3]{4 \times 3 \times 5\left(\frac{200}{2}\right)} \times R_{\text{eqn}}C_g L_n$$

$$= 18.2 \, R_{\text{eqn}}C_g L_n$$

Therefore, the input capacitance for each gate can be computed by setting the fanout delay to the above result:

$$\tau_{\text{nor}}\left(\frac{C_{\text{load}}}{C_{j+2}}\right) = 5R_{\text{eqn}}C_g L_n\left(\frac{200 \text{ fF}}{C_{j+2}}\right) = 18.2 \, R_{\text{eqn}}C_g L_n$$

$$\therefore C_{j+2} = 55 \text{ fF}$$

$$\tau_{\text{inv}}\left(\frac{C_{j+2}}{C_{j+1}}\right) = 3R_{\text{eqn}}C_g L_n\left(\frac{55 \text{ fF}}{C_{j+1}}\right) = 18.2 \, R_{\text{eqn}}C_g L_n$$

$$\therefore C_{j+1} = 9.1 \text{ fF}$$

$$\tau_{\text{nand}}\left(\frac{C_{j+1}}{C_{\text{in}}}\right) = 4 \, R_{\text{eqn}}C_g L_n\left(\frac{9.1 \text{ fF}}{C_{\text{in}}}\right) = 18.2 \, R_{\text{eqn}}C_g L_n$$

$$\therefore C_{\text{in}} = 2 \text{ fF}$$

The final result is consistent with the input capacitance specified in the problem. The device sizes are determined by the relative sizes of the transistors in Figure 6.4.

For the NAND gate: $C_{\text{in}} = 2$ fF. Therefore, $W_p = W_n = 0.5 \; \mu$m.

For the inverter: $C_{\text{in}} = 9.1$ fF. Therefore, $W_p = 3 \; \mu$m and $W_n = 1.5 \; \mu$m.

For the NOR gate: $C_{\text{in}} = 55$ fF. Therefore, $W_p = 22 \; \mu$m and $W_n = 5.5 \; \mu$m.

6.6 Optimizing Paths with Logical Effort

6.6.1 Derivation of Logical Effort

We need a more convenient method to optimize logic circuits based on the results of the previous section. Fortunately such an approach exists. Rather than carrying around the various τ values for each type of gate, one approach to simplifying the expressions is to normalize them relative to the inverter characteristic, τ_{inv}.

We can define a new term, called the *logical effort (LE)*, which is the ratio of the intrinsic time constant for a gate to the intrinsic time constant of an inverter. For example, the logical effort for an inverter would be $\tau_{inv}/\tau_{inv} = 1$; the logical effort of a NAND gate would be τ_{nand}/τ_{inv}; and, the logical effort of a NOR gate would be τ_{nor}/τ_{inv}. Using the *LE*, we can write normalized delay equations.

For example, Equation (6.25) for the total delay can be rewritten as

$$\frac{\text{total\_delay}}{\tau_{inv}} = \frac{\tau_{nand}}{\tau_{inv}}\left(\frac{C_{j+1}}{C_j} + \gamma_{nand}\right) + \frac{\tau_{inv}}{\tau_{inv}}\left(\frac{C_{j+2}}{C_{j+1}} + \gamma_{inv}\right) + \frac{\tau_{nor}}{\tau_{inv}}\left(\frac{C_{j+3}}{C_{j+2}} + \gamma_{nor}\right)$$

In normalized form, the delay equation is

$$D = (LE_{nand}FO_1 + P_{nand}) + (LE_{inv}FO_2 + P_{inv}) + (LE_{nor}FO_3 + P_{nor})$$

Each gate produces a term $LE \times FO + P$ in the delay expression. This may be written in a more compact form:

$$D = \sum (LE \times FO + P)$$

where LE = logic effort = τ_{gate}/τ_{inv}, FO_j = fanout = (C_{j+1}/C_j), and P = parasitic term = $LE \times \gamma_{gate}$.

Using these definitions, we can go back to the earlier equations for optimal delays and realize that, for the minimum delay, we need to equalize $LE \times FO$ for all gates. When we have only one type of gate, we try to make each gate delay the same as the others. This is possible since their P terms are all the same. When we have many different types of gates in the logic path, we require only that the fanout portion of the delay, $LE \times FO$, be the same for all gates, since their P terms may all be different.

The basic elements of logical effort have been described, but a number of questions remain unanswered at this stage:

1. How do we obtain the logical effort (*LE*) of any type of logic gate?

2. How do we compute the parasitic term (*P*) for any type of logic gate?

3. How do we use the *LE* and *P* values to find the optimal delay and device sizes along a critical path in a logic circuit?

To determine the *LE* of a gate, we revisit the definition of τ of an inverter:

$$\tau_{inv} = 3R_{eqn}C_gL_n$$

The corresponding values for the NAND and NOR gates are

$$\tau_{nand} = R_{eff}C_{in} = R_{eqn}\left(\frac{L_n}{W_n}\right)4W_nC_g = 4R_{eqn}C_gL_n$$

$$\tau_{nor} = R_{eff}C_{in} = R_{eqn}\left(\frac{L_n}{W_n}\right)5W_nC_g = 5R_{eqn}C_gL_n$$

Using these values, we find that

$$LE_{\text{inv}} = \frac{\tau_{\text{inv}}}{\tau_{\text{inv}}} = 1 \qquad LE_{\text{nand}} = \frac{\tau_{\text{nand}}}{\tau_{\text{inv}}} = \frac{4}{3} \qquad LE_{\text{nor}} = \frac{\tau_{\text{nor}}}{\tau_{\text{inv}}} = \frac{5}{3}$$

We can also use another approach to compute LE. If we take the definition of τ and multiply it by C_{load}, we have the following:

$$\tau \times C_{\text{load}} = R_{\text{eff}} C_{\text{in}} C_{\text{load}} = R_{\text{eff}} C_{\text{load}} C_{\text{in}}$$

$$\therefore LE = \frac{(R_{\text{eff}} C_{\text{load}} C_{\text{in}})_{\text{gate}}}{(R_{\text{eff}} C_{\text{load}} C_{\text{in}})_{\text{inv}}}$$

Using this form, there are two other ways to produce the logical effort:

1. Set the delays of the inverter and the gate to be the same; then, take the ratio of the input capacitances, or

2. Set the input capacitances to be same; then, take the delay ratio.

The first approach is illustrated using Figure 6.27, where the widths have been omitted for convenience. The NAND and NOR gates have already been sized to have the same delay as the inverter. Therefore, we can simply use the input capacitance ratios. Consider input A:

$$\text{For the NAND gate:} \quad LE = \frac{(C_{\text{in}})_{\text{nand}}}{(C_{\text{in}})_{\text{inv}}} = \frac{2 + 2}{3} = \frac{4}{3}$$

$$\text{For the NOR gate:} \quad LE = \frac{(C_{\text{in}})_{\text{nor}}}{(C_{\text{in}})_{\text{inv}}} = \frac{4 + 1}{3} = \frac{5}{3}$$

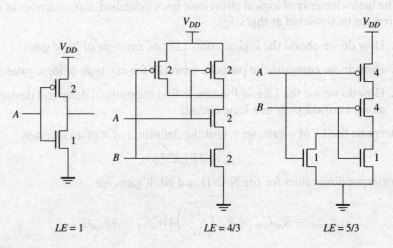

$$LE = 1 \qquad\qquad LE = 4/3 \qquad\qquad LE = 5/3$$

Figure 6.27
Logical effort for gates with equal delays.

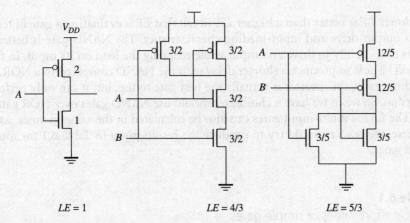

$LE = 1$ $LE = 4/3$ $LE = 5/3$

Figure 6.28
Logical effort using equal input capacitances.

The second approach is illustrated using Figure 6.28. Here, the device sizes of Figure 6.27 have been uniformly scaled such that the input capacitances of all three gates are equal. This is possible because the *LE* of a gate does not change if all devices are scaled uniformly. Since they all have the same input capacitance, we can take the ratio of the delays to obtain the *LE* values.

For the NAND gate, the two pull-down devices in series are 3/2 each. Their combination generates an equivalent device with size 3/4. The equivalent resistance is given by $(4/3)\,R_{eff}$. Therefore,

$$LE_{nand} = \frac{\left(\dfrac{4}{3}\,R_{eff}\right)C_{out}}{R_{eff}C_{out}} = \frac{4}{3}$$

For the NOR gate, the equivalent resistance of the pull-down device with size 3/5 is $(5/3)R_{eff}$. Therefore,

$$LE_{nor} = \frac{\left(\dfrac{5}{3}\,R_{eff}\right)C_{out}}{R_{eff}C_{out}} = \frac{5}{3}$$

In effect, we are taking the ratio of the driving resistance of gates that have equal input capacitance. This approach is somewhat more complicated than the first approach but may be used where the input capacitances of two gates are known to be equal.

The logical effort of the NOR gate is higher than the NAND gate. This implies that the NAND gate is better than a NOR gate in the context of logical effort; that is, a lower *LE* is better than a higher *LE*. Recall that *LE* is evaluating a gate in terms of its output-drive and input-loading characteristics. The NAND gate is better in terms of its ability to drive an output while reducing the load on its input. In fact, we will be able to produce a shorter delay with the NAND compared to a NOR. Of the three gates, the inverter is actually the best gate to use, but it can only perform inversion. So when we have a choice, we should use NAND gates over NOR gates.

The *LE* for multi-input gates can also be calculated in the same manner. As an exercise, the reader should try to produce the results given in Table 6.1 for multi-input gates.

Table 6.1
Logical effort values of simple gates

Type of Gate	1 input	2 inputs	3 inputs	4 inputs
Inverter	1	—	—	—
NAND	—	4/3	5/3	6/3
NOR	—	5/3	7/3	9/3

The next step is to compute the parasitic term, *P*. Unfortunately, this term is technology- and gate-dependent. For a given technology, this term will have to be recomputed for all the different types of gates. Let's begin with a simple inverter and determine its *P* value. Recall that this term is given by

$$P = LE_{inv} \times \gamma_{inv} = LE \times \frac{C_{self}}{C_{in}} = LE \times \frac{C_{eff}3W}{C_g3W} = LE \times \frac{C_{eff}}{C_g}$$

In effect, the value of *P* depends on the coefficient for junction capacitance and the coefficient for gate capacitance. Substituting in the *LE* and technology-dependent parameters, we obtain

$$P_{inv} = (1) \times \frac{1 \text{ fF}/\mu m}{2 \text{ fF}/\mu m} = \frac{1}{2}$$

For the NAND gate, we refer to Figure 6.27 to determine *P*. Accounting for shared source/drain regions in the layout:

$$P_{nand} = LE_{nand} \times \gamma_{nand} = LE \times \frac{C_{self}}{C_{in}}$$

$$= LE \times \frac{C_{eff}(2W + 2W + 2W)}{C_g(2W + 2W)} = LE \times \frac{C_{eff}}{C_g} \times \frac{3}{2} = \frac{4}{3} \times \frac{1}{2} \times \frac{3}{2} = 1$$

For the NOR gate, we again refer to Figure 6.27 to determine P. With proper accounting for shared source/drain regions in the layout:

$$P_{nor} = LE_{nor} \times \gamma_{nor} = LE \times \frac{C_{self}}{C_{in}}$$

$$= LE \times \frac{C_{eff}(W + 4W + 4W)}{C_g(W + 4W)} = LE \times \frac{C_{eff}}{C_g} \times \frac{9}{5} = \frac{5}{3} \times \frac{1}{2} \times \frac{9}{5} = \frac{3}{2}$$

The best way to accurately compute the value is through simulation. However, for the purposes of rapid hand calculations, we can use the following *approximate* table:

Table 6.2
Table of parasitic terms for simple gates

Type of Gate	1 input	2 inputs	3 inputs	4 inputs
Inverter	0.5	—	—	—
NAND	—	1	2	3
NOR	—	1.5	3	4.5

Path Optimization Using Logical Effort   **Example 6.11**

Problem:

Repeat Example 6.10 using logical effort techniques. However, before specifying the sizes, compute the optimal delay.

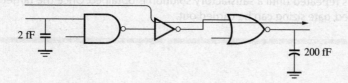

Solution:

We need to equalize the $LE \times FO$ components of the delay for all gates. First compute the product of $LE \times FO$ for all the gates:

$$\text{total path effort} = LE_{nand} \times LE_{inv} \times LE_{nor} \times \left(\frac{C_{load}}{C_{in}}\right)$$

$$= (4/3)(1)(5/3)(200/2) = 222.2$$

Next, take the geometric mean of the result:

$$\text{Stage Effort} = \sqrt[3]{222.2} = 6$$

This is the fanout portion of the delay. The normalized path delay is three times this value (one for each gate) plus the parasitic term for each gate:

$$D = 3(6) + P_{nand} + P_{inv} + P_{nor}$$

$$= 18 + 1 + \left(\frac{1}{2}\right) + \left(\frac{3}{2}\right) = 21$$

The physical delay value is obtained by multiplying the normalized delay by $\tau_{inv} = 7.5$ ps:

$$\text{min\_path\_delay} = \tau_{inv} D = (7.5 \text{ ps})(21) = 157.5 \text{ ps}$$

Assuming that the delay is acceptable, we work backwards from the output to the input to compute the device sizes:

$$\therefore LE_{nor}\left(\frac{C_{out}}{C_{j+2}}\right) = 6 \Rightarrow LE_{nor}\left(\frac{C_{j+3}}{6}\right) = C_{j+2} = (5/3)(200 \text{ fF}/6) = 55 \text{ fF}$$

$$\therefore LE_{inv}\left(\frac{C_{j+2}}{C_{j+1}}\right) = 6 \Rightarrow LE_{inv}\left(\frac{C_{j+2}}{6}\right) = C_{j+1} = (1)(55/6) = 9.1 \text{ fF}$$

$$\therefore LE_{nand}\left(\frac{C_{j+1}}{C_{in}}\right) = 6 \Rightarrow LE_{nand}\left(\frac{C_{j+1}}{6}\right) = C_{in} = (4/3)(9.1/6) = 2 \text{ fF}$$

These are the same results as obtained in Example 6.10. The device sizing would proceed in the same manner as shown in that example.

It is interesting to note that we can determine the minimum delay without sizing the gates. This is one of the key advantages of the *LE* approach. If this minimum possible delay is not within specifications, the logic can be modified and the process repeated until a satisfactory solution is obtained. Once the target delay is achieved, gate sizing can be carried out.

6.6.2 Understanding Logical Effort

Further insight into logical effort can be obtained by examining the plot of normalized delay (D) versus electrical effort (FO) in Figure 6.29. The delay normalization is with respect to τ_{inv} while the electrical effort is the ratio of fanout capacitance to input capacitance. The slope of the inverter delay versus fanout is set to 1 by definition. The y-intercept is the parasitic term, which is $\frac{1}{2}$ for the inverter. The NAND gate has a y-intercept at 1 and a slope of 4/3, and the NOR gate has a y-intercept at 1.5 and a slope of 5/3. If we compare the delay of each gate with a fanout loading of 1, we see that the inverter is the fastest, the NAND is next and the NOR is the slowest.

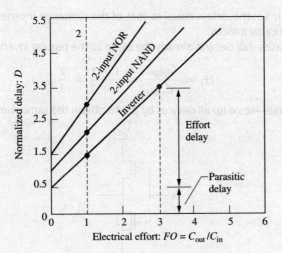

Figure 6.29

Practical interpretation of logical effort.

For improved accuracy of the *LE* method, these plots may be obtained directly from SPICE to determine more precise values of *LE* and *P* for a given technology.

LE for a Skewed Inverter

Example 6.12

Problem:

What is the *LE* of this inverter?

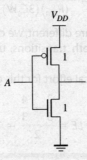

Solution:

The delays are not the same and input capacitance is not the same as the reference inverter. One of the two must be adjusted to obtain the *LE*. We will show two methods of obtaining the *LE*. The rising and falling cases must be handled separately for this gate.

Method 1: Set the delays equal to that of the reference inverter and take the ratio of input capacitances.

Falling case—fall delay is already the same as the regular inverter:

$$LE_F = \frac{C_{in}|_{gate}}{C_{in}|_{inv}} = \frac{1+1}{1+2} = \frac{2}{3}$$

Rising case—scale up all devices by 2× to obtain the same rise delay:

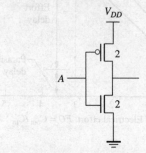

$$LE_R = \frac{C_{in}|_{gate}}{C_{in}|_{inv}} = \frac{2+2}{1+2} = \frac{4}{3}$$

Method 2: Use the definition of logical effort:

$$LE = \frac{(R_{eff} C_{in})_{gate}}{(R_{eff} C_{in})_{inv}}$$

For the falling case:

$$LE_F = \frac{(R_{eqn})(2C_g W)}{(R_{eqn})(3C_g W)} = \frac{2}{3}$$

For the rising case:

$$LE_R = \frac{(2R_{eqn})(2C_g W)}{(R_{eqn})(3C_g W)} = \frac{4}{3}$$

Since the rising and falling *LE*s are different, we can optimize based on either one. But if we want to optimize both transitions, use the *average LE* to determine the transistor sizes.

Therefore, the average logical effort for this gate is

$$LE = \frac{\dfrac{2}{3} + \dfrac{4}{3}}{2} = 1$$

Example 6.13 **Path Optimization Using Logical Effort**

Problem:

For the given logic circuit, determine the optimal stage effort, total path delay, and the sizes of the gates. Use normalized values of input and output capacitances, as given in the schematic, and compute the normalized delay and gate sizes.

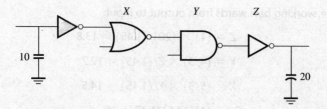

Solution:

First compute the total path effort:

$$\text{Total path effort} = \prod (LE \times FO)$$

$$= 1\left(\frac{X}{10}\right) \times \frac{5}{3}\left(\frac{Y}{X}\right) \times \frac{4}{3}\left(\frac{Z}{Y}\right) \times 1\left(\frac{20}{Z}\right)$$

$$= \frac{20}{9} \times \frac{20}{10} = \frac{400}{90}$$

In this example, we sequenced through each stage and computed the $LE \times FO$. Then the total path effort was obtained by multiplying these factors together. Another way to obtain the same answer is to multiply the LEs together (to obtain 20/9), then multiply the FOs together (to obtain 20/10), and finally multiply these two terms together (to obtain 400/90). This approach works only for single paths with no branches.

Next compute the optimal stage effort, SE^*, by taking the geometric mean of the above result.

$$SE^* = \text{Optimal stage effort} = \left(\frac{400}{90}\right)^{1/4} = 1.45$$

We take the fourth root of the path effort since there are four stages in this example. This is the optimal stage effort that we assign to all gates in the path. The total path delay can be computed as

$$D = 4(SE^*) + 2P_{inv} + P_{nor} + P_{nand}$$

$$= 4(1.45) + 1.0 + 1.5 + 1.0 = 9.3$$

Note that the optimal stage effort, hence the optimal solution, is completely determined by the input and output capacitances, and the number and type of logic gates in the path of interest. The optimal value of the total path delay is known before the gate sizes have even been determined.

The actual sizes are obtained by working backwards from the output to the input. We use the fact that for each gate,

$$SE^* = LE \times FO = LE \times \frac{C_{out}}{C_{in}}$$

$$\therefore C_{in} = LE \times \frac{C_{out}}{SE^*}$$

Therefore, working backwards from output to input:

$$Z = (1) \times (20)/(1.45) = 13.8$$

$$Y = (4/3) \times Z/(1.45) = 12.7$$

$$X = (5/3) \times Y/(1.45) = 14.5$$

$$C_{in} = (1)(14.5)/1.45 = 10$$

The first inverter size can be verified by the last equation, which is consistent with the specified input capacitance value. This is a good way to confirm that your sizing is correct.

Example 6.14

Designing an 8-Input AND Gate

Problem:

An 8-input AND gate is to be designed to drive a load of 200 fF but is limited to an input capacitance of 20 fF. Since a single 8-input CMOS NAND gate is out of the question, choose two configurations that are more suitable and identify the solution with the fastest speed.

Solution:

1. The first option is the NAND4-INV-NAND2-INV as shown below. Here the *LE* and parasitic terms are all known for these gates since they are standard gates. So the following computation can be used to determine the delay:

$$D = 4(\text{Path Effort})^{1/4} + \sum P = 4((2)(4/3)(10))^{1/4} + 3 + 1/2 + 1 + 1/2 = 14$$

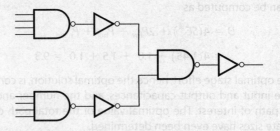

2. Next, a NAND2-NOR2-NAND2-INV cascade is examined. Again, the *LE* and γ values are known. Therefore,

$$D = 4(\text{Path Effort})^{1/4} + \sum P$$

$$= 4((4/3)^2(5/3)(10))^{1/4} + 1 + 3/2 + 1 + 1/2 = 13.3$$

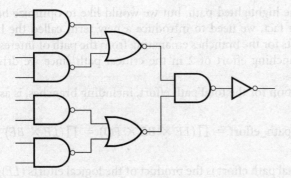

Option 2 is better than option 1.

We can make a few conclusions based on these results. The *LE* of the gates in a logic path, by themselves, do not tell us which configuration is faster. A delay calculation must be performed to make the determination. This is because the delay depends on the fanout capacitance. If the fanout capacitance is small, the parasitic terms will influence the answer. If the fanout is very large, then the delay is a function of the types of gates and the number of stages used. In practice, only single stage gates driving large capacitances can be compared purely on *LE*. Therefore, we should always use delay calculation to determine if one configuration is superior to another.

6.6.3 Branching Effort and Sideloads

So far we have considered a single path through the logic circuit. What if there are one or more branches from a given node? This would affect the sizing of gates and therefore must be taken into account in logical effort. For this purpose, we introduce a *branching factor* into the analysis. Alternatively, if a node has an additional load of fixed size, we treat it as a *sideload*. These methods are described below.

The first situation is one where the branch is identical to the path of interest. In Figure 6.30, we have an inverter driving two other inverters. This doubles the loading on the first inverter since both are sized in the same way. We are interested in

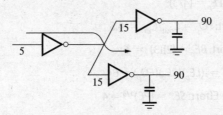

Figure 6.30
Branching factor.

optimizing the highlighted path, but we would like to optimize both paths at the same time. In fact, we need to introduce a new term called the branching effort which accounts for the branches emanating from the path of interest. In this circuit, there is a branching effort of 2 in the critical path since we drive two identical inverters.

The equation for the total path effort, including branches, is as follows:

$$\text{total\_path\_effort} = \prod(LE \times BE \times FO) = \prod(LE \times BE) \times \frac{C_{\text{load}}}{C_{\text{in}}}$$

That is, the total path effort is the product of the logical efforts (LE) times the product of the branching efforts (BE) times the product of the fanouts (FO). The branching effort is often known in advance or can be estimated based on the circuit topology. The use of BE is best illustrated in an example.

Example 6.15   **Branching Effort Example**

Problem:

Select gate sizes y and z to minimize delay in the highlighted path:

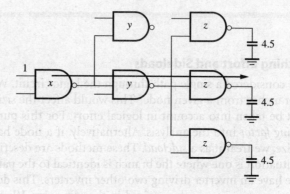

Solution:

Logical Effort: $LE_p = (4/3)^3$

Electrical Effort: $FO_p = C_{\text{out}}/C_{\text{in}} = 4.5$

Branching Effort: $BE_p = (2)(3) = 6$

Path Effort: $PE = (LE_p)(BE_p)(FO_p) = 64$

Optimal Stage Effort: $SE^* = (PE)^{1/3} = 4$

Delay: $D = (N)(SE^*) + \text{Parasitics}$

Delay: $D = (3)(4) + (3)(1) = 15$

Work backwards for gate sizes:

$$z = (1)(4.5)(4/3)/4 = 1.5$$

$$y = (3)(1.5)(4/3)/4 = 1.5$$

$$x = (2)(1.5)(4/3)/4 = 1$$

Another situation arises where we have a known fixed load in a circuit along the path of interest. The notion of branching effort cannot be used here. The reason is that branching effort should only be applied where the other fanouts uniformly scale in size with the path of interest. This does not handle the case where a node has a fixed capacitance value. We refer to these capacitances as *sideloads*. The approach is best illustrated using an example.

Computing Delay with Sideloads   **Example 6.16**

Problem:

Compute the gate sizes w, x, and y for the following logic circuit to produce the minimum delay. Assume that $A = 8$ and $B = 64$. Here, A should be considered as a sideload.

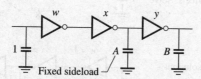

Fixed sideload

Solution:

If we remove the sideload and use FO4 sizing rules, we would size the inverters as $w = 1, x = 4$, and $y = 16$. This satisfies the geometric relationship between consecutive stages and would produce the minimum delay.

If we now insert the sideload, we would derive the following delay equations

First two stages: $D_1 = LE_{inv}\left(\dfrac{x}{w} + \gamma_{inv}\right) + LE_{inv}\left(\dfrac{A + y}{x} + \gamma_{inv}\right)$

$$\frac{\partial D_1}{\partial x} = \frac{1}{w} - \frac{A + y}{x^2} \Rightarrow \frac{x}{w} = \frac{A + y}{x}$$

Next two stages: $D_2 = LE_{inv}\left(\dfrac{A + y}{x} + \gamma_{inv}\right) + LE_{inv}\left(\dfrac{B}{y} + \gamma_{inv}\right)$

$$\frac{\partial D_2}{\partial y} = \frac{1}{x} - \frac{B}{y^2} \Rightarrow \frac{y}{x} = \frac{B}{y}$$

We can use the two equations to iterate the solution:

$$y^2 = Bx \rightarrow y = \sqrt{Bx} = \sqrt{64(4)} = 16$$
$$x^2 = (A + y)w \rightarrow x = \sqrt{(A + y)w} = 4.9$$
$$y = 17.7 \qquad x = 5.1$$
$$y \approx 18 \qquad x \approx 5$$

Setting up the iterative equations is complicated and prone to error. An alternative approach is recommended that is much simpler and produces a reasonable solution. First solve the sizing problem using logical effort without the sideload. Next, add in the sideload and the loading of the next gate. Then, remove the downstream gates and solve the remaining circuit again with logical effort to obtain their sizes.

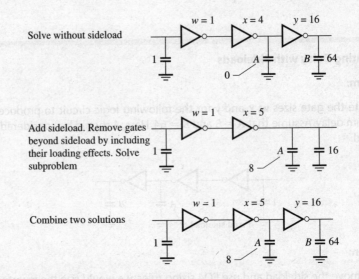

The results obtained are slightly different from the exact solution but produce a similar delay. More importantly, it is much easier to carry out hand calculation using this method compared to the iterative approach.

It should be noted that logical effort is a useful tool for back of the envelope timing optimization. It allows the designer to quickly determine the optimal delay for a given path, and the corresponding device sizes to achieve this delay. It provides insight into the key factors in the delay of logic paths. There are many other aspects of logical effort that were not covered in this chapter. The reader is encouraged to read further in the references. The concepts outlined here will be extended in the chapters to follow.

6.7 Summary

Propagation delay:

$$t_P = \frac{t_{PLH} + t_{PHL}}{2}$$

Driving resistance:

$$R_{eqn} \approx 12.5 \text{ k}\Omega/\square$$

$$R_{eqp} \approx 30 \text{ k}\Omega/\square$$

$$R_N = R_{eqn} \left(\frac{L}{W}\right)_n$$

$$R_P = R_{eqp} \left(\frac{L}{W}\right)_p$$

Load capacitance components:

$$C_{\text{load}} = C_{\text{self}} + C_{\text{wire}} + C_{\text{fanout}}$$

Input capacitance:

$$C_g = C_{ox}L + 2C_{ol} \cong 2 \text{ fF}/\mu\text{m}$$

Self-capacitance:

$$C_{eff} = C_j + 2C_{ol} \cong 1 \text{ fF}/\mu\text{m}$$

Wire capacitance:

$$C_{\text{int}} = 0.2 \text{ fF}/\mu\text{m}$$

Total delay:

$$\text{Total\_delay} = \sum_i R_i C_i$$

Inverter delay equation:

$$t_{\text{delay}} = \tau_{\text{inv}} \left[\frac{C_{\text{out}}}{C_{\text{in}}} + \gamma_{\text{inv}}\right]$$

where

$$\tau_{\text{inv}} = R_{\text{eff}}C_{\text{in}} = R_{eqn}\left(\frac{L_n}{W_n}\right)C_g(3W_n) = 3R_{eqn}C_gL_n$$

$$\gamma_{\text{inv}} = \frac{C_{\text{self}}}{C_{\text{in}}}$$

NAND and NOR intrinsic time constants:

$$\tau_{\text{nand}} = R_{\text{eff}}C_{\text{in}} = R_{eqn}\left(\frac{L_n}{W_n}\right)4W_nC_g = 4R_{eqn}C_gL_n$$

$$\tau_{\text{nor}} = R_{\text{eff}}C_{\text{in}} = R_{eqn}\left(\frac{L_n}{W_n}\right)5W_nC_g = 5R_{eqn}C_gL_n$$

Normalized delay equation:

$$D = \sum \left(LE \times FO + P\right)$$

where

$$LE = \text{logic effort} = \tau_{\text{gate}} / \tau_{\text{inv}} \text{ (normalized to inverter)}$$

$$FO_j = \text{fanout} = \frac{C_{j+1}}{C_j}$$

$$P = \text{parasitic term} = LE \times \gamma_{\text{gate}}$$

Logical effort for inverter, NAND2, and NOR2:

$$LE_{\text{inv}} = \frac{\tau_{\text{inv}}}{\tau_{\text{inv}}} = 1$$

$$LE_{\text{nand2}} = \frac{\tau_{\text{nand2}}}{\tau_{\text{inv}}} = \frac{4}{3}$$

$$LE_{\text{nor2}} = \frac{\tau_{\text{nor2}}}{\tau_{\text{inv}}} = \frac{5}{3}$$

Path effort:

$$\text{total\_path\_effort} = \prod (LE \times BE \times FO) = \prod (LE \times BE) \times \frac{C_{\text{load}}}{C_{\text{in}}}$$

Optimal stage effort:

$$SE^* = (\text{Path Effort})^{1/N}$$

Gate sizing based on optimal stage effort:

$$C_{in} = LE \times \frac{C_{out}}{SE^*}$$

Normalized delay:

$$D = N \, (\text{Path Effort})^{1/N} + \sum P$$

REFERENCES

1. I. Sutherland, B. Sproull, and D. Harris, *Logical Effort: Designing Fast CMOS Circuits*, Morgan Kaufman Publishers, San Francisco, CA, 1999.

2. D. Harris, *Skew-Tolerant Circuit Design*, Morgan Kaufman Publishers, San Francisco, CA, 2001.

3. J. Rabaey, A. Chandrakasan, and B. Nikolic, *Digital Integrated Circuits: A Designer Perspective*, Second Edition, Prentice-Hall, Upper Saddle River, NJ, 2003.

4. S. M. Kang and Y. Leblebici, *CMOS Digital Integrated Circuits, Analysis and Design*, Third Edition, McGraw-Hill, New York, NY, 2003.

5. H. Veendrick, *Deep-Submicron CMOS ICs*, Second Edition, Kluwer Academic Publishers, Boston, MA, 2000.

6. J. P. Uyemura, *CMOS Logic Circuit Design*, Kluwer Academic Publishers, Boston, MA, 1999.

PROBLEMS

P6.1. Plot the on-resistance of a unit-sized NMOS device as a function of V_{DS}. Use 0.13 μm technology parameters and assume that $V_{DD} = 1.2$ V. How does this plot compare to the design value of 12.5 kΩ? Derive an expression for the average resistance value between V_{DD} to $V_{DD}/2$ using the velocity saturated model.

P6.2. Compute the oscillation frequency of a seven-stage ring oscillator using 0.13 μm technology parameters. Does the size of the inverters make any difference in the result? Compare your result with SPICE.

P6.3. Extract values of R_{eqn}, R_{eqp}, C_g, and C_{eff} using SPICE for a 0.13 μm technology. How do they compare against the values used for hand calculation?

P6.4. In each of the circuits of Figure P6.4, determine the self-capacitance at the output assuming step changes at the inputs shown.

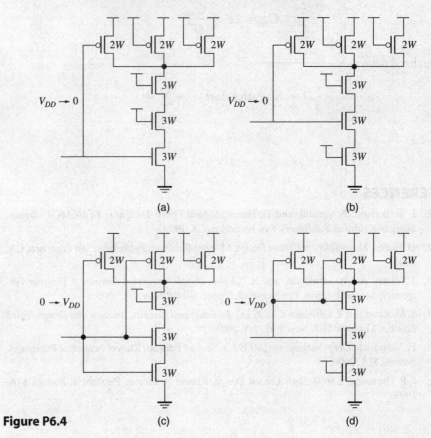

Figure P6.4

(a)   (b)   (c)   (d)

P6.5. In this problem, we examine the effect of the input selected and the velocity saturation model on the delay for the two circuits of Figure P6.5.

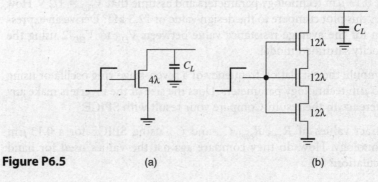

Figure P6.5   (a)   (b)

(a) Using HSPICE and a 0.13 μm technology file, compare the t_{PHL} delay for the two cases. The output capacitance is 50 fF. The input should be a step going from 0 V to 1.2 V. You can ignore parasitics in your simulation by setting *AS*, *AD*, *PS*, and *PD* to zero in the netlist. Which case has a shorter delay and why?

(b) Now, adjust the sizes of all three devices in circuit (b) until the delay for circuit (a) and (b) are the same. By what factor is the device size reduced in case (b)?

P6.6. Without adding additional inverters, size the inverters in Figure P6.6 to minimize the propagation delay, and then calculate the path delay. Next, calculate the number of devices in the path for optimum delay and recalculate the size of devices. Finally calculate the new path delay and compare it with the first case. C_{inv} is the input capacitance of a minimum size inverter.

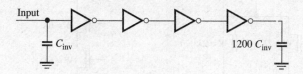

Figure P6.6

P6.7. Show that the logical effort of a gate does not change as you uniformly increase all the device sizes. Demonstrate this with a NAND3 and a NOR4 circuit.

P6.8. One way to improve the power dissipation of pseudo-NMOS gates is to connect one of the inputs to the pull-up device as shown in Figure P6.8. If we connect input *A* to the pull-up, we can reduce the size of the NMOS device to *W*/2. This configuration behaves as a static CMOS gate if the input comes through node *A*, but like the pseudo-NMOS gate if

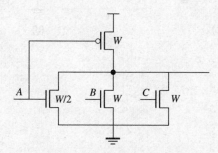

Figure P6.8

the input comes through B or C. Therefore, the power dissipation is smaller if node A goes high but will be the same as a pseudo-NMOS gate if B or C go high. Clearly, this type of configuration is suitable if we knew that A would arrive first.

(a) What is the LE of input A?

(b) What is the LE of inputs B and C?

P6.9. Calculate the logical effort of the gates in Figure P6.9. (All transistors have minimum length, $L = 2\lambda$). Use input A for the calculation.

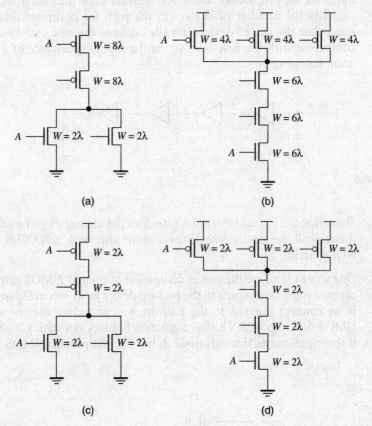

(a)

(b)

(c)

(d)

Figure P6.9

P6.10. What is the rising LE_R at input B of the first gate, and falling LE_F of the subsequent gate in Figure P6.10?

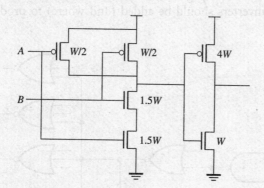

Figure P6.10

P6.11. In Figure P6.11, calculate the optimum delay and size of the transistors. (All devices are standard CMOS and all transistors have minimum length, $L = 0.1\ \mu$m). C_{inv} is the input capacitance of a minimum size inverter.

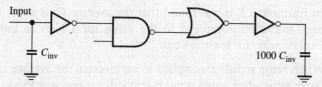

Figure P6.11

P.6.12. In Figure P6.12, calculate the optimum path delay and the transistor sizes. (All devices are standard CMOS and all transistors have minimum length, $L = 0.1\ \mu$m). Use 0.13 μm technology parameters. C_{inv} is the input capacitance of a minimum size inverter.

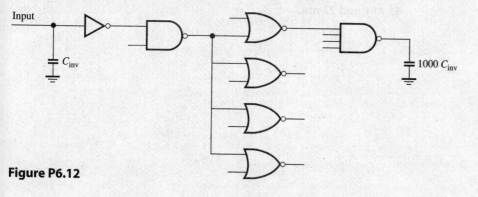

Figure P6.12

P6.13. Without adding additional inverters, size the gates in Figure P6.13 to minimize the propagation delay, and then calculate the path delay. How many inverters should be added (and where) to produce the optimal delay?

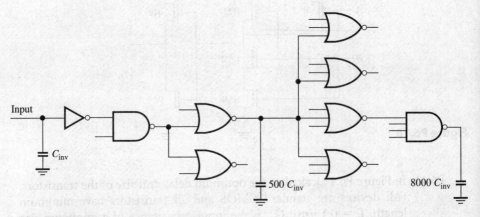

Figure P6.13

P6.14. In Example 6.2, it was found that the average C_g is larger for a low to high transition compared to the value for a high to low transition. Explain why this is always true.

P6.15. When ramp inputs are applied to an inverter, the average value of C_g is larger than when a step input is applied. Explain why this is always true.

P6.16. Derive a simple formula for the FO4 delay that can be used for back of the envelope calculations. It should have the form:

$$\text{FO4 delay} = \text{constant} \times L$$

where the constant is in units of picoseconds/μm and L is the minimum channel length. Compute the constant based on 0.18 μm and 0.13 μm technologies. Use the formula to estimate the FO4 delay for $L = 90$ nm, 45 nm, and 22 nm.

Transfer Gate and Dynamic Logic Design

7.1   Introduction

In previous chapters, we examined the characteristics of *static* logic gates. Two varieties of static gates were presented: conventional CMOS and pseudo-NMOS gates. Standard CMOS gates dissipate far less power than their pseudo-NMOS counterparts but require more area due to the number of complementary PMOS transistors needed, and their size requirements to achieve equal rise/fall delays. Usually the PMOS device is twice the size of the NMOS device in a conventional CMOS inverter. However, the pseudo-NMOS gates require ratioed devices to set the desired value of V_{OL}; typically, the NMOS device is four times the size of the PMOS device in a pseudo-NMOS inverter. Unfortunately, this produces asymmetric rise and fall times. If we increase the size of the PMOS device to try to equalize the delays, the value of V_{OL} increases. In order to strike a balance between conventional CMOS and pseudo-NMOS circuits in terms of area, timing, and power, we turn our attention to *dynamic logic* techniques.

Earlier, we found that all nodes of a static gate have direct paths to V_{DD} or Gnd. So long as the power remains on, the value of the output node is held indefinitely.

Dynamic gates, on the other hand, store their value on a capacitor. The storage nodes are often isolated from the rest of the circuit for long periods of time. Therefore, node values may decay over time if not refreshed or updated periodically. A dynamic node is also more susceptible to noise events than static gates. It is in this sense that the name *dynamic* is applied—the node voltage is held somewhat precariously by the charge stored at the node. This feature renders dynamic logic less desirable than static circuits for most designers. However, if we are careful about how we design this type of circuit, it can outperform static logic circuits. For this reason, we explore dynamic design techniques in this chapter.

One form of dynamic logic uses transfer gates as switches to propagate information through the circuit. When the switches are off, their outputs are held in a *high-impedance* (or high-Z) state implying that the gate is no longer driving the output. In this condition, the previous value is stored as charge on the output capacitance. A second form of dynamic logic relies on additional clocking signals for proper operation. On one part of the clock cycle, all logic gate outputs are *precharged* to an initial value. On the other part of the cycle, the gates *evaluate* their correct output values. We now discuss these two types of dynamic logic circuits in detail.

7.2   Basic Concepts

We begin our study of dynamic circuits by considering the pass transistor or transfer gate (sometimes referred to as a pass gate or transmission gate). These devices will expose the advantages and limitations of using a single transistor as a switch. There are three basic concepts that are important to dynamic circuits. These are charge sharing, feedthrough, and charge leakage.

7.2.1   Pass Transistors

The role of a pass transistor is to transfer an input signal, unaltered, to the output node when the gate is *on*. When the gate is turned *off*, the output enters the high-Z state and holds its previous value. This type of logic gate has an input, an output, and a third terminal that controls whether the device is *on* or *off*. In Figure 7.1, single *n*-channel and *p*-channel implementations of the transfer gate are shown under various input conditions. The source and drain nodes serve as inputs and outputs, while the gate node serves as the control input.

Figure 7.1 illustrates the signal transmission capability of each type of transfer gate in the *on* and *off* conditions. Figure 7.1a demonstrates that the *n*-channel device can successfully pass 0 V when its control input is at V_{DD}. Similarly, the PMOS device propagates V_{DD} from input to output when its control input is 0 V, as in Figure 7.1b. However, both NMOS and PMOS devices have problems passing the opposite signal level. The NMOS device in Figure 7.1c has trouble passing V_{DD}, since it shuts off when the output rises to $V_{DD} - V_{TN}$, with full accounting for body effect. The PMOS has a similar problem with low inputs, as shown in Figure 7.1d. When the control input shuts the device *off*, the output enters the high-Z state, as in Figure 7.1e and Figure 7.1f.

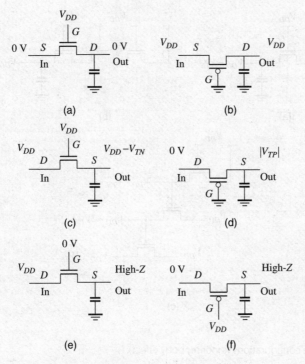

Figure 7.1
NMOS and PMOS pass transistor configurations.

The reason for difference in transmission capability of the NMOS device can be understood by comparing Figure 7.1a and Figure 7.1c. The drain (D), gate (G), and source (S) have been identified to clarify the description. For an NMOS device, the drain is the higher of the two nodes. Since the MOS transistor is a symmetric device, the determination of the drain and source can only be carried out after the node voltages have been assigned. In Figure 7.1c, the drain is connected to V_{DD} since this is guaranteed to be the highest node. If the source node starts at 0 V, the device is *on* and in the saturation of operation. Current flows from drain to source to charge up the output capacitance and the source node voltage begins to increase. It continues to increase until $V_{GS} = V_{TN}$. At this point, the output voltage is $V_{DD} - V_{TN}$. In Figure 7.1a, the drain and source terminals are reversed. The value of V_{GS} is always V_{DD}. As such, the device is always *on* and will pull the output node low until $V_{DS} = 0$, at which point the output is 0 V.

For the *p*-channel device, we can go through the same exercise for Figure 7.1b and Figure 7.1d. This time the definition of the drain and source are reversed such that the higher voltage is the source and the lower voltage is the drain. In Figure 7.1b, the drain node begins at 0 V and rises as the PMOS device charges it to V_{DD}. The output can reach V_{DD} since the value of V_{GS} is constant at $-V_{DD}$ implying that

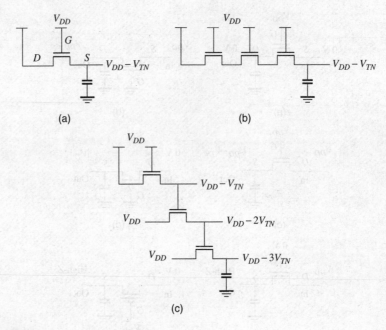

Figure 7.2

NMOS pass gate configurations (ignoring body effect).

the PMOS device is always *on*. In Figure 7.1d, the source node begins at V_{DD} and drops in voltage as the output capacitance is discharged until the value of $V_{GS} = |V_{TP}|$. At this point, the device shuts off. Therefore, the lowest voltage that the output can reach is $|V_{TP}|$.

Figure 7.2 shows three n-channel pass transistor configurations to further clarify the operation. Note that the two circuits of Figure 7.2a and Figure 7.2b produce the same output, $V_{DD} - V_{TN}$. At first glance, it would seem that Figure 7.2b with three series transistors would produce an output of $V_{DD} - 3V_{TN}$, but this is incorrect. Each pass transistor is able to pass a value of $V_{DD} - V_{TN}$ from input to output when the gate voltage is V_{DD}. Figure 7.3c illustrates the actual configuration that would produce an output of $V_{DD} - 3V_{TN}$. In each successive pass transistor, the gate voltage is V_{TN} lower than the previous transistor. The output can only climb within a threshold voltage of the gate voltage before the device shuts off. Note that the more accurate value of the output is in fact $V_{DD} - V_{TN1} - V_{TN2} - V_{TN3}$ due to the change in the body effect term in each transistor. The reader should be aware that this example is contrived since designers should avoid using the output of a pass transistor to drive the gate of another pass transistor.

For completeness, the p-channel equivalents for Figure 7.2 are given in Figure 7.3. The same arguments for the n-channel configurations can be applied to the p-channel devices, with the corresponding changes in output voltage levels.

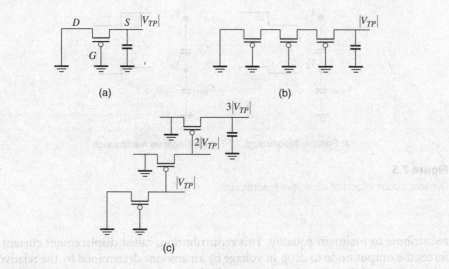

Figure 7.3
PMOS pass gate configurations (ignoring body effect).

7.2.2 Capacitive Feedthrough

The role of the control node of a pass transistor is to place the device in the *on* and *off* states. As such, it is often driven by a clock signal. Ideally, this input should not have any direct influence on the output, except to enable or disable the transfer gate. However, there exists a capacitance, C_f, between the gate and output nodes that causes the clock signal to feed through to the output. This effect is illustrated in Figure 7.4. The control signal undergoes a voltage swing from V_{DD} to 0 V, thereby shutting off the device. This places the output in the high-Z state since $V_{GS} < V_{TN}$. At this point, the two capacitors, C_f and C_{gnd}, are isolated from the rest of the circuit. As the gate voltage decreases in value, the charges associated with the two capacitors

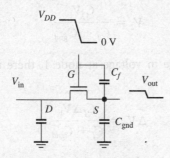

Figure 7.4
Clock feedthrough.

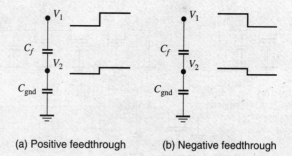

(a) Positive feedthrough   (b) Negative feedthrough

Figure 7.5
Dynamic circuit effects of capacitive feedthrough.

redistribute to maintain equality. This redistribution, called displacement current, forces the output node to drop in voltage by an amount determined by the relative values of C_f and C_{gnd}. The fact that a small replica of the clock appears at the output led to the terminology of *clock feedthrough* for this effect. The same effect would be observed at the drain node if it were isolated from the rest of the circuit. However, we have assumed that drain is driven by a static gate in this example.

The capacitive effects associated with feedthrough may occur in the positive or negative direction. We can understand these effects by examining isolated capacitors in series as shown in Figure 7.5. For a series combination of two capacitors, positive and negative feedthrough result in noise injection at an internal node when the external node rises or falls. The change at the external node 1 produces a replica change at the internal node 2, which is a high-impedance node.

The exact voltage change at the internal node can be determined for the idealized cases of Figure 7.5. The charges associated with the two capacitors must be the same at equilibrium:

$$C_f(V_1 - V_2) = C_{gnd}V_2 \tag{7.1}$$

Therefore,

$$V_2 = \frac{C_fV_1}{C_f + C_{gnd}} \tag{7.2}$$

If there is an abrupt change in voltage at node 1, there is a corresponding but smaller change at node 2:

$$\Delta V_2 = \frac{C_f\Delta V_1}{C_f + C_{gnd}} \tag{7.3}$$

In Figure 7.5a, when there is a large positive change in V_1, the internal node voltage will change by an amount dictated by the ratio of C_f to $(C_f + C_{gnd})$. The change at node 2 will be in the positive direction. This is sometimes referred to as bootstrapping.[1] In Figure 7.5b, we have a negative going step at node 1 that produces a replica negative going step at node 2. Consider the two extreme cases of feedthrough. If C_f is much larger than C_{gnd}, then ΔV_2 approaches ΔV_1. On the other hand, if C_{gnd} is much greater than C_f then ΔV_2 approaches 0. For the pass transistor, the value of C_f is determined by C_{GS} while C_{gnd} is determined by the junction capacitance, C_{BS}, plus the loading capacitance of the next gate. To reduce the feedthrough effect, we should ensure that $C_{gnd} \gg C_f$.

V_T Drop and Clock Feedthrough Effects

Example 7.1

Problem:

In the circuit below with the input at 1.2 V, what is the initial value of the output when the clock is at 1.2 V. Estimate the final value after the clock goes low. Repeat the problem for the case when the input is 0 V. Assume that the device is 4λ/2λ in 0.13 μm technology.

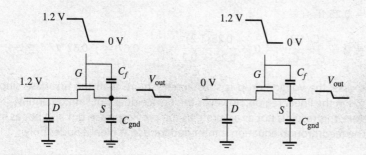

Solution:

Initially, the output will be a threshold voltage below 1.2 V:

$$V_{out} = V_{DD} - V_{TN} = 1.2 - (0.4 + 0.2(\sqrt{0.88 + V_{out}} - \sqrt{0.88}))$$

$$\therefore V_{out} = 0.73 \text{ V}$$

When the clock switches from high to low, the feedthrough effects will act to reduce the value at the output:

$$V_{out} = 0.73 - \Delta V = 0.73 - \frac{C_f(1.2)}{C_f + C_{gnd}}$$

In this example, C_f is due to the overlap capacitance since the transistor is in the cutoff region. Therefore,

$$C_f = C_{OL} = C_{ol}W = (0.25 \text{ fF}/\mu m) \times 0.2 \ \mu m = 0.05 \text{ fF}$$

---

[1] Bootstrapping is usually associated with increasing a node voltage above V_{DD} using active devices. We use the term here more generally to refer to any increase in the voltage due to series capacitor effects.

The value of C_{gnd} is due to the junction capacitance. Therefore,

$$C_{gnd} = C_{eff} \times W = 1 \text{ fF}/\mu m \times 0.2 \ \mu m = 0.2 \text{ fF}$$

The resulting value of V_{out} is

$$V_{out} = 0.73 - \frac{C_f(1.2)}{C_f + C_{gnd}} = 0.73 - \frac{0.05(1.2)}{0.05 + 0.2} = 0.73 - 0.24 \approx 0.5 \text{ V}$$

For this particular case, the clock feedthrough effect is significant even though we are only considering the overlap capacitance. The resulting voltage is below typical switching thresholds and this would be a problem. In a realistic situation, there is always additional grounded capacitance at the output due to the fanout gates. This would greatly reduce the degree of clock feedthrough.

When the input is 0 V, the output is 0 V. However, in this case, the device is in the linear region of operation. Therefore,

$$C_f = 1/2 \ C_g W + C_{ol} W = (1/2)(2 \text{ fF}/\mu m)(0.2 \ \mu m) + (0.25 \text{ fF}/\mu m)(0.2 \ \mu m)$$

$$= 0.25 \text{ fF}$$

$$V_{out} = 0 - \frac{C_f(1.2)}{C_f + C_{gnd}} = 0 - \frac{0.25(1.2)}{0.25 + 0.2} = 0 - 0.67 = -0.67 \text{ V}$$

In this case, the voltage drop is substantially more than the first case since the device is in the linear region. However, the device does not shut off until $V_{GS} < V_{TN}$. Therefore, this result is not as accurate as the previous case, but also not as important. The feedthrough equation is intended for use at high-Z nodes only.

7.2.3 Charge Sharing

Another important issue in dynamic circuits is charge sharing which tends to reduce the voltage levels even further. This phenomenon occurs when two isolated nodes with different voltage levels are suddenly connected together when a pass transistor turns on, as shown in Figure 7.6. The key requirement is that the two nodes are in the high-impedance state and store different voltages. When the switch turns on, the charge redistributes until the voltage levels at the two nodes are equal. This reduces the voltage at one node while increasing the voltage at the other. If the voltage is reduced at an output node, it is of concern to us. We can analyze charge sharing by examining the total charge before and after the charge-sharing event.

In Figure 7.6a, the total charge in the closed system is

$$Q_{total} = C_1 V_1 + C_2 V_2 \tag{7.4}$$

When the gate node is switched from 0 to V_{DD}, as in Figure 7.6b, the transistor turns on and a charge transfer occurs between the two nodes until an equilibrium voltage

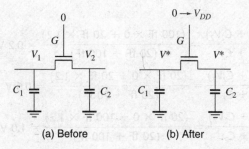

(a) Before   (b) After

Figure 7.6
Dynamic charge sharing.

is reached. At equilibrium, the total charge in the system remains constant. If V^* is the final voltage after charge exchange is completed, the total charge is given by

$$Q_{\text{total}} = (C_1 + C_2)V^* \qquad (7.5)$$

Combining (7.4) and (7.5), we obtain

$$V^* = \frac{(C_1V_1 + C_2V_2)}{C_1 + C_2} \qquad (7.6)$$

As an illustration of charge sharing, assume that $V_1 = 0$ and $V_2 = V_{DD} - V_T$ in Figure 7.6a. After the transistor turns on, the voltage at V_2 will drop in value and the voltage at V_1 will increase. Equation (7.6) specifies the final voltage on the two nodes. If V_2 drops below the switching threshold of the next gate, it will trigger the gate to produce an incorrect output. This is a serious consequence of charge sharing. To reduce charge sharing in this case, C_2 should be made much larger than C_1. There are additional techniques that can be employed to reduce the effects of charge sharing that will be described later in this chapter.

Equation (7.6) should be used carefully in conjunction with Figure 7.6 since it is only valid if V^* does not exceed $V_{DD} - V_{TN}$. If the computed voltage goes beyond this value, then V_1 should be set to this value and then V_2 re-calculated with the remaining charge, $Q_{\text{total}} - C_1 (V_{DD} - V_{TN})$. In this case, $V_1 \neq V_2$ after charge sharing.

Charge Sharing Example   **Example 7.2**

Problem:

In Figure 7.6a, compute the charge-sharing effects for the following cases assuming 0.13 μm technology parameters:

(a) $C_1 = 100$ fF, $C_2 = 20$ fF, $V_1 = 0$, $V_2 = 1.2$ V

(b) $C_1 = 20$ fF, $C_2 = 20$ fF, $V_1 = 0$, $V_2 = 1.2$ V

(c) $C_1 = 20$ fF, $C_2 = 100$ fF, $V_1 = 0$, $V_2 = 1.2$ V

Solution:

(a) $V^* = \dfrac{(C_1V_1 + C_2V_2)}{C_1 + C_2} = \dfrac{(100 \text{ fF} \times 0 + 20 \text{ fF} \times 1.2)}{(20 \text{ fF} + 100 \text{ fF})} = 0.2 \text{ V}$

(b) $V^* = \dfrac{(C_1V_1 + C_2V_2)}{C_1 + C_2} = \dfrac{(20 \text{ fF} \times 0 + 20 \text{ fF} \times 1.2)}{(20 \text{ fF} + 20 \text{ fF})} = 0.6 \text{ V}$

(c) $V^* = \dfrac{(C_1V_1 + C_2V_2)}{C_1 + C_2} = \dfrac{(20 \text{ fF} \times 0 + 100 \text{ fF} \times 1.2)}{(20 \text{ fF} + 100 \text{ fF})} = 1.0 \text{ V}$

This last solution is not possible since the voltage of node V_1 cannot rise above V_{DD} − V_{TN}. Ignoring body effect, the maximum voltage at node V_1 is 0.8 V. The total charge in the system is 120 fC. Node V_1 requires $0.8 \times 20 \text{ fF} = 16 \text{ fC}$ of charge. That leaves $120 - 16 = 104 \text{ fC}$ of charge on node V_2. This implies that the voltage at node $V_2 = 104 \text{ fC}/100 \text{ fF} = 1.04 \text{ V}$.

7.2.4   Other Sources of Charge Loss

When a pass transistor shuts off, the output node enters a high-Z state and retains the value of the node as charge on a capacitance. Unfortunately, the charge tends to leak away over time unless the value is updated or refreshed periodically. If a high value is stored, there are two possible sources of charge leakage. One source is reverse-bias leakage current from the drain junction. This current is rather small as it depends on the area of the junction which continues to shrink as technology scales. Of greater concern is the subthreshold current as described in Chapter 2.

A second source of charge loss is noise injection from neighboring wires. For example, if a wire is routed too closely to a dynamic node, capacitive coupling between the wire and the node could result in noise injection during switching events. The mechanism is similar in nature to feedthrough and bootstrapping. This form of noise injection can have serious consequences and must be considered carefully when designing dynamic circuits. Coupling noise is the subject of Chapter 10 on interconnect.

Another problem is associated with α-particles which are also responsible for data loss in memory circuits. These are high-energy particles that may be present in device packaging materials, such as solder bumps, or due to cosmic rays arriving from space. Particles of this nature can enter the silicon substrate and generate hole-electron pairs that act to discharge the output. This occurs over a very short amount of time and leads to unexpected functional failures in the circuit. The detailed mechanisms are beyond the scope of this book, but the importance of α-particles as a leading cause of so-called *soft errors* in both dynamic and static circuits should be recognized.

7.3   CMOS Transmission Gate Logic

In the previous section, we observed the limitations of using either a single NMOS or a single PMOS device as a transfer gate. Each one is capable of transmitting one

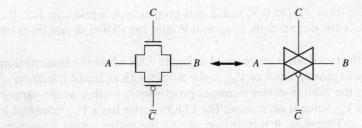

Figure 7.7
CMOS transmission gate and logic symbol.

of the levels accurately but neither device is capable of transmitting both high and low voltages properly, as evidenced by Figure 7.1. A natural improvement can be constructed by placing an NMOS device in parallel with a PMOS device to create a CMOS transmission gate, as shown in Figure 7.7. The two devices in combination can fully transmit any signal value between V_{DD} and Gnd. The cost of this feature is not only an extra transistor, but also an extra inverter since each transistor requires a complementary control input. Therefore, a total of four transistors are necessary for the CMOS version. The corresponding symbol for the transmission gate is also shown in Figure 7.7.

To understand the transmission capability of the CMOS transfer gate, consider the two cases shown in Figure 7.8. The two transistors have been separated out to clearly identify their role in transmitting 0 V or V_{DD}. In Figure 7.8a, a 0 V signal is being transmitted through both devices with an initial output of V_{DD}. The NMOS device has $V_{GS} = V_{DD}$ for the entire duration of the transition of the output from V_{DD} to 0 V. Therefore, it can pull the output to 0 V by itself. The PMOS device can only pull the output to $|V_{TP}|$ since it shuts off at that point. Note the positions of the gate and source terminals. The V_{GS} value of the PMOS device decreases in magnitude

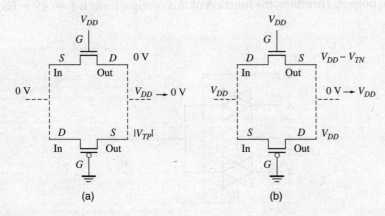

(a)   (b)

Figure 7.8
Transmitting low and high signals.

as the output falls from V_{DD} to 0 V, and it gets progressively weaker. In fact, the NMOS device pulls the output from $|V_{TP}|$ to 0 V after the PMOS device shuts off completely.

The roles of the two devices are reversed in Figure 7.8b, where the transmission gate is attempting to pass an input of V_{DD} to the output with an initial condition of 0 V. In this case, the NMOS device becomes progressively weaker as the output increases since its V_{GS} value is decreasing. The PMOS device has a V_{GS} value that is constant at $-V_{DD}$. Therefore, it remains on during the entire output transition. When the output reaches $V_{DD} - V_{TN}$, the NMOS device shuts off and the PMOS device pulls the output the rest of the way to V_{DD}. By examining these two cases, it is clear that the weakness of one device is overcome by the strength of the other device, whether the output is transmitting a high or low value. This is a clear advantage of the CMOS transfer gate over the single transistor counterpart.

Another advantage of the CMOS transfer gate is that the degree of capacitive feedthrough is reduced. This is because it is clocked with the true and complement values of the enable signal. Referring to Figure 7.7, when the signal C falls, there may be feedthrough at node B, but it would be canceled by the transition to a high voltage at $\overline{C}$. If the target voltage of B is low, feedthrough due to C would only make it lower. So this case is not a problem. If the intended voltage at B was high, then feedthrough would normally make the voltage lower. But since the p-channel device remains on for slightly longer than the n-channel device, it is able to pull the output back to V_{DD}.

7.3.1 Multiplexers Using CMOS Transfer Gates

CMOS transmission gate logic can be used to reduce the number of transistors needed to implement certain logic functions. They can be used in a variety of situations, but the most popular is in the role of a multiplexer as shown in Figure 7.9. The control signal S turns the transfer gates on and off depending on its value. Specifically, when $S = 1$, the upper transfer gate is on and that allows A to flow to the output. When $S = 0$, the lower transfer gate is on, and that allows B to flow from input to output. Therefore, the function of this configuration is $F = AS + B\overline{S}$. This

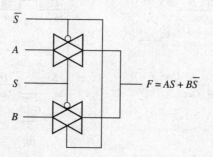

Figure 7.9
Multiplexer configuration.

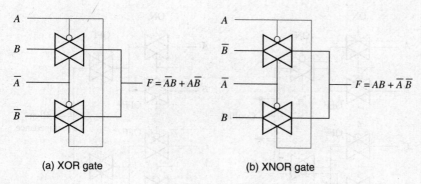

Figure 7.10

XOR and XNOR gates using CMOS transmission gates.

is a multiplexer where one of two input signals is selected based on the value of a control signal.

Assuming that certain rules are followed, it is a simple matter to construct other useful circuits using the multiplexer of Figure 7.9. By specifying the inputs and control signals in a particular pattern, we can construct XOR and XNOR gates as shown in Figure 7.10. A static CMOS gate version would require 16 transistors whereas the transfer gate version requires only 8 transistors (including all necessary inverters).

Another example is shown in Figure 7.11. Here, two multiplexer configurations that select one-of-four inputs are shown. In Figure 7.11a, a two-level strategy is used, while in Figure 7.11b a single-level is used. The two-level approach requires

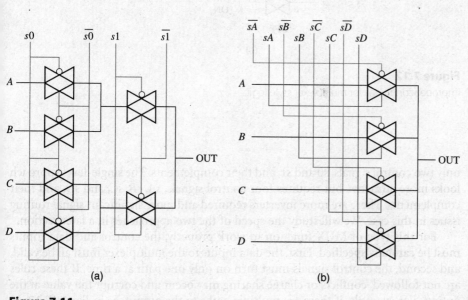

Figure 7.11

Two-level and single-level multiplexer configurations.

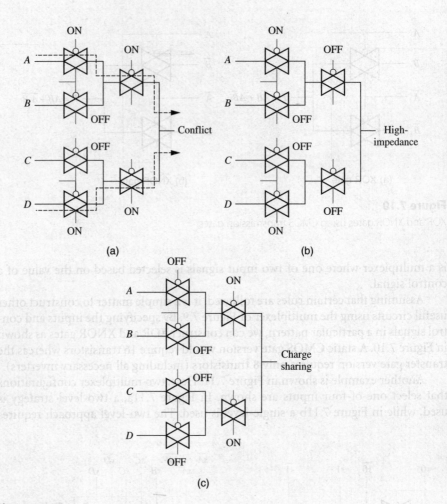

Figure 7.12
Improper conditions for multiplexer style logic.

only two control signals, $s0$ and $s1$, and their complements. The single-level approach looks more attractive but requires four control signals, sA, sB, sC, and sD, and their complements. There are more inverters required and more significant signal routing issues in this case. We will study the speed of the two approaches in a later section.

For this type of MUX function to work properly, the control and data inputs must be carefully specified. First, the data inputs to the multiplexer must all be valid, and second, the control signals must turn on only one path at a time. If these rules are not followed, conflicts or charge sharing may occur and corrupt the value at the output. For example, if there are multiple paths to the output, as in Figure 7.12a, a

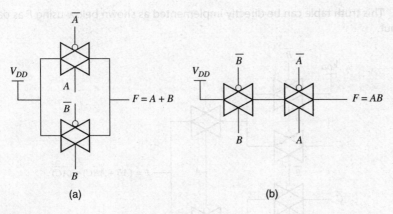

Figure 7.13
OR and AND functions using CMOS transmission gates.

conflict would arise at the output if A and D had different values. If there is no path to the output due to *off* devices in all paths, the output will assume a high-impedance state as in Figure 7.12b. If intermediate gates are *on*, as in Figure 7.12c, then an unknown may result at the output (possibly due to charge sharing).

To build general logic functions using transmission gates, the first step is to select the control signals and build a truth table for all the possible combinations. Then, the truth table is converted to a multiplexer-style design by creating a signal path in the circuit for each row of the truth table. Next, the desired output values specified in the truth table are routed from the data inputs to the output. Any needed OR and AND operations can be realized using parallel and series transmission gates as shown in Figure 7.13. Finally, optimization of the design may be carried out to combine paths or remove unnecessary transistors.

Implement the function $F = AB + A\bar{B}C + \bar{A}\bar{C}$ using transmission gates. **Example 7.3**

Solution:

Identify A and B as control signals and build a truth table.

A	B	F
0	0	$\bar{C}$
0	1	$\bar{C}$
1	0	C
1	1	1

This truth table can be directly implemented as shown below using F as data input.

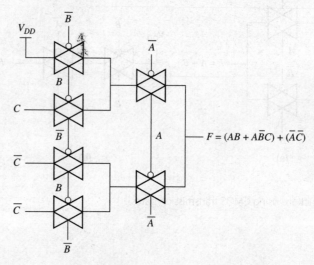

$$F = (AB + A\bar{B}C) + (\bar{A}\bar{C})$$

The first two lines of the truth table are associated with the lower part of the multiplexer. They can be combined to simplify the implementation. In addition, the transfer gate connected to V_{DD} does not need an n-channel device since it is only passing a high value. With these two optimizations, the following circuit results:

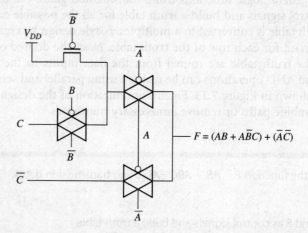

$$F = (AB + A\bar{B}C) + (\bar{A}\bar{C})$$

CMOS transmission gates can also be used with combinational blocks to implement certain functions efficiently. The first circuit in Figure 7.14 is a six-transistor XOR gate. The second circuit simply illustrates the use of transmission gate logic with standard CMOS logic to implement a complex function. In order to quickly extract the function F from the given circuit, follow the NMOS side of the transmission gates.

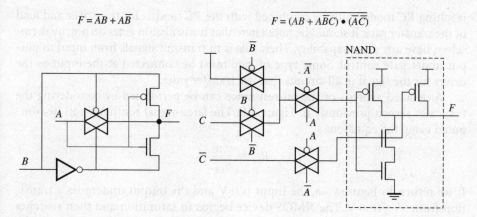

$$F = \overline{A}B + A\overline{B}$$

$$F = \overline{(AB + A\overline{B}C) \cdot (\overline{AC})}$$

NAND

Figure 7.14
Transmission gates and standard gate combinations.

In this case, the NAND operation is being performed on the two inputs. One input is $\overline{AC}$, while the other input is $AB + A\overline{B}C$. The resulting function F is the NAND of these two terms as shown in the diagram.

| Describe the operation of the XOR gate of Figure 7.14. Discuss its advantages and disadvantages relative to other XOR circuits considered so far in this textbook. | **Exercise 7.1** |

7.3.2   CMOS Transmission Gate Delays

In order to evaluate the timing performance of circuits containing transmission gates, an RC model of these gates must be developed. The model for a CMOS transfer gate (TG) consists of an on-resistance, R_{TG}, and two capacitances, C_1 and C_2, as shown in Figure 7.15. The on-resistance of the transfer gate is a parallel combination of the on-resistances of the NMOS and PMOS devices. The value of the resistances will depend on whether a 0 or a 1 is being propagated through the gate. The

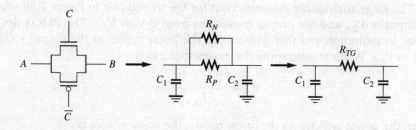

Figure 7.15
RC model for CMOS transmission gate.

resulting *RC* model must be combined with the *RC* models for the driver and load of the transfer gate. It should be noted here that transmission gates do not, by themselves, have any drive capability. Their role is to transmit signals from input to output under gate control. Some type of gate must be connected at the input as the driver for the signal in all circuits that use transfer gates.

A detailed analysis of the on-resistance can be performed by considering the two cases shown previously in Figure 7.8. The large-signal resistance can be computed using the equation:

$$R_{\text{on}} \approx \frac{V_{DS}}{I_{DS}}$$

If we return to Figure 7.8a, the input is 0 V and the output undergoes a transition from V_{DD} to 0 V. The NMOS device begins in saturation and then switches to the linear region as the output voltage drops to 0 V. When in saturation, the on-resistance is

$$R_N = \frac{V_{\text{out}}}{I_{Dsat,n}}$$

When the device switches to the linear region, the on-resistance is

$$R_N = \frac{V_{\text{out}}}{I_{Dlin,n}}$$

The PMOS device is biased in the saturation region until the output reaches $|V_{TP}|$. At this point, it enters cutoff and the resistance increases to infinity. In the saturation region, the resistance is given by

$$R_P = \frac{V_{\text{out}}}{I_{Dsat,p}}$$

The on-resistances for unit size NMOS and PMOS devices, and their parallel combination are plotted in Figure 7.16a. Note that the resistance of the PMOS device increases dramatically as the output voltage switches from V_{DD} to $|V_{TP}|$, while the NMOS resistance drops linearly over the same range. However, the parallel combination of the two resistances is relatively constant. It is convenient to model this resistance by a constant value based on the average during the transition.

The same analysis can be carried out for the second case in Figure 7.8b where the input is V_{DD} and the output transitions from 0 V to V_{DD}. The PMOS device begins in saturation and then switches to the linear region as the output voltage rises to V_{DD}. When in saturation, the on-resistance is

$$R_P = \frac{V_{DD} - V_{\text{out}}}{I_{Dsat,p}}$$

When the device switches to the linear region, the on-resistance is

$$R_P = \frac{V_{DD} - V_{\text{out}}}{I_{Dlin,p}}$$

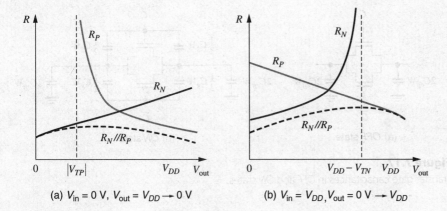

Figure 7.16

NMOS and PMOS on-resistances for falling and rising cases.

The NMOS device stays in the saturation region until the output reaches $V_{DD} - V_{TN}$. At this point, it enters cutoff and the resistance increases to infinity. In the saturation region, the resistance is given by

$$R_N = \frac{V_{DD} - V_{out}}{I_{Dsat,n}}$$

The on-resistance for unit size NMOS and PMOS devices, and their parallel combination for the second case is shown in Figure 7.16b. Here, the resistance of the NMOS device increases to infinity as the output voltage approaches $V_{DD} - V_{TN}$, while the PMOS resistance decreases linearly over the same interval. Again, the parallel combination of the two resistances is relatively constant and of similar magnitude as the falling case.

A simplified analysis can be carried out to estimate the on-resistance of the combined devices for the rising and falling cases. If we are propagating V_{DD}, the PMOS device behaves as a regular pullup with an on-resistance of approximately $R_{eqp} = 30 \text{ k}\Omega/\square$. For a unit size device, the resistance is 30 kΩ. On the other hand, the n-channel device is trying to pass a high value and its on-resistance will increase as its source node voltage approaches V_{DD}. Since the NMOS device is shutting off, the resistance will eventually reach infinity. The average on-resistance will be roughly *double* its nominal value of $R_{eqn} = 12.5 \text{ k}\Omega/\square$. For a unit device, this value is 25 kΩ. The parallel combination of the two devices produces a value that is close to the NMOS on resistance:

$$R_{TG} = R_N//R_P = 2R_{eqn}//R_{eqp} \approx 2R_{eqn}//2.4R_{eqn} = 1.1R_{eqn} \approx R_{eqn}$$

Now consider the case when we are propagating 0 V through the transmission gate. In this case, the n-channel device is *on* and has a resistance of R_{eqn}. The p-channel

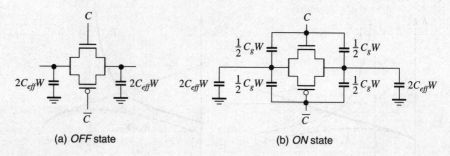

Figure 7.17
Transfer gate capacitances in *OFF* and *ON* states.

device is initially *on* and then begins to shut off as the voltage drops to 0 V. Therefore, its resistance is roughly $2R_{eqp}$, which is about five times R_{eqn}. The parallel combination of the two values produces

$$R_{TG} = R_N//R_P = R_{eqn}//2R_{eqp} \approx R_{eqn}//4.8R_{eqn} = 0.83R_{eqn} \approx R_{eqn}$$

In effect, the on-resistance of the CMOS transfer gate is approximately R_{eqn} regardless of the rising or falling conditions. Therefore, we will use this value for all resistance calculations with suitable adjustment for different W/L values:

$$R_{TG} = R_{eqn}\left(\frac{L}{W}\right) \tag{7.7}$$

We now turn our attention to the capacitance calculation. The transfer gate capacitance can be determined by examining the capacitances at the input and output for the *on* and *off* cases. When the transfer gate is *off*, as in Figure 7.17a, the C_{GS} and C_{GD} capacitances for both devices are zero, except for the overlap capacitances (not shown). In this condition, the input and output capacitances are due to the junction capacitances of the *n*-channel and *p*-channel devices.

Using C_{eff}, the input and output capacitances are

$$C_{in} = C_{out} = C_{eff}(W_n + W_p) \tag{7.8}$$

Since the two devices are the same size this simplifies to

$$C_{in} = C_{out} = C_{eff}2W \tag{7.9}$$

Next, consider a transfer gate in the *on* state, as shown in Figure 7.17b. Here the devices are assumed to be in the linear region (which is true for some part of the transition for both devices). Therefore, the input and output nodes see half the gate capacitance from each device along with the junction capacitances (and overlap

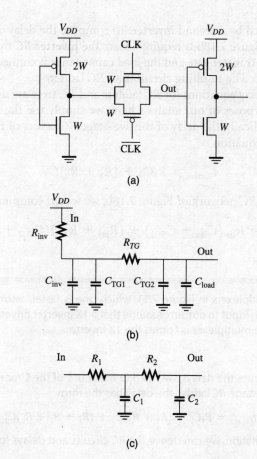

Figure 7.18

Transmission gate with driver and load.

capacitances). The total input and output capacitances are equal and can be computed as

$$C_{in} = C_{out} = C_{eff}(W_n + W_p) + \frac{1}{2}(C_g W_n + C_g W_p) \tag{7.10}$$

Note that both devices are the same size so this can be simplified to

$$C_{in} = C_{out} = C_{eff} 2W + C_g W \tag{7.11}$$

With the complete *RC* model defined as above, it is now possible to compute the path delay of circuits containing transmission gates. However, accurate delay calculation must involve the characteristics of the driver and load of the transmission gate. This is illustrated in Figure 7.18a where an inverter is driving the transmission gate which is loaded by a second inverter. To compute the delay accurately, the RC model shown in Figure 7.18b is required. Here the inverter RC model is connected at the input of the transfer gate and the load capacitance is connected at the output of the transfer gate. The resulting circuit is an RC ladder.

The Elmore delay equations for RC ladders and RC trees are described in Chapter 10. For the purposes of our analysis here, we simply use the results derived in that chapter. Specifically, the delay of the two-stage RC ladder of Figure 7.18c using the Elmore delay equation is

$$t_{\text{Elmore}} = R_1 C_1 + (R_1 + R_2) C_2$$

Therefore, for the RC network of Figure 7.18b, we would compute the delay as

$$t_{\text{Elmore}} = R_{\text{inv}}(C_{\text{inv}} + C_{\text{TG1}}) + (R_{\text{inv}} + R_{\text{TG}})(C_{\text{TG2}} + C_{\text{load}})$$

Example 7.4   For the two multiplexers in Figure 7.11, which one is faster, assuming that there exists a path from input to output? Assume that a 1X inverter drives each input and the fanout of the multiplexer is f times the 1X inverter.

Solution:

In order to compute the delays, we need to make use of the Elmore delay calculation. For a three-stage RC ladder, the delay has the form

$$t_{\text{Elmore}} = R_1 C_1 + (R_1 + R_2) C_2 + (R_1 + R_2 + R_3) C_3$$

Using this formulation, we can derive the RC circuits and delays for the two cases as follows:

MUX1:

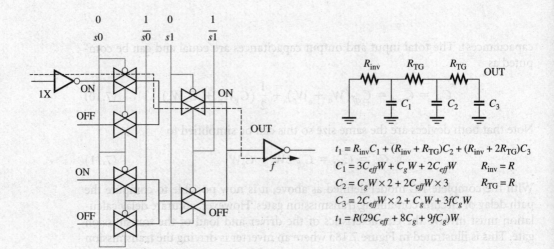

$$t_1 = R_{\text{inv}} C_1 + (R_{\text{inv}} + R_{\text{TG}}) C_2 + (R_{\text{inv}} + 2R_{\text{TG}}) C_3$$

$$C_1 = 3C_{\text{eff}} W + C_g W + 2C_{\text{eff}} W \qquad R_{\text{inv}} = R$$

$$C_2 = C_g W \times 2 + 2C_{\text{eff}} W \times 3 \qquad R_{\text{TG}} = R$$

$$C_3 = 2C_{\text{eff}} W \times 2 + C_g W + 3f C_g W$$

$$t_1 = R(29C_{\text{eff}} + 8C_g + 9f C_g) W$$

MUX2:

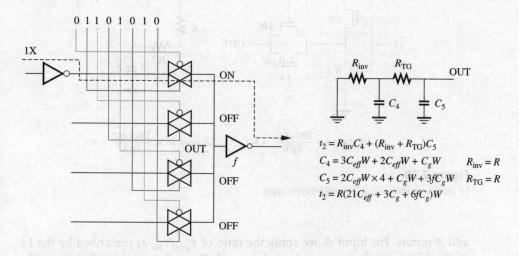

$$t_2 = R_{inv}C_4 + (R_{inv} + R_{TG})C_5$$
$$C_4 = 3C_{eff}W + 2C_{eff}W + C_gW \qquad R_{inv} = R$$
$$C_5 = 2C_{eff}W \times 4 + C_gW + 3fC_gW \qquad R_{TG} = R$$
$$t_2 = R(21C_{eff} + 3C_g + 6fC_g)W$$

Comparing the two cases, MUX1 is slower than MUX2. If we have too many transfer gates without any buffering, the delay increases very quickly. Also, we will eventually drive a large load, and transfer gates do not have the needed driving capability. However, MUX2 requires more routing resources than MUX1.

7.3.3   Logical Effort with CMOS Transmission Gates

We now address the topic of logical effort (LE) and its application to CMOS transmission gates. Consider the circuit of Figure 7.19 with a minimum size transmission gate. This is another type of tristate driver which performs a similar function to the tristate inverter seen in Section 4.9 of Chapter 4. Here, we have three inputs: A, sel, and $\overline{sel}$. Since both sel and $\overline{sel}$ are related, we can compute the LE for the sel

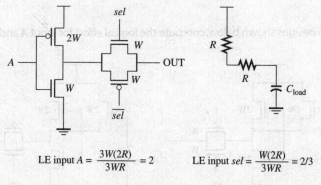

$$\text{LE input } A = \frac{3W(2R)}{3WR} = 2 \qquad \text{LE input } sel = \frac{W(2R)}{3WR} = 2/3$$

Figure 7.19

Logical effort computation for transmission gates.

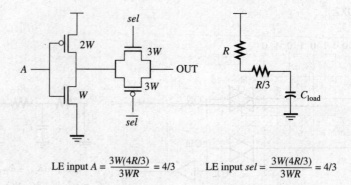

$$\text{LE input } A = \frac{3W(4R/3)}{3WR} = 4/3 \qquad \text{LE input } sel = \frac{3W(4R/3)}{3WR} = 4/3$$

Figure 7.20
LE computation with a 3X transmission gate.

and A inputs. For input A, we apply the ratio of $\tau_{\text{gate}}/\tau_{\text{inv}}$ as prescribed by the LE method. This involves the product of C_{in} with R_{eff} as described in Chapter 6. The expression for C_{in} is $3WC_g$ for the inverter. R_{eff} is $2R$, given that the inverter and TG each have a resistance of R. Therefore, $\text{LE}_A = 2$. For input sel, the input capacitance is WC_g and the total path resistance is $2R$ (including the inverter). Therefore, $\text{LE}_{sel} = 2/3$.

If we increase the size of the transmission gate to three times the minimum size, we see from Figure 7.20 that the LE of the A input decreases while the LE for the sel input increases. This makes sense intuitively since input A experiences a smaller output resistance without any change in its input capacitance, while input sel experiences an increase of three times its input capacitance but not a reduction of three times its output resistance.

Example 7.5   Logical Effort for NAND Driving CMOS TG

Problem:

For the two designs shown below, compute the logical effort for input A and input sel.

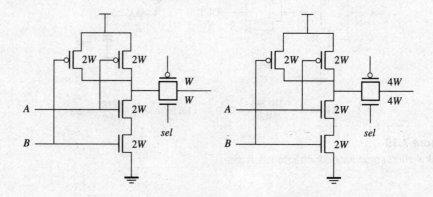

Solution:

$$\text{LE input } A = \frac{4W(2R)}{3W\,R} = 8/3 \qquad \text{LE input } A = \frac{4W(5R/4)}{3W\,R} = 5/3$$

$$\text{LE input } sel = \frac{W(2R)}{3W\,R} = 2/3 \qquad \text{LE input } sel = \frac{4W(5R/4)}{3W\,R} = 5/3$$

7.4 Dynamic D-Latches and D Flip-Flops

The operation and design considerations of latches and flip-flops were described in Chapter 5. The D flip-flop and D-latch are perhaps the most widely used circuits in CMOS design. In this section, we describe design improvements associated with these types of sequential elements when implemented with transfer gates. The major advantage in using transfer gates is that the circuits require many fewer transistors than the configurations shown in Chapter 5.

We begin with the simplest possible D-latch, shown in Figure 7.21a. Surprisingly, a single NMOS pass transistor functions as a D-latch. It is transparent since the value of D is propagated to Q while CLK is high. When the clock transitions from high to low, the last value is stored on the capacitor C_2. However, there are a number of obvious problems with this circuit based on material presented earlier in

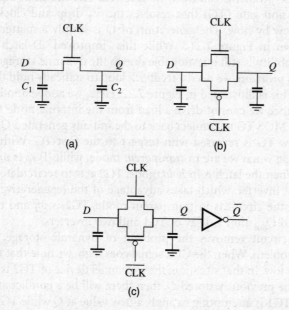

Figure 7.21

Progression of simple D-latches.

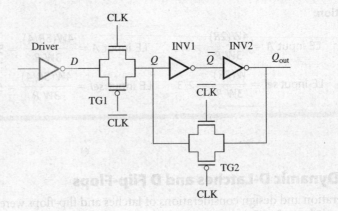

Figure 7.22

CMOS D-latch using transfer gates.

this chapter. First, the voltage at the output can only rise to $V_{DD} - V_T$. Second, there is clock feedthrough at Q when the clock goes low. The level of feedthrough is given by Equation (7.3). Third, there is no $\overline{Q}$ output available. Finally, and perhaps most importantly, the output is in a high-Z state after the clock goes low so it is susceptible to all of the charge loss mechanisms.

Most of these problems can easily be resolved. The circuit of Figure 7.21b is a CMOS transmission gate (TG) that resolves the V_T drop and clock feedthrough issues, as we know by now. The generation of $\overline{Q}$ is simply a matter of adding an inverter as shown in Figure 7.21c. While this "improved" D-latch will work as required, its reliability is still questionable due to the dynamic storage at node Q.

To solve this problem, we need a feedback loop to statically hold the value when the latch is *off*. This is illustrated in Figure 7.22. Here, we added another inverter to generate Q_{out} (since we cannot drive a load from the internal node Q), and introduced another CMOS TG to connect back to the initially generated Q. Note that the clock on the new TG is reversed with respect to the first TG. With this clocking scheme, TG1 is *on* when we are in *transparent* mode, while TG2 is *on* when we are in *hold* mode. When the latch is in *hold* mode, TG2 acts to recirculate Q back to the input of the first inverter, which takes advantage of the regenerative nature of the inverters. When the circuit is in transparent mode, TG2 is *off* and the value of D passes through to Q_{out} after a delay of TG1 and two inverters.

While this circuit removes the problem of dynamic storage, it introduces another small problem. When the CLK signal goes high, we note that there is a delay before $\overline{CLK}$ goes low. In that situation, the n-channel device of TG2 is still *on*. If D is different from the previously stored Q, then there will be a conflict at node Q for a short duration. TG1 is attempting to apply a new value at Q while TG2 is recirculating the old value through the loop. The problem can be resolved with proper sizing

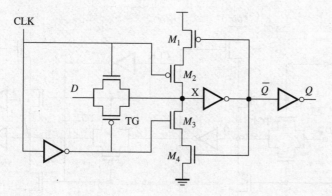

Figure 7.23

Typical D-latch implementation in CMOS.

of the INV2, TG2, TG1, and the gate that is driving D. The basic idea is to ensure that the forward path is "stronger" than the feedback path. Therefore, the driver and TG1 must be large enough such that the devices driving the forward path can swing the voltage at Q past the switching threshold V_S when competing with INV2 and TG2. If they are not sized properly, the old value will remain latched until TG2 turns *off*.

A more popular version of the D-latch is shown in Figure 7.23. This circuit employs the same principles as the one shown in Figure 7.22 but avoids any conflicts at internal nodes. The operation of this latch is as follows. When the CLK is high, the latch operates in transparent mode. Any changes at the input D are reflected at the output after a delay of TG + 2 INV. If the input data is high, then the value of $\overline{Q}$ is low. Therefore, M_1 is *on* and M_4 is *off*. When CLK goes low, then M_2 is turned *on* while M_3 is turned *off*. The internal node X is pulled high through M_1 and M_2. Note that there is no conflict situation in this circuit, and node X is not a dynamic node. A similar analysis can be done with a low input data. This time M_3 and M_4 would act to pull the internal node low after the clock goes low. Again, there are no conflicts in this configuration.

The circuit for a master-slave D flip-flop can be constructed from two D-latches, as shown in Figure 7.24. The flip-flop is simply a cascade of two D-latches. The connection of the clock signals to the master and slave are important to note. The positive edge of the clock shuts off the first latch and enables the second latch. The operation of the flip-flop is as follows: when the clock is low, the first latch is transparent, while the second latch is disabled. The data will flow up to TG2, but no further since TG1 is *on* and TG2 is *off*. When CLK goes high, TG1 shuts off and holds D at the internal node Q. Either the pull-up or pull-down path for the internal Q is enabled depending on the data value. Meanwhile, TG2 turns on and allows Q to flow to the outputs. Since D is only transmitted to the output on the rising edge of CLK, this is a positive edge-triggered flip-flop.

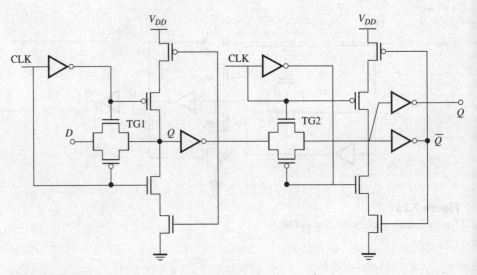

Figure 7.24
Positive edge-triggered D-type flip-flop.

7.5   Domino Logic

We have already seen the numerous difficulties that may arise with dynamic logic: charge sharing, feedthrough, charge leakage, single-event upsets, etc. These problems have limited the use of dynamic logic in industry. Furthermore, the CAD tool support needed to verify these types of designs are not readily available. Nevertheless, it is worthwhile to understand this approach for two reasons. First, static gates require numerous PMOS devices with relatively large sizes. Trying to implement a high fanin gate (i.e., a gate with more than four inputs) is difficult because either the N-complex or P-complex will require a large series stack. Pseudo-NMOS gates help to reduce the high fanin problem at the expense of static power when the output is low. The dynamic approach allows us to design circuits that are faster than static gates, with lower power than pseudo-NMOS, so they are worth exploring. We limit the treatment here to the most prominent dynamic configurations used in industry.

The structure of a dynamic logic gate can be derived from a static logic gate, as shown in the diagram of Figure 7.25. The conversion from static CMOS to pseudo-NMOS is straightforward, as shown in the first and second diagrams. We know that the second gate suffers from excessive power dissipation when the output is low. We need a way of shutting off the PMOS device when the output is low so as to reduce the power. What if we turned on the PMOS device to precharge the output to a high value, and then shut off the PMOS device during the period when the output would go low? For this purpose, we could introduce a new clock signal, $\Phi_{precharge}$, to turn the PMOS device *on* and *off* as needed. However, if we tried to charge up the output using the clocked PMOS device while a path to Gnd existed through the NMOS devices, we would have contention between the pull-up and pull-down paths.

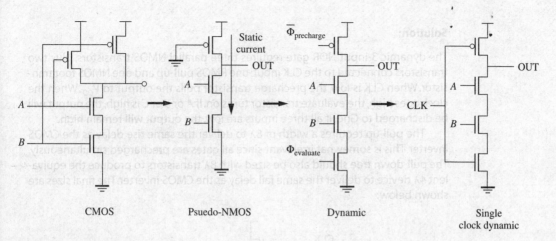

Figure 7.25
Evolution from static gate to dynamic gate.

Therefore, we must add another NMOS transistor, called a *foot* transistor or *evaluation* transistor, in the pull-down path. This transistor is turned on only after the PMOS load is shut off using another clock signal, $\Phi_{evaluate}$.

The configuration described above is depicted in the third circuit of Figure 7.25 where $\Phi_{precharge}$ is used to turn on the *p*-channel device and pull the output high (precharge phase), while $\Phi_{evaluate}$ is used to turn on the *n*-channel device to potentially pull the output node low (evaluation phase). The precharge signal is active low since it is connected to the PMOS device. The evaluate signal is active high since it turns on the NMOS device. Since the precharge and evaluate clocks are in phase, we can simply use one signal called CLK to drive the precharge and foot transistors. This is shown in the fourth circuit for the dynamic 2-input NAND gate.

The operation of the 2-input dynamic NAND gate is as follows. Initially, the precharged signal goes low and the output is precharged high. It is as if we are postulating a "1" at the output of all nodes during this phase. The precharge phase is intended to be a small portion of the clock cycle. Then, the CLK goes high and we enter the evaluation phase when the dynamic gates either remain high or are pulled low. For this NAND gate, if both *A* and *B* are high, then a path exists to Gnd. Otherwise, the output remains high and we preserve the value on the capacitance at the output node. This charge storage at the output node makes it a dynamic gate.

Dynamic Gate Implementations   **Example 7.6**

Problem:

Implement a 3-input NOR gate in dynamic logic and explain its operation. Size the transistors to deliver the same delays as a conventional CMOS inverter (PMOS $8\lambda{:}2\lambda$, NMOS $4\lambda{:}2\lambda$).

Solution:

The dynamic 3-input NOR gate requires three parallel NMOS transistors, plus two transistors connected to the CLK input: one PMOS pull-up and one NMOS foot transistor. When CLK is low, the precharge transistor pulls the output to V_{DD}. When the clock goes high, the evaluate transistor turns on. If A or B or C is high, the output will be discharged to Gnd. If all three inputs are low, the output will remain high.

The pull-up requires a width of 8λ to deliver the same rise delay as the CMOS inverter. This is somewhat irrelevant since all gates are precharged simultaneously. The pull-down tree should also be sized with 8λ transistors to produce the equivalent 4λ device to deliver the same fall delay as the CMOS inverter. The final sizes are shown below:

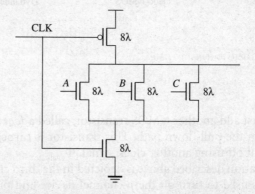

In reality, the CLK signal arrives first so A, B, and C can be considered as late arriving signals. In that case, the transistors can be reduced to half the size to deliver the same delay as the inverter.

Most logic functions can be implemented as dynamic circuits using the structure shown in Figure 7.26. The desired function is implemented in the NMOS complex. Transistors M_P and M_N are the precharge and evaluate transistors, respectively. The foot transistor is the only extra device relative to pseudo-NMOS gates. Note that all dynamic gates require a clock signal for proper operation. Furthermore, the clock must be routed to all dynamic gates, as opposed to static gates which do not require a clock. This places an additional burden on the physical layout tools.

There is a notable complication when one dynamic gate feeds another, as shown in Figure 7.27a. Since all output nodes are precharged high, all inputs to subsequent gates are high, implying that there will be an active path to Gnd from each output node as soon as the foot transistor is turned on. Once an output node has been discharged, it cannot go high until the next precharge phase. Therefore, a direct connection is not suitable.

A simple solution exists for this problem: add a static inverter to the output of all dynamic gates. Then define a "stage" as the dynamic gate plus the inverter. The

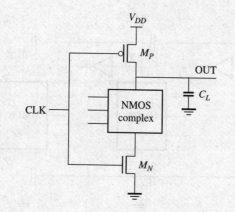

Figure 7.26

General structure of a dynamic gate.

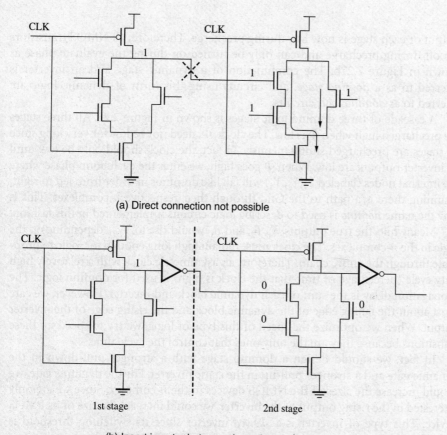

(a) Direct connection not possible

(b) Insert inverter between dynamic gates

Figure 7.27

Connecting dynamic gates.

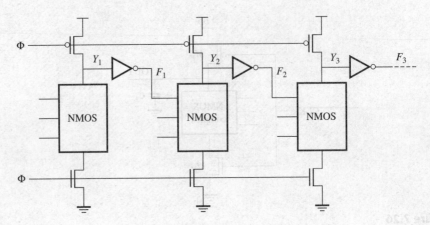

Figure 7.28
Domino cascaded gates.

output of each stage is now low during precharge. Therefore, all NMOS transistors are off during precharge and can only be turned on during the evaluate phase as shown in Figure 7.27b. The combination of a dynamic stage and an inverter is referred to as a *domino stage,* and circuits using this form of dynamic logic are referred to as *domino logic* circuits.

A cascade of three domino logic stages is shown in Figure 7.28. All three stages are precharged high when Φ is low. The clock, Φ, need not be low for very long since all stages are precharged simultaneously. In fact, the clock should only be low until all inverter outputs are low. When Φ goes high, we enter the evaluation phase where the internal nodes (labeled Y_1, Y_2, Y_3) will fall like dominos in order from left to right, assuming there is a path to the Gnd through their respective n-complexes. This is why the name *domino* is used to describe logic circuits implemented in this fashion.

Meanwhile, the true outputs, F_1, F_2, and F_3, would rise to V_{DD}, depending on the logic in the n-complexes. The clock must remain high long enough for logic to propagate through the entire chain. Therefore, an asymmetric clock with a relatively high duty cycle (percentage of time that the clock is high) is used for domino logic. The propagation delay is the sum of each dynamic block and inverter. However, we care most about the falling edge of the dynamic block and the rising edge of the inverter output. When we optimize the speed of this type of logic, we try to speed up these transitions because they are the only ones that control the cycle time.

In fact, we should design a domino stage with a stronger pull-down in the dynamic gate and a stronger pull-up in the static inverter. For the dynamic gate, we should increase the sizes of the NMOS devices in the n-complex. Since we are only interested in the rising output of the inverter, we could increase the size of its PMOS device. This type of inverter is a *skewed* inverter since its switching threshold is skewed relative to the conventional inverter. As a side-effect of the sizing operations, the V_S is higher for the static inverter. Furthermore, there is no pull-up fighting the pull-down in the first gate so its V_S is actually lower than expected (roughly equal to the V_{TN} of the NMOS device). Therefore, a domino stage will actually switch earlier than a regular gate.

There is also a power savings in domino logic. Only those gates that discharge to Gnd will dissipate power. There will be no power dissipation due to crowbar current since a direct path between V_{DD} and Gnd is not allowed in this type of logic. In addition, glitches can be effectively removed since all inputs switch from low to high.

One disadvantage of domino logic is that it can only be used to create noninverting functions. This may not seem to be a problem at first glance, but one quickly realizes that *an inverter cannot be implemented* in domino logic. This is not a serious problem since we can push the inversions around the circuit as required until they appear at a primary input or output. We can also generate the true and complement values if necessary using two precharged gates. In the worst case, we will require twice as many gates but the overall speed will still be faster.

Adder Function in Domino Logic

Example 7.7

Problem:

Implement the function $sum = a \oplus b \oplus c$ in domino logic. Assume that the literals $a, \bar{a}, b, \bar{b}$ are available as stable inputs to the gates.

Solution:

We need to create the XOR and XNOR of a and b using domino gates and then apply them to a third XOR gate. Note that we need the true and complement of X to implement the function.

$$X = a \oplus b = a\bar{b} + \bar{a}b$$
$$\bar{X} = \overline{a \oplus b} = ab + \bar{a}\bar{b}$$
$$Sum = c \oplus X = c\bar{X} + \bar{c}X$$

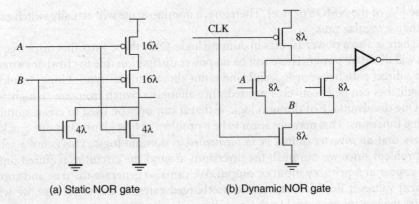

Figure 7.29
Comparison of static and dynamic logical effort.

7.5.1 Logical Effort for Domino Gates

One question to pose at this stage is whether or not domino logic is actually faster than the static CMOS gates, and by how much. One way to evaluate its timing performance is to use logical effort. For comparison, consider a static NOR gate and a dynamic NOR gate as shown in Figure 7.29. The pull-down strengths of both gates have been made equal and we assume that they are driving the same output load to conduct a fair comparison. The length of all devices is 2λ.

For the static gate, we already determined its logical effort to be 5/3. This can be derived by comparing the input capacitance of the static NOR to a corresponding inverter. The inverter size of 8λ for the pull-up and 4λ for the pull-down produces a ratio of

$$\text{LE}_{\text{NOR}} = \frac{(\text{NOR input cap.})}{(\text{Inverter input cap.})} = \frac{16\lambda + 4\lambda}{8\lambda + 4\lambda} = 5/3$$

For the domino circuit, the input capacitance is simply 8λ since it is only connected to NMOS devices. Then,

$$\text{LE}_{\text{dyn\_NOR}} = \frac{(\text{Dynamic input cap.})}{(\text{Inverter input cap.})} = \frac{8\lambda}{12\lambda} = 2/3$$

Since the extra inverter in domino logic has an LE = 1, the average LE for each of the two gates is the geometric mean of the product of their logical efforts (i.e., $\text{LE}_{\text{avg}} = \sqrt{(2/3)\,(1)} \approx 0.8$). Therefore, the domino stage is better in terms of its overall drive capability and input capacitive loading.

The results above may seem counterintuitive at first since there are two stages in the domino circuit and only one in the static NOR gate. However, the fact that only one NMOS device is driven in the domino case gives it a decided advantage in terms of input capacitance. This advantage translates into a faster overall circuit.

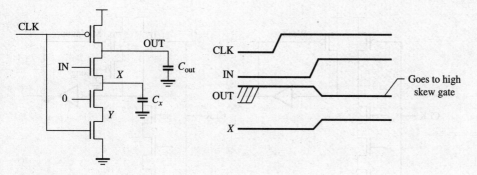

Figure 7.30

Charge-sharing example in domino logic.

Furthermore, the pull-down transistors in the domino case do not fight with the pull-up device as in the case of the static NOR gate (albeit, only for a brief period during switching). This makes the switching threshold V_S smaller for domino inputs than for static gates.

7.5.2 Limitations of Domino Logic

While the previous sections highlighted the merits of dynamic logic, there are notable disadvantages that have prevented its widespread use in industry. The main problem is the potential for logic upset due to charge loss on a capacitor, and that is not acceptable to most designers. Charge may be lost via charge sharing, noise injection due to capacitive coupling, charge leakage, or α-particle hits. Once lost, it cannot be recovered and the circuit ceases to function correctly. We address each of these issues below.

Charge sharing was described earlier in this chapter. We now apply it to the domino stage shown in Figure 7.30. Initially, CLK is low so the circuit is in the precharge phase. The *OUT* signal is unknown until the precharge is complete. We assume that signal X is low initially. When CLK goes high, we enter the evaluation phase. At some point, *IN* goes high and turns on one of the transistors connected to the output, while the other transistor in the stack remains off. As a result, we have charge sharing between the output node and the internal node X. The degree of charge sharing depends on the two capacitances C_{out} and C_x:

$$V^* = \frac{C_{out}}{C_x + C_{out}} V_{DD}$$

If they are equal, then the output value will be reduced to half its original value (i.e., $1/2 \ V_{DD}$). Since this value is being fed to an inverter, the implications of this degree of charge sharing is that the inverter may flip its value and produce an erroneous result. Furthermore, the fact that the inverter is skewed for timing reasons means that a smaller drop in the output voltage will cause the inverter to switch. There is

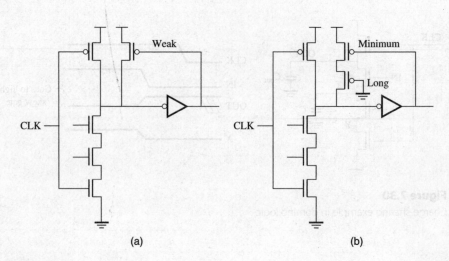

(a)   (b)

Figure 7.31

Minimizing the effects of charge sharing using keepers.

obviously a design tradeoff between timing and noise tolerance when sizing the inverter.

There are a number of ways to minimize charge sharing in these types of circuits. One way is to increase the output capacitance so that the final output will not vary significantly from its initial value. The input capacitance of the static inverter helps in this regard. Another approach is to precharge the internal node X to V_{DD} during the precharge phase with an additional transistor. This will require additional power and area. It will also increase the delay since there will be additional charge to remove from the internal nodes.

A third approach is to introduce "keepers" or "baby-sitters" to hold the output value high in the presence of charge sharing. In Figure 7.31a, a weak PMOS device is placed in a feedback path from the output to the internal node. After precharge, the PMOS device is on and it continues to pull up the node even after the precharge is complete. If there is any charge sharing, the output is pulled back up to V_{DD} by this device. On the other hand, if there is a path to Gnd from the output of the dynamic stage, the NMOS path must overpower the PMOS device so that the output actually switches. For this reason, we need to make the PMOS device very weak. That is, the length L of the device is made large which makes the W/L small.

The problem with this requirement is that it places a larger drive requirement on the output inverter. To circumvent this issue, two transistors can be used in the feedback path: one transistor is driven by the inverter output but it is a minimum size device so it does not place a significant load on the inverter. The second one is always *on* but it is a very long (and hence weak) device. The effective pull-up strength is controlled by the long device, but the capacitance seen by the inverter output is due to the small device. There is additional power dissipation, some ratioing that is required and some additional delay. Clearly, as you begin to make the dynamic circuit more tolerant to noise, it begins to take on the characteristics of a static device.

A second issue in dynamic circuits is leakage. Both subthreshold current and reverse-bias diode leakage act to remove stored charge from any *high-impedance* nodes. However, every output node is precharged on every cycle. Perhaps a more serious issue is that of α-particle hits on dynamic nodes. These are cosmic particles that may enter the substrate and discharge capacitive nodes. Depending on the size of the capacitance, and hence the total charge on a dynamic node, it could reduce the value to a point where the stored information is lost. One way to overcome this issue is to increase the size of the capacitances, but this increases the area and power of the circuits. The keeper circuit is also useful in mitigating the effects of leakage and α-particles.

A third area of concern is noise injection from the clock or capacitive coupling to neighboring nodes. Clock feedthrough was described earlier in this chapter and this effect can be observed at the dynamic output node through the C_{GD} capacitance of the PMOS precharge device. The example below illustrates that this effect does not pose a problem. The issue of capacitive coupling to other nodes is described in more detail in the chapter on interconnect. The design approach to reducing this problem is to minimize the coupling between any dynamic node and its neighbor using either spacing or shielding techniques that are described in Chapter 10.

Charge Sharing and Feedthrough in Domino Logic **Example 7.8**

Problem:

For the domino function below, assume 0.13 μm technology parameters and answer the following questions:

(a) What function does the gate perform at the output *F*?

(b) How much clock feedthrough do we observe at the internal node *X*? Is this a potential problem?

(c) What is the worst-case charge sharing voltage that we observe at node *X*?

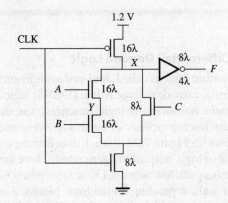

Solution:

(a) The function at the output is $F = AB + C$ (a noninverting function).

(b) Clock feedthrough is due to the clock going from low to high. The PMOS device is in the linear region after precharge. The feedthrough capacitance is

$$C_f = C_{GD} = \frac{C_g W_p}{2} = \frac{(2 \text{ fF}/\mu m)(16)(0.05 \ \mu m)}{2} = 0.8 \text{ fF}$$

The grounded capacitance at node X, assuming no source/drain sharing, is

$$C_{gnd} = C_{eff}(16\lambda + 16\lambda + 8\lambda) + C_g(8\lambda + 4\lambda)$$

$$= (1 \text{ fF}/\mu m)(40)(0.05 \ \mu m) + (2 \text{ fF}/\mu m)(12)(0.05 \ \mu m)$$

$$= 5 \text{ fF}$$

The feedthrough voltage is

$$\Delta V_x = \frac{C_f \Delta V_{clk}}{C_f + C_{gnd}} = \frac{0.8 \text{ fF}(1.2 \text{ V})}{0.8 \text{ fF} + 5 \text{ fF}} = 0.17 \text{ V}$$

Therefore the output voltage due to feedthrough is $1.2 + 0.17$ V $= 1.37$ V. Since the value is above V_{DD}, it is not a problem.

(c) The worst-case charge sharing assumes that the output is sitting at 1.2 V, $A = 1, B = C = 0$. We have already determined that $C_X = 5$ fF. The capacitance at the intermediate node between transistors A and B is

$$C_Y = (1 \text{ fF}/\mu m)(16\lambda) = 16(0.05) = 0.8 \text{ fF}$$

Therefore, the worst-case charge sharing is given by

$$V^* = \frac{C_X(1.2 \text{ V})}{C_X + C_Y} = \frac{5(1.2 \text{ V})}{0.8 + 5} = 1.0 \text{ V}$$

This level is not possible at node Y. Set $V_Y = V_{DD} - V_{TN} = 0.73$ V. The rest of the charge remains at node X. The remaining charge is $(5 \text{ fF})(1.2 \text{ V}) - 0.8 \text{ fF}$ $(0.73 \text{ V}) = 5.42$ fC. This translates to a voltage of 1.08 V at node X.

7.5.3 Dual-Rail (Differential) Domino Logic

A popular form of domino logic is called *dual-rail* or *differential* domino logic. It is also known as differential cascode voltage switch (DCVS) logic. Since standard domino can only implement noninverting logic functions, the dual-rail approach has been adopted by many microprocessor designers to overcome this limitation. The basic structure is shown in Figure 7.32. Rather than having only one output node, a complementary pair of logic outputs are generated. There are two precharge transistors that force the outputs low when CLK is low. When CLK goes high, either OUT or $\overline{OUT}$ will go high, depending on the logic blocks, $\overline{F}$ and F, respectively. Of course, both outputs cannot go high during the evaluate phase.

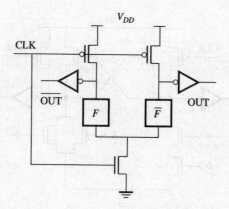

Figure 7.32
Structure of dual-rail domino logic.

An example of a dual-rail AND/NAND gate is shown in Figure 7.33. One side of the gate implements the AND function while the opposite side implements the NAND function.

This configuration has a number of problems similar to the standard domino gate. The internal nodes are susceptible to charge sharing. Therefore, a pair of *keeper* devices are needed to maintain high levels if the clock is high for a long period of time. The keeper devices are shown in Figure 7.34. It is clear that the number of devices needed to implement the gate has increased significantly from the modest levels that we expected when first considering dynamic logic. Furthermore, the power dissipation of these gates is much higher than the conventional CMOS gate or the standard domino gate since one side will always be precharged high and then

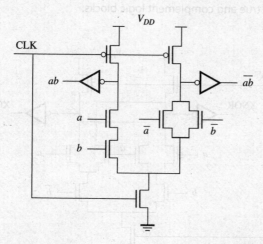

Figure 7.33
Dual-rail domino AND/NAND function.

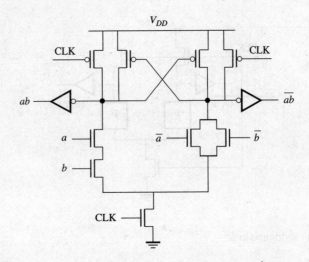

Figure 7.34
Dual-rail domino with keeper devices.

go low. This is a significant price to pay for the extra output. However, we should note that not every logic gate requires a complement function. Only those functions that explicitly require a complementary term would require the use of dual-rail gates. The rest can be implemented as standard domino gates.

Example 7.9   **Dual-Rail XOR/XNOR Domino Gate**

Problem:

Design a dual-rail XOR/XNOR domino gate and share as many transistors as possible between the true and complement logic blocks.

Solution:

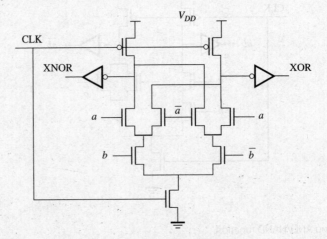

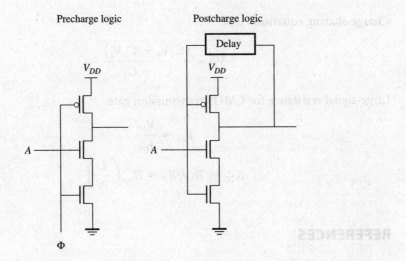

Figure 7.35
Precharge and postcharge circuits.

7.5.4   Self-Resetting Circuits

The routing of the clock to domino gates presents a problem to CAD tools and introduces issues of delay and skew into the circuit design process. There are situations that permit the use of circuits that can automatically precharge themselves (i.e., reset themselves) after a prescribed delay. These are called postcharge or self-resetting logic circuits. They find applications where a small percentage of gates switch in each cycle, such as memory decoders (described in Chapter 10). Here we will examine the basic operation of these circuits.

Figure 7.35 shows the standard precharge configuration and the postcharge configuration. In the domino case, the clock is used to operate the circuit. In the self-resetting case, the output is fed back to the precharge control input and, after a specified time delay, the pull-up is reactivated. The delay line is implemented as a series of inverters. The signals that propagate through these circuits are pulses. The width of the pulses must be controlled carefully or else there may be contention between NMOS and PMOS devices, or even worse, oscillations may occur. For example, if A is high for more than twice the delay around the loop, the circuit will oscillate. Therefore, special care must be taken to ensure correct timing.

7.6   Summary

Capacitive feedthrough and bootstrapping equation:

$$\Delta V_2 = \frac{C_f \Delta V_1}{C_f + C_{\text{gnd}}}$$

Charge-sharing equation:

$$V^* = \frac{(C_1 V_1 + C_2 V_2)}{C_1 + C_2}$$

Large-signal resistance for CMOS transmission gate:

$$R_{on} \approx \frac{V_{DS}}{I_{DS}}$$

$$R_{TG} = R_N // R_P \approx R_{eqn}\left(\frac{L}{W}\right)$$

REFERENCES

1. I. Sutherland, B. Sproull, and D. Harris, *Logical Effort: Designing Fast CMOS Circuits*, Morgan Kaufman Publishers, San Francisco, CA, 1999.

2. J. Rabaey, A. Chandrakasan, and B. Nikolic, *Digital Integrated Circuits: A Designer Perspective*, Second Edition, Prentice-Hall, Upper Saddle River, NJ, 2003.

3. S. M. Kang and Y. Leblebici, *CMOS Digital Integrated Circuits, Analysis and Design,* Third Edition, McGraw-Hill, New York, NY, 2003.

4. H. Veendrick, *Deep-Submicron CMOS ICs,* Second Edition, Kluwer Academic Publishers, Boston, MA, 2000.

5. J. P. Uyemura, *CMOS Logic Circuit Design,* Kluwer Academic Publishers, Boston, MA, 1999.

PROBLEMS

P7.1. Compute all the voltages at all the nodes for the pass transistor circuit of Figure P7.1 including the body effect. Use 0.13 μm technology parameters. Assume that all nodes are initially at 0 V.

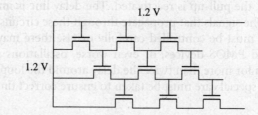

Figure P7.1

P7.2. Provide a truth table that describes the functionality of each circuit in Figure P7.2. (Note: In some cases, the output of the circuit may be high-Z.) The symbol A' refers to the complement of A.

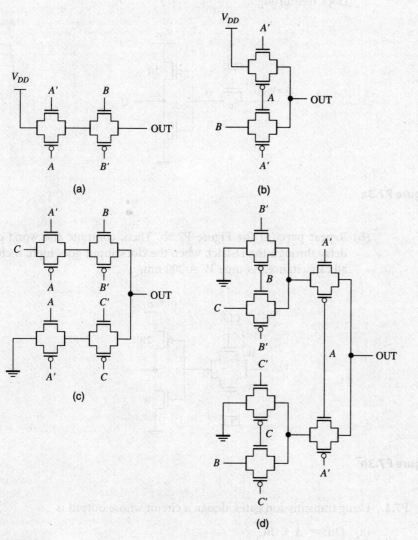

Figure P7.2

P7.3. (a) For the dynamic D-latch shown in Figure P7.3a, estimate the output voltages for Q and $\overline{Q}$ given that the input is at V_{DD} when CLK goes high (V_{DD}). Assume that $W = 200$ nm and $V_{DD} = 1.8$ V. Then, recompute the values when the CLK goes low. Include the effects of clock feedthrough.

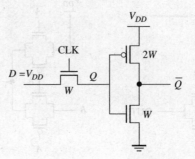

Figure P7.3a

(b) Repeat part (a) for Figure P7.3b. Then, compute the worst-case delay through the D-latch when the clock input goes high. Include all capacitance. Assume $W = 200$ nm.

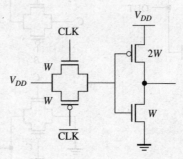

Figure P7.3b

P7.4. Using transmission gates, design a circuit whose output is

(a) Out $= A + BC$

(b) Out $= AB + BC + \overline{C}$

(c) Out $= \overline{(A + B + C)} + \overline{A}B$

(d) Out $= \overline{((A + B + \overline{C}) + \overline{A}\,\overline{B})}$

Then remove the transistors and switches that are not necessary.

P7.5. What is the output of each of the circuits in Figure P7.5?

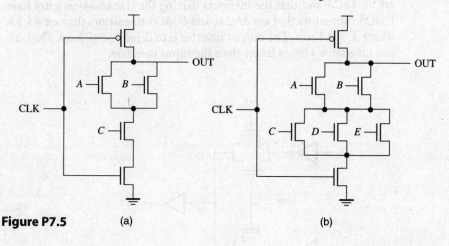

Figure P7.5   (a)   (b)

P7.6. Design a domino circuit whose output is

(a) Out $= \bar{A} + \bar{B}C$

(b) Out $= A\bar{B} + BC + \bar{C}$

(c) Out $= \overline{(\bar{A} + \bar{B} + C)} + A\bar{B}$

(d) Out $= \overline{((A + \bar{B} + C) + \bar{A}B)}$

P7.7. What is the LE (logic effort) of each input signal of the circuits of Figure P7.7? (All transistors are minimum size, $L = 2\lambda$ and $W = 2\lambda$, unless specified.)

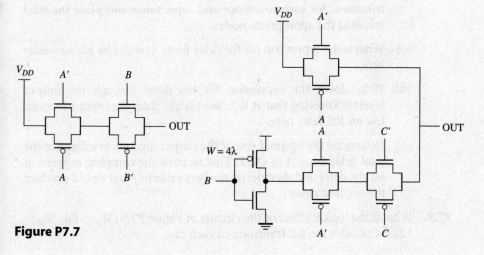

Figure P7.7

P7.8. For the circuit shown in Figure P7.8, assume that the transmission gates are all $4\lambda{:}2\lambda$ and that the inverters driving the transmission gates have PMOS transistors that are $8\lambda{:}2\lambda$, and NMOS transistors that are $4\lambda{:}2\lambda$, where $\lambda = 0.1\ \mu\text{m}$. The output inverter is to drive a 50 fF load. The output inverter is f times larger than the input inverters.

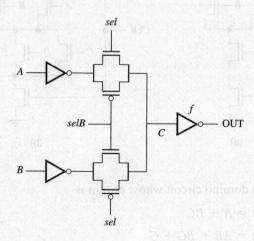

Figure P7.8

(a) Write the expression for the output function in terms of A, B, sel, and $selB$.

(b) Draw an equivalent RC circuit model for the path from A to C assuming that the sel signal is high. Write down the individual contributions for each resistance and capacitance and place the total values at the appropriate nodes.

(c) What is the expression for the delay from A to C? Use Elmore delay here.

(d) Write down the expression for the delay through the output inverter knowing that it is f times larger than the input inverters. Use an RC delay here.

(e) Determine the optimal size of the output inverter to minimize the total delay from A to OUT. That is, write the complete expression for the delay and then derive the best value of f that would produce the smallest delay.

P7.9. What is the logical effort of the circuits of Figure P7.9 ($W_P = 8\lambda$, $W_N = 12\lambda$)? Consider the fall transition in each case.

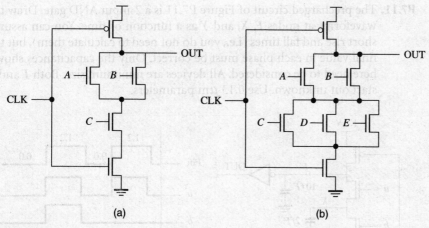

Figure P7.9

P7.10. In the circuit of Figure P7.10, determine the capacitance of each node and calculate the minimum and maximum delay. (All transistors are minimum size, $L = 2\lambda$ and $W = 2\lambda$, unless otherwise specified.)

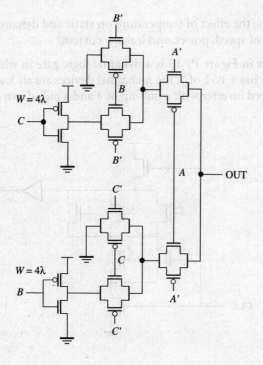

Figure P7.10

P7.11. The precharged circuit of Figure P7.11 is a 2-input AND gate. Draw the waveforms at nodes F, X, and Y as a function of time. You can assume short rise and fall times (i.e., you do not need to calculate them), but the final value in each phase must be correct. Only the capacitances shown here need to be considered. All devices are minimum size. Both F and Y start out unknown. Use 0.13 μm parameters.

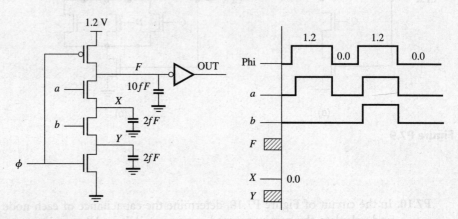

Figure P7.11

P7.12. What is the effect of temperature on static and dynamic logic circuits in terms of speed, power, and leakage current?

P7.13. Shown in Figure P7.13 is a dynamic logic gate in which the precharge device has a W/L of 5, the n-channel devices are all 3, and the inverter is a skewed inverter with a pull-up of 4 and a pull-down of 1 to reduce the delay.

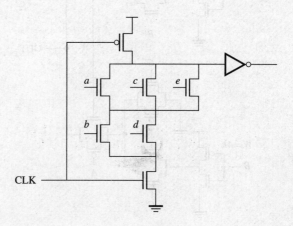

Figure P7.13

(a) What input settings give you the worst-case charge sharing?

(b) What is the amount of charge sharing in the worst-case?

(c) Does this circuit fail in the worst-case charge sharing situation? Explain.

P7.14. The two CMOS circuits in Figure P7.14 are intended to be simple latches. Do these gates work as latches? Are there any problems with using them as latches? Is one better than the other? Explain.

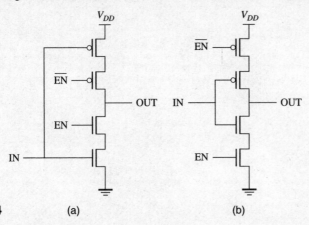

Figure P7.14   (a)   (b)

P7.15. The circuit shown in Figure P7.15 is a bootstrapped inverter. It uses a linear enhancement load, M_2, with an additional transistor, M_3, to provide gate drive to M_2. A bootstrapping capacitor, C_b, is used to pull node X up when the output is being pulled up. Answer the following questions in terms of the quantities V_{DD}, V_T, V_{OL}, C_X, C_{out}, and C_b.

(a) When the input is V_{DD}, what is the output voltage and the voltage at node X?

(b) When the input switches to a low voltage, what is the required value of C_b that allows the output to reach V_{DD}?

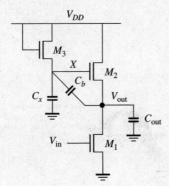

Figure P7.15

Semiconductor Memory Design

8.1   Introduction

Modern digital systems require the capability of storing and retrieving large amounts of information at high speeds. *Memories* are circuits or systems that store digital information in large quantity. This chapter addresses the analysis and design of VLSI memories, commonly known as *semiconductor memories*. Today, memory circuits come in different forms including SRAM, DRAM, ROM, EPROM, E^{2}PROM, Flash, and FRAM. While each form has a different cell design, the basic structure, organization, and access mechanisms are largely the same. In this chapter, we classify the different types of memory, examine the major subsystems, and focus on the static RAM design issues. This topic is particularly suitable for our study of CMOS digital design as it allows us to apply many of the concepts presented in earlier chapters.

Recent surveys indicate that roughly 30% of the worldwide semiconductor business is due to memory chips. Over the years, technology advances have been driven by memory designs of higher and higher density. Electronic memory capacity in digital systems ranges from fewer than 100 bits for a simple function to standalone chips containing 256 Mb (1 Mb = 2^{10} bits) or more.[1] Circuit designers usually

---

[1] Recently, a memory chip with 1 Gbit of data storage capacity has been announced.

speak of memory capacities in terms of bits, since a separate flip-flop or other similar circuit is used to store each bit. On the other hand, system designers usually state memory capacities in terms of *bytes* (8 bits); each byte represents a single alphanumeric character. Very large scientific computing systems often have memory capacity stated in terms of *words* (32 to 128 bits). Each byte or word is stored in a particular location that is identified by a unique numeric *address*. Memory storage capacity is usually stated in units of kilobytes (K bytes) or megabytes (M bytes). Because memory addressing is based on binary codes, capacities that are integral powers of 2 are most common. Thus the convention is that, for example, 1K byte = 1,024 bytes and 64K bytes = 65,536 bytes. In most memory systems, only a single byte or word at a single address is stored or retrieved during each cycle of memory operation. *Dual-port* memories are also available that have the ability to read/write two words in one cycle.

8.1.1 Memory Organization

The preferred organization for most large memories is shown in Figure 8.1. This organization is a *random-access* architecture. The name is derived from the fact that memory locations (*addresses*) can be accessed in random order at a fixed rate, independent of physical location, for reading or writing. The storage array, or *core*, is made up of simple cell circuits arranged to share connections in horizontal rows and vertical columns. The horizontal lines, which are driven only from outside the storage array, are called *wordlines*, while the vertical lines, along which data flow into and out of cells, are called *bitlines*.

A cell is accessed for reading or writing by selecting its row and column. Each cell can store 0 or 1. Memories may simultaneously select 4, 8, 16, 32, or 64 columns

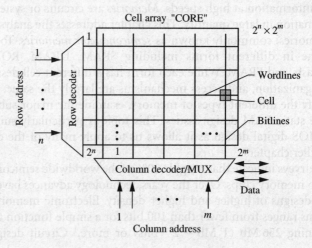

Figure 8.1

Organization of memory systems.

in one row depending on the application. The row and column (or group of columns) to be selected are determined by decoding binary address information. For example, an n-bit *decoder* for row selection, as shown in Figure 8.1, has 2^n output lines, a different one of which is enabled for each different n-bit input code. The column decoder takes m inputs and produces 2^m bitline access signals, of which 1, 4, 8, 16, 32, or 64 may be enabled at one time. The bit selection is done using a multiplexer circuit to direct the corresponding cell outputs to data registers. In total, $2^n \times 2^m$ cells are stored in the core array.

An overall architecture of a 64 Kb random-access memory is shown in Figure 8.2. For this example, $n = m = 8$. Therefore, the core array has a total of 65,536 cells. The memory uses a 16-bit address to produce a single bit output.

Memory cell circuits can be implemented in a wide variety of ways. In principle, the cells can be based on the flip-flop designs listed in Chapter 5 since their intended function is to store bits of data. However, these flip-flops require a substantial amount of area and are not appropriate when millions of cells are needed.

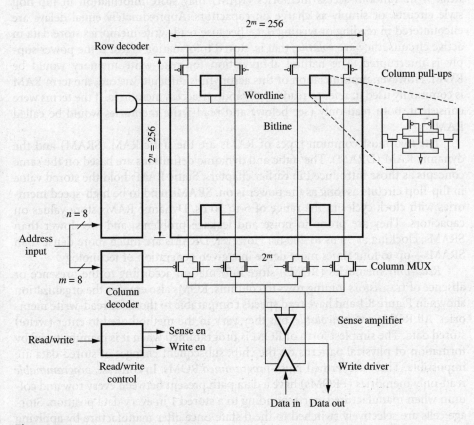

Figure 8.2

Overall architecture of memory design.

In fact, most memory cell circuits are greatly simplified compared to register and flip-flop circuits. While the data storage function is preserved, other properties including quantization of amplitudes, regeneration of logic levels, input-output isolation, and fanout drive capability may be sacrificed for cell simplicity. In this way, the number of devices in a single cell can be reduced to one to six transistors. Figure 8.2 illustrates a six-transistor memory cell.

At the level of a memory chip shown in Figure 8.2, the desired logic properties are recovered through use of properly designed *peripheral circuits*. Circuits in this category are the decoders, sense amplifiers, column precharge, data buffers, etc. These circuits are designed so that they may be shared among many memory cells. Read-write (R/W) circuits determine whether data are being retrieved or stored, and they perform any necessary amplification, buffering, and translation of voltage levels. Specific examples are presented in the following sections.

8.1.2   Types of Memory

Read-write random-access memories (RAM) may store information in flip-flop style circuits, or simply as charge on capacitors. Approximately equal delays are encountered in reading or writing data. Because read-write memories store data in active circuits, they are *volatile*; that is, stored information is lost if the power supply is interrupted. The natural abbreviation for read-write memory would be RWM. However, pronunciation of this acronym is difficult. Instead, the term RAM is commonly used to refer to read-write random-access memories. If the terms were consistent, both read-only (see below) and read-write memories would be called RAMs.

The two most common types of RAMs are the static RAM (SRAM) and the dynamic RAM (DRAM). The static and dynamic definitions are based on the same concepts as those introduced in earlier chapters. Static RAMs hold the stored value in flip-flop circuits as long as the power is on. SRAMs tend to be high-speed memories with clock cycles in the range of 5 to 50 ns. Dynamic RAMs store values on capacitors. They are prone to noise and leakage problems, and are slower than SRAMs, clocking at 50 ns to 200 ns. However, DRAMs are much more dense than SRAMs—up to four times more dense in a given generation of technology.

Read-only memories (ROMs) store information according to the presence or absence of transistors joining rows to columns. ROMs also employ the organization shown in Figure 8.1 and have read speeds comparable to those for read-write memories. All ROMs are *nonvolatile*, but they vary in the method used to enter (write) stored data. The simplest form of ROM is programmed when it is manufactured by formation of physical patterns on the chip; subsequent changes of stored data are impossible. These are termed *mask-programmed* ROMs. In contrast, *programmable read-only memories* (PROMs) have a data path present between every row and column when manufactured, corresponding to a stored 1 in every data position. Storage cells are selectively switched to the 0 state once after manufacture by applying appropriate electrical pulses to selectively open (blow out) row-column data paths. Once programmed, or *blown*, a 0 cannot be changed back to a 1.

Erasable programmable read-only memories (EPROMs) also have all bits initially in one binary state. They are programmed electrically (similar to the PROM), but all bits may be erased (returned to the initial state) by exposure to ultraviolet (UV) light. The packages for these components have transparent windows over the chip to permit the UV irradiation. *Electrically erasable* programmable read-only memories (EEPROMs, E²PROM, or E-squared PROMs) may be written and erased by electrical means. These are the most advanced and most expensive form of PROM. Unlike EPROMs, which must be totally erased and rewritten to change even a single bit, E²PROMs may be selectively erased. Writing and erasing operations for all PROMs require times ranging from microseconds to milliseconds. However, all PROMs retain stored data when power is turned off; thus they are termed nonvolatile.

A recent form of EPROM and E²PROM is termed Flash memory, a name derived from the fact that blocks of memory may be erased simultaneously. Flash memory of the EPROM form is written using the hot-electron effect[2] whereas E²PROM Flash is written using Fowler-Nordheim (FN) tunneling.[3] Both types are erased using FN tunneling. Their large storage capacity has made this an emerging mass storage medium. In addition, these types of memories are beginning to replace the role of ROMs on many chips, although additional processing is required to manufacture Flash memories in a standard CMOS technology.

Memories based on ferroelectric materials, so-called FRAMs or FeRAMs, can also be designed to retain stored information when power is off. The *Perovskite crystal* material used in the memory cells of this type of RAM can be polarized in one direction or the other to store the desired value. The polarization is retained even when the power supply is removed, thereby creating a nonvolatile memory. However, semiconductor memories are preferred over ferroelectric memories for most applications because of their advantages in cost, operating speed, and physical size. Recently, FRAMs have been shown to be useful nonvolatile memory in certain applications such as smart cards and may be more attractive in the future due to their extremely high storage density.

8.1.3 Memory Timing Parameters

The timing signals of random-access memories are illustrated in Figure 8.3. At a high level, the main inputs are the $(n + m)$-bit address, the k-bit input data, and the *read/write* signal (write operations are active low in this example). The output is the k-bit value that was stored in the memory location associated with the $(n + m)$-bit address. The *read access time*, t_{AC}, is the delay from presentation of an address until data stored at that address are available at the output. Maximum read access time is an important parameter, and it should not exceed the memory cycle time since

---

[2] Hot electrons are created by applying a high field in the channel region. These electrons enter the oxide and raise the threshold voltage of a device. Devices with this higher threshold voltage are viewed as a stored "1." Devices with the lower threshold voltage represent a stored "0."

[3] Fowler-Nordheim tunneling occurs through thin insulating material such as thin-oxide associated with the gate. Current flows through the oxide by tunneling through the energy barrier.

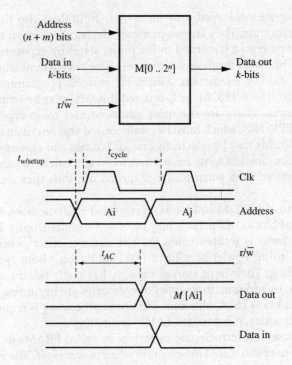

Figure 8.3

Random access memory timing parameters.

there are write setup operations needed before each memory operation, indicated by $t_{w/setup}$. The memory clock cycle time, t_{cycle}, is the minimum time needed to complete successive read or write operations.

The cycle time is essentially the reciprocal of the time rate at which address information is changed while reading or writing at random locations. Minimum access times for reading and writing are not necessarily the same, but for simplicity of design, most systems specify a single time for both reading and writing. For semiconductor read-write memories, the read access time is typically 50 to 80% of cycle time.

8.2 MOS Decoders

The row and column decoders identified in Figure 8.1 are essential elements in all random-access memories. Access time and power consumption of memories may be largely determined by decoder design. Similar designs are used in read-only and read-write applications. Row decoders take an n-bit address and produce 2^n outputs, one of which is activated. Obviously, the one that is activated depends directly on the address applied to the memory. Figure 8.4 shows two forms of decoders: AND and NOR decoders. The decoder can be implemented using AND gates or

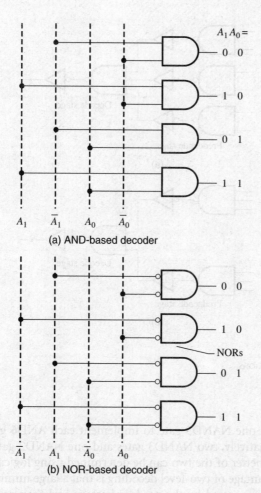

(a) AND-based decoder

(b) NOR-based decoder

Figure 8.4
AND and NOR decoders.

NOR gates that take every possible combination of the inputs. There are two address bits in this example and we require both the true and complement of each address bit. The output line activated by each input combination is shown in the figure. Note that all outputs are normally low except one.

An n-bit decoder requires 2^n logic gates, each with n inputs. For example, with $n = 6$, we need 64 NAND6 gates driving 64 inverters to implement the decoder. From previous chapters, it is clear that gates with more than 3 or 4 inputs create large series resistances and long delays. Rather than using n-input gates, it is preferable to use a cascade of gates. Typically two stages are used: a predecode stage and a final decode stage. The predecode stage generates intermediate signals that are used by multiple gates in the final decode stage. In Figure 8.5, schematics are shown for two possible alternatives to implement a 6-input AND gate. We could choose three

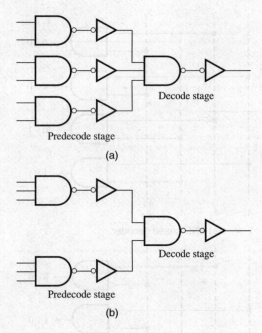

Figure 8.5
Predecoder configurations.

NAND2 gates and one NAND3 gate to implement each AND6 gate, as shown in Figure 8.5a. Alternatively, two NAND3 gates and one NAND2 gate of Figure 8.5b may be used. The better of the two can be determined using logical effort.

The main advantage of two-level decoding is that a large number of intermediate signals can be generated by the predecode stage and then reused by the final decoding stage. The result is a reduction in the number of inputs for each gate. Since this aspect is not clearly depicted in Figure 8.5, a more complete example for 6 address bits is shown in Figure 8.6. In the predecoder, a total of 12 intermediate signals are generated from the address bits and their complements. The signals that are generated in the predecoder are as follows: A_0A_1, $A_0\bar{A}_1$, $\bar{A}_0A_1$, $\bar{A}_0\bar{A}_1$, A_2A_3, $A_2\bar{A}_3$, etc. These signals may now be used by the final decoding stage to generate the 64 required outputs using NAND3/inverter combinations. This corresponds to the configuration shown in Figure 8.5a. Each predecoder output drives 16 NAND gates (i.e., 64 NAND3 gates × 3 inputs each / 12 intermediate outputs). Therefore, the branching effort $BE = 16$. The delay through the NAND2-inverter-NAND3-inverter stages can be minimized by sizing the gates using logical effort. A similar kind of two-level decoder can be constructed using the configuration of Figure 8.5b. Again, the better of the two approaches can be determined using logical effort. It is important to minimize the delay through the decoder as it may constitute up to 40% of the clock cycle.

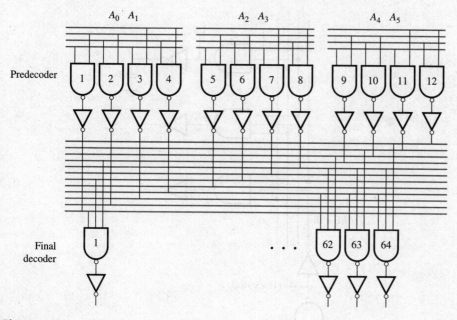

Figure 8.6
Structure of two-level decoder for 6-bit address.

Decoder Sizing Using Logical Effort Techniques

Example 8.1

Problem:

Size the decoder of Figure 8.6 using FO4 rules assuming that the normalized output loading is 1. FO4 rules imply that the optimal stage effort is equal to 4.

For each stage, $C_{in} = \dfrac{LE \times BE \times C_{out}}{4}$

Solution:

Work backwards from the output to the input, taking into account logical effort and branching effort of each stage. First, the normalized output has a size of 1. Therefore, the inverter input capacitance is 1/4 using FO4 sizing rules. The *LE* of the NAND3 gate is 5/3. Therefore, its input capacitance is $(5/3)/4^2$. The branching effort at the output of the predecode stage is 16. Therefore, the input capacitance of the inverter is $(16)(5/3)/4^3$. Finally, the NAND2 gate has an input capacitance of $(16)(4/3)(5/3)/4^4$.

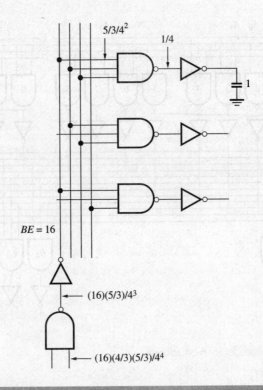

8.3 Static RAM Cell Design

Memories are said to be static if no periodic clock signals are required to retain stored data indefinitely. Memory cells in these circuits have a direct path to V_{DD} or Gnd or both. Read-write memory cell arrays based on flip-flop circuits are commonly referred to as static RAMs or SRAMs. The design issues for static memory cells are described in this section.

8.3.1 Static Memory Operation

The basic static RAM cell is shown in Figure 8.7a. It consists of two cross-coupled inverters and two access transistors. The access transistors are connected to the wordline at their respective gate terminals, and the bitlines at their source/drain terminals. The wordline is used to select the cell while the bitlines are used to perform read or write operations on the cell. Internally, the cell holds the stored value on one side and its complement on the other side. For reference purposes, assume that node q holds the stored value while node $\bar{q}$ holds its complement. The two complementary bitlines are used to improve speed and noise rejection properties, as described later in this chapter.

The VTC of cross-coupled inverters is shown in Figure 8.7b. This type of VTC was already described in Chapter 4 on single source noise margins, and in Chapter 5

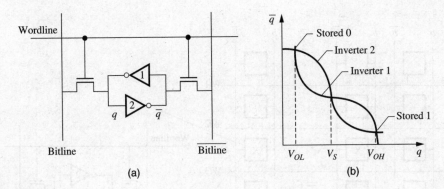

Wordline

1

2

q $\bar{q}$

Bitline $\overline{\text{Bitline}}$

(a)

$\bar{q}$

Stored 0

Inverter 2

Inverter 1

Stored 1

V_{OL} V_S V_{OH} q

(b)

Figure 8.7
Basic SRAM cell and VTC.

on flip-flops. The VTC conveys the key cell design considerations for read and write operations. In the cross-coupled configuration, the stored values are represented by the two stable states in the VTC. The cell will retain its current state until one of the internal nodes crosses the switching threshold, V_S. When this occurs, the cell will flip its internal state. Therefore, during a read operation, we must not disturb its current state, while during the write operation we must force the internal voltage to swing past V_S to change the state.

The six transistor (6T) static memory cell in CMOS technology is illustrated schematically in Figure 8.8. The cross-coupled inverters, M_1, M_5 and M_2, M_6, act as the storage element. Major design effort is directed at minimizing the cell area and power consumption so that millions of cells can be placed on a chip. The steady-state power consumption of the cell is controlled by subthreshold leakage currents, so a larger threshold voltage is often used in memory circuits. To reduce area, the cell layout is highly optimized to eliminate all wasted area. In fact, some designs replace the load devices, M_5 and M_6, with resistors formed in undoped polysilicon.

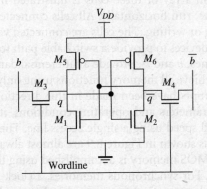

V_{DD}

b M_5 M_6 $\bar{b}$

M_3 M_4

q $\bar{q}$

M_1 M_2

Wordline

Figure 8.8
6T SRAM cell.

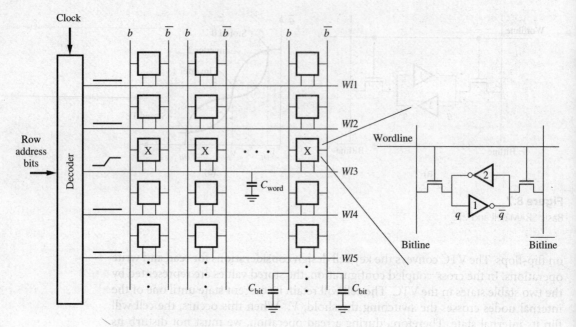

Figure 8.9
Wordline and double bitline configuration.

This is called a 4T cell since there are now only four transistors in the cell. To minimize power, the current through the resistors can be made extremely small by using very large pull-up resistances. Sheet resistance of these resistors is 10 MΩ per square or higher and the area is minimal. Standby currents are kept in the nanoampere range. Thus, power and area may be reduced at the expense of extra processing complexity to form the undoped polysilicon resistors. However, the majority of the designs today use the conventional 6T configuration of Figure 8.8.

The operation of an array of these cells is illustrated in Figure 8.9. The row select lines, or wordlines, run horizontally. All cells connected to a given wordline are accessed for reading or writing. The cells are connected vertically to the bitlines using the pair of access devices to provide a switchable path for data into and out of the cell. Two column lines, b and $\bar{b}$, provide a differential data path. In principal, it should be possible to achieve all memory functions using only one column line and one access device. Attempts have been made in this direction, but due to normal variations in device parameters and operating conditions, it is difficult to obtain reliable operation at full speed using a single access line. Therefore, the symmetrical data paths b and $\bar{b}$ as shown in Figure 8.9 are almost always used.

Row selection in CMOS memory is accomplished using the decoders described in the previous section. For synchronous memories, a clock signal is used in conjunction with the decoder to activate a row only when read-write operations are being performed. At other times, all wordlines are kept low. When one wordline goes high, say $wl3$ in Figure 8.9, all the cells in that row are selected. The access transistors are all turned on and a read or write operation is performed. Cells in other rows are effectively disconnected from their respective wordlines.

The wordline has a large capacitance, C_{word}, that must be driven by the decoder. It is comprised of two gate capacitances per cell and the wire capacitance per cell:

$$C_{word} = (2 \times \text{gate cap} + \text{wire cap}) \times \text{no. of cells in row} \qquad (8.1)$$

Once the cells along the wordline are enabled, read or write operations are carried out. For a read operation, only one side of the cell draws current. As a result, a small differential voltage develops between b and $\bar{b}$ on all column lines. The column address decoder and multiplexer select the column lines to be accessed. The bitlines will experience a voltage difference as the selected cells discharge one of the two bitlines. This difference is amplified and sent to output buffers.

It should be noted that the bitlines also have a very large capacitance due to the large number of cells connected to them. This is primarily due to source/drain capacitance, but also has components due to wire capacitance and drain/source contacts. Typically, a contact is shared between two cells. The total bitline capacitance, C_{bit}, can be computed as follows:

$$C_{bit} = (\text{source/drain cap} + \text{wire cap} + \text{contact cap}) \times \text{no. of cells in column}$$

$$(8.2)$$

During a write operation, one of the bitlines is pulled low if we want to store 0, while the other one is pulled low if we want to store 1. The requirement for a successful write operation is to swing the internal voltage of the cell past the switching threshold of the corresponding inverter. Once the cell has flipped to the other state, the wordline can be reset back to its low value.

The design of the cell involves the selection of transistor sizes for all six transistors of Figure 8.8 to guarantee proper read and write operations. Since the cell is symmetric, only three transistor sizes need to be specified, either M_1, M_3, and M_5 or M_2, M_4, and M_6. The goal is to select the sizes that minimize the area, deliver the required performance, obtain good read and write stability, provide good cell read current, and have good soft error immunity (especially due to α-particles).

8.3.2 Read Operation

We now describe the design details of the 6T RAM cell for the read operation using Figure 8.10. Assume that a "0" is stored on the left side of the cell, and a "1" on the right side. Therefore, M_1 is on and M_2 is off. Initially, b and $\bar{b}$ are precharged to a high voltage around V_{DD} by a pair of column pull-up transistors (not shown). The row selection line, held low in the standby state, is raised to V_{DD} which turns on access transistors M_3 and M_4. Current begins to flow through M_3 and M_1 to ground, as shown in Figure 8.10a. The resulting cell current slowly discharges the capacitance C_{bit}. Meanwhile, on the other side of the cell, the voltage on $\bar{b}$ remains high since there is no path to ground through M_2. The difference between b and $\bar{b}$ is fed to a sense amplifier to generate a valid low output, which is then stored in a data buffer.

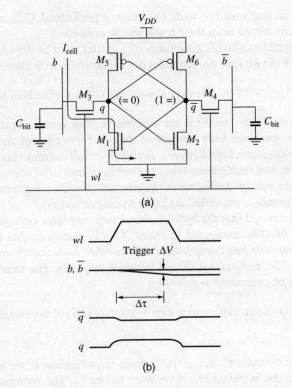

(a)

(b)

Figure 8.10
Design of transistor sizes for read operation.

Upon completion of the read cycle, the wordline is returned to zero and the column lines can be precharged back to a high value.

When designing the transistor sizes for read stability, we must ensure that the stored values are not disturbed during the read cycle. The problem is that, as current flows through M_3 and M_1, it raises the output voltage at node q which could turn on M_2 and bring down the voltage at node $\bar{q}$, as shown in Figure 8.10b. The voltage at node $\bar{q}$ may drop a little but it should not fall below V_S. To avoid altering the state of the cell when reading, we must control the voltage at node q by sizing M_1 and M_3 appropriately. We can accomplish this by making the conductance of M_1 about 3 to 4 times that of M_3 so that the drain voltage of M_1 does not rise above V_{TN}. In theory, the voltage should not exceed V_S, but this design must be carried out with due consideration of process variations and noise. In effect, the read stability requirement establishes the ratio between the two devices.

The other consideration in the read cycle design is to provide enough cell current to discharge the bitline sufficiently within 20 to 30% of the cycle time. Since the cell current, I_{cell}, is very small and the bitline capacitance is large, the voltage will drop very slowly at b, as shown in Figure 8.10b. The rate of change of the bitline can be approximated as follows:

$$I_{cell} = C_{bit} \frac{dV}{dt}$$

$$\therefore \frac{dV}{dt} = \frac{I_{cell}}{C_{bit}}$$

Clearly, I_{cell} controls the rate at which the bitline discharges. If we want a rapid full-swing discharge, we can make I_{cell} large. However, the transistors M_1 and M_3 would have to be larger. Since we have millions of such cells, the area and power of the memory would be correspondingly larger. Instead, we choose a different approach. We attach a sense amplifier to the bitlines to detect the small difference, ΔV, between b and $\bar{b}$ and produce a full-swing logic high or low value at the output. The trigger point relative to the rising edge of the wordline, $\Delta \tau$, for the enabling of the sense amplifier can be chosen by the designer based on the response characteristics of the amplifier. If the voltage swing ΔV and a target delay $\Delta \tau$ are specified according to Figure 8.10b, then

$$I_{cell} = \frac{C_{bit} \Delta V}{\Delta \tau}$$

This leads to the cell current value which, in turn, determines the final transistor sizes for M_1 and M_3. Alternatively, if the transistor sizes are determined to optimize the cell area, then the corresponding delay is computed as

$$\Delta \tau = \frac{C_{bit} \Delta V}{I_{cell}}$$

We now establish a rule of thumb for transistor sizes for the read cycle using an example.

Read Cycle Design Guidelines   **Example 8.2**

Problem:

Compute the widths of M_1 and M_3 in Figure 8.10 given that the circuit can only tolerate a rise in voltage of 0.1 V at node q during the read operation. Assume that $C_{bit} = 2$ pF and that the specification calls for a 200 mV transition of the bitline in 2 ns. Use 0.13 μm technology parameters.

Solution:

When the wordline, wl, goes high, M_3 is a saturated enhancement load for the M_1 driver. The driver transistor is expected to be in the linear region of operation. Therefore, we can write the following equation:

$$\frac{W_1}{L_1} \frac{\mu_n C_{ox}}{\left(1 + \dfrac{V_q}{E_{CN} L_1}\right)} \left[(V_{DD} - V_{T1})V_q - \frac{V_q^2}{2}\right] = \frac{W_3 v_{sat} C_{ox}(V_{DD} - V_q - V_{T3})^2}{(V_{DD} - V_q - V_{T3}) + E_{CN} L_3}$$

We first eliminate C_{ox} from both sides of the equation. Now, setting $V_q = 0.1$ V and ignoring body effect, we obtain

$$\frac{W_1}{0.1 \ \mu m} \frac{\left(270 \frac{cm^2}{V - sec}\right)}{\left(1 + \frac{0.1}{0.6}\right)} \left[(1.2 - 0.4)0.1 - \frac{0.1^2}{2}\right]$$

$$= \frac{W_3(8 \times 10^6 \ cm/s)(1.2 - 0.1 - 0.4)^2}{(1.2 - 0.1 - 0.4) + 0.6}$$

$$\therefore \frac{W_1}{W_3} \approx 1.7$$

This ratio would be smaller if body effect were taken into account. The actual values of the widths depend on the desired rate of change of the bitline voltage, the delay specification, and cell current. If we require a bitline transition of 200 mV in 2 ns, with a total bitline capacitance of 2 pF, then the cell current is

$$I_{cell} = C_{bit} \times \frac{\Delta V}{\Delta \tau} = 2 \ pF \times \frac{200 \ mV}{2 \ ns} = 200 \ \mu A$$

This is the average cell current through M_1 and M_3. As a rough estimate, we could simply use the current through the access transistor when it turns on:

$$I_{cell} \approx \frac{W_3(8 \times 10^6)(1.6 \mu F/cm^2)(1.2 - 0.1 - 0.4)^2}{(1.2 - 0.1 - 0.4) + 0.6} = 200 \ \mu A$$

$$\therefore W_3 = 0.4 \ \mu m$$

This implies that $W_1 = 0.7 \ \mu m$. These two sizes are larger than we would desire if we were trying to create a 1 Mbit SRAM. However, this example is intended to show the steps in the design process.

In practice, the device sizes are controlled by the RAM cell area constraints. As a rule of thumb, we typically use

$$\frac{W_1}{W_3} \approx 1.5 \tag{8.3}$$

and then optimize the sizes to provide the proper noise margin characteristics.

8.3.3 Write Operation

The operation of writing 0 or 1 is accomplished by forcing one bitline, either b or $\overline{b}$, low while the other bitline remains at about V_{DD}. In Figure 8.11, to write 1, $\overline{b}$ is forced low, and to write 0, b is forced low. The conditions when writing 1 are illustrated in Figure 8.11a. The cell must be designed such that the conductance of M_4 is several times larger than M_6 so that the drain of M_2 is pulled below V_S. This initiates a regenerative effect between the two inverters. Eventually, M_1 turns off and

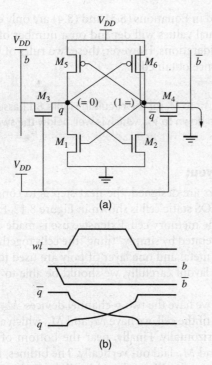

(a)

(b)

Figure 8.11
Write operation and waveforms for 6T SRAM.

its drain voltage rises to V_{DD} due to the pull-up action of M_5 and M_3. At the same time, M_2 turns on and assists M_4 in pulling output $\bar{q}$ to its intended low value. When the cell finally flips to the new state, the row line can be returned to its low standby level.

The design of the SRAM cell for a proper write operation involves the transistor pair M_6-M_4. As shown in Figure 8.11a, when the cell is first turned on for the write operation, they form a pseudo-NMOS inverter. Current flows through the two devices and lowers the voltage at node $\bar{q}$ from its starting value of V_{DD}. The design of device sizes is based on pulling node $\bar{q}$ below V_S to force the cell to switch via the regenerative action. This switching process is shown in Figure 8.11b. Note that the bitline $\bar{b}$ is pulled low *before* the wordline goes up. This is to reduce the overall delay since the bitline will take some time to discharge due to its high capacitance.

The pull-up to pull-down ratio for the pseudo-NMOS inverter can be determined by writing the current equation for the two devices and setting the output to V_S. To be conservative, a value much lower than V_S should be used to ensure proper operation in the presence of noise and process variations. Based on this analysis, a rule of thumb is established for M_6-M_4 sizing:

$$\frac{W_4}{W_6} \approx 1.5 \tag{8.4}$$

The two ratios provided in Equations (8.3) and (8.4) are only estimates. One should remember that the actual values will depend on a number of factors such as area, speed, and power considerations. However, these two rules of thumb can be used to validate the solution, once obtained.

Exercise 8.1 Compute the ratio of M_6 to M_4 for the circuit in Figure 8.11 assuming that the node $\bar{q}$ is to be pulled down to V_{TN}, which is well below the switching threshold.

8.3.4 SRAM Cell Layout

Once the cell transistors are designed, the next step is to construct a cell layout. A typical layout for a CMOS static cell is shown in Figure 8.12. Every effort is made to minimize the area of the memory cell. Extensive use is made of symmetry to allow the core array to be generated by simply "tiling" the cells together vertically and horizontally. Two levels of metal and one layer of poly are used to realize this memory cell. If we examine the layout carefully, we should be able to identify a total of six transistors.

Starting at the top, we have the two p-channel devices, M_5 and M_6, laid out horizontally. In the middle of the cell, we have M_3 and M_4, which are the two pull-down transistors laid out horizontally. Finally, near the bottom of the cell are the two access transistors, M_1 and M_2, laid out vertically. The bitlines, b and $\bar{b}$, are routed in Metal2 vertically, while the wordline is horizontally routed in both poly and Metal1

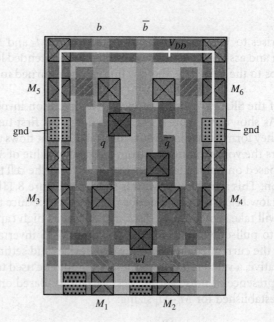

Figure 8.12
SRAM cell layout.

near the bottom of the cell. V_{DD} is routed in Metal1 at the top of the cell while Gnd is routed in Metal1 near the middle of the cell. The source/drain contacts are shared between pairs of neighboring cells by mirroring the cell vertically. The capacitance of the contacts per cell is therefore half the actual value due to sharing. The cell indicated by the center bounding box is replicated to create the core array. This cell is approximately 40λ by 30λ. Note that the substrate and well contacts are contained inside the cell. Removal of substrate and well plugs from the cell would result in a smaller cell.

The large number of devices connected to the wordline and bitlines gives rise to large capacitance (and resistance) values as described earlier. The row lines are routed in both Metal1 and poly to reduce resistance, while the bitlines are routed in Metal2. Calculations of total capacitance may be carried out using Equations (8.1) and (8.2).

Capacitance Calculations for the Wordline and Bitlines   **Example 8.3**

Problem:

What is the capacitance of the wordline and the bitlines for a 64K SRAM that uses the cell layout of Figure 8.12 with access transistors that are 0.5 μm/0.1 μm in size? The contacts on the bitlines are shared between pairs of cells and have a capacitance of 0.5 fF each. Wire capacitance is 0.2 fF/μm. Assume 0.13 μm technology parameters. The cell layout is 40λ by 30λ. Note that 1μm = 20λ.

Solution:

If we were to design a 64K SRAM, it would contain a core area of 256 × 256. Ignoring the resistance for the moment, the row capacitance would be due to the gate capacitance of 512 access transistors and the wire capacitance of 256 cells:

$$C_{word} = 512 \times 2 \text{ fF}/\mu\text{m} \times 0.5 \ \mu\text{m} + 256 \times 30\lambda \times 0.2 \text{ fF}/\mu\text{m} \times 1 \ \mu\text{m}/20\lambda$$

$$= 589 \text{ fF}$$

The bitline capacitance per cell due to the source/drain capacitance of the access transistors is lower than usual since the voltage drop across the junction is close to V_{DD}. In addition, there is wire capacitance and a half contact capacitance per cell. The total is

$$C_{bit} = 256 \times 0.5 \text{ fF}/\mu\text{m} \times 0.5 \ \mu\text{m} + 256 \times 40\lambda \times 0.2 \text{ fF}/\mu\text{m} \times 0.1 \ \mu\text{m}/2\lambda$$

$$+ 128 \times 0.5 \text{ fF} = 230 \text{ fF}$$

8.4   SRAM Column I/O Circuitry

In this section, we examine the column input/output (I/O) circuitry, which includes bitline precharge circuits, column multiplexers, write circuits, and read circuits. The column I/O must be designed with due consideration of the cell design and the timing specifications of the memory.

8.4.1   Column Pull-Ups

In both read and write operations, the bitlines are initially pulled up to a high voltage near V_{DD}. The circuits used to precharge the bitlines depend on the type of sensing that is used in the read operation. Figure 8.13 illustrates three possible precharge configurations. In Figure 8.13a, the precharge is similar to the dynamic logic precharge described earlier in Chapter 7. A precharge signal, PC, is applied to the two pull-ups and to a third transistor, called the *balance* transistor, connected between the two bitlines to equalize their voltage levels. When the wordline (*wl*) signal goes high, one bitline remains high and the other falls at a linear rate until *wl* goes low. The difference between the bitlines is fed into a voltage-sensing latch-based amplifier that is triggered when the differential voltage exceeds a certain threshold.

The precharge circuit of Figure 8.13b is reminiscent of the pseudo-NMOS circuits. Two static loads and a balance transistor form the precharge circuit. When PC is applied to the balance transistor, it simply equalizes the two voltage levels. Once the bitlines are precharged, the PC signal is turned off (raised to V_{DD}) and, at this point, the wordline can be activated. Of course, the pull-ups are still *on* so current will flow through one of them and into the cell side with the stored "0." Eventually, a steady-state output level will be reached by the bitline, as shown in the figure. This type of pull-up is suitable for current-sensing amplifiers since there is continuous

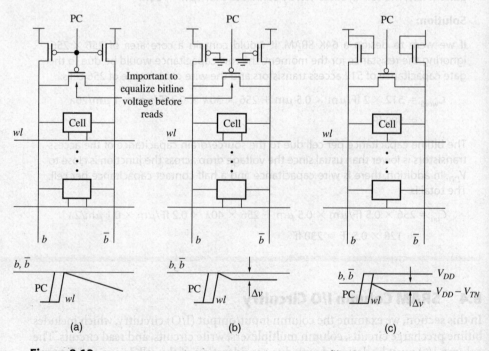

Figure 8.13
Column pull-up configurations.

current flow, or latch-based voltage-sensing amplifiers since the bitlines will establish a differential voltage, Δv.

Figure 8.13c is based on the NMOS saturated enhancement load. Therefore, the maximum possible voltage on the bitline is $V_{DD} - V_T$. When PC is applied to the balance transistor, it equalizes the two voltage levels. Once the lines are precharged high, the PC signal is turned off (raised to V_{DD}) and then *wl* goes high. At this point, the pull-ups are still active so current will flow through one of them into the cell side with the stored "0." Again, a steady-state output level will be reached by the corresponding bitline, as shown in the figure, although this value will be lower than the pseudo-NMOS case. This type of pull-up is suitable for differential voltage sensing amplifiers since the bitline voltages initially start at $V_{DD} - V_{TN}$. This lower voltage is needed for a proper biasing and output swing of the differential amplifier, as will be described later.

The PC signal may be generated in a variety of ways, but typically it is produced by an address transition detection (ATD) circuit. One form of this circuit is shown in Figure 8.14. The ATD signal is triggered by any transition on the address inputs. The basic circuit is comprised of a set of XOR gates, each with a delay element on one of the inputs. When an address line changes, it causes the XOR gate to generate a short pulse since the inputs differ in value for a short time. Circuits that generate a short pulse of this nature are called *one-shots*, which are part of the *monostable* family of circuits. The duration of the pulse, τ_D, is determined by the delay element. The delay line may be constructed from a simple inverter chain with an even number of inverters. In the figure, N is an even number and τ_{Pinv} is the inverter propagation delay.

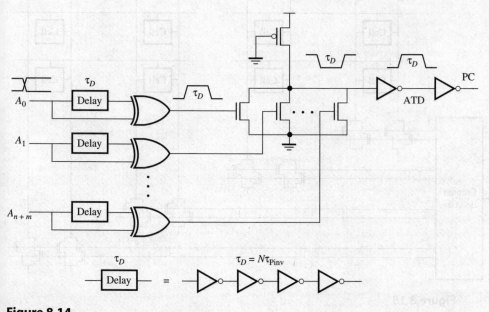

Figure 8.14
Address transition detection (ATD) circuit.

Once the pulse is generated, it turns on one of the pull-down transistors of the pseudo-NMOS NOR gate. A negative going pulse is generated at its output. This is passed through another inverter to generate the actual ATD signal. Many of the timing signals in SRAMs are derived from this basic circuit so it is required to drive a very high capacitance. Therefore, the signal should be properly buffered using logical effort or any other optimization method. Once generated, it can be inverted and applied to the bitline precharge elements as the PC signal. The address transitions usually take place before the beginning of a clock cycle and, as a result, the precharge operation typically occurs at the end of a previous memory cycle.

8.4.2 Column Selection

Once all the columns have been pulled up to a high voltage, the next step is to select the column(s) that will be involved in the read or write operation. This column selection is performed using a decoder/multiplexer combination. The m-bit column address is used to select one or more of the 2^m columns. This can be performed using a decoder, similar to the row decoder, driving a number of CMOS pass transistors as shown in Figure 8.15. The pass transistors require complementary signals. Of course, if an 8-bit output is desired, then the decoder outputs would each drive eight CMOS transmission gates, and fewer column address bits would be needed.

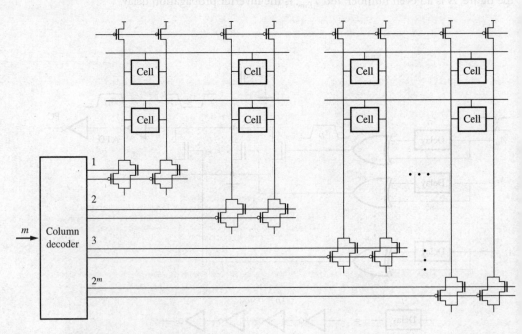

Figure 8.15
Column decoding and multiplexing.

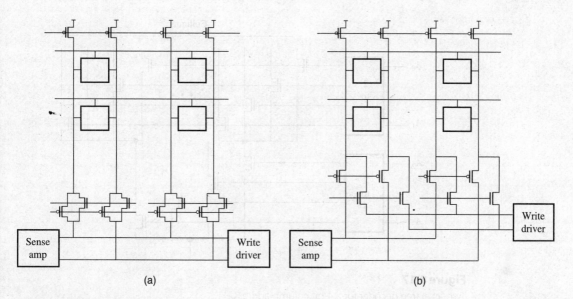

Figure 8.16
Column selection.

The optimal design of the column decoder proceeds in the same way as described earlier for the row decoder. The transmission gates driven by the decoder are also sized for optimal speed. They are connected to the sense amplifier for read operations and the write driver for write operations. This is shown in Figure 8.16a. Note that the use of the CMOS transmission gate presents a routing problem since each of the signals driving the pass transistors must be complementary (we are driving both PMOS and NMOS devices).

The routing can be simplified by realizing that the PMOS device is better at transmitting high signals while the NMOS device is better at transmitting low signals. Since the bitlines are near V_{DD} during a read, we should turn on the PMOS device during a read operation and leave the NMOS device off. During a write, one bitline is pulled to a low voltage. Therefore, we leave the PMOS device off and only turn on the NMOS device. It is possible to separate the NMOS and PMOS devices and only turn them on when needed. This is shown in Figure 8.16b. The NMOS devices are only connected to the write drivers while the PMOS devices are only connected to the sense amplifiers since they would be turned on during a read operation.

Now that the lines have been separated, there is one other improvement we can consider. Rather than a single level of multiplexing, it is possible to reduce the overall transistor count by using a tree decoding structure as shown in Figure 8.17. In this example, we have a 4-bit column address which would normally translate to 16 enable lines. Instead, we use two 2-to-4 decoders that select 1-out-of-4 pass transistors at each level. As we add more levels in the tree, the signal path is slower but the decoder size is reduced. For this example, we have shown two-level tree decoding

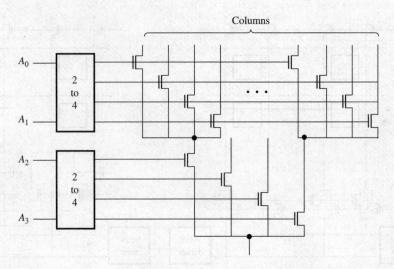

Figure 8.17

Two-level tree decoder for a 4-bit column address.

with exclusively NMOS pass transistors. We would need a corresponding set of PMOS transistors in a similar tree configuration. The tree decoding strategy requires less power but may be slower as more and more levels are added. These circuits should be designed based on the timing and power specifications for the memory.

8.4.3   Write Circuitry

Simplified write circuitry for the SRAM is shown in Figure 8.18. The operation is as follows. First, the columns are precharged to V_{DD} using M_7 and M_8. Next, the address and data signals are set up and held stable for a required amount of time before the clock is applied. The address signals are converted into column select and wordline activation signals. Before the wordline is enabled, the data and write signals are applied to pull one column to ground while leaving the other side at V_{DD}. This is done by ANDing the input data with the write signal. The pull-down transistors, M_{13}, M_{14}, and M_{15} in this case, are sized to discharge the column line in a specified amount of time. When the wordline goes high, current flows out of the cell and flips the sense of the cell. As described earlier, the internal cell voltage must be pulled below the switching threshold to enable the cell to flip state. Once it has switched, the wordline and column select lines may be returned to their standby values.

8.4.4   Read Circuitry

The read circuitry is activated when the wordline goes high. The cell transistors draw current from the highly capacitive column during a read operation. Therefore,

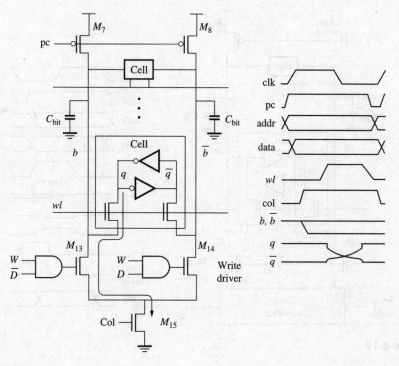

Figure 8.18
Write driver circuit.

the bitlines slowly drop in voltage and could potentially cause long access times. To reduce read access time, the memory is designed so that only a small voltage change on one column line or the other is needed to detect the stored value. Two or more amplifying stages are used to generate a valid logic output when the voltage difference between b and $\bar{b}$ is about 150–200 mV. Thus the column delay is only due to the time needed to achieve this small voltage change.

Figure 8.19 shows a simplified version of the read circuitry for a CMOS static memory. One of the precharge circuits of Figure 8.13 is used to pull the column lines high. In this case, the columns are biased at V_{DD} by transistors M_7, M_8. Then, the address, data (not used during read), and clock signals are applied. Again, the address signals translate into column enable and wordline activation signals. Usually the column selection and sense enable are activated at the same time. The sense amplifier depicted in Figure 8.19 is used to provide valid high and low outputs using the small voltage difference between inputs b and $\bar{b}$. The precharge circuit must be consistent with the sense amplifier circuit. Otherwise, the sense amplifier may not operate properly.

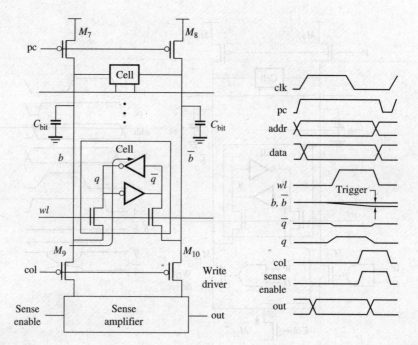

Figure 8.19

Basic read circuitry.

Figure 8.20 provides an example of a sense amplifier in the form of a conventional CMOS differential amplifier.[4] Typically, SRAMs may use eight identical sense amplifiers to provide simultaneous output of eight data bits. When using these types of sense amplifiers, the column pull-up transistors must be saturated enhancement loads (shown at the top of Figure 8.13c). Otherwise, the inputs would start at V_{DD} which would make it difficult to bias M_4 and M_5 properly for the desired output swing at node *out*.

The main reason for using this type of sense amplifier is to improve the noise immunity and speed of the read circuit. Since the voltage swing on the bitlines is limited due to the large capacitances, any noise on these lines may cause an error in the reading process. In fact, any noise that is common to b and $\bar{b}$ should not be amplified. We are only interested in the differential signal changes between the two bitlines. The sense amplifier shown in Figure 8.20 attenuates *common-mode noise* and amplifies *differential-mode signals*. The detailed operation of this circuit involves the concepts of analog circuit design. However, since we are using it for

---

[4] These are called *sense amplifiers* when used in memory applications; their role is to sense which bitline is dropping in voltage. Normally, such a circuit is used for small-signal voltage gain rather than large-signal sensing applications.

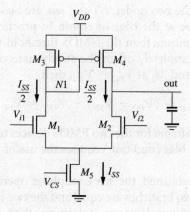

Figure 8.20
Differential voltage sense amplifier.

large-signal applications, we can study its properties from a more digital point of view.

The circuit can be divided into three components: the current mirror, common-source amplifier, and the biasing current source. All transistors are initially placed in the saturation region of operation so that the gain is large. They also use large values of channel length, L, to improve linearity.

The two transistors, M_3 and M_4, act to provide the same current to the two branches of the circuit. That is, the current flowing through M_3 is mirrored in M_4:

$$I_3 \approx I_4$$

Any difference in the two currents is due to differences in their V_{DS} values. The transistor M_5 sets the bias current, I_{SS}, which depends on the bias voltage V_{CS}. At steady-state, the current flowing through the two branches of the amplifier should be equal to $I_{SS}/2$.

The two input transistors, M_1 and M_2, form a source-coupled differential pair. The two input voltages, V_{i1} and V_{i2}, are connected to the column lines. The biasing of the circuit must be done carefully to allow the output node to have a large enough swing. Specifically, the transistors must be *on* and in the saturation region of operation for high gain. In order to accomplish this, the inputs to M_1 and M_2 must be set to approximately $V_{DD} - V_{TN}$ rather than V_{DD}. To understand this, consider the case when the inputs are precharged to V_{DD}. To keep the input devices in saturation, their two drain nodes, $N1$ and *out*, would be biased at the saturation voltage:

$$V_{N1} = V_{\text{out}} = \frac{(V_{DD} - V_{TN})E_{CN}L_N}{(V_{DD} - V_{TN}) + E_{CN}L_N} \approx (V_{DD} - V_{TN})$$

The above simplification is possible since the channel lengths are large.

A problem arises if the two nodes, N1 and *out*, are biased at this value: both *p*-channel devices would be at the edge of cutoff. In practice, the PMOS threshold voltage is higher in magnitude than the NMOS threshold voltage. Therefore, both M_3 and M_4 would be completely off in the steady-state condition. Instead, if we biased the inputs of M_1 and M_2 at $V_{DD} - V_{TN}$, then

$$V_{N1} = V_{out} \approx (V_{DD} - V_{TN}) - V_{TN} \approx V_{DD} - 2V_{TN}$$

Now there is enough *headroom* for the two PMOS devices to be comfortably *on* and in saturation. This input bias condition requires the use of the column pull-up circuits of Figure 8.13c.

With the biasing established, the sense amplifier operates as follows. Initially, the bias currents in the two branches are equal and the two inputs are at $V_{DD} - V_{TN}$. When the voltage at one input decreases, it decreases the current in that branch. At the same time, the current in the other branch increases in value to maintain a total of I_{SS} through M_5.

We examine the discharging and charging cases in Figure 8.21. Assume that M_1 is the input that has dropped below $V_{DD} - V_{TN}$ by the prescribed amount to turn it off, as in Figure 8.21a. This implies that the currents in M_3 and M_4 are both zero. However, since the current in M_5 is I_{SS}, it follows that this current must be discharging the output capacitance through M_2. Therefore, the output voltage is quickly forced to ground. In the other scenario depicted in Figure 8.21b, if the input V_{i2} drops by the prescribed amount, M_2 is turned off. Then all the current flows through M_1, M_3, and M_5. The current of M_3 is mirrored in M_4. Since the current in M_2 is zero, this current must flow to the output to charge it to V_{DD}.

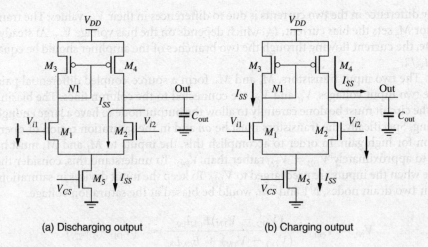

(a) Discharging output   (b) Charging output

Figure 8.21
Detecting "0" and "1" using a differential sense amplifier.

This type of differential amplifier is used in high-speed applications. The required differential voltage for proper operation is of the order of 100 mV to 200 mV. Its speed can be adjusted depending on how much power dissipation can be tolerated. Consider modeling the output transition as a current source driving a capacitor. The rate of change of the output, whether switching high or low, is given by

$$\frac{dV}{dt} = \frac{I_{SS}}{C_{out}}$$

This is called the *slew rate* (i.e., dV/dt at the output). Rearranging, the delay through the sense amplifier is

$$\Delta\tau = \frac{C_{out}\,\Delta V_{out}}{I_{SS}}$$

To reduce the delay, a large I_{SS} can be selected. However, the power dissipation in steady-state is given by

$$P = I_{SS}V_{DD}$$

Therefore, a tradeoff exists between the speed and the power dissipation; both are controlled by the choice of I_{SS}. Once a suitable value of I_{SS} is selected, the W/L of the devices can be determined. For the input devices, the W/L determines the $V_{GS} - V_{TN}$ value. This value is the gate overdrive term that establishes the desired bitline swing value. As the input transistor sizes increase, the gate overdrive term decreases. Since we require a small gate overdrive, the input devices are required to be rather large. The sizes of the other transistors are based on the bias voltages needed at the internal nodes. The complete design of such amplifier circuits falls into the realm of analog circuit design. Further details can be obtained by consulting the references at the end of the chapter.

A second option for the sense amplifier is the latch-based circuit shown in Figure 8.22. The circuit is effectively a cross-coupled pair of inverters with an enabling transistor, M_1. This circuit relies on the (slower) regenerative effect of inverters to generate a valid high or low voltage. It is a lower power option since the circuit is not activated until the required potential difference has developed across the bitlines. However, it is slower since it requires a large input voltage difference and is not as reliable in the presence of noise as the previous sense amplifier.

The initial sequence of operations is similar to the differential sense amplifier described above. The bitlines are precharged to V_{DD} with either Figure 8.13a or Figure 8.13b. Then the wordline is enabled and one of the bitlines drops in voltage. As the bitline differential voltage reaches the prescribed amount, the sense enable is activated. The timing of the sense enable is critical as described later. For now, assume that it arrives at the proper time. At this point, the bitline difference is fed into the cross-coupled inverters. One side drops in voltage faster than the other side, since one side will always have more gate overdrive than the other. Eventually, the pull-down transistors on one side act to bring down the output to Gnd while, on the other

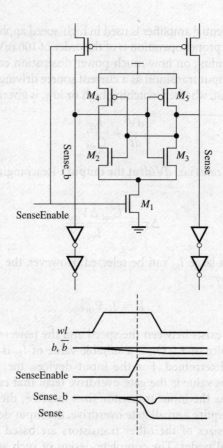

Figure 8.22
Latch-based sense amplifier.

side, the pull-up transistor acts to raise the voltage to V_{DD}. This process is shown in the timing diagram of Figure 8.22. The device sizing follows previously discussed methods for flip-flops.

The more important issue is the timing of the SenseEnable signal. If the latch is enabled too early, the latch may not flip in the proper direction due to noise. If it is enabled too late, then it will add unnecessary delay to the access time. In addition, process variations will control the actual timing of the signal. In order to guarantee that the signal will arrive at the proper time in the presence of process variations, one needs to introduce a replica circuit that mimics the delay of the actual signal path, shown in Figure 8.23. Here, the upper path emanating from the clock is the actual signal path to the bitlines. The SenseEnable should arrive as soon as the bitline swing reaches the desired value. By creating a second path (the lower path) that exhibits the same delay characteristics, we can ensure that the SenseEnable arrives at the correct time.

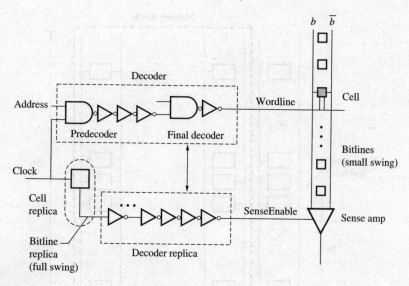

Figure 8.23

Replica circuit for sense amplifier clock enable.

The critical path for the read cycle starts from the clock and the address inputs and terminates at the sense amplifier inputs. The signal flows through the decoder and generates the wordline, which activates the memory cell that drives the bitlines. The swing on the bitlines is presented to the sense amplifier. This is the point at which we wish to enable the sense amplifier. The purpose of a replica circuit is to duplicate the delays along this path with circuits that correspond to each delay element. Essentially, we want to have a decoder replica that tracks the gate delays in the real decoder, and a cell replica that tracks the bitline discharge delay of the actual bit cell.

Note that we have placed the memory cell replica *before* the decoder in Figure 8.23. It is not appropriate to place the memory cell after the decoders in the replica path since it would have to drive all the sense amplifiers at the bottom of the memory. Since a small memory cell does not have the needed drive capability, we place the replica cell ahead of the decoder. We can keep the memory small and still deliver a full-swing signal as needed by the input to the decoder replica. The buffers of the decoder replica can be used to drive the sense amplifiers.

One issue for the replica memory cell in this configuration is that we require the full-swing output to have the same delay as the small swing on the actual bitlines. For example, if the actual cell requires 500 ps to transition by 180 mV, then the replica memory cell would require approximately 5 ns to transition by 1.8 V. This is not an acceptable delay in the replica path.

The replica cell should, in fact, be a replica column line with only enough cells to match the timing of the actual column. This is shown in Figure 8.24. For example,

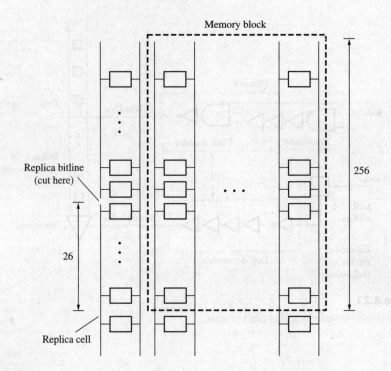

Figure 8.24
Replica cell design.

if we have 256 bits in the true bitline with a swing of 180 mV, then we only require roughly 26 cells in the replica circuit to produce a full swing of 1.8 V in the same time interval. The slight round off error in the number of cells used is not an issue since we will ensure that the replica path is slightly longer than the actual path delay. With the full swing from the replica path cells, we can drive the decoder replica gates. The needed 26 bits can be cut from a section of additional columns that are always fabricated alongside the main memory array to avoid "edge effects" on each end.

To ensure that the SenseEnable does not arrive too early for any reason, we should add an extra gate delay or two to the decoder replica. Designed in this manner, the SenseEnable will arrive at the proper time in the presence of process and environmental variations.

8.5 Memory Architecture

The overall memory architecture can now be described. In Figure 8.25, we illustrate a high-level layout of the memory array. The core array containing the cells is the largest block. The bitline precharge circuits are positioned above the core. The row

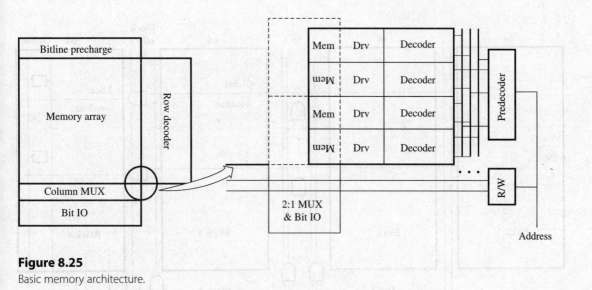

Figure 8.25
Basic memory architecture.

decoder is placed on the right side and the column multiplexer and bit I/O are located below the core array. If we zoom in on a corner region of the memory, as shown in the right-hand side of Figure 8.25, we see that the row decoder is comprised of a predecoder and a final decoder. The decoder drives the wordlines horizontally across the array. Each pair of bitlines feeds a 2:1 column decoder (in this case) which is connected to the bitline I/O circuits such as sense amplifier and write drivers. Each memory cell is mirrored vertically and horizontally to form the array, as indicated in the figure.

Several factors contribute to a limit on the maximum speed of operation. Delays in address buffers and decoders naturally increase as the number of inputs and outputs increase. Row lines are typically formed in polysilicon and may have substantial delays due to distributed RC parameters. A metal line may be placed in parallel and contacted to the poly line to reduce the delay (cf., Figure 8.12). Column lines are usually formed in metal, so resistance is not as significant, but the combined capacitance of the line and many parallel access transistors connected to them results in a large equivalent lumped capacitance on each of these lines. The large capacitances on the wordline and bitlines also contribute to excess power dissipation.

In order to reduce delay and power, a number of different partitioning approaches have been used. One technique is the divided wordline (DWL) strategy shown in Figure 8.26 for a 64K bit SRAM. Part of the 8 row address bits (6 in this case) are used to define global wordlines. A total of 64 global wordlines are created. These lines do not drive memory cells (i.e., the two access transistors within each cell) and therefore have far less capacitance than the regular wordlines. The remaining 2 bits of the address are used to generate local wordlines that actually drive the

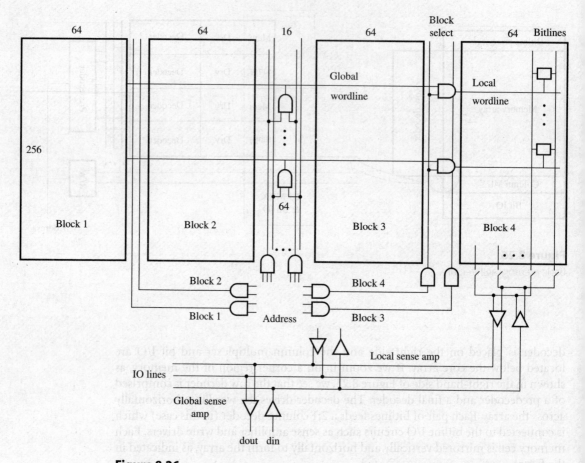

Figure 8.26
Divided wordline strategy to reduce power and delay.

cell access transistors. In this example, four blocks are created and accessed using the local wordlines. The total cell capacitance is reduced by up to a factor of 4. Therefore, the power will be reduced greatly. In addition, the delay along the wordlines is also reduced.

A similar partitioning strategy can be applied to the bitlines, as shown in Figure 8.27. An architecture without partitioning is shown in Figure 8.27a. For this case, neighboring pairs of bitlines are multiplexed to produce 128 outputs (i.e., there are 128 sense amplifiers in this example). If the bitlines are partitioned into two sections, the bitline capacitance is reduced by a factor of 2. The proper cell must be selected using a two-level multiplexing scheme of Figure 8.27b. To achieve the same bitline swing as in Figure 8.27a would only require roughly half the time. Further partitioning can be carried out with a corresponding increase in the complexity of multiplexing.

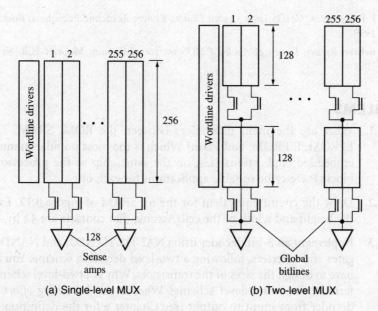

Figure 8.27

Bitline partitioning to reduce delay.

8.6 Summary

This chapter has focused on the application of material in previous chapters to the design of an SRAM. Modern memories are, of course, much more complicated but most of them can be understood with the basic concepts that have been presented in this chapter. Since memory is very regular in nature, the design process has reached a point where it can be implemented in software. Today, there are CAD tools called *memory compilers* that can generate a memory design within minutes. While the sizes of the memories that can be generated are still limited to some degree, the automatic synthesis approach for memories will be used more frequently in the future. This concludes the discussion on SRAM circuits. Other types of memory circuits are described in Chapter 9.

REFERENCES

1. B. Prince, *Emerging Memories: Technologies and Trends*, Kluwer Academic Publishers, Boston, MA, 2002.

2. K. Itoh, *VLSI Memory Chip Design*, Springer-Verlag, Heidelberg, 2001.

3. J. Rabaey, A. Chandrakasan, and B. Nikolic, *Digital Integrated Circuits: A Designer Perspective*, Second Edition, Prentice-Hall, Upper Saddle River, NJ, 2003.

4. S. M. Kang and Y. Leblebici, *CMOS Digital Integrated Circuits, Analysis and Design*, Third Edition, McGraw-Hill, New York, 2003.

5. H. Veendrick, *Deep-Submicron CMOS ICs*, Second Edition, Kluwer Academic Publishers, Boston, MA, 2000.

6. J. P. Uyemura, *CMOS Logic Circuit Design*, Kluwer Academic Publishers, Boston, MA, 1999.

7. Behrad Razavi, *Design of Analog CMOS Integrated Circuits*, McGraw-Hill, New York, 2001.

PROBLEMS

P8.1. What are the main differences between the ROM, SRAM, DRAM, EPROM, E^2PROM, and Flash? Which is the most popular memory for embedded applications (i.e., on the same chip as the processor logic blocks)? Describe suitable applications for each one.

P8.2. Draw the circuit equivalent for the 6T SRAM of Figure 8.12. Estimate the height and width of the cell. Assume that contacts are 4λ by 4λ.

P8.3. Implement an 8-bit decoder using NAND2, NAND3, and NAND4 logic gates and inverters, following a two-level decoding scheme. You do not have to design the sizes of the transistors. Why is a two-level scheme preferred over a multilevel scheme? What is the *branching effort* of the decoder from input to output (see Chapter 6 for the definition of this term)?

P8.4. Consider the SRAM cell of Figure 8.8 with a stored 0 on the left side and a stored 1 on the right side. Design the transistors of the SRAM such that node q does not exceed V_{TN} during a read operation and node $\bar{q}$ drops below V_S during a write operation. The desired cell current during a read operation is 300 μA. Use 0.18 μm technology parameters.

P8.5. Redesign the SRAM cell of the previous problem by assuming worst-case conditions for a read operation as follows: the threshold voltage of M_3 is reduced by 10%, the width M_3 is increased by 10%, the threshold voltage of M_2 is decreased by 10%, and the width of M_2 is increased by 10%. Explain why this is considered to be worst case for a read operation. Simulate the circuit in SPICE to demonstrate its operation under worst-case conditions.

P8.6. Redesign the SRAM cell of the previous problem by assuming worst-case conditions for a write operation as follows: the threshold voltage of M_4 is increased by 10%, the width M_4 is decreased by 10%, the threshold voltage of M_1 is decreased by 10%, and the width of M_1 is increased by 10%. Explain why this is considered to be worst-case for the write operation. Simulate the circuit in SPICE to demonstrate its operation under worst-case conditions.

P8.7. Consider the 6T SRAM cell of Figure 8.8. Replace M_5 and M_6 by poly resistors that are 100 MΩ in value. Explain how this new 4T cell works for read and write operations. How does the internal node get pulled to a high value? Is the new cell static or dynamic?

P8.8. For the sense amplifier shown in Figure 8.20, answer the following questions using 0.18 μm technology parameters:

(a) If the sense amplifier is driving a load of 50 fF in 500 ps, what is the required value of I_{SS}?

(b) In order to turn off the input transistors with a bitline swing of 100 mV, what values of W/L are needed?

(c) Which of the three column pull-up configurations of Figure 8.13 would be used with this sense amplifier? What is the initial voltage at the inputs to the sense amp?

(d) Given the size of the input transistors, what is the steady-state voltage at the gate node and the resulting size of M_5?

(e) Choose the sizes of M_3 and M_4 to establish a suitable steady-state output voltage.

DESIGN PROBLEM 1: Decoder Design in 0.18 μm Technology

Your task is to create a decoder for a small memory shown in Figure D8.1. The memory consists of 1K words, each containing 64 bits, arranged as a 256 $\times$ 256 array of 6T SRAM cells. A word is selected for reading by the row and column decoders. The row decoder asserts one of the 256 wordlines. Each Metal2 wordline selects a row of four 64-bit words. Four selected words feed the input of the 4:1 MUX controlled by the outputs of the column decoder.

The SRAM receives a 10-bit address. The inputs to the row decoder are the upper 8 bits of the address, while the lowest 2 bits of the address feed the column decoder. Each access transistor in the memory cell is 4λ in width. Each SRAM cell is 40λ $\times$ 40λ. The diagram in Figure D8.1 illustrates the SRAM array, with a blow-up of one of the SRAM cells in the forty-second word.

The spec allows a maximum of 10 fF of gate capacitance on any address input. Your task is to minimize the delay from the address becoming stable to the wordline rising. The general topology for the decoder is provided in Figure D8.2. Your design goal is to implement an optimal row decoder that converts 8 address bits into 256 wordlines using logical effort.

(a) What is the total load on one wordline? Include both the loading of the SRAM cells and the capacitance of a Metal2 wordline. Assume a wire capacitance of 0.2 fF/μm. You can assume that gate capacitance is 2 fF/μm.

(b) Find the total path effort in the address decode path by estimating the fanout from input (address bit) to output (wordline), the branching factor, and the logical effort. Estimate the number of stages needed in the optimal design.

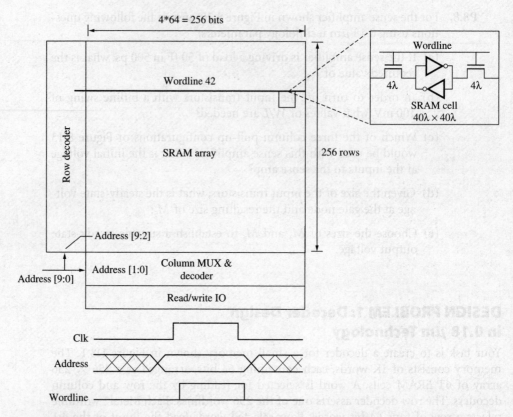

Figure D8.1

SRAM layout and timing information.

(c) You can implement the predecoder in either 2 or 4 stages as shown in Figure D8.2. Which of the two approaches is better? Using logical effort, decide which architecture you are going to use. For both cases, the final decode stage is a NAND2-INV combination. Ignore any sideload capacitances.

(d) Next choose the correct design for the decoder, and size the gates to optimize performance. What is your estimate of the delay of the decoder in terms of FO4 delay (include the delay from the parasitics of the gates in your estimate)?

(e) Now include the sideload at the outputs of the predecoder stage. The sideload is due to the wire running vertically in Figure D8.2. Compute the actual sizes when the sideload is included.

(f) Compare the hand-calculated delay against SPICE.

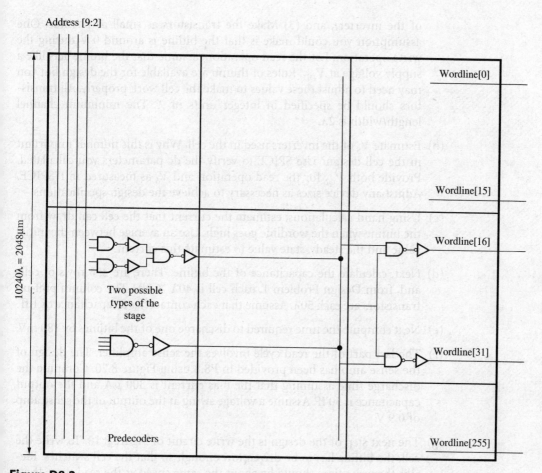

Figure D8.2

Decoder topology, branching, and wire loads.

DESIGN PROBLEM 2: Design of SRAM Cell and Read/Write Circuitry in 0.18 μm Technology

The problem explores cell and I/O design issues for a 64K SRAM based on the previous problem. Since there are 256 columns in the SRAM and 64 bits/word, it requires 64 sense amplifiers (1 per bit of output) and each one is driven by 1 of 4 possible columns (one column from each interleaved 64-bit word).

(a) First consider the cell design. Recall that in Design Problem 1, the access transistor of the SRAM cell was given as 4λ. Size the rest of the transistors to satisfy the following requirements: (1) During a read, the internal voltage should not rise above V_{TN}, (2) During a write, the access transistor must be able to pull the internal node to at least 0.8 V (i.e., well below V_S

of the inverter), and (3) Make the transistors as small as possible. One assumption you could make is that the bitline is around 0 V during the write operation. For the read operation, assume that the bitline acts like a supply voltage at V_{DD}. Rules of thumb are available for the design but you may need to adjust these values to make the cell work properly. All transistors should be specified in integer units of λ. The minimum channel length/width is 2λ.

(b) Estimate V_S of the inverters used in the cell. Why is this number important in the cell design? Use SPICE to verify the dc parameters you calculated. Provide both V_{OL} for the read operation and V_S as measured in HSPICE. Adjust any device sizes as necessary to achieve the design specifications.

(c) Using hand calculations, estimate the current that the cell can draw from the bitline when the wordline goes high. Use an average between the initial value and the steady-state value to estimate this current.

(d) Next, calculate the capacitance of the bitline. There are 256 rows of cells and, from Design Problem 1, each cell is $40\lambda \times 40\lambda$. The column pull-up transistors are each 50λ. Assume that each contact has a capacitance of 1 fF.

(e) Next compute the time required to discharge one of the bitlines by 180 mV.

(f) The last part of the read cycle involves the sense amplifier. The design of the sense amp has been provided in P8.8 using Figure 8.20. Compute the discharge time assuming that the bias current is 300 μA and the output capacitance is 50 fF. Assume a voltage swing at the output of the sense amp of 0.9 V.

(g) The next step of the design is the write circuit of Figure 8.18. To write the cell, the bitline has to be driven low enough so that the cell switches. Ideally, the write time should be about the same speed as the read time. If we work to make it faster, we are wasting our effort because the read will be the limiting factor. If it is slower than the read, then the write is in the critical path and that is not desirable either. Using a simple RC model, determine the effective resistance needed to get the bitlines to swing down to $V_{DD}/5$ in the same amount of time it takes to do the read. Size M_{13}, M_{14}, and M_{15} so that they have this effective resistance.

(h) As a last step, we need to set the values of the column pull-up transistors of Figure 8.18. They need to pull the bitlines up after a write but before the end of the precharge phase. How big do they need to be? The final difference of the bitlines should be less than 10% of the desired read swings to avoid confusing the sense amp. Typically, we make them twice the size of the pull-down devices for a fast precharge. Size these transistors accordingly.

(i) Check your results using SPICE.

Additional Topics in Memory Design

9.1   Introduction

Memory is occupying a larger and larger percentage of the total area of digital chips. When memory is integrated on the same chip with logic, it is referred to as *embedded memory*. It has been forecast by the International Roadmap for Semiconductors (ITRS) that embedded memory will represent more than 50% of the design content of digital ICs by the year 2005. Many large microprocessor and graphics processing chips already contain over 50% memory, and in some cases it is well over 80%. An important reason for using large blocks of on-chip memory is to provide high data transfer rates between logic and memory. A sophisticated graphics processor chip, for instance, might require transfer of 128 bits of data every 5 ns, requirements that would be nearly impossible to meet with memory and logic in separate packages. Other requirements for embedded memory are found in cell phones and PDAs, where the need to simultaneously minimize physical size, power consumption, and cost make it desirable to combine all logic and memory functions on a single chip. It is clear that memories, both embedded and stand-alone, will be a growing part of the integrated circuit market in the future.

Memory designs are differentiated by the cell structure, the use of static or dynamic storage techniques, access mechanisms, and whether or not the data storage is persistent even when the power is turned off. However, the most important metric for memory is the cost per bit. High-density and high-capacity memories are typically cheaper. There are a growing number of applications that require gigabytes of memory in hand-held and portable devices. Over the years, memory cells have evolved from six-transistor (6T) configurations to single-transistor (1T) configurations. The 6T cells are still the most popular in SRAMs. EEPROMs use 2T cells, and 1T cells are used by DRAMs, ROMs, EPROMs, Flash memories, and FRAMs.

The use of static versus dynamic techniques is primarily driven by the demand for high density. Static techniques are much more reliable and do not require refresh circuitry, but dynamic memories offer four times the density. On the other hand, static memories are much faster compared to dynamic memories, at the expense of additional power. When considering on-chip memories, static techniques are most frequently used due to the extra processing costs and complexity associated with dynamic memories. However, at some point, the density and cost-per-bit advantages of DRAM may outweigh many of the disadvantages.

Memories are also classified into the read/write and nonvolatile categories. Well-known members of read/write memories are obviously the SRAM and DRAM. Associative memories are a special type of read/write memory that use a keyword for the lookup process in place of address decoding. These are also called content-addressable memories (CAM). Serial memories such as FIFOs (first-in-first-out memories) and shift registers are also members of the read/write category. Nonvolatile memories retain their stored data even after the power supply is removed. Their primary role is to serve as read-only memories (ROM), although most have the ability to modify the stored data. Typically their write times are very long, but their read times are short and of the same order as other semiconductor memories. There are many ways to implement a nonvolatile memory cell. A well-known variety of this type of memory is the mask-programmable ROM. The other important members of this family are the EPROM, EEPROM, and Flash.

This chapter explores a variety of other semiconductor memories, their applications, access mechanisms, and cell configurations. Since SRAMs were described in Chapter 8, we will begin by examining CAMs, as they are a derivative of the SRAM architecture. We will also cover an important application of SRAM cells in the growing market segment of programmable logic called field-programmable gate arrays (FPGAs). Then, we will sequence through dynamic RAMs, mask-programmable ROMs, erasable programmable ROMs, electrically erasable ROMs, and Flash memories. The chapter concludes with a look at a memory cell based on ferroelectric materials called FRAMs.

*9.2   Content-Addressable Memories (CAMs)

The SRAMs discussed in Chapter 8 are used for data storage and lookup when the access mechanism is based on a known address. However, there are applications

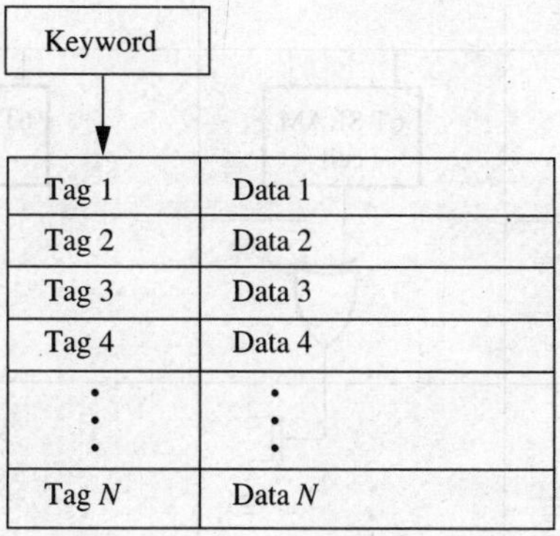

Figure 9.1

Associative memory lookup mechanism.

when the data that we seek is associated with a known binary keyword rather than a known binary address. The known keyword is compared against previously stored keywords, called *tags,* that reference the actual data that we seek. The tags are not stored in any particular order so we must match the address keyword with the tags that are already stored to access the desired data. This is illustrated in Figure 9.1. Memories that perform this type of function are referred to as content-addressable memories (CAMs). They are also called *associative memories* since we reference the data associated with a tag by matching the keyword to the stored tag.

CAMs use the basic architecture of the SRAM but allow the access of data through a matching scheme rather than an address decoding scheme. They are often used to build highly associative *cache* memories. The term *cache* is given to a local memory of a CPU that holds frequently used data by storing its address in one table and its associated block of data in another table. The addresses are not stored in any particular order, and only a small subset of the entire address space is represented in the cache. Instead of accessing data in the cache through a static address (direct mapped cache), we want to be able to access it through association with an address keyword. This requires a way of reading and writing the SRAM array based on different tags. The CAM stores the tag bits in a table that points to different parts of the SRAM array where the associated data is stored.

Another application of the CAM is to store an Internet routing table. Such a table is used to route network packets from a source to a destination. Given a destination keyword, the data portion of the table contains information about the next node (or next "hop" in Internet parlance) to send the packet in order for it to move closer to the destination. Since packets contain the Internet protocol (IP) address of the destination, it can be processed at each node in the network to extract the destination address. The destination is used as a keyword to retrieve the next hop information. The routing table can be implemented as a CAM by using the destination as a keyword to look up the next hop data in the SRAM array.

A conceptual diagram of a CAM array and the contents of each CAM cell are shown in Figure 9.2. The array contains n-bit stored tags that are to be compared to

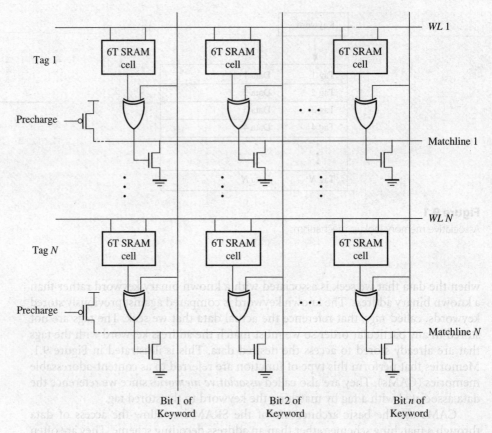

Figure 9.2
Arrangement of CAM lookup array.

the incoming n-bit keyword. Each row holds a different tag; each bit of the tag is stored in a separate 6T SRAM cell. The SRAM cell holds two values, the true value and its complement. The reference side holding the true value of the cell is fed to an XOR gate. Each of the N rows also has its own matchline to indicate that the incoming keyword matches the tag.

The operation is as follows. Initially all N matchlines are precharged high. In effect, all rows start by assuming that a match has occurred with the keyword. The XOR gate compares each keyword bit with the tag bit stored in each SRAM memory cell. If there is a match, the NMOS pull-down device does not turn on and the precharged matchline stays high. If the keyword and stored tag do not match, the NMOS device discharges the matchline. Note that all bits of the tag, and all tags are compared to the keyword in parallel. Therefore, any one of the pull-down transistors can discharge the matchline, since any single bit mismatch implies a complete tag mismatch. Therefore, the matchline will only stay high (signifying a match)

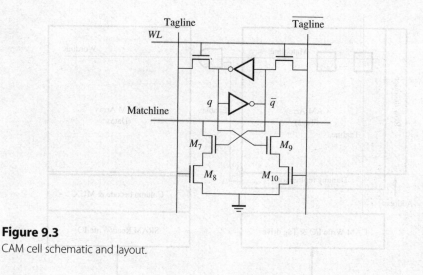

Figure 9.3

CAM cell schematic and layout.

when *all* tag bits match the keyword bits in a given row. Since all matchlines are initially precharged high, and all but one will go low, there is significant power dissipation. This is one of the limitations of large CAMs. Of course, there are cases when none of the contents of the CAM match the tag, or more than one row matches the tag. Actual CAM designs must handle a single match, multiple matches, and complete mismatches properly.

CAM cells may be implemented in many ways. One possible implementation is shown in Figure 9.3. The *WL* signal is routed in polysilicon while matchline is routed in metal 1. The two complementary bitlines, called *taglines* in this case, are routed in metal 2. The top part of the schematic is simply one SRAM cell, while the lower portion discharges the matchline if the cell contents do not match the values on the taglines. The functions of the XOR and pull-down transistor are combined and implemented using four transistors, M_7, M_8, M_9, and M_{10}. Due to these additional transistors, the layout of the CAM cell is 20–30% larger than the 6T SRAM cell. Other CAM cells can be designed to reduce area or increase speed depending on the application requirements.

> Explain how the CAM cell of Figure 9.3 works assuming that the stored tag bit is on the left side labeled *q* and the keyword bit comes in on the signal labeled *tagline*.
>
> **Exercise 9.1**

A block diagram of the CAM array (storing tags) alongside the SRAM array (holding data) is shown in Figure 9.4. The CAM array performs a parallel comparison of the incoming keyword with the stored tags. If a match occurs, it generates a matchline output that drives a wordline of the associated SRAM array. In a sense,

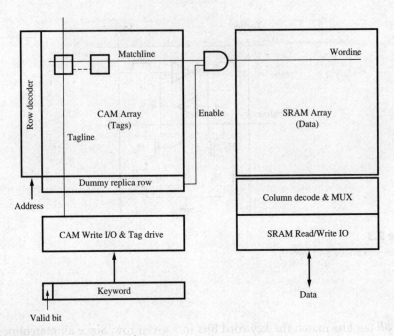

Figure 9.4
Block diagram of CAM and SRAM array.

the CAM plays the role of the decoder in a conventional SRAM. If the tag is 32 bits wide, each matchline would run horizontally through 32 CAM cells. Often, certain data in the SRAM is invalid so the corresponding tag is not valid. In order to indicate whether valid information exists, there is also a valid bit associated with each tag row. This must be matched along with the tag to activate the corresponding wordline. Additional address bits are used to select one or more of the columns out of the SRAM array, as defined by the application.

Each matchline must be ANDed with an enable signal that drives one of the wordlines high if there is a valid match. Timing of this enable signal is critical because all the matchlines start out high after precharge and only one of them will remain high at the end of a valid matching process. This means that the enable signal should not fire until the CAM has had enough time to resolve the worst case mismatch before selecting a wordline. In this case, the worst case corresponds to the condition that results in the longest time required to realize a mismatch. A replica circuit, similar to the one described in Chapter 8, is needed to generate this enable signal with the timing of a worst-case mismatch in the presence of process variations and changes in operating conditions.

A complete CAM design must handle unexpected cases, such as *multiple* matches. Of course, this can be avoided by checking if the tag already exists in the array before storing it. There can also be a complete mismatch with all the stored

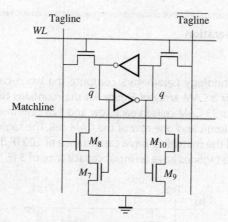

Figure 9.5

Reordering of XOR transistors for improved speed.

tags, in which case a *miss* has occurred. This requires an examination of all the matchlines to flag the case where none of them are high. This can be done with a large NOR gate. Upon detection of this case, the new tag and associated data can be written into the CAM and SRAM arrays, respectively.

Since each CAM cell has an SRAM cell within it to store the tags, arrangements must be made to write to them. Therefore, the CAM array also has wordlines driven by the decoder that access each of the rows and bitlines to write the tag data into the cells. The bitlines for the 6T SRAM cell and the taglines for matching purposes use the same wires. The write process is similar to that for the SRAM array, but instead of pulling down a tagline, a tagline must be driven high. This is because both taglines must start off low to keep the internal XOR transistors off and enable the matchline to be precharged to a high value. This can be further understood by examining the cell shown earlier in Figure 9.3. If either M_8 or M_{10} are on, and the opposite side of the SRAM cell is high, then the matchline will inadvertently be pulled low. Therefore, the *taglines must start low* to avoid this.

The cell mismatch timing can be improved by reordering the transistors in the cell. In Chapter 6, it was pointed out that late arriving signals should be placed at the top of a series stack. We can use this fact to rearrange the transistors of the CAM cell as illustrated in Figure 9.5: The two column transistors, M_8 and M_{10}, are now connected to the matchline while the other transistors, M_7 and M_9, are connected to Gnd. Since *tagline* and *$\overline{tagline}$* can be considered as late arriving signals, they should be placed closer to the outputs. Of course, nodes internal to the cell are both stable and therefore may be viewed as early arriving signals. This new configuration allows M_8 or M_{10} to carry out most of the discharging process since M_7 or M_9 have already discharged the intermediate capacitance.

Example 9.1   **Delay of Match Operation**

Problem:

Using 0.18 μm technology parameters, compute the worst-case delay of a mismatch operation for a CAM array of Figure 9.4 that contains the CAM cell shown below. The array has 33 CAM cells in each row and 128 cells in each column. Draw the cells for one column and one row of the CAM cell. The taglines have a capacitance of 450 fF and the matchline has a capacitance of 200 fF due to the cells. The input drivers for the taglines have an input capacitance of 3 fF.

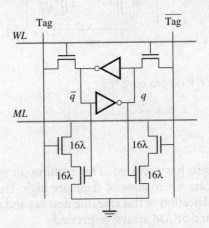

Solution:

The drawing of the row and column of the CAM should be similar to Figure 9.2. Using this figure, the total delay due to the taglines and the matchline is

$$\tau_{total} = \tau_{tag} + \tau_{matchline}$$

The delay along the taglines can be obtained using logical effort. The number of stages of drivers can be determined using FO4 rules:

$$N = \log_4\left(\frac{C_{tag}}{C_{in}}\right) = \log_4\left(\frac{450\ \text{fF}}{3\ \text{fF}}\right) = \log_4(150) = 3.6 \approx 4 \text{ stages}$$

The optimal stage effort (SE) for four stages is

$$SE^* = \sqrt[4]{150} = 3.5$$

The normalized delay is

$$D = 4(3.5) + 4(0.5) = 16$$

Note that the τ_{inv} value for 0.18 μm technology can be computed as

$$\tau_{inv} = 3C_g R_{eqn} L_n = 3(2\ \text{fF}/\mu\text{m})(12.5\ \text{k}\Omega)(0.2\ \mu\text{m}) = 15\ \text{ps}$$

The actual delay is

$$\tau_{tag} = \tau_{inv} \times D = (15\ \text{ps})(16) = 240\ \text{ps}$$

The delay for the matchline to be pulled low in the worst case can be computed using an RC delay model for the CAM cell and matchline, respectively. The output capacitance is given as 200 fF. The CAM cell has one transistor that is always on in the pull-down stack since it is connected to the internal node of the SRAM cell. Therefore, the size of the upper transistor of the stack determines the resistance seen by the output capacitance. The on-resistance of the CAM cell is approximately

$$R_{eff} = 12.5 \text{ k}\Omega/8 \cong 1.6 \text{ k}\Omega$$

Therefore,

$$\tau_{matchline} = RC = (1.6 \text{ k}\Omega)(200 \text{ fF}) = 320 \text{ ps}$$

The total delay is

$$\tau_{total} = \tau_{tag} + \tau_{matchline} = 240 \text{ ps} + 320 \text{ ps} = 560 \text{ ps}$$

*9.3   Field-Programmable Gate Array

An important category of chips is called the *field-programmable gate array (FPGA)*. An FPGA is a stand-alone, programmable logic device that allows rapid implementation of complex logic systems. They can be broadly categorized into two groups: SRAM programmed and antifuse programmed. We focus on the SRAM-programmed FPGA in this section. This type of array uses SRAM bits to configure the chip to perform a desired function. FPGA customers purchase the stand-alone chips based on the size, speed, and power requirements of the target application. User customization of the chips is performed by setting the programmable SRAM bits in the FPGA to the desired values.

Traditionally, FPGAs were widely used for prototyping an ASIC before the chip was designed. Today, the densities and speeds of FPGAs are such that these devices are often found in finished products. There are also many other examples of its use, such as interface chips for automatic test equipment. It is a fast-growing segment of the semiconductor market, competing with both ASIC and SOC design styles. Recently, the use of on-chip or embedded programmable fabrics has been proposed, and there is much research underway in this area.

The basic architecture of a stand-alone FPGA is shown in Figure 9.6. This architecture is highly regular with a programmable logic block (PLB) replicated horizontally and vertically, and I/O pads placed along the periphery. Both the logic blocks and the I/O are programmable. The task of placing and routing the logic onto the FPGA is a highly automated process. Beginning with an RTL description of the system, usually represented in Verilog or VHDL, a synthesis and optimization step is used to generate the corresponding logic level representation. The logic is then placed and routed by FPGA CAD tools for a target FPGA chip. This process ultimately produces a set of programming bits that must be written into the SRAMs inside the FPGA to implement the final system.

The logic blocks and routing architecture are illustrated in Figure 9.7. This figure shows how the logic outputs are connected to the neighboring routing channels.

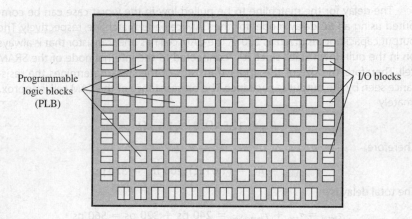

Figure 9.6
Overall architecture of FPGA chip.

The outputs of the block intersect the vertical or horizontal tracks at *connection blocks*. These connection blocks feed the vertical or horizontal tracks via programmable connections. The signals are routed along these tracks in one direction to the *switch block*, or *switch matrix*, at which point they can be routed in one of the other three directions. The design decisions at this level involve the number of vertical

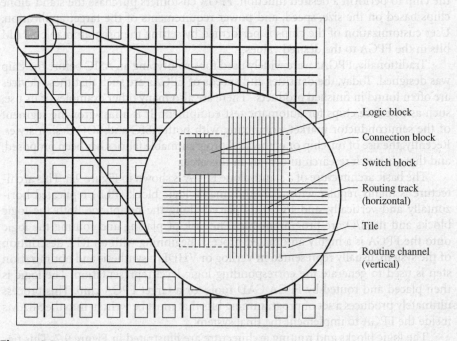

Figure 9.7
Island style FPGA architecture.

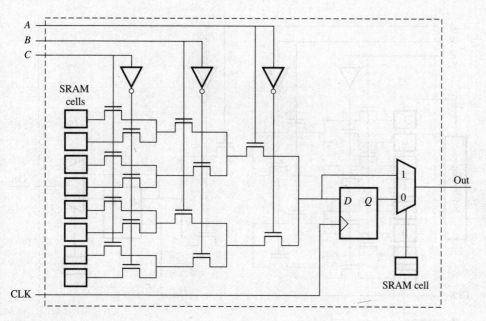

Figure 9.8

Basic programmable 3-LUT (lookup table).

and horizontal tracks in the connection block and the switch block, and the connection mechanisms between the wires. Once determined, a *tile* for the FPGA can be laid out and arrayed vertically and horizontally to form the core of the chip.

A simplified schematic of a PLB is shown in Figure 9.8. It consists of a number of SRAM cells, pass transistors, a D-flop, and a multiplexer. Actual blocks are more complicated, but this schematic is sufficient for our purposes of illustrating the basic concepts of the programmable block. The SRAM bits are programmable and serve two purposes: to store logic data and to select the configuration of the logic block.

The SRAM cells shown in the left portion of the diagram are used to store the truth table of the function being implemented. This particular implementation has three inputs and a total of eight cells for storage of the 2^3 possible combinations. This is referred to as a 3-input lookup table, or 3-LUT for short. Typically, 4-LUTs are implemented in FPGAs, but this may vary from manufacturer to manufacturer. User programming of an FPGA is performed by serially shifting desired values into the SRAM bits as shown in Figure 9.9. For this purpose, the SRAM bits need to be arranged as a shift register. There are a number of design considerations in the programming procedure, including power and overall programming time. For example, several serial chains can be used to minimize programming time, but this may increase the power dissipation.

Once the values are stored in the LUTs, they are accessed by applying the inputs *A*, *B*, and *C*. The input settings activate a single path through the pass transistor tree. In Figure 9.9, this tree can be viewed as an 8-to-1 multiplexer with the inputs acting

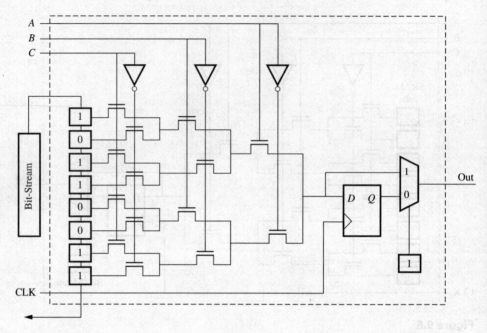

Figure 9.9
Programming the 3-LUT.

as the select variables. For example, the first stored value is accessed when $A = B = C = 1$. The second value is propagated to the output when $A = 0$, $B = C = 1$, and the eighth value is accessed when $A = B = C = 0$. The fact that these are n-channel pass transistors implies that they have a V_{TN} drop that degrades the output level. This can be overcome by boosting the gate drive above V_{DD} so that there is no reduction in the output voltage level along the pass transistor path.

On the right side of the figure are the elements that determine whether the PLB is sequential or combinational. The SRAM bit setting for the multiplexer determines whether the output is taken directly from the pass transistor tree or from the Q output of the D-flop. Choosing the pass transistor tree output produces a combinational circuit, while choosing the D-flop output creates a sequential circuit. The flop is edge-triggered and controlled by an additional CLK input to the PLB. Note that in FPGAs, the clock must be symmetrically routed to all PLBs since it is a required input to all flops. Of course, modern FPGAs have many additional clocks that must be routed to other types of blocks.

Example 9.2   FPGA Logic Blocks

Problem:

In Figure 9.9, what function is implemented in the PLB? Is the function combinational or sequential?

Solution:

Using a Karnaugh map, $Out = \bar{B} + AC$. This is a combinational function since the output of the D-flop is not gated through the multiplexer due to the "1" setting of the SRAM bit.

Connections between logic blocks are formed using prefabricated routing tracks. These routing tracks are connected to each other, and to the logic blocks, via pass transistors, each controlled by an SRAM bit. This is illustrated in Figure 9.10. Programmable connections are provided at the cross points of vertical and horizontal tracks using pass transistors. The transistors that have a stored "1" in their

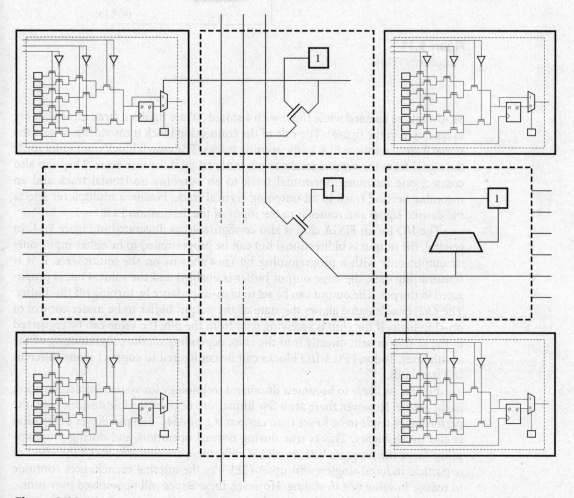

Figure 9.10

Programmable connections.

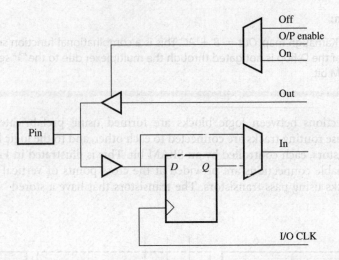

Figure 9.11
I/O buffer for FPGA.

SRAM bit are enabled while those with a stored "0" are disabled (transistor sizes are exaggerated in the figure). The role of the connection block transistors is to gate the signal from the source PLB to the routing tracks. The switch block transistors route the signal from the vertical tracks to a horizontal track, or vice versa. They can also connect one incoming horizontal track to an outgoing horizontal track and an incoming vertical track to an outgoing vertical track. Finally, a multiplexer selects the desired signal and routes it to the input of the destination PLB.

The I/O for an FPGA chip is also configurable, as illustrated in Figure 9.11. In general, the output is bidirectional but can be programmed to be either input-only or output-only with a programming bit (not shown) on the multiplexer. If it is transmitting data, the large output buffer is enabled and the value, Out, is propagated to the pin. The output can be set to high-impedance by turning off this buffer. The *O/P Enable* signal allows the state of the output buffer to be under control of on-chip logic. If the chip is receiving data from the pin, the value can be registered in the D-flop or sent directly into the chip, depending on the programming of the multiplexer. Today, FPGA I/O blocks can be configured to support many different I/O standards.

FPGAs are likely to become a dominant technology for system implementation in the future. However, there are a few limitations of these flexible devices. First, the performance tends to be lower than custom ICs or ASIC designs. Power dissipation is also much higher. This is true during normal operation, and during programming. Since the program bits are SRAM cells, there are concerns about the effect of α-particle induced single-event upset (SEU) as the internal capacitances continue to reduce in value due to scaling. However, these issues will be resolved over time.

Another limitation is associated with the size of a system that can be implemented on an FPGA. Typically an RTL description is automatically converted to a gate-level description, and then placed and routed by CAD software for a target FGPA. Depending on the type of system being implemented, the LUTs may not be fully utilized, or the desired logic may not fit within a single LUT and must span several LUTs. This creates signal routing and congestion problems due to the limitations of the number of available tracks. While the reported gate counts of these devices are 5M or higher, the effective utilization of FPGAs may only be 10–20%. In addition, higher capacity FPGAs tend to be more expensive on a per chip basis, so they are not suitable for high-volume applications. Nevertheless, the market segment of FPGAs is expected to grow over the next few years.

In the near future, the programmable fabric associated with FPGAs will begin to appear on ASIC/SOC designs to permit programmability after fabrication. There are situations where an industry standard is evolving, or a block will be tailored to the end customer requirements, or perhaps the specifications for a block not fully defined at design time. In these cases, an FPGA-like programmable fabric can be embedded on the same chip along with processors, memory, and other logic blocks. The desired function can be programmed later using CAD software similar to that for stand-alone FPGAs. This is another reason why the interest in FPGAs is continuing to grow, and expected to continue for the foreseeable future.

9.4 Dynamic Read-Write Memories

The importance of reducing the cost per bit of memory led to simpler, smaller-area memory cells that could be more densely packed on a chip. The static memory cells described in Chapter 8 all require four to six transistors per cell and four or five lines connecting to each cell. In the late 1960s, it was realized that memory cells with reduced complexity, area, and power consumption could be designed if dynamic MOS concepts, similar to those introduced in Chapter 7, were used. Static memory cells store data as a stable state of a flip-flop, and data is retained as long as dc power is supplied. In contrast, dynamic cells store binary data as charge on a capacitance. Normal leakage currents can remove stored charge in a few milliseconds, so dynamic memories require periodic restoration, or *refreshing*, of stored charge, typically every millisecond or so. For memories of 64K bytes and larger, the cost of a complete dynamic memory system including provision for refresh cycles is lower than the cost of a system based on static memory components. However, the complexity of the peripheral circuitry, refresh circuitry, and timing leads to slower devices than their static counterparts.

Our study of dynamic RAMs (DRAMs) begins with the basic static RAM cell with the PMOS devices removed, as shown in Figure 9.12. At first glance, this configuration may not appear to work as a memory cell since the pull-ups have been removed. However, the access transistors, M_3 and M_4, act as pull-ups when they are turned on. Since the bitlines are precharged high in the previous cycle, they will act to keep one side high while the other side is low. Consider the case where the left side of the cell is high and the right side is low. When the access transistors are turned off, the high value is stored on the capacitor at node q. This high value keeps M_2 turned on which maintains a low output at node $\bar{q}$. This keeps M_1 turned off. When the wordline is raised, the two access transistors turn on. Charge sharing

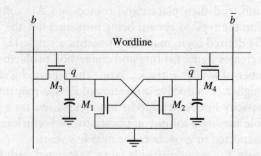

Figure 9.12
Static RAM cell with pull-ups removed.

occurs between b and q to keep node q high, while $\bar{b}$ discharges through M_4 and M_2. Since this cell relies on charge storage to maintain the value of a node, it is a dynamic cell. If we want to minimize the cell size of this dynamic memory, we can do substantially better.

9.4.1 Three-Transistor Dynamic Cell

The first widely used dynamic memory cell is shown schematically in Figure 9.13. Note that this three-transistor (3T) cell can be derived by eliminating M_2 from the NMOS cell shown in Figure 9.12. The read and write ports have been separated out and two wordlines are used in the cell. Contrary to static cell design, this cell does not require internal device ratios for proper operation. Transistors M_1, M_3, and M_4 can all be small devices to minimize cell area. Parasitic node capacitance C_1 is drawn in explicitly because it is essential to the operation. Charge stored on C_1 represents stored binary data. Selection lines for reading and writing must be separated

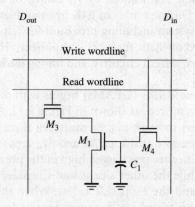

Figure 9.13
Three-transistor (3T) DRAM cell.

because the stored charge on C_1 would be lost if M_4 turned on during reading. Although separate column lines are shown here for data in (D_{in}) and data out (D_{out}), these two may be combined at the expense of some extra complexity in the read-write circuits.

The cell operates in two-phase cycles. The first phase of each read or write cycle is devoted to a precharge phase during which columns D_{in} and D_{out} are charged to a valid high logic level via column pull-up transistors. A "1" is assumed to correspond to a high level stored on C_1 and is written by turning on M_4 after D_{in} is high. The D_{in} line is highly capacitive because it is attached to many cells. The column I/O circuits do not need to hold D_{in} high because sharing the charge on D_{in} with C_1 does not significantly reduce the precharged high level. A "0" is written by turning on M_4 after the precharge phase is over, then simultaneously discharging D_{in} and C_1 via a grounded-source pull-down device (not shown) in the column I/O.

Reading is accomplished by turning on M_3 after the precharge is over. If 1 is stored, D_{out} will be discharged through M_1 and M_3. If 0 is stored, there will be no conducting path through M_1, so the precharged high level on D_{out} will not change significantly. The cell may be read repeatedly without disturbing the charge stored on C_1. Drain junction leakage and subthreshold current of M_4 reduce the stored charge over the span of milliseconds. Refreshing is performed by reading stored data before charge all leaks away, inverting the result, and writing back into the same location. This is performed simultaneously for all the bits in a row once every millisecond.

The level on the D_{out} line in principle can be detected with a simple inverter, but considerable delay would be encountered in achieving the needed 1- or 2-V swing on the D_{out} line. If a short access time is desired, a *current sensing* amplifier may be used. This amplifier would detect the flow of current into the cell and produce 1 at the output. If current did not flow into the cell, the output of the amplifier would be 0. For this 3T cell, output data is inverted compared to input data. However, memory component data input and output will have the same logic polarity if one extra inversion is included in either the read or write data path.

9.4.2 One-Transistor Dynamic Cell

Most modern dynamic RAMs have capacities of 64M bits or more. All use the one-transistor (1T) cell with a storage capacitor shown schematically in Figure 9.14. It can be derived from Figure 9.13 by removing the read access transistors, M_1 and M_3. There are many variations in the detailed realization of this cell, depending on the number of polysilicon layers, method of capacitor formation, conductors used for row and column, etc. For simplicity in this introductory evaluation we overlook the many differences and focus on the schematic representation that is common to all.

Selection for reading or writing is accomplished by turning on M_1 with the single row line. Data are stored as a high or low level on C_1. In the interests of minimum cell area, C_1 should be kept fairly small. However, as voltage levels drop, the total charge stored on this capacitor begins to diminish. Therefore, it is desirable to make C_1 large without compromising the cell size.

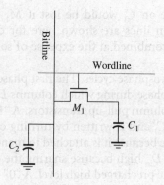

Figure 9.14
1T DRAM cell.

Data are written into the cells by forcing a high or low level on the selected column when the cell is selected. The internal node voltage should be as high as possible to further increase the stored charge. Rather than limiting the internal voltage to $V_{DD} - V_{TN}$, the wordline can be boosted above $V_{DD} + V_{TN}$ using bootstrapping or charge-pump circuits so that the internal node can rise to V_{DD}. The boosted wordline is used for both reading and writing.

When reading the cell, the charge stored on C_1 is shared with the capacitance C_2 of the column line which is typically 10 times larger. If the bitline capacitance is too large, the results of the charge sharing will not be significant enough to detect the stored value in the cell. A large value of C_1 would mitigate this problem. However, the requirement for a large C_1 is in conflict with the cell size requirements for high density. Two approaches have emerged to address this issue, as shown in Figure 9.15. On the left is the *trench capacitor* cross section where a vertical cut is made in the substrate and filled with an insulator-poly sandwich forming the capacitor. On the

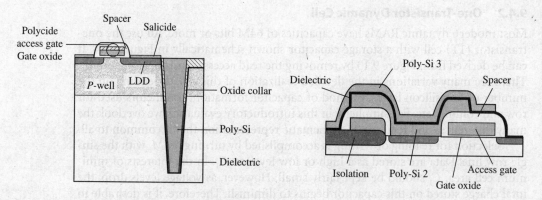

Figure 9.15
DRAM trench and stack capacitors.

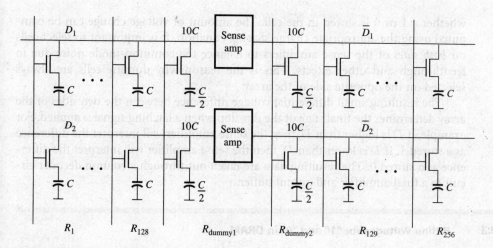

Figure 9.16

1T DRAM array configuration.

right is the *stacked capacitor* where two additional poly layers are deposited above the transistor with a dielectric material sandwiched between them. The stacked capacitor is now the preferred method to realize the cell capacitance. Both of these approaches yield capacitance values between 20–30 fF. This implies that the bitline capacitance should lie in the range of 200–300 fF for proper read operations.

During the read, the internal value of the cell is disturbed. The read process is referred to as a *destructive read-out* since the value in the cell is modified due to charge sharing. As a result, stored data must be regenerated every time they are read, in addition to refreshing them periodically even if they are not read. Read amplifier design for reliable detection of the small column signal is one of the most difficult aspects of 1T DRAM design.

The simplified schematic for a read-refresh circuit for a 1T DRAM is shown in Figure 9.16. Since the detection of a small voltage change in a single-ended configuration is difficult, the bitlines of the storage array are split in half so that equal capacitances are connected to each side of the flip-flop. This is called an open-bit architecture. The regenerative switching of a dynamic flip-flop (represented as a sense amplifier) detects the small data signal and restores the high or low signal level. As shown in Figure 9.16, each half column in the array has a single additional dummy cell that will be used as described below.

Reading from a 1T array proceeds as follows. A precharge signal sets the voltages on all column lines to $V_{DD}/2$ and sets the internal voltages in all dummy cells to $V_{DD}/2$ by turning on both R_{dummy} lines. Next, assume the wordline R_1 is pulled high so that the first set of cells on the left is selected. The dummy cells on the opposite side of the sense amplifier are selected simultaneously by raising the signal R_{dummy2}. The column voltage $\overline{D}$ on the right side connected to the selected dummy remains at $V_{DD}/2$ since the internal and bitline voltages are equal. However, the D voltage on the left side will either increase or decrease in value depending on whether a 1 or 0 is stored in the cell. The amount of voltage change can be computed using the appropriate charge sharing equation. It is important to select cells on *both sides* of the sense amplifiers to balance the common-mode noise due to feedthrough and other effects. This is the reason why dummy cells are always selected on the opposite side of the array.

The resulting small differential voltage difference between the two sides of the array determines the final state of the flip-flop when a latching signal is applied. For example, if D is higher than $\overline{D}$, then the sense amplifier will interpret the difference as a stored 1. If D is lower than $\overline{D}$, then the sense amplifier will interpret the difference as a stored 0. The resulting data are taken out through a column decoder circuit to a final amplifier and output buffer.

Example 9.3

Bitline Voltages for "1" and "0" in DRAM

Problem:

In Figure 9.16, assume that the column lines are precharged to $V_{DD}/2$ and the internal dummy cell voltages are also set to $V_{DD}/2$. Compute the voltages on the bitlines when reading a "1" and reading a "0." Assume that boosted wordlines are used so that full V_{DD} levels can be stored in each cell when writing a "1." The column capacitance is $10C$ and the cell capacitance is C. Also compute the reference voltage level and then explain why it is required.

Solution:

The output voltage is due to charge sharing. For a stored "1," we can write

$$\frac{V_{DD}}{2}C_{column} + V_{DD}C_{cell} = V^*(C_{column} + C_{cell})$$

$$\therefore V^* = \frac{\frac{V_{DD}}{2}C_{column} + V_{DD}C_{cell}}{C_{column} + C_{cell}} = \frac{\frac{V_{DD}}{2}10C + V_{DD}C}{10C + C} = 0.55\,V_{DD}$$

On the other hand, if a "0" is stored, the output on D is

$$\frac{V_{DD}}{2}C_{column} + 0 \times C_{cell} = V^*(C_{column} + C_{cell})$$

$$\therefore V^* = \frac{\frac{V_{DD}}{2}C_{column}}{C_{column} + C_{cell}} = \frac{\frac{V_{DD}}{2}10C}{10C + C} = 0.45\,V_{DD}$$

The reference voltage sits at $0.5\,V_{DD}$. For a 1.8 V supply, there is approximately 90–100 mV of change relative to the reference level. This difference is converted to a full-swing value by the regenerative sense amplifier. The dummy cells are used to balance feedthrough and noise effects on both sides of the differential amplifier.

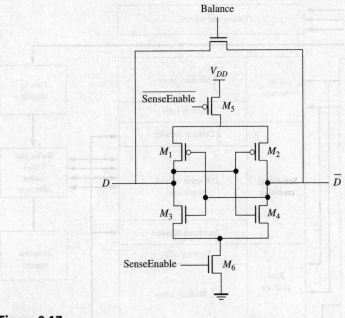

Figure 9.17
Simplified diagram of flip-flop style sense-refresh circuit.

The sense amplifier design is somewhat complicated but can be viewed as a latched-based clocked sense circuit as discussed in Chapter 8. A simplified version of the circuit is shown in Figure 9.17. Initially, a balance transistor is turned on to equalize the voltage on the two sides of the flip-flop, D and $\overline{D}$, to $V_{DD}/2$. The *SenseEnable* signal is held low until the difference voltage has been established on these lines with the activation of a regular wordline and a dummy wordline. Next, the pull-up transistor, M_5, and pull-down transistor, M_6, are turned on using the SenseEnable signal. The flip-flop then uses its regenerative property to establish true high and low values. These values are written back into the cell to complete the DRAM operation.

9.4.3   External Characteristics of Dynamic RAMs

The internal circuit design and timing diagram for widely used dynamic RAMs are much more complicated than described above, involving, for instance, a total of more than 20 internally generated clock phases for read, write, and refresh functions. These matters are beyond the scope of this book. To complete our study of dynamic RAMs, we provide a user's point of view and consider the terminal characteristics of these components.

The block diagram for a 64K-bit dynamic RAM is shown in Figure 9.18. The capacity of a single block can be increased by a factor of 4 to 16 without any serious penalty in operating speed. However, larger storage capacity on a single chip is best

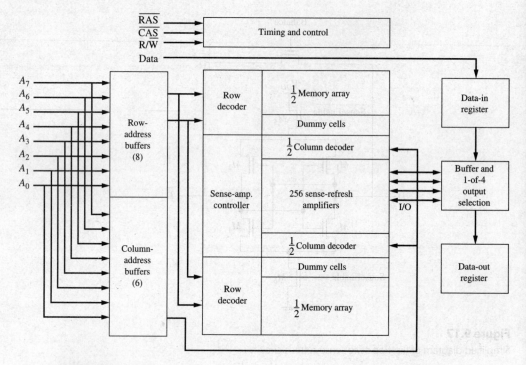

Figure 9.18

Block diagram of 64-kbit DRAM.

realized by replicating blocks like these many times over. Although internal process and circuit details vary, the block shown here is similar to those found in designs from many vendors. The 1T cells are organized in two halves as described above.

A read cycle would proceed as follows, with specific reference to the internal design of this particular diagram. First, row selection is achieved using eight row address bits that are latched into eight row address buffers. These buffers provide true and inverted outputs for each input bit. Seven address bits are routed to either the upper or lower set of row decoders, as determined by the state of the eighth row address bit. The upper or lower group of row decoders performs a 1 out of 128 selection, driving a single row line to a high level.

The high or low level stored in each of 256 cells along the selected row line is transferred to the column line, followed by a charge sharing event to establish a new voltage level. One flip-flop sense amplifier for each of the 256 columns is used to capture the relatively small change in column voltage and regeneratively restore it to a full 1 or 0 voltage level. The correct levels are restored to all selected cells without any involvement by column address selection circuits.

Address information for column selection comes in via the same eight pins used for row addresses. This is accomplished by a time-division multiplexing of these pins, as follows. After the row addresses are latched, they are disconnected from the address pins. Address changes at the pins do not affect row selection for the remainder of the cycle. Therefore the pins are used for column selection. The purpose of address multiplexing is to reduce the package pin count, size, and cost. The column address is latched into eight column address buffers. Six of the column address bits are used to select one of 64 groups of four sense amplifiers for connection to four data buffers and a 4-to-1 multiplexer (using the last two address bits). A single selected bit is passed to the data output buffer and to an off-chip data bus.

A write cycle proceeds with many similarities, except that a single data input bit is used to set the state of one sense amplifier flip-flop, overriding the effect of the data previously present in the selected cell. An externally applied active low write enable signal, $\overline{W}$, specifies the write operation. Regardless of any other activity, every storage cell must be *refreshed* at least once every few milliseconds. This can be achieved by ensuring that every row in each half of the array is accessed at least this often. During each row access, the sense amplifiers perform their function of regenerating stored signal levels. The digital timing and control functions needed to perform the refresh functions can be provided by additional hardware on the memory board or by additional software executed by the central processing unit. Most systems (but not all) can be designed to allow the necessary refresh cycles without serious effects.

Dynamic RAMs derive the signals needed to perform these dynamic functions from two externally generated timing signals, known as the *row address strobe (RAS)* and *column address strobe (CAS)*. The complements of these signals, known as $\overline{RAS}$ (RAS bar) and $\overline{CAS}$ (CAS bar), are actually applied to the component pins. Complete specification of the read cycle timing relationships involves many timing parameters, all of which must be held within specified limits to ensure proper operation. Write cycle timing is similarly complex. Data sheets and application notes are the best source of detailed information for any particular component.

9.5 Read-Only Memories

Since we have reduced the memory cell contents to a single transistor in the DRAM, it is appropriate to examine other types of memory that contain only one cell transistor. These are collectively referred to as *nonvolatile* memory because they store values in the cells permanently, or at least semipermanently. The first memory in this category is the read-only memory or ROM. This type of memory is used to store constants, control information, and program instructions (*firmware*) in digital systems. ROMs may be thought of as components that provide a fixed, specified binary output for every binary input. In principle, the values are considered to be permanent and therefore do not expect to be changed after they are initially specified. In this section, we will study the internal circuits in the basic ROMs and then follow up with a look at other types of memories that can be reprogrammed to store new data.

9.5.1 MOS ROM Cell Arrays

The ROM architecture is constructed from the intersection of a set of wordlines and bitlines. A bit is stored in a ROM by the presence or absence of a transistor at the cross point. The absence of a path is achieved simply by having no circuit element

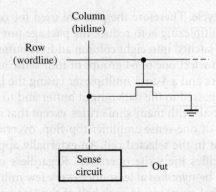

Figure 9.19
Basic ROM cell.

joining row and column. Figure 9.19 shows a single ROM cell with the gate attached to the wordline and the drain attached to the bitline. If the transistor is present at this cross point, it will pull the bitline low when the wordline goes high. However, if it is absent, the bitline will remain at its precharged voltage. This is the key concept in single transistor ROMs and provides the high density levels of the DRAM. This is different from DRAM cells since a transistor is present in every DRAM cell position and its operation relies mainly on charge sharing. In the case of the ROM, the cell may or may not contain a transistor and does require a capacitor for data storage.

Figure 9.20 shows the two basic forms of MOS ROM cell arrays: NOR arrays and NAND arrays. In each array, bits are stored according to the presence or absence of a transistor switch at each row-column intersection. The NMOS array of Figure 9.20a implements the NOR function in the sense that each column is one big NOR gate. A column goes low when any row, joined to the column with a transistor, is raised to a high level. In normal operation, all but one row line is held low. When a selected wordline is raised to V_{DD}, all transistors present in that row are turned on. The columns to which they are connected are pulled low. The remaining columns with transistors missing in their respective rows are held high by the pull-up or load devices shown at the top in this example. Column selection is performed using a decoder/MUX combination that enables a pass transistor in the data path.

ROMs of this type can be programmed by adjusting the contents of the masks, the so-called *mask-programmable* ROMs. Using positive logic, a stored "1" is defined as the absence of a transistor and a stored "0" by the presence of a transistor. Usually the array is formed with transistors at every row-column intersection. The desired bit pattern is placed in the array by omitting the drain or source connection at locations where a "1" is desired. Alternatively, a threshold implant can be used to raise the threshold voltage well above normal levels to "remove" a transistor from the array.

The array shown in Figure 9.20b is called a NAND ROM since each column forms one big NAND gate. The column output goes low only when all series bit

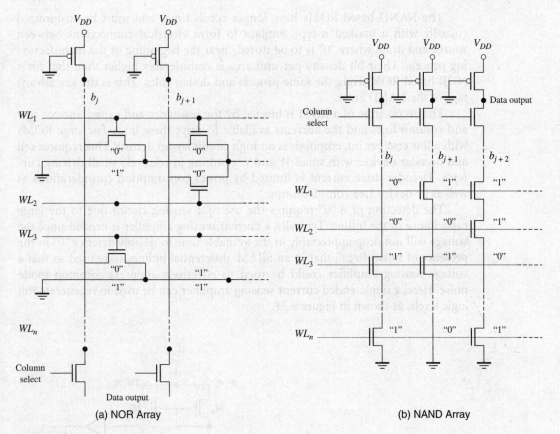

(a) NOR Array   **(b) NAND Array**

Figure 9.20
Alternative ROM array configurations.

locations provide a conducting path toward ground. In the NAND case, all the wordlines are normally held at V_{DD} in the standby condition. The selected row line is *pulled low*, and all transistors with gates connected to that line will turn off. The data output is taken at the top. In positive logic, a stored "1" is defined as the presence of a transistor, while a stored "0" is achieved with a direct connection (i.e., short) in place of the transistor. The array is formed with transistors at every intersection, but the source-drain paths of transistors at the desired "0" locations are shorted out by an implant or diffusion. Column selection transistors are placed in series with the bits to limit power dissipation.

The NOR array usually exhibits a faster access time and has the advantage that the stored bit pattern can be determined by the mask defining contacts to the transistors or the metal interconnection layer. Therefore, these ROMs may be kept in inventory with most of the fabrication processing completed, then customized quickly to a particular bit pattern by preparing and using a mask that makes contact only to transistors at 0-bit locations.

The NAND-based ROMs have longer access times and must be customized (usually with a masked n-type implant to form electrical connections between source and drain where "0" is to be stored) near the beginning of the manufacturing process. Their bit density per unit area is considerably higher than that for a NOR-based ROM using the same process and design rules. This is the key advantage of the NAND array.

The access time of a ROM is limited by the resistance and capacitance of row and column lines and the currents available to drive these lines. For large ROMs with a low cost per bit, emphasis is on high circuit layout density. This requires cell and decoder devices with small W and L, resulting in relatively small driving currents. Decoder drive current is limited by power consumption considerations as well as by device area considerations.

The detection of a "0" requires the use of a sensing circuit due to the large capacitance of the bitline. Typically, a current sensing amplifier is needed since the voltage will not drop appreciably in the available time to reliably detect a "0" in the presence of noise. Recall that in an SRAM, differential bitlines were used so that a voltage sensing amplifier could be used to effectively suppress common-mode noise. Here, a single-ended current sensing amplifier can be used to regenerate full logic levels, as shown in Figure 9.21.

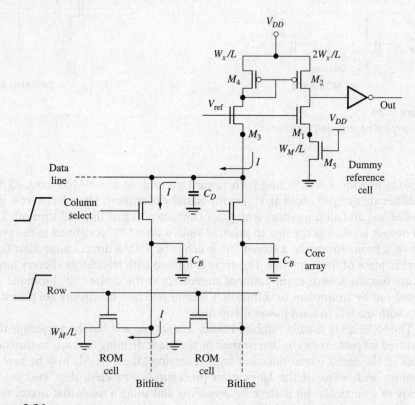

Figure 9.21

Current sensing amplifier.

The amplifier consists of a current mirror load for a common-gate amplifier controlled by a voltage, V_{ref}. When a row line selects a cell, current begins to flow in that cell. With the column select line high, this current flows from the data line capacitance and pulls the line down slightly. This turns on transistor M_3 and, as a result, current flows through M_4. This current is mirrored and doubled in M_2 since it is twice as large as M_4. Half of this current flows through M_1 while the rest flows to the gate of the inverter to charge up its input. Finally, node *Out* is discharged to zero. Hence, the presence of a transistor produces 0 V at the output.

If the transistor were not present in the ROM cell, no current would flow in the left branch of the amplifier. Therefore, M_4 and M_2 would have no current flowing through them. However, since V_{ref} keeps M_1 on, when M_5 turns on, the input of the inverter is pulled low. Therefore, its output is high. Hence, the absence of the transistor implies a 1 at the output. The dummy transistor, M_5, represents the cell transistor. In reality, the dummy cell is much more complicated than a single transistor since it must track process and operating condition variations that are experienced by the ROM cell transistor. However, it is shown as a single device connected to V_{DD} for simplicity.

9.6 EPROMs and E²PROMs

There are many applications where it is necessary to reprogram the ROM from time to time. For this purpose, the memory cell must be made erasable in some manner and then rewritable. This is not possible in conventional mask-programmable ROMs, but there are other more flexible ROM cells that are appropriate. This section describes two such memories: the EPROM and E²PROM.

The most widely used form of erasable and programmable ROM (EPROM) relies on a special MOS device structure shown in Figure 9.22a. Two layers of polysilicon form a double gate; gate 1 is a *floating gate* that has no electrical contact, while gate 2 is the *control gate* used to apply an external gate voltage. A circuit equivalent for the structure, with critical capacitances drawn, and its corresponding circuit symbol are provided in Figure 9.22b.

Initially, assume no charge on gate 1 or gate 2 and that the drain and source are connected to Gnd. As V_{G2} is increased, V_{G1} also rises but at a lower rate as determined by the capacitive divider. The effect of the series capacitances should be familiar from the bootstrapping and feedthrough concepts of Chapter 7. From Figure 9.22b, the series capacitance gives rise to the following relationship:

$$\Delta V_{G1} = \frac{C_2 \Delta V_{G2}}{C_1 + C_2}$$

$$\therefore V_{G1,new} = V_{G1,old} + \frac{C_2(V_{G2,new} - V_{G2,old})}{C_1 + C_2} \tag{9.1}$$

Since the transistor uses V_{G1} as its gate-source voltage, the control gate 2 must be made higher than usual to turn on the device. If V_T is the nominal threshold voltage of the device, it is not sufficient to make $V_{G2} > V_T$ to turn on the device. In

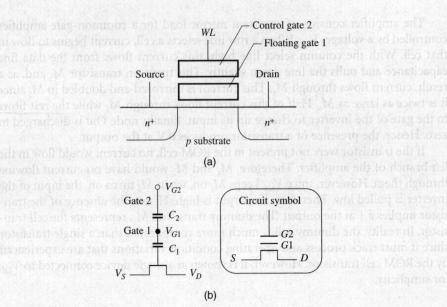

Figure 9.22
EPROM cell structure.

fact, we must make $V_{G1} > V_T$. Using this criteria and Equation (9.1), it is possible to determine the required voltage at V_{G2} to turn on the device. Assuming that all voltages initially start at 0 V, we require that

$$V_{G1} \geq V_T$$

$$\therefore V_{G1} = \frac{C_2 V_{G2}}{C_1 + C_2} \geq V_T$$

$$\therefore V_{G2} \geq \frac{(C_1 + C_2) V_T}{C_1}$$

Clearly, the voltage at V_{G2} must be higher than V_T by a factor of $(C_1 + C_2)/C_1$ so that V_{G1} exceeds the threshold voltage of the device to turn it on. Seen from external gate 2, the effective threshold voltage of the device has been increased.

The EPROM uses this feature to define the notion of a stored "0" and stored "1." The key is to program the value of the initial voltage of gate 1, called $V_{G1,old}$ in Equation (9.1), so that the external threshold voltage appears to be modified. If we can lower initial gate voltage at V_{G1} to some suitable negative value, then a nominal V_{DD} value at V_{G2} would not be able to turn on the device. From Equation (9.1), if $V_{G1,old}$ is negative then $V_{G1,new}$ will not be above V_T. This would be a stored "1." If we program V_{G1} to 0 V, then when $V_{G2} = V_{DD}$, the device would turn on as usual. This

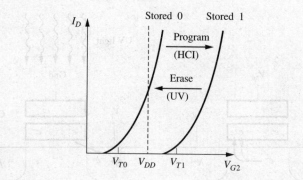

Figure 9.23

V_T adjustment when programming and erasing EPROM device.

would be considered a stored "0" as it would discharge the bitline like any other ROM cell.

The proper operation of this EPROM cell relies on the ability to store and remove charge from the internal floating gate. When programming the cell, we inject electrons through the oxide to the floating gate. From the perspective of gate 2, lowering the internal voltage is equivalent to raising the threshold voltage of this transistor from its initial value, V_{T0}, to a new value of V_{T1}. This is shown in Figure 9.23 in the plot of I_D versus V_{G2}. After programming, the effective threshold voltage is V_{T1}. When $V_{G2} = V_{DD}$, the device remains *off* because the voltage does not exceed V_{T1}. Since the device does not discharge the bitline, it is interpreted as a stored "1." To erase the cell, we must somehow remove the stored charge thereby increasing the internal voltage and reducing the effective threshold back to V_{T0}. When V_{DD} is applied at the gate in normal operation, the device will turn *on*.

To write a "1" in this cell, we use a mechanism called *hot-electron* injection. To initiate this mechanism, both gate 2 and the drain are raised well above 5 V while source and substrate remain grounded. A relatively large drain current flows due to normal device conduction characteristics. The high field in the drain-substrate depletion region results in an avalanche breakdown of the drain-substrate junction, with a considerable additional flow of current. The field accelerates electrons to high velocity, at which point they are referred to as *hot carriers*. A fraction of these carriers are injected into the thin oxide and become trapped on gate 1, as shown in Figure 9.24a. This so-called hot-carrier injection (HCI) reduces the internal node voltage until the vertical field is no longer sufficient to generate hot carriers—in this sense, it is a self-limiting process. When gate 2 and drain potentials are forced back to zero, the negative charge remains on gate 1 and forces its potential to a negative value through the capacitive feedthrough process. If V_{G2} for reading is limited to a few volts, a channel never forms since V_{G2} does not exceed V_{T1}. Thus, a logic "1" is stored in the cell as shown in Figure 9.23.

Once programmed, the data is preserved even if the power is turned off. Gate 1 is completely surrounded by silicon dioxide (SiO_2), an excellent insulator, so charge can be stored for many years. Data may be erased, however, by exposing the cells to

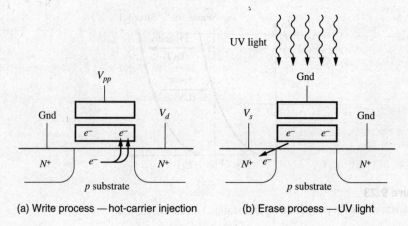

(a) Write process — hot-carrier injection   (b) Erase process — UV light

Figure 9.24
E^2PROM write/erase process.

strong ultraviolet (UV) light, as illustrated in Figure 9.24b. The *UV radiation* renders the SiO_2 slightly conductive by direct generation of hole-electron pairs in this material. With proper transistor biasing, the store charge can be removed. Unfortunately, these EPROMs must be assembled in packages with transparent covers so that they may be exposed to UV radiation. As such, these devices are only suitable as stand-alone parts. For embedded applications, other alternatives such as E^2PROMs and Flash memories must be considered.

Example 9.4

EPROM Programming

Problem:

An EPROM with a threshold voltage of 1 V relative to gate 1 starts with the floating gate voltage at 0 V as shown in (a). What is the threshold voltage relative to gate 2? An external voltage of 10 V is applied. The internal node voltage reaches 5 V since the two series capacitances have the same value as shown in (b). After hot-carrier injection, the internal node reduces to 2 V as shown in (c). Will this device turn on if an external voltage at gate node 2 is 5 V? If not, at what external voltage will it turn on?

(a) Initial state   (b) After applying 10 V   (c) After programming

Solution:

The V_T relative to gate 2 is 2 V based on the capacitive divider equation. After programming, when the external voltage is returned to 0 V, the internal voltage will drop to -3 V. When 5 V is applied, the internal voltage will reach -0.5 V which means that the device is off. To reach 1 V at the internal node, the external node will have to rise to 8 V. Therefore, the new threshold voltage relative to gate 2 is 8 V. Relative to Figure 9.23, $V_{T0} = 2$ V and $V_{T1} = 8$ V.

Electrically erasable PROMs (EEPROMs or E²PROMs) employ a somewhat different structure and mechanism for writing and erasing. The two-transistor (2T) structure for an E²PROM cell is shown in Figure 9.25. Since each cell requires two transistors, the bit density is lower than regular ROMs or EPROMs. In E²PROM cells, one transistor stores the content of the cell while the other is used for cell selection. The selection transistor has a normal gate oxide thickness. The storage transistor looks like the EPROM cell except that it has two oxide thicknesses. As seen in Figure 9.25, a portion of the dielectric separating gate 1 from body and drain is reduced in thickness to a value 10 nm or below. This is referred to as a *floating gate tunneling oxide* (FLOTOX) structure.

When approximately 10 V is applied across this thin dielectric, electrons flow to/from gate 1 by a conduction mechanism known as Fowler-Nordheim (FN) tunneling. That is, when the electric field across the oxide exceeds 10^7 V/cm, current flow through the oxide is possible using tunneling. The current due to tunneling increases linearly with the applied voltage, as indicated in Figure 9.26, and this mechanism is reversible. Therefore, erasure is achieved simply by reversing the applied voltage. The effect of injecting electrons into the floating gate is the same as before: the effective threshold voltage increases. Therefore, a normal voltage level applied at the gate of the FLOTOX device does not turn on the device after programming. If electrons are removed from the floating gate in the reverse process, the effective threshold voltage is reduced. At typical high gate voltage levels, the device will turn on.

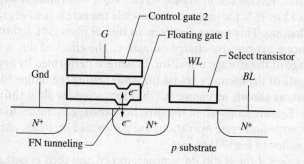

Figure 9.25
E²PROM 2T structure.

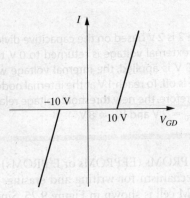

Figure 9.26
Fowler-Nordheim tunneling characteristic for 10 nm oxide.

Unfortunately, the tunneling mechanism is not self-limiting like HCI. A problem occurs if too much charge is removed during erasure. The V_T may go below 0 V to effectively create a device that does not turn off even when 0 V is applied at the gate. The reason for the select device is that the threshold voltage is difficult to control precisely since it depends on variations in the fabrication process and on the initial charge stored on the floating gate. If the desired internal voltage levels cannot be reached reliably due to initial stored charge, then the memory cell will not function properly. To avoid this problem, a select transistor is placed in series with the FLOTOX transistor and connected to the wordline and bitline. The select transistor uses the normal wordline voltage levels, whereas the FLOTOX transistor has an appropriate gate voltage that sits between the two possible thresholds, as shown in Figure 9.23. This way, the proper gate voltage can be selected after fabrication to ensure reliable operation.

The arrangement of eight E²PROM cells in an array is shown in Figure 9.27 using the 2T cells of Figure 9.25. The wordline drives the selection transistors while a separate control is used for the gate of the storage transistors. Consider the write operation for an E²PROM cell in Figure 9.27a. When a wordline is selected, the bitline is raised to 12 to 15 V for programming while the gate is held at ground and the source is left floating. This forces electrons to tunnel from gate 1 through the thin oxide to produce a net positive charge on gate 1. The effect of this is to reduce the threshold voltage of the storage transistor. Erasure is performed by applying a large voltage at the gate of the memory transistor while setting the bitline to 0 and letting the source float, as shown in Figure 9.27b. Electrons now flow through the thin oxide to gate 1. Erasure stops when the threshold voltage increases to a value above V_{DD}. Typically, write and erase operations are performed on bytes, although bit-by-bit access is possible in E²PROMs.

One issue arises if the E²PROM is programmed and then erased on a frequent basis. The two threshold voltages of Figure 9.23 begin to shift towards each other. In fact, after one million write/erase cycles or more, the difference in the two threshold voltages is too small to be of value in this application. E²PROMs require thresholds

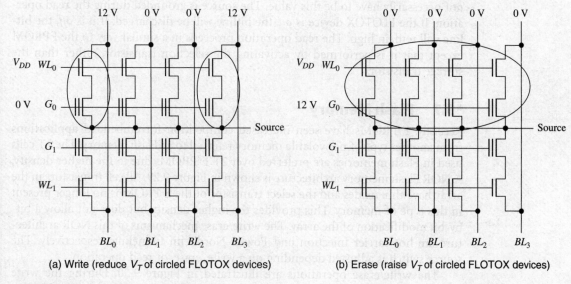

(a) Write (reduce V_T of circled FLOTOX devices)   (b) Erase (raise V_T of circled FLOTOX devices)

Figure 9.27
E^2PROM array configurations for write/erase operations.

that are well separated as in Figure 9.23. Therefore, these devices are suitable only for 10^5–10^6 write/erase cycles before reliability becomes a problem.

To read from the array, the wordline for the select transistor is raised while the gate drive of the FLOTOX transistor is held at a constant voltage. This is illustrated in Figure 9.28. Here we assume that the FLOTOX gate drive is V_{DD}, although it does

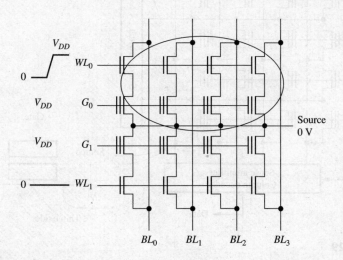

Figure 9.28
E^2PROM read operation.

not necessarily have to be this value. The source is grounded during the read operation. If the FLOTOX device is *on*, the bitline will be discharged. If it is *off*, the bitline will remain high. The read operation proceeds in a similar way to the EPROM except that it is performed by activating the selection transistor, rather than the storage transistor.

*9.7 Flash Memory

Recently, E^{2}PROMs have seen increased competition for embedded applications from another type of nonvolatile memory referred to as *Flash* memory. The 1T cells used in Flash memories are preferred over 2T E^{2}PROMs due to the higher density. A NOR Flash memory architecture is shown in Figure 9.29. All cell transistors in the array have thin oxides and the select transistor of the E^{2}PROM is no longer present in this type of memory. This provides the higher density but does not allow a bit-by-bit modification of the array. The write/erase mechanisms of this NOR architecture are hot-carrier injection and Fowler-Nordheim tunneling, respectively. The source switch is adjusted depending on a write, erase, or read operation.

The write/erase operations are illustrated in Figure 9.30. During the write process, the source voltage is connected to Gnd as shown in Figure 9.30a. Then, a high value of V_d is applied to the selected bitline while a high value of V_{pp} is applied to the wordline. This creates channel hot carriers that enter the gate oxide and get trapped at the floating gate, thus raising the threshold voltage. This device will now

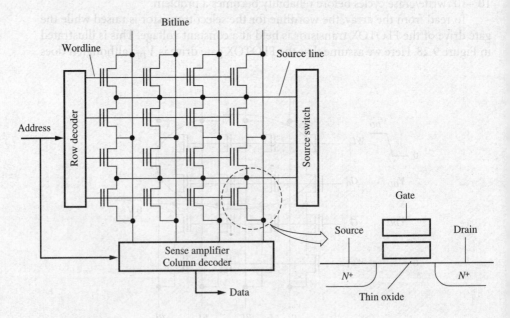

Figure 9.29
NOR Flash memory architecture.

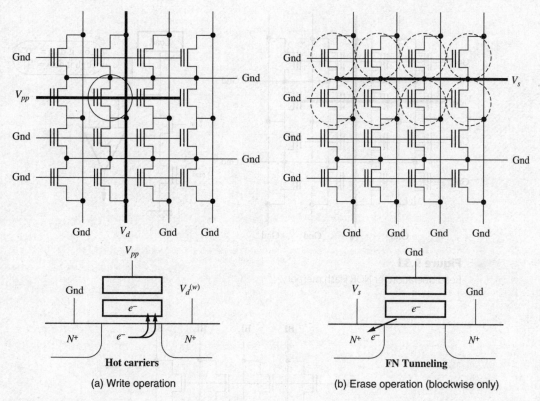

(a) Write operation

(b) Erase operation (blockwise only)

Figure 9.30
Write/erase operations of NOR Flash memory.

remain off even when the wordline is activated. Write operations can take place on a bit-by-bit basis. The erase operation requires the application of Gnd to the gate node and a high voltage of V_S to the source node. The erase mechanism is FN tunneling through the thin oxide. As shown in Figure 9.30b, the other transistors connected to the source connection are all erased as the same time, hence the term *Flash*. As such, erase operations are always carried out in block-mode in Flash memories.

The read operation is performed by applying Gnd to the source connection, precharging the bitline to V_d, and enabling the wordline with a voltage V_{read}. This is shown in Figure 9.31. The proper value of V_{read} must be selected to lie between the two thresholds of the device. If a drain current flows, then the bitline is discharged and interpreted as a stored "0." Otherwise, the bitline stays high and a "1" can be inferred. A sense amplifier needed for this type of memory is also shown in Figure 9.31.

A smaller and more dense Flash memory can be implemented if a NAND array is used, as illustrated in Figure 9.32. This type of memory uses FN tunneling for

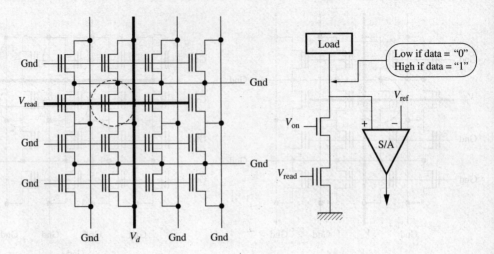

Figure 9.31
Read operation for NOR Flash memory.

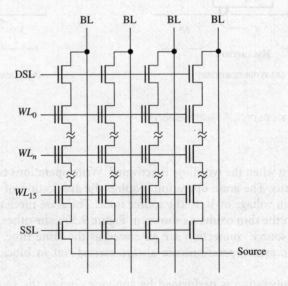

Figure 9.32
NAND Flash array.

write and erase which allows a much larger write/erase cycle limit, above 10^6 cycles. This is because programming using HCI damages the device more rapidly than programming with FN tunneling. The NAND Flash operates similar to the NAND ROM that was described earlier in this chapter. Wordlines are normally high, but one will go low when the decoder is activated. Programming is carried out by setting the V_T to a high value using FN tunneling. Memories with 2 Gbits of storage capacity have been developed using this architecture which has applications in mass storage, MP3 players, and digital cameras.

*9.8   FRAMs

There is another flavor of nonvolatile memory based on ferroelectric materials called *FRAMs*. Recently, FRAMs have been shown to be useful in certain applications such as smart cards and may be more attractive in the future due to their extremely high storage density. The FRAM cell, shown in Figure 9.33, is similar to the DRAM cell with one transistor and one capacitor. However, the capacitor is composed of a *Perovskite crystal* material that can be polarized in one direction or the other to store the desired value.

When an electric field is applied in one direction or the other, the crystals polarize and hold that state even when the power supply is removed, thereby creating a nonvolatile memory. The polarization characteristic, P, exhibits hysteresis, as shown in the curves in Figure 9.33, which allows the capacitor to retain the direction of polarization. During a write operation, a voltage is applied in one direction ($-V_{CC}$) to store a "0" and in the opposite polarity (V_{CC}) to store a "1."

When reading, the bitline is held high and the wordline is enabled. The current level associated with the cell depends on the direction of the stored polariziation, P_r. If the dipoles switch state due to the applied field, a high current is detected by a sense amplifier. Otherwise, the current level is lower. Unfortunately, during the read process, the stored value of the cell is disturbed. That is, FRAMs also have a *destructive read-out*. Therefore, the value must be read and then written back into the cell similar to DRAM cells.

FRAMs require much less power and provide high density. The other notable feature of FRAMs is that they can endure hundreds of billions of read/write cycles

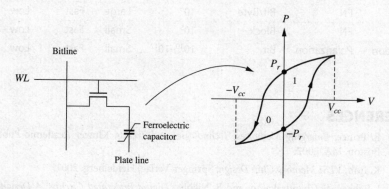

Figure 9.33
FRAM cell and polarization characteristic.

before reliability becomes an issue. In this respect, they are superior to all of the other nonvolatile memories discussed in this chapter. However, semiconductor memories are preferred over ferroelectric memories for most applications because of their advantages in cost, operating speed, and physical size.

9.9 Summary

A summary of the different types of semiconductor memories covered in Chapters 8 and 9 are shown below:

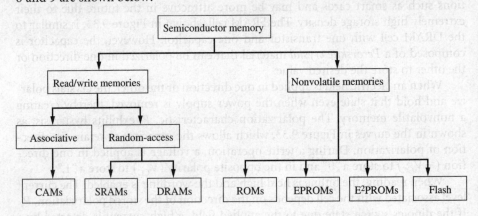

A summary of programmable nonvolatile memories is given in Table 9.1.

Table 9.1
Summary of programmable nonvolatile memories

Memory	Program Type	Erase Type	Erase Resolution	Cycles	Cell Size	Speed	Power
EPROM	HCI	UV	Full Memory	10^2	Small	Fast	High
E²PROM	FN	FN	Bit/Byte	10^6	Large	Fast	Low
Flash	HCI/FN	FN	Block	10^5	Small	Fast	Low
FRAM	Polarization	Polarization	Bit	10^{10}–10^{12}	Small	Fast	Low

REFERENCES

1. B. Prince, *Emerging Memories: Technologies and Trends,* Kluwer Academic Publishers, Boston, MA, 2002.

2. K. Itoh, *VLSI Memory Chip Design,* Springer-Verlag, Heidelberg, 2001.

3. J. Rabaey, A. Chandrakasan, and B. Nikolic, *Digital Integrated Circuits: A Designer Perspective,* Second Edition, Prentice-Hall, Upper Saddle River, NJ, 2003.

4. S. Trimberger, *Field-Programmable Gate Array Technology,* Kluwer Academic Publishers, Boston, MA, 1994.

5. V. Betz, J. Rose, and A. Marquardt, *Architecture and CAD for Deep-Submicron FPGAs*, Kluwer Academic Publishers, Boston, MA, 1999.

6. H. Veendrick, *Deep-Submicron CMOS ICs*, Second Edition, Kluwer Academic Publishers, Boston, MA, 2000.

PROBLEMS

P9.1. In the CAM design of Figure 9.3, the taglines are first precharged low and then the matchline is precharged high. Why are the tag lines precharged low rather than high? Why are they precharged low before the matchline is precharged high?

P9.2. You want to build a CAM cell with fewer transistors and one of your fellow designers comes up with the two designs shown in Figure P9.2. Which one do you prefer and why?

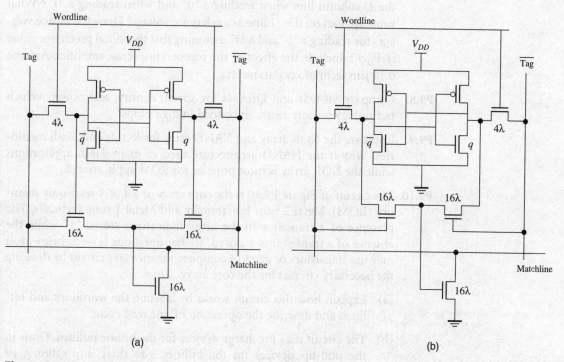

Figure P9.2

P9.3. Using the CAM cell of Problem P9.2(a), estimate the worst-case match-line delay. Assume that the CAM array portion is 33 cells across × 128 cells vertically. The cells are each 50λ wide by 80λ high. Identify the worst-case delay condition in the array. Then, compute the tagline capacitance and matchline capacitances in detail. Assume that the input capacitance for the first tagline driver is 3 fF. Next, compute the tagline and matchline delays. Use 0.18 μm technology parameters.

P9.4. Redesign the transistor sizes for the CAM cell in Figure 9.5 to minimize the tagline and matchline delays. All transistors should be the same size. Use 0.18 μm technology parameters.

P9.5. Design a replica circuit for the CAM described in the problem above, assuming that the overall architecture is given in Figure 9.4. Describe the considerations in constructing an effective replica for this architecture.

P9.6. Consider the FPGA architecture shown in Figure 9.10. How would you implement a 4-input logic function in this array? Note that the PLBs contain 3-LUTs, not 4-LUTs so your function must span at least two PLBs.

P9.7. For the dynamic RAM cell shown in Figure 9.16, what value appears on the D column line when reading a "0" and when reading a "1"? What value appears on the $\bar{D}$ line as a reference voltage? Draw the bitline voltages for reading a "0" and a "1" assuming that the initial precharge value is $V_{DD}/2$. Include the effect of the regenerative sense amplifier. Assume 0.18 μm technology parameters.

P9.8. Compare SRAMs and DRAMs for speed, density, and power. Which technology is more easily embedded in logic chips?

P9.9. Compare the NOR array and NAND array for ROMs and Flash memories. Why is the NAND architecture used in many Flash applications while the NOR array is most popular for ROM applications?

P9.10. The circuit of Figure P9.10 is the core array of a 4 × 4 read-only memory (ROM). Metal 2 runs horizontally and Metal 1 runs vertically. The presence of a transistor in the array indicates a stored "1" while the absence of a transistor is a stored "0." For questions (a)–(d) below, you may use transistors or gates to complete the memory circuit by drawing the necessary circuits for the core array.

(a) Explain how this circuit works by labeling the wordlines and bitlines, and describe the operation of one read cycle.

(b) The circuit uses precharge devices for the bitline pullups. Draw in the pull-up devices on the bitlines. Are there any ratioing or charge-sharing issues to worry about? If so, explain. If not, why not?

(c) The circuit wordlines are to be controlled by a decoder circuit. Draw the appropriate decoder circuits using gates (not transistors) with the appropriate clock qualification. Why do we need the wordline to be driven by a qualified clock (i.e., ANDed with the clock signal)?

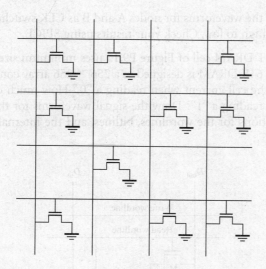

Figure P9.10

(d) The output of this circuit is a single bit from the bitlines (i.e., a bit addressable ROM). Draw a multiplexer circuit to select one bitline using transistors and gates to accomplish this on the diagram. Ensure that there is no V_T loss in the output and use any inverters/buffers that you need to produce the correct value at the output. Should we use qualified clock signal here? Why or why not?

P9.11. Explain why the select transistor is needed in an E^2PROM cell? How does the EPROM cell avoid the need for this extra transistor?

P9.12. Consider the charge pump circuit shown in Figure P9.12 that is intended to generate a boosted wordline for a memory application. Assume that CLK is high initially and the output of the inverter is at Gnd. Also assume that node A is at $V_{DD} - V_T$ and node B is at Gnd.

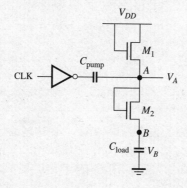

Figure P9.12

Draw the waveforms for nodes A and B as CLK switches back and forth from high to low. Check your results using SPICE.

P9.13. The 3T DRAM cell of Figure P9.13 uses minimum size devices. Assume that a 64K DRAM is designed in a 256 × 256 array configuration. Compute the cell current when reading a "0." How much cell current flows when reading a "1"? Draw the signal waveforms for the read and write operations for the wordlines, bitlines, and the internal node associated with C_1.

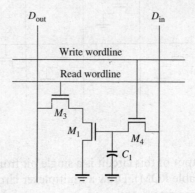

Figure P9.13

P9.14. Explain the difference between Fowler-Nordheim tunneling and hot-carrier injection. Which mechanism causes more damage to the oxide, and therefore limits the number of programs/erase cycles of nonvolatile memories?

Interconnect Design

10.1   Introduction

This chapter is devoted to the study of interconnect issues that the IC designer faces when designing in deep submicron technologies. The relative importance of interconnect in deep submicron cannot be overstated. In fact, the topic of interconnect should actually appear much earlier in the text to stress its importance, but it is more appropriate at this stage since the discussion of transistor level circuit design has been completed. Initial coverage of interconnect topics was provided in Chapters 1 and 3. This chapter addresses the issues associated with *RLC* aspects of wires in detail. We begin by reexamining the *RC* delay calculation using the Elmore delay, and address the issue of buffer insertion in long wires. Then, we examine the capacitances associated with 3D interconnect. This topic is rather complex but we provide a simplified treatment to convey the most important concepts. This leads to a discussion of the effect of coupling capacitance on delay and noise injection in logic circuits. The chapter continues with a discussion of inductance effects and concludes with a brief look at antenna effects.

"Interconnect is everything" was an often-used expression starting in the mid-1990s to characterize the importance of interconnect in deep submicron technologies.

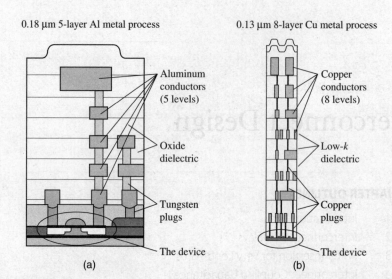

Figure 10.1
Cross sections of aluminum and copper processes.

While device sizes were shrinking with each technology generation, multilevel metal structures rose higher and higher above the surface of the silicon and soon began to dominate the landscape of the integrated circuit. This is illustrated in the cross-sectional views of 0.18 μm aluminum and 0.13 μm copper technologies in Figure 10.1. The number of layers of metal has increased from a few layers in the 1980s, to four or five layers in the 1990s, to eight or more layers today. The fabrication of these superstructures required significant advances in integrated circuit processing. However, the impact on design was even more significant. Suddenly, interconnect controlled timing, power, noise, design functionality, and reliability. It controlled all of these important electrical characteristics on the chip, even though the tiny devices (buried under a multilevel structure of wires and vias) defined the actual logic functions. Today interconnect still controls the design process in advanced technologies and will continue to do so for the foreseeable future.

The dimensions associated with a cross section of interconnect are shown in Figure 10.2. The rectangular wires are W wide and T thick, as shown. The separation between layers is a distance H (insulator thickness), and from other conductors is a distance S. The length of the wire, L, is shown only for Metal 2. The Metal 1 wires run into the page and so their lengths are not shown. It is important to realize that the vertical dimensions $H1$, $T1$, $H2$, and $T2$ are determined during the fabrication process. The designer has no control over these quantities. On the other hand, the horizontal dimensions $W1$, $S1$, $L1$, $L2$, etc. are all under the control of the designer.

There are a number of reasons to emphasize the importance of interconnect. First, as the width W of wires is decreased, the resistance increases. This increase in wire resistance causes an RC delay phenomenon that had not been experienced before

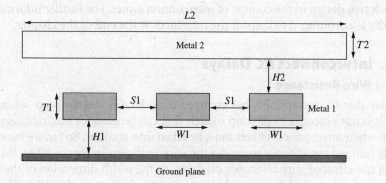

Figure 10.2
Wire dimensions for resistance and capacitance calculations.

1990. By the mid-1990s, a noticeable increase in wire delay led to widespread concern that it would soon be greater than gate delay. Second, the spacing S between wires has been decreasing to the point where the coupling between wires is significant. The resulting capacitive coupling introduces additional delay and noise effects that can cause failures in the design, requiring respins of silicon[1] in order to fix the problem. The overall term for all these problems is *signal integrity*. Recent issues of inductance in wires have been included in the growing list of signal integrity problems.

Other problems have surfaced due to the scaling of interconnect. The increase in resistance in the power supply lines due to scaling causes voltage drop along interconnect, referred to as *IR drop*. This affects the timing and functionality of gates connected to the power lines if the drop becomes too significant. A similar issue concerns the *Ldi/dt* drop in the power grid due to inductance. Still other effects such as charge storage on metal lines during manufacture, called *antenna effects*, lead to gate oxide breakdown or a threshold voltage shift. Further reliability problems exist due to the migration of the aluminum or copper material in the wires as high levels of current flow through them. Eventually, cracks and other imperfections in the metal cause material erosion until opens or shorts occur. This phenomenon is called *electromigration*, a long-term reliability issue.

Indeed, interconnect is more important than devices in many respects. This chapter and the next should be studied carefully as they contain valuable information pertaining to interconnect design issues. The material on interconnect in the open literature is rather extensive. Our purpose here is to convey the major issues and provide useful insight into the design methods to circumvent these issues. This chapter considers resistance, coupling capacitance, and inductance effects on delay and noise. Antenna effects are also described. The next chapter considers power grid

---

[1] A spin of silicon is the process of designing a chip and then having it fabricated. When errors are found in the design after fabrication, the whole process must be repeated. This is a very expensive and time-consuming exercise. Often several "spins of silicon" are needed to produce a working design for large complex chips.

and clock tree design in the context of interconnect issues. For further information, the reader is encouraged to consult the references at the end of the chapter.

10.2 Interconnect *RC* Delays

10.2.1 Wire Resistance

The delay due to interconnect has changed considerably due to deep submicron effects. It is our objective to develop models that can be used for accurate delay calculation when interconnect effects must be taken into account. So far, we have used a simple lumped capacitance to model the wire as shown in Figure 10.3a. We now consider the effect of wire resistance on delay. As the width dimension of the wires is reduced, the increased resistance has a pronounced effect on the delay. This was first observed at the 0.8 μm technology node at a number of semiconductor companies, but became a widespread issue at the 0.35 μm technology node. The interconnect model shown in Figure 10.3b is required when interconnect resistance is important.

The resistance of a material is given by

$$R = \frac{\rho L}{A} = \frac{\rho L}{TW} \tag{10.1}$$

where ρ is the resistivity of the material in Ω-cm, L is the length of the wire, T is the thickness of the wire, and W is the wire width. The leading term in Equation (10.1) is an important one:

$$R_{sq} = \frac{\rho}{T} \tag{10.2}$$

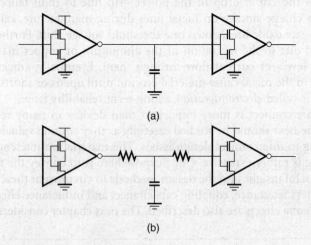

(a)

(b)

Figure 10.3

(a) Lump capacitance model. (b) *RC* interconnect model.

where R_{sq} is the *sheet resistance* of the material and has the units of *ohms per square* ($\Omega/\square$). The sheet resistance of any metal layer can readily be computed from the resistivity and the thickness, T. To keep resistance relatively low in each technology generation, the thickness has not been scaled at the same rate as the minimum line width. However, the thickness of the metal lines will vary, depending on the metal layer. To simplify our description, we assume that two different thicknesses are used, one for the lower layers and one for the upper layers. Because the upper layers carry much larger currents over longer distances, they require a lower resistance, and therefore a higher thickness.

The two most common materials for interconnect are aluminum, with $\rho = 2.7\ \mu\Omega$-cm, and copper, with $\rho = 1.7\ \mu\Omega$-cm.[2] The metal hierarchies for a 0.18 μm aluminum process and a 0.13 μm copper process were shown in Figure 10.1. The approximate sheet resistances for a 0.18 μm, 5-layer aluminum process assuming that metals 1 to 4 have a thickness of 0.5 μm and metal 5 has a thickness of 1.0 μm are as follows:

$$R_{sq} = \frac{\rho}{T} = \frac{2.7\ \mu\Omega\text{-cm}}{0.5\ \mu\text{m}} = 54\ \text{m}\Omega/\square \quad \text{Al} \quad \text{metals 1–4}$$

$$R_{sq} = \frac{\rho}{T} = \frac{2.7\ \mu\Omega\text{-cm}}{1.0\ \mu\text{m}} = 27\ \text{m}\Omega/\square \quad \text{Al} \quad \text{metal 5}$$

(10.3)

The approximate sheet resistances for a 0.13 μm, 8-layer copper process assuming that metals 1–6 have a thickness of 0.4 μm and metals 7–8 have a thickness of 0.8 μm are as follows:

$$R_{sq} = \frac{\rho}{T} = \frac{1.7\mu\Omega\text{-cm}}{0.4\ \mu\text{m}} = 42\ \text{m}\Omega/\square \quad \text{Cu} \quad \text{metals 1–6}$$

$$R_{sq} = \frac{\rho}{T} = \frac{1.7\mu\Omega\text{-cm}}{0.8\ \mu\text{m}} = 21\ \text{m}\Omega/\square \quad \text{Cu} \quad \text{metals 7–8}$$

(10.4)

Given these parameters, the actual resistance of a segment of wire is:

$$R = R_{sq}\left(\frac{L}{W}\right)$$

(10.5)

The ratio of L/W is referred to as the *number of squares* of wire. It is the aspect ratio of the wire in terms of length and width. Designers count squares of interconnect as a way of obtaining a relative resistance value for a wire since R_{sq} is fixed for a given technology. As we know by now, the number of squares of resistance has continued to increase over the years since L is increasing and W is decreasing for the longest wires on the chip. Therefore, these are the wires that cause significant RC delay problems.

---

[2] As a point of comparison, tungsten plugs have a much higher resistivity of 5.5 $\mu\Omega$-cm.

10.2.2   Elmore Delay Calculation

In long wires, the increased resistance presents a distributed RC load to a driving gate, as shown in Figure 10.4. For simplicity, the driver is represented as an ideal voltage source. The distributed RC line has been converted to a lumped RC ladder structure with n segments. The total resistance for the line is the sum of all the individual resistances, $R_{wire} = nR_W$. The same holds for the total capacitance, $C_{wire} = nC_W$.

The wire capacitance in the delay calculation is computed using the capacitance per unit length of interconnect, C_{int}. In modern technologies, there are multiple levels of metal and each one has a different C_{int}. In fact, as we shall see later, interconnect capacitance is distributed in nature and highly dependent on the layout. Today, there is more coupling capacitance between lines than there is capacitance to ground. For the moment, we use an average capacitance value and assume that all layers have the same C_{int} for hand calculations. The effective wire capacitance for metal interconnect is $C_{int} = 0.2$ fF/μm for densely packed lines (3–4λ apart) and of the order of $C_{int} = 0.1$ fF/μm for loosely packed lines (30–40λ apart). We will often use $C_{int} = 0.2$ fF/μm for the capacitance for an interconnect line to be somewhat pessimistic.

To determine the delay of an RC ladder, consider an aluminum wire in 0.18 μm technology. Assume a wire width of $W = 0.4$ μm, and $C_{int} = 0.2$ fF/μm and $R_{sq} = 0.054$ $\Omega/\square$. Then for a length of wire 1mm, the total resistance is $R_{wire} = 0.054$ $\Omega/\square$ $\times$ 1000/0.4 = 125 Ω and the total capacitance is $C_{wire} = 0.2$ fF/μm $\times$ 1000 μm = 200 fF. It is tempting to compute the total RC delay as $0.7\, R_{wire}C_{wire} = (0.7)125$ $\Omega \times$ 200 fF = 17.5 ps. However, the actual delay is closer to 10 ps. Clearly, we need an accurate way to compute the delay of such RC ladders.

By multiplying R_{wire} and C_{wire} together, we assumed that the response was exponential in nature, as shown in Figure 10.5a. In actual fact, the response of a distributed RC line is given in the graph of Figure 10.5b. The key to developing a convenient way of computing the delay for a ladder network is to examine the area under the two graphs and establish a relationship between the two responses.

The area underneath the curve in Figure 10.5a is called the *first moment of the impulse response* and is given by

$$\text{Area} = \int_0^\infty e^{-t/RC}dt = R_{wire}C_{wire}$$

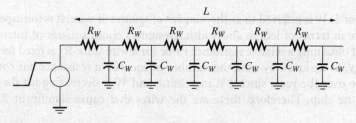

Figure 10.4

Distributed RC line as a lumped RC ladder.

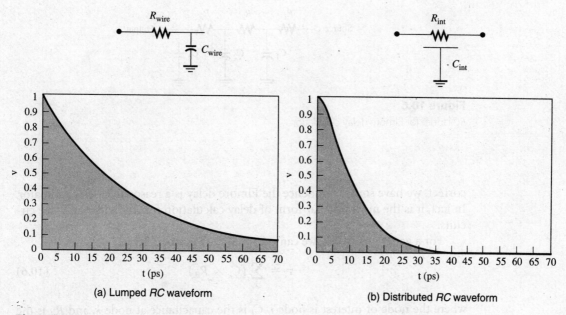

Figure 10.5
Lumped *RC* versus distributed *RC* output waveforms.

This gives us exactly the time constant for a lumped *RC* circuit. Apparently the area under the curve provides first-order delay information. If we apply this observation to the waveform for the distributed *RC* given by Figure 10.5b, we find that the area under this curve is some value which we call τ given by

$$\text{Area} = \int_0^\infty v(t)\,dt = \tau$$

This quantity is also the first moment of the impulse response but is more commonly referred to as the *Elmore delay* by circuit designers. It can be shown that this is the dominant time constant of the network and is a good estimate of the delay. While this value is difficult to compute in general, it is fairly straightforward for *RC* networks. The Elmore delay for an *RC* ladder involves visiting each node in the circuit and multiplying the capacitance at that node by the sum of all the resistances from the source node to the node being visited.

To further illustrate this procedure, consider the circuit in Figure 10.6. It has an Elmore delay of

$$\tau = R_1 C_1 + (R_1 + R_2)C_2 + (R_1 + R_2 + R_3)C_3$$

We can examine two extreme cases of this delay value to see if the Elmore delay is consistent. Specifically, if $C_1 = C_2 = 0$, then the Elmore delay and the *RC* time constant are equal to $(R_1 + R_2 + R_3)C_3$. Similarly if $R_2 = R_3 = 0$, then the Elmore delay and the *RC* time constant are both $R_1(C_1 + C_2 + C_3)$. Since both cases are

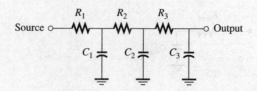

Figure 10.6

RC ladder for Elmore delay calculation.

correct, we have some confidence the Elmore delay is a reasonable delay estimator. In fact, it is the most popular form of delay calculation for *RC* ladder and tree circuits.

For a general network, we can compute the Elmore delay as

$$\tau_i = \sum_k \left(C_k \times R_{ik} \right) \tag{10.6}$$

where the node of interest is node *i*, C_k is the capacitance at node *k*, and R_{ik} is the sum of all the *resistances in common* from the source to node *i* and the source to node *k*. In other words, we visit each node and multiply the capacitance at that node by a resistance value that is the sum of the resistances that are common when we draw two paths: one from the source to node *i* and another from the source to node *k*. The process is best illustrated with an example.

Example 10.1

Elmore Delay of a Simple *RC* Tree

Problem:

Compute the Elmore delay from the input to nodes 1, 2, and 3 in the following *RC* tree. The Elmore delay is not accurate for internal nodes such as node 1. However, we are not usually interested in the delay from the input to an internal node in *RC* trees. In any case, write the expression for the time constant due to Elmore for each node.

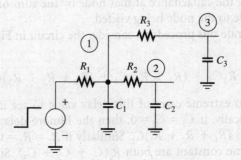

Solution:

$$\tau_1 = R_1C_1 + R_1C_2 + R_1C_3$$

$$\tau_2 = C_1R_1 + C_3R_1 + C_2(R_1 + R_2)$$

$$\tau_3 = C_1R_1 + C_2R_1 + C_3(R_1 + R_3)$$

10.2.3   *RC* Delay in Long Wires

For a long wire, we can compute the *RC* delay in terms of the total resistance and total capacitance. Consider Figure 10.4 once again. If the total wire length is L, and each segment is ΔL in length, then $L = n\Delta L$. For convenience, set the wire resistance per unit length to $R_{int} = r$ and the wire capacitance unit length to $C_{int} = c$. The total resistance is $R_{wire} = rL$ and the total capacitance is $C_{wire} = cL$. Using the Elmore delay calculation assuming n segments, we obtain

$$\tau_{Elmore} = (r\Delta L)(c\Delta L) + 2(r\Delta L)(c\Delta L) + \cdots + n(r\Delta L)(c\Delta L)$$

$$= (\Delta L)^2 rc(1 + 2 + \cdots + n)$$

$$= (\Delta L)^2 rc(n)(n+1)/2 \tag{10.7}$$

$$\approx (\Delta L)^2 rcn^2/2 = L^2rc/2 = R_{wire}C_{wire}/2$$

The actual propagation delay value is closer to $0.38R_{wire}C_{wire}$ which is slightly less than what Elmore predicts, so Elmore can be viewed as being somewhat pessimistic. Note that, according to Equation (10.7), the *delay increases as the square of the length.* This alerts us to the fact that long wires will create significant delays.

In practice, there must be a buffer or inverter driving the interconnect as shown in Figure 10.7. The driver can be represented as a source voltage and a source resistance. The source voltage is either Gnd or V_{DD} depending on the direction of the switching event. The source resistance is the on-resistance of the buffer.

We should always compute the total delay with the buffer attached to the interconnect. In addition, we must include all fanout loading capacitances on the interconnect for accurate delay estimation. To simplify the calculation, we replace the distributed *RC* line with a lumped *RC* model after computing R_{wire} and C_{wire} of the line. There are three forms of *RC* models as shown in Figure 10.8. While they all

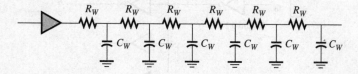

Figure 10.7
Driver and interconnect.

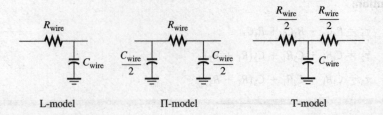

Figure 10.8

Three possible lumped RC models.

appear to be similar in form, they are not all suitable for the purposes of delay calculation. We can evaluate each one by computing its corresponding time constant.

First, the L-model produces a time constant of $R_{wire}C_{wire}$. We already know from Equation (10.7) that the delay should be $R_{wire}C_{wire}/2$ so this model should not be used. The second model is the π-model where the capacitance has been divided in half and assigned to the input and output. The time constant is $R_{wire}C_{wire}/2$. The third model is a T-model where the resistance has been divided in half and assigned to the input and output. Here, the time constant is also $R_{wire}C_{wire}/2$. Therefore, the L-model is not an accurate model for long distributed RC lines, whereas the π-model and the T-model produce the correct answer, so they are both suitable for the delay calculation. The T-model has an extra node that may increase the number of calculations. As a result, the π-model is the most popular lumped model for a distributed RC line.

Example 10.2

Delay with and without Resistance Effects for Short Wires

Problem:

What is the propagation delay through the first inverter shown below, ignoring the wire resistance? Assume all inverters are equal in size. Include all capacitances and use 0.18 μm technology parameters. Recompute the delay including interconnect resistance. Assume that the metal is Al and that the width of the wire is 0.2 μm. Is wire resistance significant?

Parameters: $C_{eff} = 1$ fF/μm, $C_{int} = 0.2$ fF/μm, $C_g = 2$ fF/μm.

Solution:

Fanout capacitance: inverter is driving four identical inverters.

$$C_{fanout} = 4 \times C_g(W_N + W_P) = 4(2\,\text{fF}/\mu m)(0.8\,\mu m + 0.4\,\mu m) = 9.6\,\text{fF}$$

Self-capacitance:

$$C_{self} = C_{eff}(W_N + W_P) = (1\,\text{fF}/\mu m)(0.8\,\mu m + 0.4\,\mu m) = 1.2\,\text{fF}$$

Wire capacitance:

$$C_{wire} = C_{int}L_{wire} = (0.2\,\text{fF}/\mu m)(20\,\mu m) = 4\,\text{fF}$$

Total capacitance:

$$C_{load} = C_{fanout} + C_{self} + C_{wire} = 9.6 + 1.2 + 4 = 14.8\,\text{fF}$$

Based on this total capacitance, the delay assuming a ramp input is given by

$$\tau_{driver} = R_{eff}C_{load} = (12.5k)\left(\frac{L}{W}\right)(14.8\,\text{fF})$$

$$= (12.5k)\left(\frac{1}{2}\right)(14.8\,\text{fF}) = 6.25k(14.8\,\text{fF}) = 92.5\,\text{ps}$$

To include wire resistance, we first compute the resistance for the 20 μm wire:

$$R_{wire} = R_{sq}\left(\frac{L}{W}\right) = 54\,\text{m}\Omega/\ \times \left(\frac{20\,\mu m}{0.2\,\mu m}\right) \approx 5.4\,\Omega$$

Next, use π-model for the wire:

Use Elmore delay calculation:

$$\tau_{driver} = (6.25\,\text{k}\Omega)(3.2\,\text{fF}) + (6.25\,\text{k}\Omega + 5.4\,\Omega)(11.6\,\text{fF})$$

$$= 92.6\,\text{ps}$$

Conclusion: the inclusion of wire resistance made no appreciable difference to the solution.

The above example illustrates that short wires can (and should) be handled as a lumped capacitance with little or no error in the calculations. The definition of a short wire depends on the technology but typically wires that are a few microns long or as high as 20 μm should be handled as a lumped capacitance. Over 90% of the wires in a chip are short wires and, therefore, can be computed in this way.

While the analysis above is appropriate when the length of interconnect is relatively short, it is not appropriate when the interconnect line is long. In this case, the wire should be treated as a distributed *RC* line rather than a simple lumped capacitance. Consider the example below that illustrates the impact of a long wire.

Example 10.3   **Delay for Inverter Driving a Long Wire**

Problem:

Consider an isolated metal 5 Al wire that is 20 mm long and driven by a 100X inverter (i.e., 100 times larger than the minimum size inverter). Since the wire is isolated, its capacitance is 0.1 fF/μm. Estimate the total line resistance and the total line capacitance assuming that the width of the wire is 0.5 μm. What is the propagation delay as calculated by Elmore for the π-model from the input of the inverter to the end of the wire?

Solution:

The wire resistance is

$$R_{wire} = R_{int}L = \left(\frac{0.027\ \Omega/\square}{0.5\ \mu m}\right)(20,000\ \mu m) = 1080\ \Omega$$

The wire capacitance is

$$C_{wire} = C_{int}L = (0.1\ fF/\mu m)(20,000\ \mu m) = 2\ pF$$

The inverter on-resistance is

$$R_{eff} = R_{eqn}/100 = 12.5\ k\Omega/100 = 125\ \Omega$$

The inverter output capacitance is

$$C_{self} = C_{eff}(2W + W)100 = (1\ fF/\mu m)(0.6\ \mu m)100 = 60\ fF$$

We can ignore the junction capacitance since it is rather small. Using the π-model, the wire capacitance is split in half while the full wire resistance is used in the model.

The resulting Elmore delay is

$$\tau_{Elmore} = (125\ \Omega)(1\ pF) + (125\ \Omega + 1080\ \Omega)(1\ pF) \approx 1.3\ ns$$

In order to appreciate the large delays associated with long wires, we plot the FO4 gate delay and the wire delay for a number of different wire lengths as technology scales in Figure 10.9. As reference points, the FO4 delay for 350 nm is approximately 150 ps; for 130 nm, the FO4 delay is reduced to approximately 40 ps; for 65 nm, the value reduces to about 25 ps. On the other hand, for $L = 1$ mm the interconnect delay increases from 3 ps, to 27 ps, to 116 ps, respectively. For $L = 2$ mm the delay

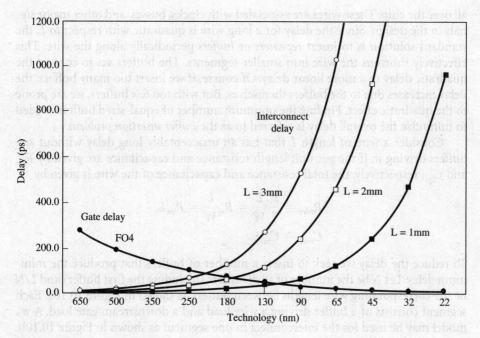

Figure 10.9

Gate delay versus interconnect delay.

values are 12 ps, 110 ps, and 460 ps, respectively. For $L = 3$ mm the delay values are 30 ps, 240 ps, and 1035 ps, respectively. The wire delay doubles with each technology node and increases quadratically as a function of wire length. Clearly, when a single buffer drives a long wire, the interconnect delay will eventually dominate the FO4 delay as technology scales or as the length increases.

We can define a rule of thumb for long wires by setting the FO4 delay equal to the interconnect delay in each technology. A critical wire length can be derived as follows:

$$FO4 = 0.38 R_{int} C_{int} L_{crit}^2$$

$$\therefore L_{crit} = \sqrt{\frac{FO4}{0.38 R_{int} C_{int}}}$$

For example, in a 0.18 μm technology, the value of L_{crit} can be computed using this equation or estimated from the graph in Figure 10.9 to be approximately 2.5 mm. Of course, this value will vary depending on the values of R_{int} and C_{int} for a given wire.

10.3 Buffer Insertion for Very Long Wires

For very long wires, the quadratic delay characteristics described above cannot be tolerated in any design. The interconnect delay would be so long that it would dominate the gate delay. In ICs, global wires tend to be very long since they must be distributed all over the chip. These wires are associated with clocks, busses, and other major signals in the design. Since the delay for a long wire is quadratic with respect to L, the standard solution is to insert *repeaters* or *buffers* periodically along the wire. This effectively shortens the wire into smaller segments. The buffers act to convert the quadratic delay to a more linear delay. Of course, if we insert too many buffers, the delay increases due to the buffers themselves. But with too few buffers, we are prone to the quadratic effect. Finding the optimum number of equal-sized buffers needed to minimize the overall delay is referred to as the *buffer insertion problem.*

Consider a wire of length L that has an unacceptably long delay without any buffers driving it. If the per unit length resistance and capacitance are given by R_{int} and C_{int}, respectively, the total resistance and capacitance of the wire is given by

$$R_{wire} = \frac{\rho}{T}\frac{L}{W} = R_{sq}\frac{L}{W} = R_{int}L$$

$$C_{wire} = C_{int}L$$

To reduce the delay we seek to insert a number of buffers that produce the minimum delay. Let N be the number of such buffers (including the first buffer) and L/N be the corresponding wire lengths between buffers as shown in Figure 10.10a. Each segment consists of a buffer driving a wire load and a downstream gate load. A π-model may be used for the interconnect in one segment as shown in Figure 10.10b.

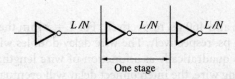

(a) Wire of length L with N buffers inserted

(b) One segment of buffer and interconnected

(c) *RC* model for one segment

Figure 10.10
Buffer insertion for very long wires.

Assuming that a minimum size buffer is 1X, the corresponding input and output capacitances are as follows:

$$C_{out} = C_{eff}W(1 + \beta) = C_J(1 + \beta) \quad \text{(in fF)}$$

$$C_{in} = C_gW(1 + \beta) = C_G(1 + \beta) \quad \text{(in fF)}$$

Here, β is the ratio of the PMOS to NMOS device size. The value of C_J is $C_{eff} \times W$, where W is the size of the NMOS device for a 1X inverter. Similarly, C_G is $C_g \times W$.

Let the multiplier M represent the optimal buffer size for the buffer insertion problem. Then, for a buffer which is M times larger than a 1X buffer:

$$R_{eff} = R_{eqn}/M$$

$$C_{out} = C_{eff}W(1 + \beta)M = C_J(1 + \beta)M$$

$$C_{in} = C_gW(1 + \beta)M = C_G(1 + \beta)M$$

In Figure 10.10c, we illustrate the RC model used for each stage during delay calculation. Using the Elmore delay, the delay for each segment is given by

$$t_{segment} = \frac{R_{eqn}}{M}\left(C_JM(1 + \beta) + \frac{C_{int}L}{2N}\right)$$

$$+ \left(\frac{R_{eqn}}{M} + \frac{R_{int}L}{N}\right)\left(\frac{C_{int}L}{2N} + C_GM(1 + \beta)\right)$$

The total delay is N times the segment delay. After some rearrangement, we find that it produces a quadratic equation with respect to L.

$$t_{total} = N \times t_{segment} = N(C_G + C_J)R_{eqn}(1 + \beta)$$

$$+ \left(C_G(1 + \beta)R_{int}M + \frac{C_{int}R_{eqn}}{M}\right)L + \left(\frac{C_{int}R_{int}}{2N}\right)L^2 \quad (10.8)$$

When we examine each delay term, we find that the first term is due solely to the buffer while the last term is due solely to the interconnect. The middle term has two components: one is due to the wire resistance driving the input capacitance of the next buffer, and a second RC term is due to the buffer driving the wire capacitance.

To find the optimal values for N and M, we apply the derivative with respect to each of the variables, as follows. The number of wire segments is

$$\frac{\partial t_{total}}{\partial N} = 0 = R_{eqn}(C_J + C_G)(1 + \beta) - \frac{R_{int}C_{int}L^2}{2N^2}$$

$$\therefore N = \sqrt{\frac{R_{int}C_{int}L^2/2}{R_{eqn}(C_J + C_G)(1 + \beta)}} = \sqrt{\frac{t_{wire}}{FO1}} \quad (10.9)$$

The buffer size, assuming all buffers are equal, is

$$\frac{\partial t_{total}}{\partial M} = 0 = R_{int}LC_G(1 + \beta) - \frac{R_{eqn}C_{int}L}{M^2}$$

$$\therefore M = \sqrt{\frac{R_{eqn}}{C_G(1 + \beta)} \frac{C_{int}}{R_{int}}} \tag{10.10}$$

Using these values of N and M, we can obtain the optimal delay through the interconnect. We can further understand these values by examining the total delay equation provided in Equation (10.8). The variable N exists in the first and last term of t_{total}; the terms are due to the buffer and interconnect, respectively, each one acting as if the other did not exist. If we set these two terms to be equal to one another, we arrive at the equation for the optimal N. The expression under the square-root sign in Equation (10.9) can be viewed as the interconnect delay (t_{wire} according to Elmore) divided by the inverter delay when driving an identical inverter (FO1 delay).

The middle term of the total delay expression in Equation (10.8) is dependent on M. If we set the two expressions in the middle term to be equal to one another, we arrive at the optimal M. This value does not depend on the length of the wire but rather the physical characteristics of the transistors and wires. In fact, this quantity depends only on technology parameters of the wire and the minimum-size inverter. Therefore, we can compute this value once the process parameters have been determined. Note that precise values of the terms in the expressions are needed to produce accurate results.

It is useful to compare and contrast the buffer insertion problem to the logical (LE) effort problem described in Chapter 6. For buffer insertion, we are concerned with driving a long wire so we break up the wire into segments and insert very large equal-sized buffers between the wire segments. For logical effort, the objective is to drive a very large output capacitance starting from a small input capacitance. The solution is obtained by determining the number of buffers and then sizing up the buffers by a given factor, typically by 4X. In LE, the delay through each buffer stage is the same at the optimal solution. In the case of buffer insertion, the delay due to the buffer and the wire are the same at the optimal point.

Example 10.4 **Buffer Insertion Example**

Problem:

From Example 10.3, consider the 20 mm Al metal 5 wire again, but this time reduce the delay using optimal buffer insertion. What is the new delay through the wire after buffer insertion?

Solution:

Using the following values:

$R_{int} = 54\ m\Omega/\mu m$ $C_{int} = 0.1\ fF/\mu m$ $L = 20{,}000\ \mu m$

$R_{eqn} = 12.5\ k\Omega/\square$ $C_g = 2\ fF/\mu m$ $C_{eff} = 1\ fF/\mu m$ $W = 0.2\ \mu m$ $\beta = 2$

The number of segments in the wire is

$$N = \sqrt{\frac{R_{int}C_{int}L^2/2}{R_{eqn}(C_G + C_J)(1 + \beta)}} = 6.9 \approx 7$$

The buffer size, assuming all equal buffers, is

$$M = \sqrt{\frac{R_{eqn}C_{int}}{C_G(1 + \beta)R_{int}}} \approx 140$$

Then, the buffer resistance is

$$R_{eff} = \frac{12.5k\,\Omega}{140} \approx 90\,\Omega$$

The buffer output capacitance is:

$$C_{self} = C_{eff}(2W + W)140 = (1\,fF/\mu m)(0.6\,\mu m)140 = 84\,fF$$

The buffer input capacitance is

$$C_{fanout} = C_g(2W + W)140 = (2\,fF/\mu m)(0.6\,\mu m)140 = 168\,fF$$

Each segment produces this *RC* delay model.

In ○—⟋⟍⟋⟍— 90 Ω —•— ⟋⟍⟋⟍— 154 Ω —•— ○ Out
84 fF ⊥   143 fF ⊥   143 fF ⊥   168 fF ⊥

The total Elmore delay is

$$\tau_{Elmore} = 7 \times \left[(90\,\Omega)(84\,fF + 143\,fF) + (90\,\Omega + 154\Omega)(143\,fF + 168\,fF) \right]$$

$$= 0.67\,ns$$

The total delay has been cut in half using buffer insertion.

10.4 Interconnect Coupling Capacitance

In this section, the issues associated with coupling capacitance are described. The goal is to understand the various components of wire capacitance and to develop formulas for hand calculation. In reality, IC interconnect structure is three-dimensional in nature as seen in Figures 1.1 and 1.2 of Chapter 1. However, for hand calculations, we can develop simple formulae that work well in practice. Thus far, we have been using 0.2 fF/μm for wire capacitance without really knowing its origin or range of validity. This section attempts to clarify its origin and justify the use of this value from a modeling perspective.

10.4.1 Components of Coupling Capacitance

In modern integrated circuits, interconnect capacitance modeling is a complex task. The capacitance of such wires is dependent on their topology, on the distances from other wires above or below, and on the separation between wires. To acquire a basic

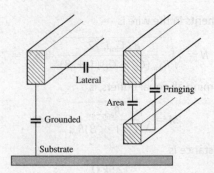

Figure 10.11
Area, lateral, and fringing components.

understanding of the problem, we can use simple first-order models to describe interconnect capacitances and derive useful constants for design purposes.

Before beginning the analysis, we describe the different components of capacitance. These components are all shown in Figure 10.11. The first capacitance worth noting is between a line and the substrate, called the *grounded* capacitance. This was the dominant capacitance in the past, but its value has been diminishing due to scaling effects. The next capacitance to note is between metal lines on the same layer. This is called the *lateral* capacitance. This is the main coupling capacitance that is the source of delay and noise issues. This capacitance has been increasing over the years. There are two other capacitances that may give rise to coupling between lines. One is referred to as the *fringing* capacitance which occurs between various edges and surfaces between two crossing lines. One of many such fringing capacitances is shown in the figure.[3] The other type of coupling capacitance occurs when two wires on different metal layers overlap. It is called the *area* capacitance.

Over the years, coupling capacitance has been increasing while the grounded capacitance has been decreasing. The general trend is depicted in Figure 10.12, where the coupling capacitance due to area, lateral, and fringing components is overtaking the grounded component as the line widths shrink. In a typical 0.13 μm design, over 70% of the wire capacitance at a node may be due to coupling between wires. This is usually the case for long nets, although short nets may also have significant coupling to their neighbors. Most nets have significant junction and gate capacitances due to the logic gates that increase the overall grounded capacitance. However, the coupling to other nodes is still significant.

To obtain a quantitative view of coupling capacitance, consider the interconnect structure shown in Figure 10.13. We would like to determine the capacitance of the center wire on a component by component basis so that it can be used for delay and noise calculations. The capacitances associated with the middle conductor are given in Figure 10.13. The dimensions of the wires were shown earlier in Figure 10.2. The total values of area, lateral, and fringing capacitances are all indicated in the figure. The grounded capacitance is treated as an area capacitance since the

---

[3] Actually, there are many other fringe capacitances that are not shown in the figure to keep it simple.

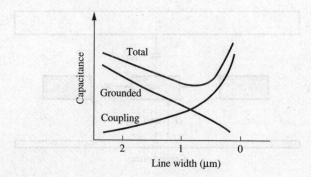

Figure 10.12

Coupling capacitance, grounded capacitance, and total capacitance.

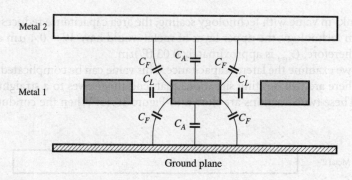

Figure 10.13

Capacitances associated with middle conductor.

calculation will be the same for both. While the capacitance cannot be exactly partitioned as shown, we model it this way for convenience. Once computed, we sum them together to compute the total wire capacitance. We now compute each one in units of capacitance per unit length.

The easiest component to compute is the area capacitance per unit length. There are two such capacitances, one from the conductor to ground and the other from the conductor to Metal 2 above it. This is illustrated separately in Figure 10.14. Assuming silicon dioxide with a dielectric constant of 4 is used as the insulating material, each of these capacitances is computed as

$$C_{area} = \varepsilon_{ox} \frac{W}{H} \tag{10.11}$$

The numerical value of this capacitance is

$$C_{area} = \varepsilon_{ox} \frac{W}{H} = 4\varepsilon_0 \frac{W}{H} = 4(88.5 \times 10^{-4} \text{ fF}/\mu\text{m}) \frac{W}{H} = 0.035 \frac{W}{H} \text{ fF}/\mu\text{m}$$

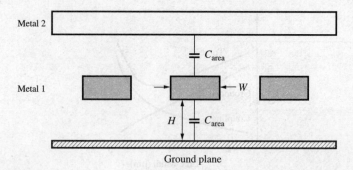

Figure 10.14
Modeling area capacitance.

As W shrinks in value with technology scaling, the area capacitance reduces linearly. In 0.18 μm technology, the upper layer of metal would have $W = 0.4$ μm and $H = 0.5$ μm. Therefore, C_{area} is approximately 0.03 fF/μm.

Next, we examine the lateral capacitance. This value can be complicated to compute but there are two limiting situations that lend themselves to a straightforward formula. These two situations are shown in Figure 10.15. When the conductors are

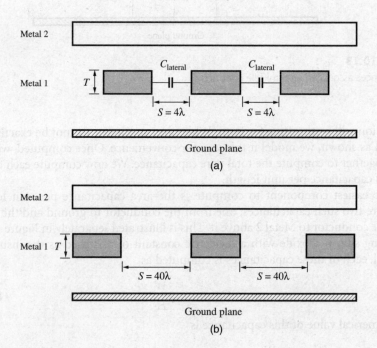

Figure 10.15
Modeling lateral capacitance.

very closely spaced by 4λ, as shown in Figure 10.15a, the capacitance can be computed using the parallel-plate formula:

$$C_{\text{lateral}} = \varepsilon_{\text{ox}} \frac{T}{S} \tag{10.12}$$

The capacitance is inversely proportional to the spacing, S. Applying the dielectric constant value to the equation:

$$C_{\text{lateral}} = \varepsilon_{\text{ox}} \frac{T}{S} = 4\varepsilon_0 \frac{T}{S} = 4(88.5 \times 10^{-4}\ \text{fF}/\mu\text{m}) \frac{T}{S} = 0.035 \frac{T}{S}\ \text{fF}/\mu\text{m}$$

In our generic 0.18 μm technology, the upper layer metal has $T = 0.8\ \mu$m and $S = 0.4\ \mu$m. Therefore, C_{lateral} is 0.070 fF/μm. When the conductors are spaced out by 40λ as in Figure 10.15b, then C_{lateral} is 0.007 fF/μm and can effectively be ignored.

The last capacitance to consider is the fringing capacitance. Again, its complexity prohibits any sort of simplified analysis. However, for hand calculations, it is sufficient to consider two cases as shown in Figure 10.16. The first case in Figure 10.16a consists of densely packed wires where the lateral capacitance dominates. For this case, C_{fringe} is approximately zero. However, if the conductors are widely spaced, as in Figure 10.16b, there is a fringe capacitance on each edge of approximately

$$C_{\text{fringe}} = \varepsilon_{\text{ox}} \ln\left(1 + \frac{T}{H}\right) \tag{10.13}$$

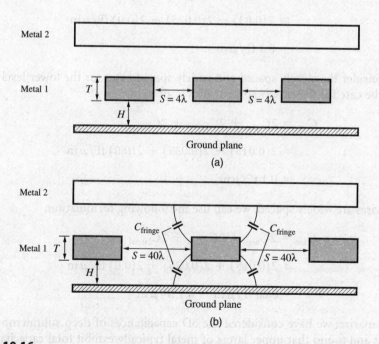

Figure 10.16
Modeling fringing capacitance.

Since T and H are fixed by the technology, this capacitance is almost independent of the topology. While this is not strictly true, it is sufficient for our modeling purposes here. We can compute the value of the fringing component as follows:

$$C_{\text{fringe}} = \varepsilon_{\text{ox}} \ln\left(1 + \frac{T}{H}\right) = 4(88.5 \times 10^{-4}\,\text{fF}/\mu\text{m})\ln\left(1 + \frac{0.5}{0.5}\right)$$

$$= 0.025\,\text{fF}/\mu\text{m}$$

Now that each of the components has been derived, we are ready to compute the quantity C_{int}.

The total capacitance for the middle wire depends on whether the wires are closely spaced or widely spaced. The case for the closely spaced wires on the upper layers is given by

$$C_{\text{int}} = 2C_{\text{area}} + 2C_{\text{lateral}} + 2C_{\text{fringe}}$$

$$\cong 2(0.03) + 2(0.070) + 2(0.0)\,\text{fF}/\mu\text{m}$$

$$= 0.2\,\text{fF}/\mu\text{m}$$

If the wires are widely spaced, we can use the following formulation:

$$C_{\text{int}} = 2C_{\text{area}} + 2C_{\text{fringe}} + 2C_{\text{lateral}}$$

$$\cong 2(0.03) + 2(0.025) + 2(0.0)\,\text{fF}/\mu\text{m}$$

$$\approx 0.1\,\text{fF}/\mu\text{m}$$

Now consider the closely spaced and widely spaced cases for the lower level metal lines. The case for the closely spaced wires is given by

$$C_{\text{int}} = 2C_{\text{area}} + 2C_{\text{lateral}} + 2C_{\text{fringe}}$$

$$= 2(0.015) + 2(0.035) + 2(0.0)\,\text{fF}/\mu\text{m}$$

$$= 0.1\,\text{fF}/\mu\text{m}$$

If the wires are widely spaced, we can use the following formulation:

$$C_{\text{int}} = 2C_{\text{area}} + 2C_{\text{fringe}} + 2C_{\text{lateral}}$$

$$\cong 2(0.015) + 2(0.025) + 2(0.0)\,\text{fF}/\mu\text{m}$$

$$= 0.08\,\text{fF}/\mu\text{m} \approx 0.1\,\text{fF}/\mu\text{m}$$

To summarize, we have considered the 3D capacitances of deep submicron interconnect and found that upper layers of metal typically exhibit total capacitance of about 0.2 fF/μm for closely spaced lines and 0.1 fF/μm for widely spaced lines. The capacitance of wires that are spaced between the two extremes would lie between 0.1 fF/μm and 0.2 fF/μm but the calculations are much more complex. However, capacitance extraction tools are available to obtain these components accurately. The lower levels of metal exhibit wire capacitances of about 0.1 fF/μm in both situations. Individual values of the coupling capacitances may be estimated using Equations (10.11), (10.12), and (10.13). These first-order equations provide valuable insight into the origin and nature of the 3D effects. Worst-case capacitances lie in the range of 0.2 – 0.3 fF/μm. We now consider the effect of coupling capacitance on delay and noise.

10.4.2   Coupling Effects on Delay

The *RC* equations given in Section 10.3 using the Elmore delay did not properly take the coupling effects into account. A more realistic situation for delay calculation is shown in Figure 10.17 where neighboring lines are coupled together. The grounded capacitances shown include self-capacitance, fanout capacitance, and wire capacitance (to substrate). The coupling capacitances due to area, lateral, and fringing effects are actually distributed along the nets. The fact that the coupling capacitors exist between all neighboring lines implies that delay is a function of not only what is happening on the line of interest, but also what is happening on the neighboring lines.

To understand this effect, consider the case of two adjacent buffers driving their respective lines with a single coupling capacitance, as shown in Figure 10.18. To simplify the problem, we ignore the wire resistance and concentrate on the effects of coupling capacitance on delay. The line of interest is called the *victim* net while the neighboring line is called the *aggressor* for reasons that will become clear in the descriptions that follow. Consider the delay associated with the switching of net 2. It is coupled to net 1 with a large capacitor C_c. How should the coupling capacitance be handled? One is tempted to connect the other side of the capacitance to ground while computing the delay for net 2. However, this may not be correct depending on what is happening at net 1. The actual delay depends on whether net

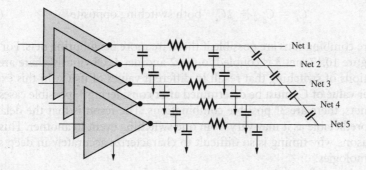

Figure 10.17

Coupling capacitance between lines.

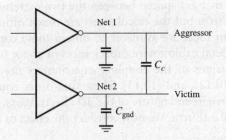

Figure 10.18
Circuit for analysis of coupling delay and noise effects.

1 is switching from high to low or low to high, or perhaps not switching at all. If it is not switching at all, then it is appropriate to ground the other side of the capacitance. This would make the total capacitance at net 2 equal to $C_{gnd} + C_c$. That covers only one of the three possible cases that may occur.

To complete the story, we examine the total loading capacitance, C_L, of net 2 for a number of different cases. Again, if the neighboring net is stationary, then

$$C_L = C_{gnd} + C_c \quad \text{aggressor not switching} \tag{10.14}$$

since the adjacent net is not switching and the coupling capacitor behaves like a grounded capacitor. If the two nets are switching in the same direction, then

$$C_L = C_{gnd} \quad \text{both switching together} \tag{10.15}$$

since net 2 does not have to charge the coupling capacitance. However, if net 1 is switching in the opposite direction to net 2, then we should include the so-called Miller effect. Since net 2 must supply twice the charge on the coupling capacitor to compensate for the switching process:

$$C_L = C_{gnd} + 2C_c \quad \text{both switching opposite} \tag{10.16}$$

Even more combinations are possible if there are more neighboring nets. For example, in Figure 10.17, net 3 is coupled to net 2 and net 4. Obviously, there are many combinations of switching that result in different values of its C_L. In this example, the proper value of C_L must be determined after considering 3^2 possible cases. For n coupled nets, there are 3^n possible combinations. The result is that the delay for a net is unpredictable as it may vary from one switching event to another. This is one of the reasons why timing is so difficult to characterize accurately in deep submicron technologies.

A number of layout-based approaches have been developed to cope with this unpredictable delay, as shown in Figure 10.19. One approach is to *space out* the wires so that the lateral capacitance term decreases. Equation (10.12) tells us that

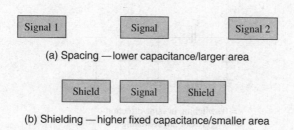

(a) Spacing — lower capacitance/larger area

(b) Shielding — higher fixed capacitance/smaller area

Figure 10.19

Spacing versus shielding to reduce coupling effects.

there is a $1/S$ relation between lateral capacitance and spacing, so we can reduce the amount of coupling by *spacing* signals apart from one another as in Figure 10.19a. Of course this will cost area, but it is effective when applied to a subset of the signals. Another approach is to interleave switching signals with nonswitching signals (such as power and ground) wherever possible. This is referred to as *shielding* as in Figure 10.19b. We can place well-behaved signals on either side of a signal so that its delay may be more predictable. However, in this case the total capacitance increases since there will always be a fixed capacitance to ground due to the shields.

Process engineers are also working to reduce the effects of coupling. Typically SiO_2 is used as the insulator in most CMOS processes. It has a relative dielectric constant of approximately 4. If the relative dielectric constant of the insulating material could be reduced from 4 to 2, the coupling capacitance would be cut in half. The pursuit of these so-called *low-k* dielectrics has been ongoing for years. Currently, the relative constant is roughly 3 but there are many issues to resolve to reach the target value of 2.

Timing verification tools can be used to obtain more accurate delay information since they have some notion of when signals switch. These tools require input from capacitance extraction tools that provide detailed coupling information. One way to characterize the effective load capacitance for these tools is to create a pre-multiplier for the coupling capacitance called a k-factor.[4] Each coupling capacitor can be multiplied by this factor to adjust its value according to switching activity. This k-factor is nominally in the range 0 to 2.

To handle coupling effects, the timing verifier would ground all coupling capacitances after taking the k-factors into account. While this is a simplistic solution, it is one of the more practical approaches to coupling analysis. Figure 10.20 shows this process for a pair of adjacent nets. The load capacitance for net 2 is adjusted by the k-factor depending on the switching of net 1. One complication is that the k-factors may vary over time due to the switching conditions associated with adjacent nets. Fortunately the designer is primarily interested in the worst-case values of k since it

---

[4] This is not the same as the k used in low-k dielectrics. This one is used to adjust capacitance values taking into account the switching behavior. To distinguish them, we will use the terms low-k and k-factor when referencing them.

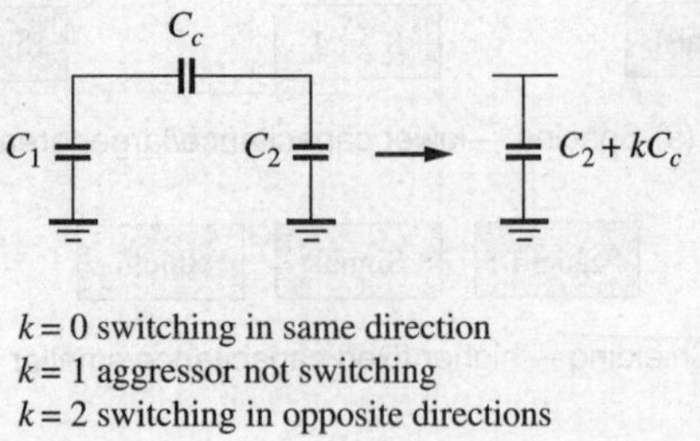

$$C_c$$

$C_1 \rightleftharpoons \quad C_2 \rightleftharpoons \quad \longrightarrow \quad \rightleftharpoons C_2 + kC_c$

$k = 0$ switching in same direction
$k = 1$ aggressor not switching
$k = 2$ switching in opposite directions

Figure 10.20
Handling coupling using k-factors.

will produce the worst-case delay values. This also simplifies the analysis significantly because it would be impractical to analyze the circuit exhaustively with case-dependent k-factors. For example, setup and hold time checks are important for the timing verification of flip-flops. When checking setup time, the designer uses the maximum k-factor on signal nets and the minimum on the clock net. The opposite settings are applied for hold time violations.

If this were not complicated enough, it turns out that the exact timing of the aggressor and victim signals also plays a role in the observed delay. Figure 10.21 illustrates the effect of signal timing in the presence of wire coupling in a SPICE transient analysis. The uncoupled waveforms of the victim (net 2) and aggressor nets (net 1) are shown along with a second plot of the victim waveform when many aggressors switch against it. Because of the early timing of the aggressors, the coupling actually causes capacitive feedthrough in the wrong direction before the proper transition begins. The resulting propagation delay in this example doubles

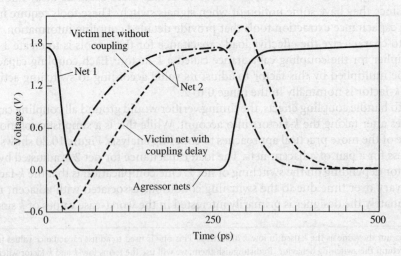

Figure 10.21
Transient analysis of coupled nets.

when compared to the case without any signal coupling. It is clear that the k-factor can lie outside of the range of 0 to 2 due to feedthrough.[5] For the designer, the use of structured layout to avoid coupling wherever possible, and careful timing verification using k-factors are the two main approaches to cope with this signal integrity problem.

10.4.3 Capacitive Noise or Crosstalk

The second type of problem is noise injection due to capacitive coupling. This problem arises when there is a nonswitching net, again the victim net, surrounded by aggressor nets that are switching. When the aggressor nets switch, noise is injected into the victim line due to capacitive feedthrough effects. We have already observed this effect during a transition in Figure 10.21. Here, we consider the case where the victim line is quiet while aggressor lines are switching and injecting unwanted noise. Depending on the size and duration of the noise, it may act to upset the functionality of a design—that is, a "soft" error may occur. Coupling noise at latch or flip-flop inputs and in dynamic logic circuits is particularly troublesome. Specifically, incorrect values can be captured in flip-flops, or voltage levels at dynamic nodes may be upset due to noise injection. Noise may also propagate through logic gates, assuming that the noise level is high enough. This can cause problems for downstream logic circuits, particularly for dynamic logic. Tracking down this type of problem in a multimillion transistor chip has consumed many engineers for months, often without success. It can also increase the power consumption unnecessarily.

To understand coupling noise, consider Figure 10.22 which depicts our aggressor and victim nets connected only by a coupling capacitance, C_c. The feedthrough equation for the noise injected from net 1 into net 2 is

$$\Delta V_2 = \frac{C_c \Delta V_1}{(C_{gnd} + C_c)} \tag{10.17}$$

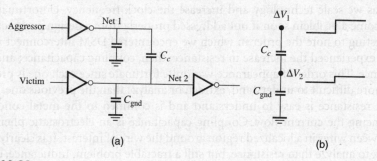

(a) (b)

Figure 10.22

Coupling noise analysis.

---

[5] The k-factor actually lies in the range of −1 to 3 when feedthrough is taken into account.

where ΔV_1 is the voltage transition at net 1 during a switching event. This equation was described in Chapter 7 on dynamic logic. If the change on the aggressor net is V_{DD}, then the injected noise is

$$\Delta V_2 = \frac{C_c V_{DD}}{(C_{gnd} + C_c)}$$

This first-order analysis is useful in obtaining an idea of the relative magnitude of noise due to coupling capacitance. To compute the noise level more accurately, a number of other factors must be taken into account such as the driver resistances, wire resistance, switching times of the aggressor signals, the switching direction of the signals, the slew rates of the signals, resistive shielding of driver, etc. Of course, once the noise is injected, the victim acts to restore the original level as quickly as possible. Complex situations that include these factors require detailed transient simulation in SPICE to obtain accurate results. Linear RC simulators are also useful for this purpose.

In practice, designers try to minimize coupling to neighboring signals to reduce noise. This can be accomplished by spacing the signals apart to reduce the C_c term, or by shielding signals with V_{DD} or Gnd, thereby eliminating the C_c term. These two approaches were illustrated in Figure 10.19.

To summarize, the delay and noise effects are difficult to analyze by hand, except for the smallest circuits. Designers must use structured design methodologies to avoid coupling effects as much as possible, especially when critical nets are involved. CAD tools must be used extensively to identify problem areas and apply the spacing and shielding approaches to resolve the problems. Process engineers must continue to develop *low-k* dielectric material to further reduce the effect of coupling capacitance. Ultimately, signal integrity-aware CAD tools, good design practices, and improved dielectrics are all needed to cope with these problems.

*10.5 Interconnect Inductance

A relatively new and even more complex issue of inductance is lurking around the corner as we scale technology and increase the clock frequency. Unfortunately, it may become a problem soon if not addressed properly from a design perspective. It is interesting to note the order in which we encountered DSM interconnect issues: first we experienced the increase in resistance; then, coupling capacitance; and now inductance. This order of appearance was quite fortunate since each one is progressively more difficult to understand, extract, or analyze than the previous one. Interconnect resistance is easy to understand and is confined to the metal conductor experiencing the current flow. Coupling capacitance is an electrostatic phenomenon between wires in a localized region around the wire of interest. It is clearly more complex to analyze than resistance, but still a tractable problem. Inductance, on the other hand, is an electromagnetic phenomenon and its effect is not necessarily confined to a localized region. It is more complicated to understand and almost impossible to extract and analyze, except for small sections. Nevertheless, we must understand its effects and explore options to avoid its impact.

The first step is to review inductance from an electromagnetic point of view. When current flows through a conductor, it sets up an electromagnetic field around it with a flux that stores energy. This flux is linearly related to the current, as follows:

$$\phi = Li \tag{10.18}$$

The proportionality constant is obviously the inductance, L, which is measured in *Henrys* (H). As the current changes, the magnetic flux acts on the wire itself and induces a voltage drop. For a linear inductor, we can take the time derivative of Equation (10.18) to obtain

$$\Delta V = L\frac{di}{dt} \tag{10.19}$$

This equation implies that the voltage drop is zero for a dc current. That is, the inductor can be treated as a short circuit for low-frequency operation. As the current demand of a chip increases, the voltage drop associated with the inductor increases. In high-speed designs, the rate of change of current with respect to time is increasing rapidly. Therefore, inductance effects are especially important at the package pins and in the power distribution system. We will examine this issue in more detail in Chapter 11.

Signal lines are also beginning to exhibit increased effects of inductance. It is important to realize that interconnect is really a distributed RLC line, not simply a distributed RC line. As such, it behaves like a transmission line under certain circumstances. We now elaborate these circumstances and describe how the inductance effects modify the delay equation. We will use R_{int}, C_{int}, and L_{int} to represent the resistance, capacitance, and inductance per unit length, respectively. An estimate of the inductance per unit length can be obtained from a well-known relationship in electromagnetic theory

$$C_{int}L_{int} = \varepsilon_{ox}\mu_{ox} \tag{10.20}$$

where the insulating material is assumed to be oxide with permittivity, ε_{ox}, and permeability, μ_{ox}. This equation only applies to a conductor that is completely surrounded by a uniform dielectric, but it is useful in obtaining first-order inductance values. Assuming that $C_{int} = 0.1$ fF/μm, $\varepsilon_{ox} = (4)(8.85 \times 10^{-14}$ F/cm) and $\mu_{ox} = 12.6 \times 10^{-7}$ Wb/amp, then $L_{int} = 0.45$ pH/μm. This is a very crude estimate but does provide the correct order of magnitude for inductance.

In Figure 10.23, a lumped model of the RLC line is shown. We can analyze this simple circuit to develop some intuition before proceeding on to the distributed line. First, consider the complex impedance associated with the resistance and inductance of the signal line

$$Z_{RL} = R + j\omega L \tag{10.21}$$

where $\omega = 2\pi f$ is the signal frequency in radians/second. If $R \gg j\omega L$, then Equation (10.21) tells us that inductance is not important. If $R < j\omega L$, then inductance

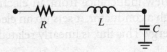

Figure 10.23
Lumped model of *RLC* interconnect.

effects will be observed in the signal line. In the past, the resistance was larger than the reactive component so that *RC* effects were dominant. In recent years ω has been increasing significantly in very high-speed designs to the point where the reactance term is important. At the same time, process engineers and designers have been working to reduce wire resistance. First, the resistance of the metal lines has been reduced with the introduction of copper as a replacement for aluminum. Second, certain signals use very wide wires to lower the resistance significantly. This reduction in resistance combined with an increase in the operating frequency has made the reactive term non-negligible in certain signals. Interestingly, while inductance values have not increased over the years, the increase in frequency and decrease in resistance have combined to raise concerns about inductance.

The above analysis is somewhat localized to the interconnect itself. When considering the significance of inductance, it is important to consider both wire resistance and the on-resistance of the buffer driving the wire. In most cases, the buffer resistance is very large (on the order of kilo-ohms) and will dominate. That is,

$$R_{\text{buffer}} + R_{\text{wire}} \gg j\omega L$$

Therefore, we should be able to ignore self-inductance for most signals on the chip. Of course, if the buffer is large and the wire is wide, we would have

$$R_{\text{buffer}} + R_{\text{wire}} < j\omega L \tag{10.22}$$

and inductance would be noticeable. This is most prominent in clock lines. Therefore, the delay should be computed using *RLC* delay equations.

Next, we include capacitance in the analysis. The lossless transmission line of Figure 10.24 has inductance and capacitance but no resistance. It is driven by a voltage source V_S with a source resistance of R_S. Since the interconnect has no resistance, it can be represented by a characteristic impedance of Z_0 given by

$$Z_0 = \sqrt{\frac{L_{\text{int}}}{C_{\text{int}}}}$$

When we apply a step input to the interconnect, the response depends on the relative values of R_S and Z_0. When the resistance is much greater than the characteristic impedance, i.e., $R_S \gg Z_0$, the *RC* effect will dominate the transient response. We expect an exponential response given by

$$V_{\text{out}}(t) = 1 - e^{-t/RC}$$

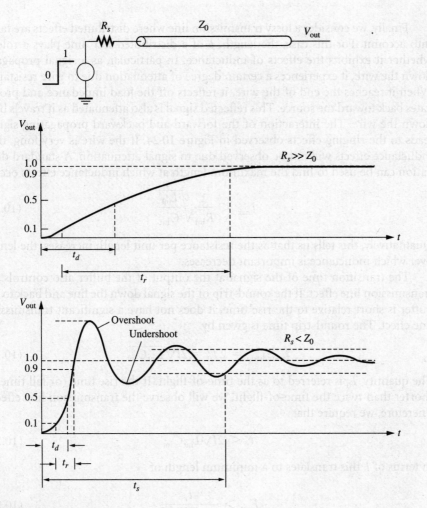

Figure 10.24

Responses of *RLC* interconnect.

As shown in the figure, the propagation delay, t_p, and rise time, t_r, are rather large.

However, if $R_S < Z_0$, inductance effects will be important and we obtain an oscillatory response within an exponential envelope. The response has a general form given by

$$V_{out}(t) = 1 - re^{-t/a}\cos(bt + c)$$

where r, a, b, and c depend on the *RLC* values. The figure illustrates the nature of the response. Note that t_d and t_r are much shorter in this case, but the tradeoff is a relatively large overshoot and undershoot of the waveform, and a longer settling time, t_s. These delay values can be computed from the response equation above.

Finally, we consider a lossy transmission line where distributed effects are taken into account. For this case, the length, l, of a distributed RLC line plays a role in whether it exhibits the effects of inductance. In particular, as a signal propagates down the wire, it experiences a certain degree of attenuation due to wire resistance. When it reaches the end of the wire, it reflects off the load impedance and propagates back toward the source. This reflected signal is also attenuated as it travels back down the wire. The interaction of the forward and backward propagating signals leads to the ringing effects observed in Figure 10.24. If the wire is very long, then inductance effects will not be observed due to signal attenuation. A standard derivation can be used to find the maximum length at which inductance effects occur

$$l_{max} < \frac{2}{R_{int}} \sqrt{\frac{L_{int}}{C_{int}}} \qquad (10.23)$$

Qualitatively, this tells us that as the resistance per unit length increases, the length over which inductance is important decreases.

The transition time of the signal at the output of the buffer also controls the transmission line effect. If the round-trip of the signal down the line and back to the buffer is short relative to the rise time, it does not have a significant transmission line effect. The round-trip time is given by

$$t_{round\text{-}trip} = 2T_0 = 2l\sqrt{L_{int}C_{int}} \qquad (10.24)$$

The quantity T_0 is referred to as the time-of-flight. If the rise time (or fall time) is shorter than twice the time-of-flight, we will observe the transmission line effects. Therefore, we require that

$$t_r < 2l\sqrt{L_{int}C_{int}} \qquad (10.25)$$

In terms of l, this translates to a minimum length of

$$l_{min} > \frac{t_r}{2\sqrt{L_{int}C_{int}}} \qquad (10.26)$$

Combining the results of Equations (10.23) and (10.26), we find that

$$\frac{t_r}{2\sqrt{L_{int}C_{int}}} < l < \frac{2}{R_{int}} \sqrt{\frac{L_{int}}{C_{int}}} \qquad (10.27)$$

This result tells us that the wire must be larger than the length specified by $t_r/2\sqrt{L_{int}C_{int}}$ but smaller than the value specified by $(2/R_{int})\sqrt{L_{int}/C_{int}}$ for inductance to be important in delay calculation. We should view these results as being more qualitative than quantitative since the terms in the equations are difficult to compute with great precision. Furthermore, the effect of buffer resistance must also be considered to obtain accurate results.

What makes the inductance problem particularly difficult is that, fundamentally, inductance can only be defined for a closed current loop, not simply for a segment of wire. The inductance of the loop is proportional to the area of the loop. Knowing the forward path of the current is not sufficient; the *return* path must also be identified. This is not easy to determine for most signals. In the past, the return path was assumed to be in the substrate. For high-speed designs, the return path often occurs in the power and ground distribution systems, and even in other signal lines. Worse yet, there may be multiple return paths, some through power/ground rails, and others through signal lines that are not close to the signal of interest. The extraction of inductance values is difficult since the effect of inductance is not confined to a localized region around the conductor.

More problematic is *mutual inductance* since it causes noise and delay effects on unsuspecting neighboring lines in unexpected ways. This type of problem is a growing concern for most integrated circuit designers, as it is difficult to extract and analyze. Mutual inductance refers to time-varying current in one line giving rise to a voltage drop in a second line. Two *RLC* lines are coupled via mutual inductance, as follows

$$v_1 = L_1 \frac{di_1}{dt} + M \frac{di_2}{dt}$$

$$v_2 = M \frac{di_1}{dt} + L_2 \frac{di_2}{dt}$$

$$(10.28)$$

where L_1 and L_2 are the self-inductances of the two wires and M is the mutual inductance between the two wires. When a current flows in one line, it induces a return current in the other line due to its mutual inductance. The voltage drop on each line is the sum of the drop due to its self-inductance and its mutual inductance with the other line. This effect can occur over distances of 100 μm or more and create functional failures that are intermittent in nature. The details of mutual inductance effects, while important in future technologies, are beyond the scope of this book. The interested reader is encouraged to consult the references at the end of this chapter for further information.

To summarize, self and mutual inductance effects have been observed most frequently in clocks and busses. Clocks are prone to self-inductance effects whereas busses are more likely to experience mutual inductive effects. To limit the effects of self-inductance, wire lengths can be kept within the boundaries suggested by Equation (10.27). For mutual inductance, shielding techniques of the form shown in Figure 10.19 can be used to limit its effects.

*10.6 Antenna Effects

Another important issue associated with interconnect is the *antenna effect*. This is a reliability issue that may destroy the thin-oxide of transistors during fabrication or modify the threshold voltage of devices. During the fabrication process, charge builds up on each metal layer during plasma etching, sputtering, or chemical-mechanical polishing (CMP). This phenomenon is referred to as an antenna effect since charge is attracted to each metal layer like an antenna. Since $Q = CV$, the accumulated charge creates a potential difference across the gate oxide of a MOS transistor. When too much charge accumulates on the gate, the voltage drop across the oxide damages the transistor by shorting the gate to the substrate. A less dramatic, but still undesirable, effect is a shift in the V_T due to injection of mobile carriers into the oxide through Fowler-Nordheim tunneling.

The antenna effect manifests itself as an interconnect design issue since the metal layer selection and routing determine the impact of this phenomenon. When Metal 1 is processed, its charge buildup is rather small since the lengths of the wires associated with Metal 1 tend to be short. As we add more and more layers, the area tends to increase since the wires are longer and thicker. Higher levels of metal have more surface area and therefore accumulate more charge, so they tend to be more troublesome with respect to the antenna effect. If a transistor survives the process on a given layer, that layer does not play as significant a role in the antenna effect during subsequent processing operations. Therefore, we usually assess antenna problems for each metal segment in each layer separately.

The *antenna rules* specify maximum allowable ratios of metal (or poly) area to gate area for each layer.

$$\text{Antenna Ratio} = \frac{\text{Area}_{\text{metal}}}{\text{Area}_{\text{gate}}} \tag{10.29}$$

For example, if the antenna ratio is set to 100, the area of a metal line would have to be 100 times larger than the gate area for an antenna rule violation to occur. There is a different ratio for each metal line. The design-rule checking (DRC) tools can check to see if each wire segment on each layer causes a violation, and flag those that are potential problems. For threshold voltage shifting, all metal layers connected to a gate need to be combined to obtain $\text{Area}_{\text{metal}}$ in Equation (10.29).

An example of the antenna effect is shown in Figure 10.25. Relative to the indicated device, poly, Metal 1, or Metal 2 may act to damage the gate region. For example, when Metal 1 is deposited and polished, charge develops on it and builds up a potential difference that could damage the oxide of the indicated transistor. If it tolerates the voltage level, then the corresponding Metal 1 segment is not considered to be a problem in the rest of the processing sequence. However, when the next layer of metal is applied, the corresponding charge on this second layer alone is checked against its antenna ratio. A more conservative approach recognizes that process induced damage is a cumulative effect. In that case, the total area of poly + Metal 1 + Metal 2 is divided by the gate area for the antenna check.

A number of different approaches have been used to avoid antenna effects. First, the insertion of diodes along the wire can be used to discharge the metal lines during the processing sequence. This approach is illustrated in Figure 10.26 where a *pn* junction has been connected to Metal 1. The job of this diode is to discharge each layer of metal as it is deposited so that the transistor does not see any significant voltage drop. It is reverse-biased and harmlessly removes charge as it accumulates.

The use of antenna diodes is very effective but presents some practical problems. Diodes cost area and their location must be decided based on the metal structure. Ideally, the diode should be near the transistor gate as shown in Figure 10.27. There is already a reverse-biased junction at the output of the inverter, but the

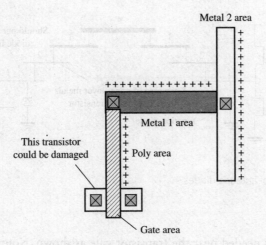

Metal 2 area

Metal 1 area

Poly area

This transistor
could be damaged

Gate area

Figure 10.25
Antenna effects during IC processing.

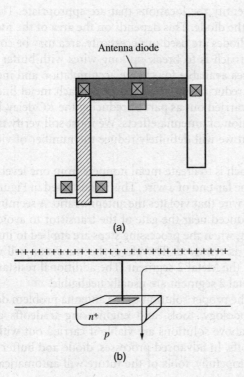

Antenna diode

(a)

(b)

Figure 10.26
Antenna diodes to discharge metal lines.

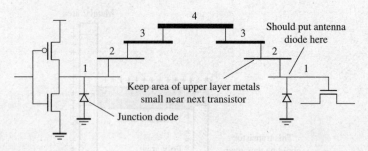

Figure 10.27

Proper placement of antenna diodes.

antenna diode is needed near the transistor gate as shown. Note that as each layer in the example is deposited, the far-end transistor must be able to handle all the charge accumulation on each successive layer in this configuration. Therefore, the far-end metal lines must be kept short or we must place diodes near the transistor. However, it would be too expensive in terms of area to place diodes near all transistor gate inputs, or embed the antenna diodes inside cell libraries. It should only be used where absolutely necessary. This involves a complete DRC verification of the entire layout to identify the locations that are appropriate. The second issue is to define the area of the diode. This depends on the area of the metal segments that it supports. If large diodes are used unnecessarily, area may be compromised.

A second approach is to break up long wires with buffer insertion. This will reduce the total area available for charge accumulation and increase the transistor gate area, thereby reducing the total charge on each metal line. Of course, such a process is already carried out as part of reducing the RC delay, but we obtain a side benefit of a reduction of antenna effects. We must still verify that no segment creates a problem, but we will definitely reduce the number of violations after buffer insertion.

A third approach is to create metal jumpers from one level to the next to break up the lines near the far-end of a wire. This is illustrated in Figure 10.28. In this case, we show a Metal 1 wire that violates the antenna ratio. A seemingly unnecessary jog to Metal 2 is introduced near the gate of the transistor to avoid the total charge of Metal 1. Recall that, when the processing steps are applied to introduce the vias, the charge of Metal 1 is removed. Therefore, the transistor will only experience the small charge from the Metal 2 segment. The additional resistance and capacitance of the vias and Metal 2 segment are usually negligible.

In summary, the proper solution to the antenna problem depends on the physical design methodology, tools, and engineering tradeoffs associated with the design. All of the above solutions are viable if carried out with careful considerations of the tradeoffs. In advanced processes, diode and buffer insertion appear to be most helpful. Hopefully, tools of the future will automatically take care of this issue on behalf of the designer.

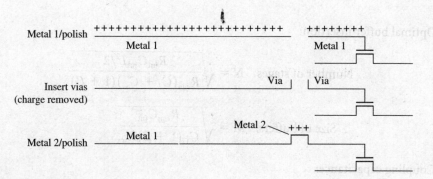

Figure 10.28
Metal line jogs to avoid antenna effects.

10.7   Summary

Interconnect data:

(a) 0.18 μm 5-layer aluminum process: $\rho = 2.7\ \mu\Omega$-cm; Metals 1–4, $T = 0.5\ \mu$m, $H = 0.5\ \mu$m, $W_{min} = 0.3\ \mu$m; and Metal 5, $T = 1\ \mu$m, $H = 0.5\ \mu$m, $W_{min} = 0.4\ \mu$m

(b) 0.13 μm, 8-layer copper process: $\rho = 1.7\ \mu\Omega$-cm; Metals 1–6, $T = 0.4\ \mu$m, $H = 0.5\ \mu$m, $W_{min} = 0.2\ \mu$m; and Metals 7–8, $T = 0.8\ \mu$m, $H = 0.5\ \mu$m, $W_{min} = 0.4\ \mu$m

Wire resistance calculations:

$$R = \frac{\rho L}{A} = \frac{\rho L}{TW} \qquad R_{sq} = \frac{\rho}{T} \qquad R = R_{sq}\left(\frac{L}{W}\right)$$

$$R_{sq} = \frac{\rho}{T} = \frac{2.7\ \mu\Omega\text{-cm}}{0.5\ \mu\text{m}} = 54\ \text{m}\Omega/\square \quad \text{Al}\quad \text{Metals 1–4}$$

$$R_{sq} = \frac{\rho}{T} = \frac{2.7\ \mu\Omega\text{-cm}}{1.0\ \mu\text{m}} = 27\ \text{m}\Omega/\square \quad \text{Al}\quad \text{Metal 5}$$

$$R_{sq} = \frac{\rho}{T} = \frac{1.7\ \mu\Omega\text{-cm}}{0.4\ \mu\text{m}} = 42\ \text{m}\Omega/\square \quad \text{Cu}\quad \text{Metals 1–6}$$

$$R_{sq} = \frac{\rho}{T} = \frac{1.7\ \mu\Omega\text{-cm}}{0.8\ \mu\text{m}} = 21\ \text{m}\Omega/\square \quad \text{Cu}\quad \text{Metals 7–8}$$

Elmore delay calculation:

$$\tau_i = \sum_k \left(C_k \times R_{ik}\right)$$

Optimal buffer insertion:

$$\text{Number of stages} \quad N = \sqrt{\frac{R_{\text{int}} C_{\text{int}} L^2/2}{R_{eqn}(C_J + C_G)(1 + \beta)}}$$

$$\text{Size of buffers} \quad M = \sqrt{\frac{R_{eqn} C_{\text{int}}}{C_G(1 + \beta) R_{\text{int}}}}$$

Coupling capacitance:

$$C_{\text{area}} = \varepsilon_{\text{ox}} \frac{W}{H}$$

$$C_{\text{lateral}} = \varepsilon_{\text{ox}} \frac{T}{S}$$

$$C_{\text{fringe}} = \varepsilon_{\text{ox}} \ln\left(1 + \frac{T}{H}\right)$$

Coupling capacitances in delay calculation:

$$C_L = C_{\text{gnd}} + C_c \quad \text{aggressor not switching}$$

$$C_L = C_{\text{gnd}} \quad \text{both switching together}$$

$$C_L = C_{\text{gnd}} + 2C_c \quad \text{both switching opposite}$$

Crosstalk noise:

$$\Delta V_2 = \frac{C_c \Delta V_1}{(C_{\text{gnd}} + C_c)}$$

Self-inductance:

$$\Delta V = L \frac{di}{dt}$$

Mutual inductance:

$$v_1 = L_1 \frac{di_1}{dt} + M \frac{di_2}{dt}$$

$$v_2 = M \frac{di_1}{dt} + L_2 \frac{di_2}{dt}$$

Conditions where inductance should be considered in delay calculation:

$$R_{\text{buffer}} + R_{\text{wire}} < j\omega L$$

$$\frac{t_r}{2\sqrt{LC}} < 1 < \frac{2}{R}\sqrt{\frac{L}{C}}$$

Antenna rule:

$$\text{Antenna Ratio} = \frac{\text{Area}_{\text{metal}}}{\text{Area}_{\text{gate}}}$$

REFERENCES

1. M. Celik, L. Pileggi, and A. Odabasioglu, *IC Interconnect Analysis*, Kluwer Academic Publishers, Boston, MA, 2002.

2. Y. Ismail and E. Friedman, *On-chip Inductance in High-Speed Integrated Circuits*, Kluwer Academic Publishers, Boston, MA, 2001.

3. H. Bakoglu, *Circuits, Interconnections, and Packaging for VLSI*, Addison-Wesley Publishing, Reading, MA, 1990.

4. N. Arora, K. V. Raol, R. Schumann, and L. Richardson, "Modeling and Extraction of Interconnect Capacitances," *IEEE Transactions on Computer-Aided Design*, vol. 15, no. 1, pp. 58–67, Jan. 1996.

PROBLEMS

P10.1. Compare the resistance of a 20 mm Metal 5 wire in 0.18 μm technology with a 20 mm Metal 8 wire in 0.13 μm technology (a non-scaled wire). Use the information provided in the Summary section. Compute the delay for each wire assuming an ideal source and a wire capacitance of $C_{\text{int}} = 0.1$ fF/μm.

P10.2. Compare the resistance of a 20 mm Metal 5 wire in 0.18 μm technology with a 14 mm Metal 8 wire in 0.13 μm technology (a scaled wire). Use the information provided in the Summary section. Compute the delay for each wire assuming that the wire capacitance is $C_{\text{int}} = 0.1$ fF/μm.

P10.3. Two adjacent Metal 5 wires in 0.18 μm technology are spaced out from 4λ to 40λ in 4λ increments. Plot the capacitance per unit length of these wires as a function of spacing, assuming that they are shielded above and below. Use minimum width dimensions for the wire.

P10.4. Simulate a distributed *RC* line as an *RC* ladder circuit in SPICE with 1 stage, 3 stages (as shown in Figure P10.4), and 20 stages. You can choose your own sizes but ensure that the total resistance and total capacitance are the same in all three cases. Measure the propagation delay for the three cases when a step input is applied at the source. Derive a delay formula of the form:

$$\tau = \alpha R_{\text{wire}} C_{\text{wire}}$$

and compute α for the three cases. Comment on the resr·

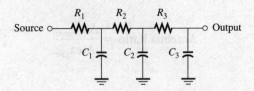

Figure P10.4

P10.5. Repeat the same experiment as described in Problem P10.4 but this time use each of the following three models shown in Figure P10.5 in place of the *RC* ladder. Which model produces accurate results?

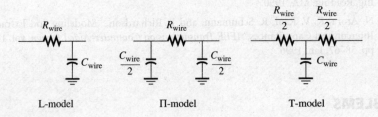

Figure P10.5

P10.6. Simulate the *RC* circuit shown in Figure P10.6 using SPICE. Set $R_1 = R_2 = R_3$ and $C_1 = C_2 = C_3$. Compare the Elmore delay with the delay derived from SPICE. How accurate are the results for each node using Elmore? Explain why any particular result is not accurate.

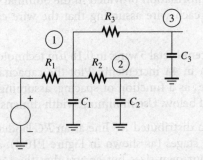

Figure P10.6

P10.7. Wires can be placed into short, medium, long, and very long categories. Establish rules of thumb for a Metal 5 wire in 0.18 μm technology that quantify each of these categories based on the following definitions:

(a) Short wires do not require any resistance or capacitance calculations if they contribute less than 5% to the delay. What is the maximum short wire length?

(b) Medium wires must include capacitance in the delay calculation, but do not require any resistance information. What is the maximum medium wire length?

(c) Long wires require both resistance and capacitance information but do not require buffer insertion. What length of wire can remain unbuffered?

(d) Very long wires require buffer insertion.

P10.8. Figure P10.8 shows a circuit that has two interconnect lines with a large coupling capacitance between them.

(a) Estimate the peak value of noise on the victim line when the aggressor line switches by 1.8V.

(b) What is the effective capacitance loading on the victim for delay calculation if the aggressor switches in the opposite direction of the victim?

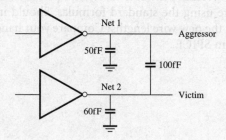

Figure P10.8

P10.9. For a 0.13 μm technology, estimate the range over which inductance is important assuming a Metal 8 wire. You can assume typical numbers in the given technology. How does this range compare against the critical length in the same technology? (See Section 10.2.3.)

P10.10. The amount of noise injected on a wire depends on the strength of the driver, rise time of the aggressor, as well as the percent of the total capacitance that is due to coupling. Create a simple *RC* model based on Figure P10.8 that you can use to help you estimate the size of noise caused by the coupling.

P10.11. Compare the number of repeaters required in a 0.18 μm technology versus a 0.13 μm technology for a 10 mm wire. Use the top layer of metal and the standard technology parameters to compute the numbers.

P10.12. Consider an 18 mm Metal 7 wire in a 0.13 μm technology. Assume the wire is 0.4 μm wide and 0.8 μm thick with a spacing to adjacent wires of 2 μm. The height above and below to Metal 8 and Metal 6 is 0.5 μm. Assume Cu for interconnect (ρ = 0.017 Ω-μm) and a low-k dielectric material (ϵ_r = 3.0). Assume a worst-case coverage of Metal 6 below, Metal 8 above, and Metal 7 for adjacent lines that are shielding the wire of interest.

(a) Compute the resistance per unit length and capacitance per unit length for this wire.

(b) Estimate the delay of the distributed RC wire, assuming that the driver is a perfect voltage source and that the load capacitance is 50 fF.

(c) Assume that the wire is being driven by a 25X inverter. What is the new delay?

(d) Now, assume that the inductance is 0.5 pH/μm. Will the inductance be a factor in the delay calculation for this buffer size? Compare hand analysis with results in SPICE.

(e) Now remove the 25X buffer and perform buffer insertion on this wire using the standard formulas. Should inductance be a factor for the new wire lengths? Compare your hand analysis with results from SPICE.

Power Grid and Clock Design

11.1   Introduction

In this chapter, we address two chip-level design challenges that are dominated by interconnect issues: power and clock distribution. Here, the word *power* is intended to mean the power and ground distribution systems, which include V_{DD} and Gnd (or V_{SS}). The power supply, up to this point in the book, has been assumed to be a constant value that is available everywhere on the chip. However, it must actually be routed from the power pads to the gates, memory circuits, and all other functions on the chip. Furthermore, its value fluctuates over time, depending on the switching activity on the chip. These variations in the voltage must be tolerated by the gates on the chip. The same applies to the clock signal. It has been assumed to be available at all required points on the chip with a well-defined clock period. However, it too must be routed from the clock source or root node to the appropriate destinations inside the chip. It also has some variability in its period and arrival times across the chip that must be tolerated by the logic circuits.

Power distribution and clock design are now complex tasks that must be done with great care in deep submicron technology. Gone are the days of simply laying out metal tracks for the power supply or running a clock signal to all the flip-flops in the design. Today, many issues come into play and affect the integrity of the power grid or the clock network. This chapter addresses many of these issues, although it is difficult to completely describe all of the issues and their interactions in a single chapter. The chapter will highlight the interaction of the power system with the clock design. Many design groups work on power system and clock design together so that the complete problem is properly addressed. We will also address clock generation and phase-lock loop (PLL) circuits as part of this chapter.

11.2 Power Distribution Design

Power distribution, when considered in its entirety, actually involves on-chip and off-chip issues starting from off-chip dc-dc converters, printed circuit boards (PCBs), power planes, packages, sockets, power pins or solder bumps, and finally the connection to the gates. Proper power grid design requires interaction of system designers, thermal designers, system architects, board designers, and chip designers. The problem demands global optimization rather than localized chip-level optimization. This section will focus on the chip-level issues, but the reader should keep in mind that this is only one part of the complete design problem.

Much of the complexity of power distribution systems arises due to the large number of transistors on a chip, the *RLC* nature of interconnect, the frequency of operation, and the current demand of high-speed circuits today. The highest frequency of operation is well over 1 GHz, while power has exceeded 100 W and current levels have reached 100 A in state-of-the-art designs. Meanwhile, supply voltage scaling to reduce power has led to V_{DD} values of 1.2 V and below. Fluctuations in the power system at these levels lead to timing variations and, eventually, design failure. Allowable voltage noise in the supply is budgeted at $\pm 10\% \times (V_{DD} - \text{Gnd})$ as a rule of thumb.

In order to manage fluctuations, the total impedance seen from the V_{DD} pads to the gate connection must be controlled based on the needed current. The target impedance of the power grid as seen from the pads is given by

$$Z = \frac{V_{DD} \times (\text{fractional noise budget})}{I_{DD}} \tag{11.1}$$

For a supply voltage of $V_{DD} = 1.2$ V and a supply current of $I_{DD} = 100$ A, $Z = 1.2$ V $\times (10\%)/100$ A $= 1.2$ mΩ. This is an incredibly small number to achieve over the gigahertz frequency range and makes power distribution design very challenging.

The noise on the supply is primarily due to *IR* drop and *Ldi/dt* as will be explained later. At this stage, it is sufficient to realize that voltage drops occur on the power grid due to the resistance and inductance along the current path. These voltage drops affect clock skew, gate performance, and clock and PLL timing jitter.

There are also issues of power grid electromigration that affect long-term reliability. The metal migrates due to the eroding effects of large currents and eventually breaks. Ultimately, the power system design will limit the system performance and may lead to failures in the field. Therefore, it must be designed carefully to avoid such potential problems that are collectively called *power integrity* issues.

One approach that has been used in the past is to overdesign the system to avoid any potential failures. *Overdesign* is a term used often by designers when design risks are removed by going well beyond the needed safeguards and recommended guidelines. One example of this is the use of decoupling capacitance on the chip to control IR and Ldi/dt. In the case of overdesign, most of the available area would be committed to decoupling capacitance rather than to devices. However, there is a large area penalty associated with this overdesign (and an even larger one for underdesign—nonworking chips!) so it is important to understand the key issues and make the proper tradeoffs wherever possible. With this brief overview, we now describe the main issues in power system design and then examine a few basic structures of the power distribution system.

11.2.1   *IR* Drop and *Ldi/dt*

The conditions contributing to the complexity of power distribution systems are primarily due to interconnect and its impact on chip performance. IR drop due to resistance on V_{DD} lines impacts overall timing and functionality. These effects are made worse by the presence of Ldi/dt voltage variations at package pins due to the increased rate of change of current in high-speed designs. Together, the total voltage drop at any point in the power grid is given by

$$V = IR + L\frac{di}{dt} \tag{11.2}$$

We consider each of these effects separately starting with IR drop. The basic concept of IR drop is illustrated in Figure 11.1, which depicts two large buffers connected to a resistive power supply. Initially, all voltage levels in the power grid are at V_{DD}. As the large driver, inv2, begins to switch, the demand for current reduces the voltage in the power grid. Specifically, the wire resistance creates voltage drops that increase as the current moves from the external supply toward inv2. The voltage remains relatively high near the V_{DD} connection at the periphery of the chip, and drops by ΔV at the connection to inv2. In practice, IR drop is caused by simultaneous switching of clock buffers, bus drivers, memory decoder drivers, etc. These simultaneous

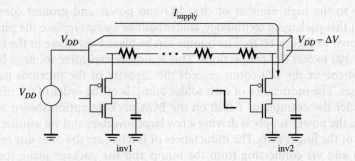

Figure 11.1

IR drop in power distribution system.

switching events can occur anywhere on the chip and, therefore, all regions are susceptible to *IR* drop violations. The ground grid is subject to the same type of problem when the outputs switch low, except that the value will increase in voltage. This is sometimes referred to as *ground bounce*.

Voltage drops on the power grid primarily affect timing. The effect of *IR* drop on performance can be significant. *IR* drop reduces the drive capability of the gates and increases the overall delay. Typically, a 5% drop in supply voltage can affect delay by 10–15%, or more. Such an increase becomes serious when managing clock skews in the range of 100 picoseconds. In the previous chapter, we found that path delays are no longer predictable due to interconnect issues. This problem is exacerbated by *IR* drop. Ideally, timing calculations should account for worst-case *IR* drop to ensure a working design. The analysis can be carried out using process corner simulation, as described in Chapter 3.

IR drop also compromises the noise margins of logic gates, due not only to voltage drop in the power grid, but also to the increase in voltage in the ground grid. Once the noise margins drop below the budgeted amount, typically 10%, the design is not guaranteed to operate properly. Over the years, supply voltage has been shrinking to avoid transistor punch-through conditions, hot-electron effects, and device breakdown. More recently, V_{DD} scaling has been driven by the need to reduce power dissipation rather than the other issues. Either way, this has resulted in smaller and smaller noise margins. With *IR* drop, the margins are reduced even further which makes it more difficult to manage the effects of interconnect coupling noise in a multimillion-transistor design.

Now consider the *Ldi/dt* term of Equation (11.2). This is another source of voltage drop in the power supply due to package pin inductance—typically around 1–2 nH. The inductance arises from the bonding wire used to connect the chip I/O pads to the lead frame in a traditional dual-inline package (DIP), as in Figure 11.2a. While the inductance *L* has not changed significantly over the years, the value of *di/dt* has continued to increase and the supply voltage has been decreasing from 5 V to 3.3 V, 2.5 V, 1.8 V, and recently 1.2 V and below. These trends have reached a point where the *Ldi/dt* drop can contribute significantly to an overall voltage drop in the power grid, especially in peak demand situations.

Today, many companies have moved to a ceramic *ball-grid array (BGA)* packaging due to the high number of chip I/O and power and ground connections needed. In this packaging technology, solder balls or *bumps* replace the pins of the DIP as shown in Figure 11.2b. The bumps can be placed anywhere in the chip area and allow 300 to 500 I/O connections. This is a more expensive solution but must be used whenever the I/O count exceeds the capacity of the previous packaging technologies. The inductance of each solder bump is of the order of 0.1 nH.

Consider the example of *Ldi/dt* on the BGA package option shown in Figure 11.3. Here, the power supply is driving a few large inverters and we assume that the resistance of the line is zero. The inductances of interest are the ones due to the solder bump and via connecting from the bump and the package plane (providing clean power). A current level of 25 mA is supplied by V_{DD} and flows into the circuit over a 100 ps time interval. At this same time, some of the buffers are discharging

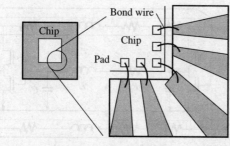

(a) Dual-inline packaging

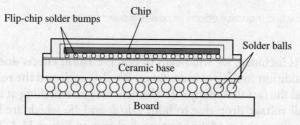

(b) Ball grid array packaging

Figure 11.2
Chip packaging options.

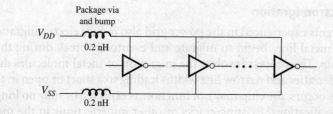

Figure 11.3
Effect of off-chip inductance.

through V_{SS} with roughly the same level of current in the same time period. If the bump and via generate 0.2 nH of inductance, then the total voltage drop due to the inductance on both rails is

$$V_L = 2 \times L \frac{di}{dt} = 2 \times 0.2 \text{ nH} \times \frac{25 \text{ mA}}{100 \text{ ps}} = 100 \text{ mV}$$

This is a significant drop considering that the supply voltage may only be 1.2 V. Furthermore, this is only one of the voltage drops to consider. If the inductance of the

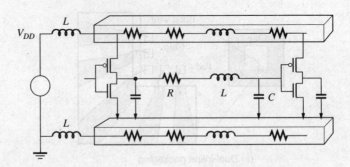

Figure 11.4
Combined resistive and inductive effects of power/ground system.

power system is included, we will begin to observe Ldi/dt effects due to the power grid itself, in addition to the pin inductance. We also neglected the resistance of the power grid, and the fact that many other buffers may be switching at the same time.

The overall voltage drop due to both Ldi/dt and IR, which are both dynamic phenomena, requires the modeling approach shown in Figure 11.4. The packaging inductances, power grid inductances, and power grid resistances must all be considered together with an RLC model of interconnect. Of particular concern are situations that give rise to simultaneous switching noise (SSN) where many buffers switch together producing large IR drops and ground bounce.

11.2.2 Electromigration

The high currents experienced in the power grid also induce electromigration (EM) effects where metal lines begin to migrate and eventually break during the operation of the chip. The process involves the migration of metal molecules due to the high current densities and narrow line widths leading to a short or open in the metal line. Once this occurs, the chip may not function as expected or may no longer meet the timing specifications. Existing cracks or other imperfections in the metal lines are particularly prone to this problem since they are already weak links in the power system. Failures due to EM can be catastrophic because they occur in the field when the chip is in a system and in a customer's hands.

An example of an electromigration failure is shown in Figure 11.5. In the past, low current densities and wide metal lines, combined with special processing, reduced the likelihood of EM. As we exceeded speeds of 100 MHz, and reached geometries below 0.8 μm, the potential for EM problems increased in aluminum. One of the reasons for switching to copper was its superior performance with respect to electromigration. Cu is approximately 10 times better in terms of EM than Al, but Cu diffuses quickly through oxide and it was not used in ICs because of this problem. However, advances in processing technology to solve this problem led to the eventual switch from Al to Cu. Initial EM results of Cu indicate that it is slightly better than Al, but large improvements are expected as the technology matures. Unfortunately, today the copper vias experience a greater degree of EM failures compared to the tungsten vias used with aluminum.

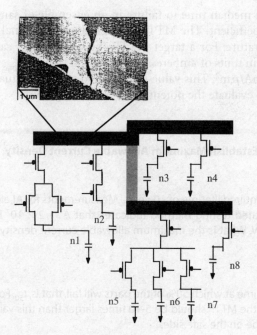

Figure 11.5
Electromigration failure in power bus.

Electromigration in the power grid is a function of the average current flow in metal lines and vias. Current flows primarily in one direction in each power bus, since it is delivering current from the power pad to the gate in the case of V_{DD} (see Figure 11.1). Therefore, it is called a dc phenomenon. To assess the EM tolerance of a piece of metal, we can examine its average dc current density, J, and compare it to some allowable level, J_{max}, when EM failure occurs. Since metal lines vary in height and material properties at different levels in the design, each metal layer may have a different failure criteria.

It is useful to characterize the lifetime of a chip due to long-term reliability problems through a metric called the *mean time to failure (MTTF)*. If the value of MTTF is 5–10 times greater than the expected lifetime of the product in which the chip is embedded, then we can safely ship the design to customers. However, if the chip lifetime is less than the product lifetime, improvements to the design must be made. Black's law is used to estimate MTTF of a metal line using the average current density, J, and the activation energy[1] of the failure, ΔH:

$$\text{MTTF} = \frac{A}{J^2} \exp(\Delta H/kT) \qquad (11.3)$$

---

[1] Electromigration is modeled as a diffusion process that is thermally activated at a given energy level. The activation energy depends on the diffusion mechanism, either through the lattice ($\Delta H = 1.4$ eV) or across the grain boundaries ($\Delta H = 0.6$ eV).

Here, MTTF is the median time to failure in an ensemble of samples and A is an empirical fitting coefficient. The MTTF is inversely proportional to J^2 and is very sensitive to temperature. For a target MTTF, the value of J_{max} can be determined from the equation in units of amperes/cm^2. A typical value of J_{max} is approximately 10^6 A/cm^2, or 10 mA/μm^2. This value is compared with the actual current density in each segment to evaluate the potential for electromigration.

Example 11.1   **Use of MTTF to Establish Maximum Allowable Current Density**

Problem:

A design has a required lifetime of 10 years. Measurements for Al electromigration using an accelerated testing method indicates that A = 2×10^7 hr-cm^2/ampere and ΔH = 0.85 eV. What is the maximum allowable current density in Al interconnect at 125 °C?

Solution:

The MTTF is the time at which 50% of the parts will fail, that is, t_{50}. For a desired lifetime of 10 years, the MTTF should be 5-10 times larger than this value. We will use a factor of 10 to be on the safe side:

$$t_{50} = \text{MTTF} = 10 \times 10 \text{ years} \times 365 \text{ days} \times 24 \text{ hours} = 8.8 \times 10^5 \text{ hours}$$

Using Equation (11.3), we can solve for J_{max}:

$$J_{max} = \sqrt{\frac{A}{t_{50}} \exp\left(\frac{\Delta H}{kT}\right)} = \sqrt{\frac{2(10^7)}{8.8(10^5)} \exp\left(\frac{0.85eV}{8.62 \times 10^{-5}eV/°K(398°K)}\right)}$$

$$= 8.95(10^5) A/cm^2$$

This value can be used as the maximum tolerable current density for electromigration.

The current density in each wire segment is computed using the wire dimensions

$$J_{avg} = \frac{I_{avg}}{W \times T} \tag{11.4}$$

where W is the wire width and T is the wire thickness. The criterion for electromigration failure is

$$J_{avg} > J_{max} \tag{11.5}$$

This comparison must be performed for every segment and via in the power grid to identify those nets that are prone to EM failure in the prescribed lifetime. Failing metal segments and vias must be modified, typically by adjusting the wire width according to Equation (11.4), until condition (11.5) is no longer violated. Not all

EM failures must be fixed since a break in the metal line does not necessarily mean that the part will fail. However, it may increase the likelihood of failure in other branches since there are usually many different current paths to each gate. The failures should be ordered in some manner, and then fixed in that order, until the probability of failure is below some predetermined threshold.

11.2.3 Power Routing Considerations

Integrated circuit power distribution systems are designed to provide the needed voltages and currents to the transistors that perform the logic functions of a chip. IC designers must design power systems with Equations (11.2) and (11.3) in mind for reliable operation. A complete picture of power grid integrity can only be obtained when effects such as IR drop, ground bounce, Ldi/dt, and electromigration are considered together. These are full-chip issues that must be addressed by interconnect verification tools that have the capacity and performance required to analyze detailed representations of the chip in a reasonable time. We will leave these higher-level issues to CAD tools and vendors. Instead we will focus on the methods needed to avoid these types of issues.

Initially, one can make estimates of the IR drop and Ldi/dt from R, C, and L calculations. Designers typically compute resistance along a conductor by counting the number of squares along the line and multiplying by the sheet resistivity. Similarly, the capacitance along the line is computed by multiplying the length of the line times the capacitance per unit length. Inductance can be estimated for the bonding wire or solder bumps, and crude estimates can be obtained for the power lines. Using this information and the expected current levels and rates of change, the anticipated voltage drops can be computed, along with electromigration lifetimes. Carrying out this type of analysis for a whole chip is difficult so rules of thumb have emerged to help guide the power grid design. These rules are associated with the metal width needed to keep the resistance low enough for the expected current levels and current densities.

A simplified method of power distribution is illustrated in Figure 11.6. The outer ring is V_{DD} and the inner ring is V_{SS}. The power and ground straps are routed

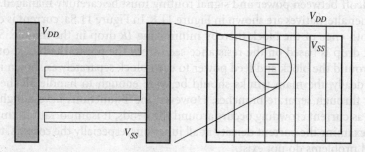

Figure 11.6
Large block level power distribution.

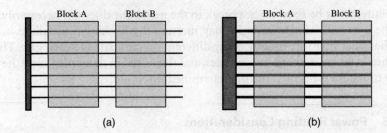

Figure 11.7
Power routing options.

vertically and interleaved so that at the lowest level they can be connected to the gates at the appropriate contact points. Of course, this type of routing does not fully account for the different types of blocks at the lower level, such as memory, logic, clock, and bus drivers, that may be connecting to the supply. However, the general idea of distributing power routes around the chip is conveyed in this diagram.

The power distribution system should be designed to route current to the gates, taking into account *IR* and EM. This requires a more careful consideration of the routing methodology. For example, consider the two blocks in Figure 11.7a. If power is routed through Block A to Block B, a larger *IR* drop will occur in Block B since power is also being consumed by Block A before it reaches Block B. As more and more blocks are added, the complex interactions between blocks determine the actual voltage drops. The placement of these blocks is typically based on the timing requirements of the system or the size and shape of blocks at the floor-planning stage. Therefore, sizing the power buses properly to minimize *IR* drop, while satisfying the required timing and area constraints, is a key design challenge.

The power busses could be widened to lower the resistance of the lines as in Figure 11.7b. The large metal trunks of power have to be sized to handle all the current for each block. Although routing power in this way makes it easier to manage *IR* drop, it also requires more area to implement. This forces designers to set aside large areas for power busing that takes away from the available global signal routing area. Since the same routing tracks are used for clocks, busses, and other global signals, the tradeoff between power and signal routing must be carefully managed.

Other alternatives are shown in Figure 11.8. In Figure 11.8a, current is delivered from both ends of the block thereby minimizing *IR* drop in the middle. Since the total *IR* drop is based on the resistance seen from the pin to the block, one could route around the block and feed power to each block separately as shown in Figure 11.8b. Ideally, the main trunks should be wide enough to handle all the current flowing through separate branches. However, the T-junctions have a high current density as current crowding occurs around the bends. It is important in this type of grid to examine the current density at all junctions, especially the corners, to ensure that EM problems do not exist.

Another approach to minimizing *IR* drop, depicted in Figure 11.9, is to have a grid of two metal layers. In the figure, assuming a five-layer metal process, Metal 4

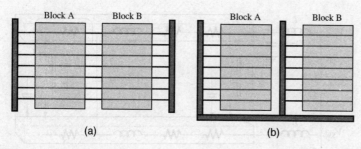

Figure 11.8
Simple techniques to reduce *IR* drop.

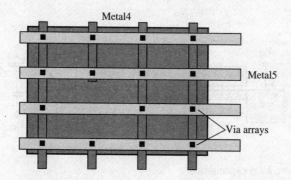

Figure 11.9
Vias in a mesh array methodology.

and Metal 5 use a via array to connect the two layers, effectively tying the whole grid to V_{DD}. However, part of the grid may have to be removed to route some signals. If you arbitrarily remove a strap that is conducting a large amount of current, the excess current must flow in adjacent straps that may push the current density in them beyond acceptable levels for electromigration. These examples all illustrate that design tradeoffs must be made with both EM and *IR* in mind.

11.2.4   Decoupling Capacitance Design

On-chip decoupling capacitances (decaps) are commonly used to keep the power supply within the noise budget, especially during peak demand periods in high-frequency switching applications. The decoupling capacitors are large-valued capac-itances that hold a reservoir of charge located near the power pins and any large driv-ers, as shown in Figure 11.10. When large buffers switch from low to high, these decaps are the first line of defense for *IR* drop and *Ldi/dt* effects. The needed current for the switching process is obtained from the local decap. Later, current flows from the V_{DD} pad to refill the reservoir of charge for the next switching operation.

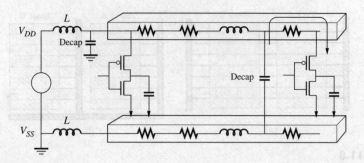

Figure 11.10

On-chip decoupling capacitance.

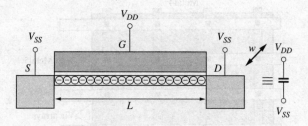

Figure 11.11

On-chip decap using MOS capacitance.

The on-chip decoupling capacitance is usually implemented using an NMOS transistor with the gate connected to V_{DD} and the source/drain connected to V_{SS}. The device is therefore in the linear region of operation. This is illustrated in Figure 11.11 where the parallel-plate capacitor is formed by the poly on one side and the channel inversion layer on the other. A first-order calculation of the capacitance is given by

$$C_{decap} = C_{ox}WL$$

and therefore the required decoupling value can be obtained with the proper choice of W and L.

A more accurate model would include the fringing and overlap capacitances of the poly edge to the source/drain regions:

$$C_{decap} = C_{ox}WL + 2C_{ol}W$$

The two main design issues are to decide how much decoupling capacitance to include and where to place them. Assuming that we somehow know the amount of decap needed, we must select the proper values of W and L to optimize the decap while achieving a target capacitance value. The selection of the proper value of W

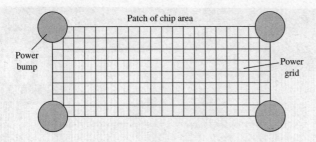

Figure 11.12
Simulation of patch area of chip.

and L can be based on a large number of simulations of inverter circuits with decaps as in Figure 11.10. The location of the decaps should be based on the location of the large buffers that are switching during the peak demand periods. Simulations can be carried out on a representative patch of the power grid between power bumps, shown in Figure 11.12. The power bumps are essentially the solder bumps connected to V_{DD}. Any circuitry connected to the grid should represent the types of buffers and drivers that will typically be found in the design.

There are many factors to consider when deciding how much capacitance to employ and where to place them. First, there is a certain amount of decoupling that is already present in the circuit due to the devices that do not switch. This includes gate and source/drain capacitances, as well as wire capacitances, for all nodes that are charged up to V_{DD}. This value may be subtracted off the target decoupling capacitance needed in the circuit. We also need to know the noise budget, the switching activity of the circuit, the current provided by the power grid and the rate of change of current with respect to time. Since the actual location and amount of decoupling capacitance are difficult to determine in an optimal way, some rules of thumb are used to ensure proper performance. Typically, the decap amount should be 10 times the switching capacitance, and decaps should be placed in as many open areas of the chip as possible. In addition, decaps should be located near the power pins to offset any effects of inductance due to solder bumps or bonding wires.

11.2.5 Power Distribution Design Example

To reinforce many of the concepts described in the previous sections, we sequence through a power distribution design example. Figure 11.13 shows an actual power distribution system for a large digital chip. Only the metal lines associated with the power grid are shown here. There are large blocks that are clearly distinguishable in this design. Each block was designed by a separate group. The horizontal and vertical patterns of the power grid are quite evident in each block. The memory block in the lower middle portion has a high-density grid as would be expected by the density of memory circuits. This chip example will be used several times in this chapter.

To illustrate a possible tradeoff between *IR* drop and electromigration, we first plot a contour map of the *IR* drop for the chip, as shown in Figure 11.14. The two

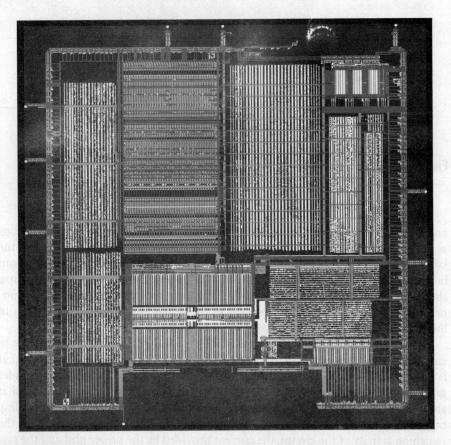

Figure 11.13
Example of a chip power distribution system.

plots show the voltage drop in the power grid with different shading levels to indicate the severity of the drop. This type of plot is generated by extracting all the resistors in the physical power grid and assembling a large resistive mesh; the logic circuits and memory blocks are then represented as ideal current sources and attached to the resistive grid. Each current source is assigned the average current level of the corresponding gate. A simulation is performed to compute the voltage drop at every point in the grid, and this voltage is assigned a grayscale value and plotted in the figure.

Consider the *IR* drop plot on the left side of Figure 11.14. The large oval region near the center of the chip is a region of excessive *IR* drop. In fact, it violates the 10% noise budget assigned to the power grid. The reason for the violation is that the lower part of the grid is not connected to the upper part of the grid. This was inadvertent since the chip was assembled simply by connecting the separately designed blocks together. Unfortunately, the upper portion of the grid must derive all needed current from the six or seven V_{DD} pads around the periphery of the top portion of the chip. To remedy this problem, the designer simply connected the lower portion

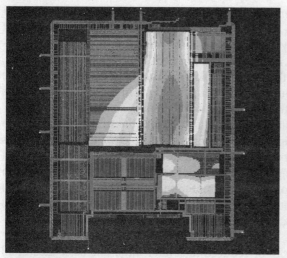
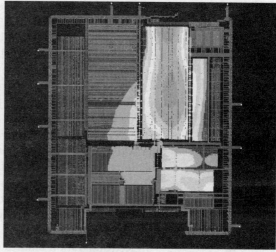

Figure 11.14
IR drop plots before and after repairs.

of the chip to the upper portion with a number of power straps (i.e., metal connections). The resulting *IR* drop plot is shown in the right-hand side figure. The power grid now satisfies the noise budget.

The side effect of the changes made to the grid is illustrated in Figure 11.15. Here, the electromigration failures have been plotted as dots on the power grid.

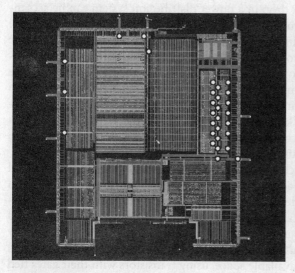
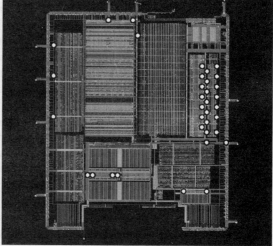

Figure 11.15
Electromigration plots before and after repairs.

Each failure is based on whether or not a given section of metal satisfies the EM criterion based on Equation (11.5). The equation requires a calculation of the current density, J_{avg}. This value is simply the dc current in the metal line divided by its cross-sectional area. Once computed, if the J_{avg} of the segment is less than a specified level, J_{max}, then the metal segment is flagged as a violation. Since large currents flow at the boundaries of the chip, we would expect more violations in these regions. This is confirmed by the locations of the dots in the two figures.

The left-hand side figure shows the violations before the straps were added to fix the *IR* drop problem. The right-hand side figure is the picture for EM violations after adding straps. Notice that the lower portion of the grid experiences more EM violations than in the other diagram. This is due to the fact that the lower portion of the grid is now supplying more of the current to the upper portion and the metal segments have a higher current density. Some of the densities are high enough to violate the EM criteria. Clearly, the power system must be redesigned by considering both *IR* and EM together.

Electromigration failures can be reduced in several ways. The basic idea in all approaches is to reduce the average current density experienced by any metal segment. The simplest approach is to widen the metal lines. However, increasing the width beyond a certain point leads to overdesign, which costs area and can reduce yields. Another approach is to change the current flow in the power grid itself by adding jumpers and straps between different points in the grid. This would reroute current from the affected areas, but such changes would require another verification pass to confirm that the problem has not simply been moved to another part of the design. Switching to copper is perhaps the most significant step toward reduction or elimination of these types of failures in metal segments. However, electromigration in vias and the local heating of neighboring lines may be limiting factors in the ultimate improvement that can be achieved using Cu.

Reducing the impact of *IR* drop in a power distribution system can be accomplished in several ways. The simplest approach is to widen the lines that experience the largest voltage drops since increasing the width decreases the resistance (and the *IR* drop). However, this may not always be possible due to constraints in the routing area. Another approach is to add/remove metal straps as mentioned above. Since *IR* drop is due primarily to simultaneous switching events, another approach is to stagger the gates that are switching together such that they switch at slightly different times—at least enough to keep the problem within the noise budget. Alternatively, buffer sizes can be reduced, but this may not be possible if the design fails to meet performance requirements with smaller devices.

The most effective approach is to use *decoupling capacitors* between power and ground, which can deliver the additional current needed by the power distribution system. As described earlier, a decoupling capacitor is a large capacitance that is connected from V_{DD} to Gnd typically using a large MOS transistor. The charge stored in the decoupling capacitors is used to initially provide current to the gates, thereby reducing the *IR* drop and *Ldi/dt* effects. These decoupling caps are usually scattered throughout the design in any available space, using transistors with their gates tied to V_{DD} and their source-drain regions tied to Gnd. All empty regions of the chip are filled with decoupling caps using the philosophy that you can never have enough (i.e., overdesign). However, the large area overhead may act to reduce yield. Typically designers add a total decoupling capacitance that is 10 times the amount of capacitance switched on every cycle, as a rule of thumb. Package and pin Ldi/dt effects can be mitigated by placing large capacitances near the pins.

The number of pins assigned to V_{DD} and Gnd can also be increased to reduce IR drop. By providing more supply pins, the current requirements for a given section can be satisfied from a number of sources. Of course, this limits the number of pins available for I/O. A more aggressive solution is to use a ball-grid array where the power supply connections can be placed at various points within the chip. The key design issue is proper placement of the bumps around the chip. Note that solder bumps cannot be used in sensitive areas such as memories and dynamic logic because the bumps generate α-particles that may cause logic value upsets on the sensitive nodes. Nevertheless, when used appropriately, solder bump technology can reduce IR drop significantly.

11.3   Clocking and Timing Issues

11.3.1   Clock Definitions and Metrics

In modern VLSI systems, the clock is perhaps the most important signal because it controls the rate of data processing and communication. It provides a structured framework for dealing with high-complexity digital systems. A clock network distributes the clock signal from the clock generator, or source, to the clock inputs of the synchronizing components. We typically build the FSMs (finite state machines) from combinational logic (for next state logic) and flip-flops (for storage elements). The logic elements have differing delays and, as a result, the path delays through the logic blocks will differ. We control the storage elements with a clock to keep everything synchronized. Unfortunately, we can have fast or slow signals in the combinational logic, and fast or slow clocks that make timing synchronization more difficult.

There are a number of important definitions and figures of merit associated with the clock as shown in Figure 11.16. Ideally, the clock should arrive at all flip-flops at the same time, have a fixed period, T_{cycle}, and near zero rise/fall times. Actual clocks fall short of this ideal model. First, the arrival times of the clock to the flip-flop (FF)

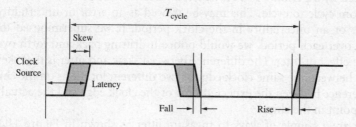

Figure 11.16
Clock latency and skew definitions.

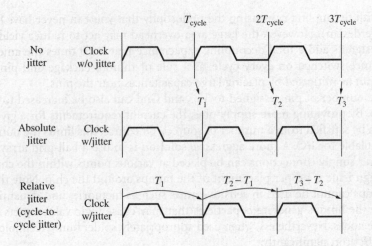

Figure 11.17
Definitions for clock jitter.

inputs around the chip are different. The *clock skew* is defined as the maximum difference of the clock arrival times to the inputs of FFs. Another important parameter is clock *latency*, as shown in Figure 11.16. The latency is defined as the maximum delay from the clock source to any FF clock input. This is important since it determines whether the external system clock is properly synchronized with the internal clock. Ideally, we would like the internal and external clock edges to be positioned at the same point in time. Otherwise, the chip I/O will require large setup and hold times to account for latency. The clock *rise/fall times* should be small and kept about equal, but this requires the use of large buffers. Unfortunately, clock networks with large buffers can consume a large portion of the total power of synchronous VLSI systems (up to 40%). The clock design objectives must be attained while minimizing the use of system resources such as power and area.

Another important metric for the quality of a clock is the clock *jitter*. This is the variation of the clock period from one cycle to another, as seen in Figure 11.17. Normally, we expect the clock edge, either rising or falling, to be at the same point in time, spaced by a period T_{cycle}. However, a variety of factors move the clock edge around from cycle to cycle. This may be viewed as an error or uncertainty in the clock edge or an uncertainty in the clock period. If we superimposed the clock waveform over each period, we would notice it drifting back and forth over time. This is the effect of jitter. The difference between skew and jitter is that skew is the difference between the same clock edge at two different locations on the chip; jitter is the difference between the expected time of the clock edge and the actual time at the same point in the chip.

There are a couple of ways to measure jitter as shown in Figure 11.17. One approach is to use a clock signal without jitter as a reference, such as the first clock that is evenly spaced by a given period T_{cycle}. The second clock has jitter and its clock

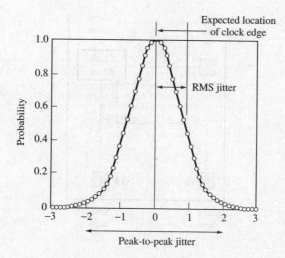

Figure 11.18

Jitter measurements.

edges are measured against the absolute points in time where the jitter-free clock edges occur. That is, T_1 is compared to T_{cycle}, and T_2 is compared to $2T_{\text{cycle}}$, and so on. This is an *absolute jitter* measurement: $T_n - nT_{\text{cycle}}$.

Another approach is to ignore errors in the edge locations up to the last cycle and measure jitter relative to the last clock edge. This is indicated using the third clock waveform which has the same error as the second clock. In this case, we simply compare the current period of the clock with the expected period. This is *cycle-to-cycle jitter*: $(T_n - T_{n-1}) - T_{\text{cycle}}$. For on-chip applications, we are mainly interested in cycle-to-cycle jitter since we care only if the logic functions can be completed within the current clock cycle and not on any absolute time reference. Absolute jitter is more important for off-chip timing synchronization between two chips.

Cycle-to-cycle jitter is typically smaller than absolute jitter since it is always measured relative to the last clock edge. If we measured the jitter over thousands of cycles, we would produce a histogram with a distribution of the form shown in Figure 11.18. Here, the normalized probability of the clock edge is plotted against its arrival time. The expected arrival time is at the point marked "0" on the x-axis. Some edges will arrive earlier than this time, while others will arrive later. The x-axis is labeled in terms of the standard deviation, or σ, of the distribution. Jitter measurements are usually provided as peak-to-peak values (4σ) or RMS values (one σ), as shown. The goal in clock design is to minimize jitter, especially within the clock generation circuits.

11.3.2 Clock Skew

Much of the effort in clock design centers on minimizing the clock skew. An example of the clock skew problem is shown in Figure 11.19. The clock driver is located

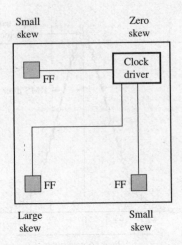

Figure 11.19
Clock skew example.

in one corner of the chip while the target flops are scattered around the chip. The arrival times of the clock to each of the FFs will be slightly different; some will receive the clock early while others receive the clock late, relative to each other. The delay differences are due to differences in the length of the global wire from clock to FF, gate delays along the different paths, and the fanout driven by FF signal. If we examine the FFs in each corner, the two near-end FFs will have a smaller skew relative to each other (early clock), whereas the one that is diagonally opposite to the clock will have a large skew (late clock).

At first, this skew appears to be more an annoyance than a problem. In reality, it can greatly affect the performance and proper functionality of the overall system. To illustrate this, consider the situation shown in Figure 11.20. In the upper part of the figure, a sequential system is shown with positive-edge triggered flip-flops at each end and a combinational "cloud" representing the logic gates between the flops. There are multiple paths through the logic that can be characterized by two parameters: the worst-case path with delay T_{dMAX}, and best-case path with delay, T_{dMIN}.

Now, consider the effect of skew on cycle time. In Figure 11.20, assume that the clock arrives early at the far-end flop and late at the near-end flop. When the clock arrives at the near-end flop, it launches new data into the combinational cloud (i.e., into the logic block) after a delay of T_{clk-q} which is a property of the flop, as discussed in Chapter 5. This is followed by a maximum delay of T_{dMAX} through the logic. Upon arriving at the far-end flop, a setup time for the flop, T_{setup}, must be satisfied. The three components, $T_{clk-q} + T_{dMAX} + T_{setup}$, would normally comprise the cycle time, T_{cycle}.

However, if the clock arrives early at the far-end flop due to skew, we may have a problem as shown in the waveforms of Figure 11.20. The early clock of the next cycle would arrive and latch data that are not yet stable from the current cycle, according to the setup time. This would cause a functional error in the circuit.

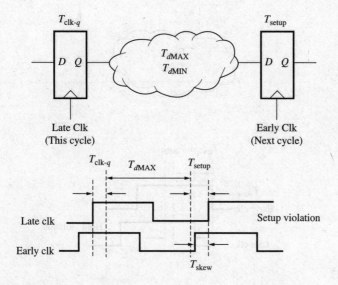

Figure 11.20

Effect of skew on cycle time.

When circuits do not meet the requirements of the cycle time, it is usually referred to as a *setup time violation*, even though it is due to skew. There is a simple solution to this problem. If we increase the clock period by T_{skew} we can guarantee that the circuit always works. However, the penalty is that the cycle time is longer by the skew value. The new cycle time is given by

$$T_{cycle} = T_{clk-q} + T_{dMAX} + T_{setup} + T_{skew} \qquad (11.6)$$

Next, consider Figure 11.21. Here the arrival times of the clock at the flip-flops are reversed. This time we are concerned about the shortest path through the logic block. When the early clock arrives at the first flop, the logic propagates through the combinational cloud and the fastest signal path reaches the second flop in a time $T_{clk-q} + T_{dMIN}$. If this is too fast, there is a problem. When the late clock arrives at the second flop in the same cycle, it latches the incoming data regardless of whether they are the correct data or not. It may inadvertently capture the new (incorrect) data. The skew is working against the goal of latching the right data. Why? Because if the new data arrives before the hold time of the previous data is satisfied, the second FF incorrectly samples the new data instead of the correct data. This is referred to as a *hold time violation* as shown in Figure 11.21. Note that this problem cannot be solved by slowing down the clock. The criterion for proper operation is that

$$T_{skew} + T_{hold} < T_{clk-q} + T_{dMIN} \qquad (11.7)$$

To overcome hold time problems, the designer must increase the delay of the shortest paths that violate Equation (11.7). This can be accomplished by adding buffers

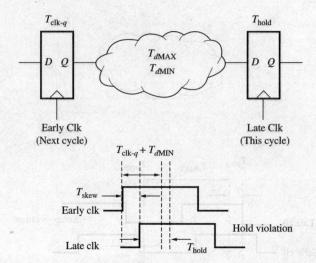

Figure 11.21
Effect of clock skew on functionality.

or reducing the size of some of the existing gates. Care must be taken so as not to inadvertently increase the delay of the longest paths. Ultimately, the clock circuit must be designed with minimum skew to reduce the number of potential setup and hold problems.

11.3.3 Effect of Noise on Clocks and FFs

At this stage, it is useful to point out some of the serious consequences of noise due to crosstalk, as described in Chapter 10, especially relating to clocks and flip-flops. Consider the positive edge-triggered D-flop of Figure 11.22a. Normally, when the clock goes from high to low, the D-flop continues to hold the output signal at its previous value. However, if a capacitive or inductive noise event couples to the clock node and is fed to the FF, it may inadvertently capture a random value at the D input. Here, the clock has a short positive-going edge during a fall transition. It is positioned at the switching threshold of the flop and triggers a capture event at the input. It is critical that noise events due to interconnect be eliminated when designing the clock distribution network.

A second case is shown in Figure 11.22b where the clock is free of any glitches, but the data input experiences a coupling noise event. Again, it occurs exactly when it cannot be tolerated (according to *Murphy's Law*)—on the positive-edge of the clock—and therefore the wrong value is captured. The noise does not satisfy the setup and hold requirements of the FF, but it still produces an unwanted change at the output. Therefore, a significant amount of noise cannot be tolerated at the data input to the FF.

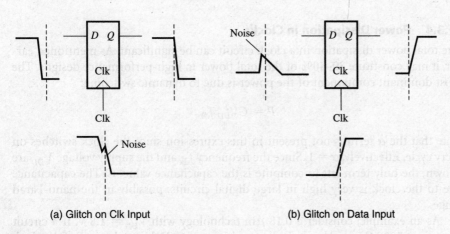

(a) Glitch on Clk Input   (b) Glitch on Data Input

Figure 11.22
Effect of coupling noise on FF performance.

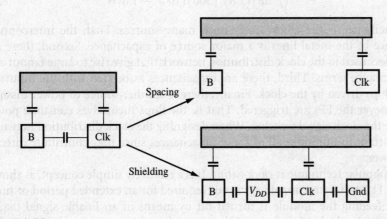

Figure 11.23
Layout solutions to coupling problems.

To limit noise events around FFs, one can employ the spacing and shielding techniques described earlier. For example, in Figure 11.23, signal B and the Clk signal are situated very close to one another. There is a potential for noise events between these signals due to coupling capacitance. The possible layout solutions are to separate B and Clk by a sufficient spacing or to shield the Clk with V_{DD} and Gnd. The spacing approach has a lower capacitance and therefore reduces power to some degree. However, the shielding is beneficial for both capacitive coupling and inductive coupling. Typically, clocks are shielded to protect them from unwanted noise, but also to protect other sensitive signals from unexpected mutual coupling to the clock. The price of shielding is increased capacitance and power dissipation.

11.3.4 Power Dissipation in Clocks

The total power dissipation in a clock circuit can be significant. As mentioned earlier, it may constitute 30–40% of the total power in high-performance designs. The most dominant component of the power is due to dynamic switching:

$$P = CV_{DD}^2 f_{clk}$$

Note that the α term is not present in this expression since the clock switches on every cycle. Effectively, $\alpha = 1$. Since the frequency f_{clk} and the supply voltage V_{DD} are known, the only term left to compute is the capacitance value, C. The capacitance due to the clock is very high in large digital circuits, possibly in the nano-Farad range.

As an example, consider a 0.18 μm technology with $V_{DD} = 1.8$ V. If a circuit operates at 500 MHz and has a clock capacitance of 1 nF, the total power of the clock circuit alone is

$$P = (1 \text{ nF})(1.8)^2 (500)(10^6) = 1.6 \text{ W}$$

The capacitance of the clock arises from many sources. First, the interconnect capacitance of the metal lines is a major source of capacitance. Second, there are large buffers used in the clock distribution network that give rise to large fanout and self-capacitance terms. Third, there are capacitances associated with the inputs of the flip-flops driven by the clock. Finally, there is another source of power dissipation whenever the FFs are triggered. That is, the flops themselves consume power each time the clock signal switches. When designing the clock distribution network, it is important to minimize all of these capacitances since they contribute directly to the power.

One popular technique is *clock gating*. It is a relatively simple concept, as shown in Figure 11.24. If a functional unit is not required for an extended period of time, the clock feeding the module is turned off by means of an Enable signal that is ANDed with the clock. Most functional units are inactive a majority of the time. For example, a floating-point unit may be inactive while a number of integer operations are being performed. If the clock continues to toggle the D-flops associated with

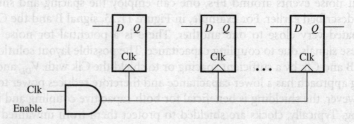

Figure 11.24
Gated clock to reduce power.

this unit, power is being dissipated unnecessarily. Clock gating can disable the unit to save the power that would be consumed by the flops.

There are a number of issues associated with clock gating. First, it is important to decide whether gating is appropriate for a given block. Clearly, a gated clock at the input of all flops does not save much power. Therefore, the location of such gates around the chip should be determined carefully. Second, the gate may add skew to the clock, so it must be inserted in a balanced way. That is, even if certain blocks do not require it, a gate should be added to maintain balance. But this runs counter to the first issue. Third, a certain amount of logic circuitry is needed for the Enable signal that may affect performance or consume power. Depending on the complexity of the clock gating, this tradeoff should be monitored to ensure that a gain here is not offset by a loss elsewhere. And finally, timing verification complexity and reusability of a block are additional considerations for this approach. Nevertheless, this technique is very popular as it saves unnecessary clock activities inside the gated module.

11.3.5   Clock Generation

With the basic definitions and design considerations completed, we now turn our attention to the design of the clock circuit itself. A simple technique for on-chip generation of a primary clock signal is to use a ring oscillator as shown in Figure 11.25. A ring oscillator has an odd number of inverter stages and produces an oscillating signal at each node. The period of oscillation is determined by the delay of each stage and the number of stages. This type of clock circuit has been used in low-end microprocessor chips. However, the generated clock signal can be quite process-dependent and unstable. Consequently, separate clock chips that use crystal oscillators have been used for high-performance VLSI circuits.

Usually, a VLSI circuit receives one or more primary clock signals from the external clock source and then generates necessary derivates for its internal use. Typically, we must generate both true and complementary clock signals for internal use. Figure 11.26 shows a CMOS generator/driver that uses a transmission gate (TG) delay element. The first driver of the chain is an inverter with transistors Mp1

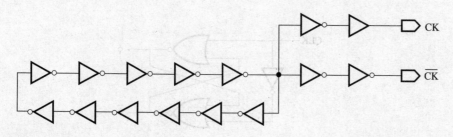

Figure 11.25
A simple on-chip clock generator using a ring oscillator.

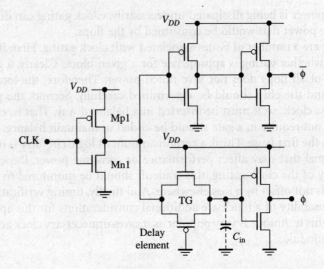

Figure 11.26

A clock generator with a transmission gate delay.

and Mn1. The top branch of the chain consists of two cascaded inverters and generates a signal $\phi \equiv \overline{CLK}$, whereas the bottom branch consists only of a single inverter and a transmission gate and provides $\phi \equiv CLK$. The TG is used as a delay element to minimize the clock skew between the two generated signals.

Another simple approach uses an SR latch to generate two-phase clock signals (see Figure 11.27). This circuit has two weaknesses that should be checked and properly designed. First, the input CLK signal propagates through an additional inverter to generate $\overline{\phi}$. The second problem is related to the first one. The NOR gates should not be designed to be equal in size, but rather their output signals should have an identical response. The design should also take into account the total capacitance of the interconnect that is dependent on the layout topology.

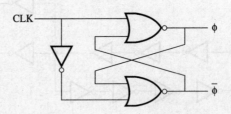

Figure 11.27

Latch-based clock generator.

11.3.6   Clock Distribution for High-Performance Designs

Once the clock signal is generated, it is necessary to distribute it around the chip. This is a complicated task due to the issues of skew, noise, and power. Since clock signals are required almost uniformly over the chip area, it is desirable that all clock signals be distributed with a uniform delay. Ideal distribution networks are the H-tree and X-tree structures shown in Figure 11.28. In an H-tree structure, the distances from the center to all branch points are the same and, hence, the signal delays are expected to be the same. The limitation of this structure is a difficult implementation due to routing constraints and nonuniform fanout requirements. Another configuration that yields equal-length interconnections is the X-clock tree. Compared to an H-tree, it suffers from the following:

- The clock line produces sharper corners than 90°; inductive discontinuities are significant and, as a result, reflections are larger.

- The fanout at the branching points is always 4 as opposed to a fanout of 2 in the H-tree. An increased fanout degrades matching the line impedance and increases the reflections.

- Two clock lines are in a close proximity (farther apart in an H-tree) which increases the crosstalk.

To avoid reflections at the branching points, the line separates into two branches with characteristic impedances twice the impedance of the incoming line. In parallel, they act like a single line and have the same impedance as the incoming line. In order to obtain such a perfect impedance matching, wiring-oriented approaches have to be applied. The designer has to narrow the line width at the branching points because the line impedance is inversely proportional to its capacitance. This type of layout construction is shown in Figure 11.29a. Other alternative approaches are a wide-bus technique and a fat clock bus. The wide-bus technique increases the capacitance and decreases the resistance on source-to-sink paths (Figure 11.29b).

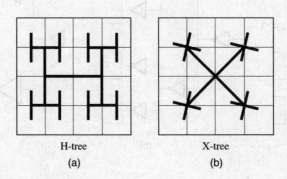

H-tree   X-tree
(a)   (b)

Figure 11.28
Symmetric clock trees.

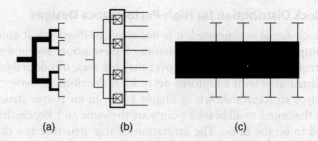

(a)   (b)   (c)

Figure 11.29
(a) Clock tree with tapered wire widths. (b) Clock tree using a wide-bus. (c) Fat bus clock tree implementation.

The construction of a fat clock bus (Figure 11.29c) requires a very large clock driver, thus the driver and the interconnect will consume large amounts of power. However, since delays of the clock tree are dominated by the capacitance of the wide-bus, the bus-to-clock interconnection can be done simply and efficiently.

Because of the significant delays associated with long wires in clocks, the designer must insert buffers at various points along the clock wire. In essence, buffer-oriented solutions partition the large clock network into small segments. The main challenge of any buffered clock architecture is to maintain balance in the delays. Several examples of buffered clock distributions are shown in Figure 11.30 and Figure 11.31. Figure 11.30 shows three conventional clock-tree networks. The

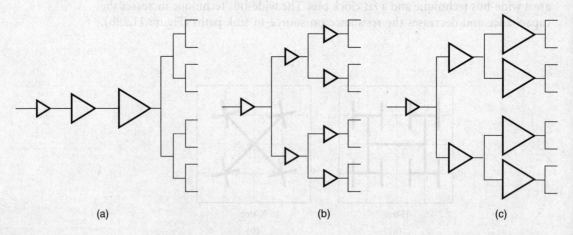

(a)   (b)   (c)

Figure 11.30
(a) Buffer chain with tapered sizes driving clock tree. (b) Clock power-up tree with uniform buffer size. (c) Clock power-up tree with tapered buffer sizes.

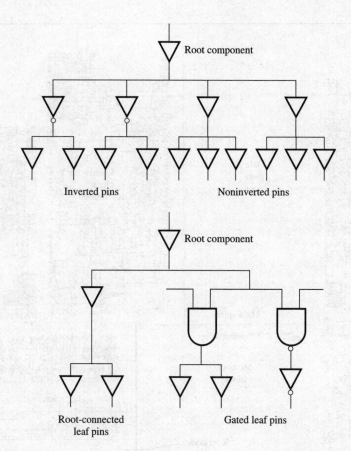

Figure 11.31
Clock tree examples.

first one uses a super buffer technique to drive the clock tree. The second approach inserts equal-sized buffers in the clock tree. The third approach increases the buffer sizes as they get closer to the loads.

Figure 11.31 shows two clock networks with additional characteristics. In the top picture, the tree generates an inverted clock in addition to a standard clock signal, and in the bottom picture, the tree generates a gated clock signal and a standard clock signal. Gated clocks are useful when we want to prevent the clock from triggering a flip-flop to reduce power.

11.3.7 Example of a Clock Distribution Network

Figure 11.32 illustrates a clock network extracted from an industrial chip. It is the same example used in Section 11.2.5. The interconnect associated with the entire clock is shown in the figure. The clock tree starts at a root node and splits off into a

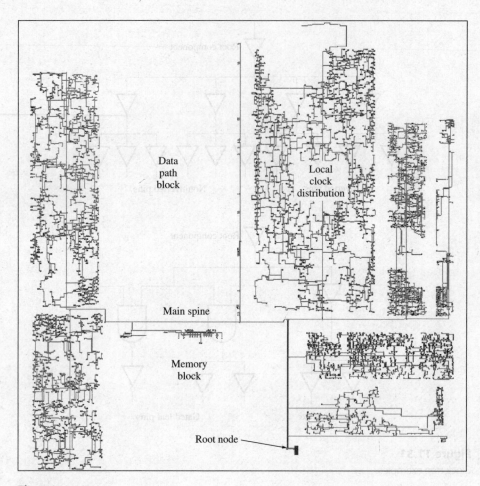

Figure 11.32
Clock tree routing for industrial chip.

number of major spines, from which local clocks emanate. The two empty regions are the memory and data path areas. The clock drives the decoders in the memory circuit (just below the *main spine* label) and the data path is driven by the clock spine on the right side. The rest of the blocks obtain their local clocks from internal spines that run through them.

The buffers in this clock tree are of the form shown in Figure 11.30b with uniform sizes. These buffers draw a significant amount of current when switching. In fact, the section labeled *local clock distribution* has such a large number of buffers that, when they switch simultaneously, it creates significant *IR* drop in the power grid. Recall from Figure 11.14 that the *IR* drop was most significant in this region

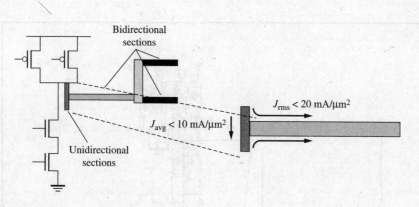

Bidirectional
sections

$J_{rms} < 20$ mA/μm^2

$J_{avg} < 10$ mA/μm^2

Unidirectional
sections

Figure 11.33
Electromigration effects in signal lines due to ac and dc current flow.

and violated the 10% noise budget. This *IR* drop translates into additional delay, resulting in additional clock skew. Ironically, the clock itself is causing the problem of *IR* drop. This is why the clock and power distribution systems are often designed together.

Recently, electromigration (EM) problems have been encountered on clock signal lines as a result of large currents that flow back and forth on these lines. EM on signal lines is therefore an ac phenomenon. As a result, we must compute the *root-mean-square (RMS)* value of the current rather than the average current (which tends to be close to zero for the ac case). The RMS current density, J_{rms}, is compared to another EM limit, $J_{AC,max}$, that is based on ac *Joule heating* as current moves back and forth in the wire. A typical value of $J_{AC,max}$ is 20 mA/μm^2. The failure criterion is

$$J_{rms} > J_{AC,max} \tag{11.8}$$

If the actual RMS current density is below the tolerable amount, the signal line is expected to have a lifetime well beyond the life of the corresponding product.

Consider Figure 11.33 which illustrates the EM problem areas for the clock. The metal segments at the output of the gate experience both unidirectional (dc) and bidirectional (ac) current flow mechanisms. Most of the wire encounters bidirectional current due to charging and discharging of capacitances. Therefore, the current density criteria would be based on Equation (11.8) for EM failure. However, a short unidirectional segment of metal connects the PMOS devices to the NMOS devices. It would be evaluated using the criteria in Equation (11.5) for EM failure. In the figure, the criteria to *pass* the EM checks are shown for each of the two segments.

Figure 11.34 shows the results of an EM analysis on a portion of the clock tree of Figure 11.32. The areas that are highlighted with squares have violated the EM criteria, either (11.5) or (11.8). All signal EM failures must be fixed since any break in the wire is catastrophic. Again, wire widening is the typical solution to this problem.

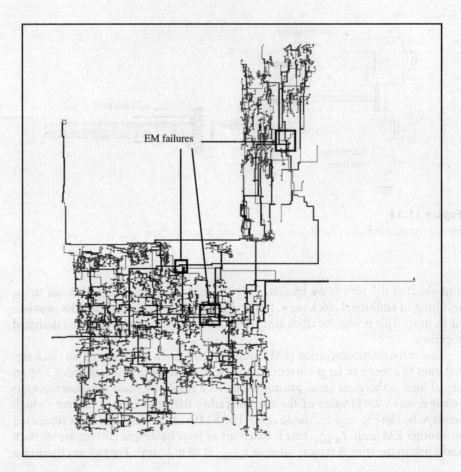

Figure 11.34
Signal EM failures in clock tree.

*11.4 Phase-Locked Loops/Delay-Locked Loops

In this section, we examine the problem of synchronizing the externally supplied master clock with the internal clock of the chip. In digital VLSI systems with multiple chips on a printed circuit board (PCB) or in system-on-chip (SOC) applications, severe problems may arise due to latency between the master reference clock and locally generated slave clocks. The value of the on-chip clock latency may differ from chip to chip or from module to module. Since the data transfers are synchronized with the slave clocks, timing hazards may occur and/or data errors may be generated (data may be sampled at a wrong time). These problems can be rectified using *phase-locked loop* (PLL) and *delay-locked loop* (DLL) circuits.

On-chip PLLs can be used to synchronize the internal clock of a chip with the external clock and data, and to generate the internal clock signal running at a higher rate of operation than the external clock input. Consider the timing diagram of

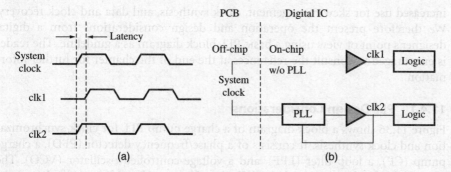

Figure 11.35
On-chip PLL for clock synchronization.

Figure 11.35a. The external system clock of the PCB is the off-chip clock. This clock is fed into a chip to be used as the internal clock as shown in the top portion of Figure 11.35b. The on-chip clock is buffered to drive the flops or latches of the logic blocks. However, the delay through the clock buffers and wires (i.e., clock latency) creates a difference between the internal and external clocks as seen in clk1 of Figure 11.35a. This leads to additional setup and hold requirements at the I/O pins of the chip. Ideally, we would like the two edges to line up so that the internal clock is synchronized with the external clock, as in the clk2 waveform of Figure 11.35a. To do this, we could use a delay-locked loop or phase-locked loop, as shown for clk2 in Figure 11.35b.

The PLL and DLL circuits are closely related.[2] Both use feedback control to lock the output clock to the incoming clock. PLLs must lock on to the frequency and phase of the reference clock, whereas DLLs simply lock to a constant phase of the reference clock. Therefore, the locking process in a PLL requires more time (since it must first lock on to the frequency and then the phase) than a DLL (since it must only lock on to the phase). If we simply want synchronization, we could use a DLL. However, if we needed the internal clock to run at a multiple of the external clock frequency, we must use a PLL.

The PLL and DLL feedback control systems have very similar architectures, as will be seen shortly. The main difference is the use of a voltage-controlled oscillator (VCO) in the PLL and a voltage-controlled delay line (VCDL) in the DLL. There are also differences in the stability properties of the two types of loops, and their ability or inability to perform frequency synthesis. Many books on analog design cover these types of circuits and their properties in great detail due to their widespread use in other applications.

As digital designers, it seems that PLLs/DLLs are beyond the scope of this book due to their analog nature. This is essentially a true statement. However, it is important to understand the basic operation of a PLL circuit, as well as DLL, due to their

---

[2] Even their names imply that they are related. That is, the term *delay* in the time domain has the same meaning as *phase* in the frequency domain.

increased use for skew management, clock synthesis, and data and clock recovery. We therefore present the operation and design considerations from a digital designer's point of view using a basic PLL block diagram as a guideline. The reader is encouraged to consult the references at the end of the chapter for further information.

11.4.1 PLL Design Considerations

Figure 11.36 shows a block diagram of a charge pump PLL for clock synchronization and clock synthesis. It consists of a phase/frequency detector (PFD), a charge pump (CP), a loop filter (LPF), and a voltage-controlled oscillator (VCO). The phase detector detects the phase difference between the reference clock and the VCO output and applies charge-up or charge-down pulses to the charge pump. These pulses are used to switch voltage or current sources, which charge or discharge its output. The pulses are filtered by the loop filter and applied as the control voltage of the VCO. The VCO changes its oscillation frequency according to the control voltage. If the VCO oscillates at a multiple of the input frequency, it must be divided down before a comparison is performed in the PFD.

The phase/frequency detector (PFD) is a circuit that detects the difference between the edges of the reference clock (Ref) and the feedback clock (FB). A simple version is shown in Figure 11.37a consisting of two D-flops and an AND gate. The D-inputs are tied to 1. The role of this circuit is to control the VCO by moving its frequency up or down depending on the edges of the incoming clocks.

The truth table for the PFD is given in Figure 11.37b. If the *up* and *down* signals are both 0, then the desired frequency and phase have been obtained and the PLL is in the locked condition. However, if the reference clock switches ahead of the feedback clock, the *up* signal is raised to indicate that the frequency of the VCO should be increased. Similarly, if the feedback clock switches ahead of the reference clock, a *down* signal is generated to slow down the VCO. If both the *up* and *down* signals are high, it is viewed as a reset condition, so the AND gate acts to reset the flops to 0.

To understand its operation further, consider the timing diagram of Figure 11.37c. Initially Ref Clk switches high ahead of FB Clk. This is a phase error in the two signals. The initial rise of Ref Clk sets its flop output to 1 while the rising edge

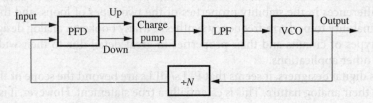

Figure 11.36
A basic PLL block diagram.

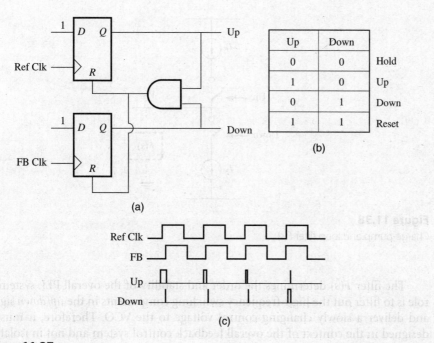

Up	Down	
0	0	Hold
1	0	Up
0	1	Down
1	1	Reset

(b)

(a)

(c)

Figure 11.37
Phase-frequency detector.

of FB Clk sets its flop output to 1. The combination of the two high outputs forces a reset. The pulse width on the *up* signal is proportional to the phase delay of the two signals. The *down* signal produces a short pulse that can easily be removed by the next stage, as will be seen. Since the VCO receives a "speedup" signal, the next set of edges of the two clocks will have a smaller phase difference. This shortens the *up* pulse. This continues until the phase difference switches signs, at which point the *down* signal is enabled. Eventually, the system stabilizes and there is a negligible difference between the two clocks.

Once the *up/down* signals have been generated, they are applied to a charge-pump which is illustrated in Figure 11.38 along with the output filter. Assume that the filter is a capacitor for the time being. The *up* signal will switch on the upper current source, I_P, and raise the output voltage at V_C. Similarly, the *down* signal will discharge the output capacitance and lower the control voltage, V_C. There are situations when both switches turn on simultaneously. However, as long as $I_P = I_N$, the overlapping pulses for the *up* and *down* signals do not create a problem since both switches are on and the current flows harmlessly from V_{DD} to Gnd.[3]

---

[3] In practice, it is difficult to get these two currents to match over supply and process variations, and temperature changes. This leads to a dc offset in the output that must be removed in some way (typically with a unity-gain amplifier and some additional switches).

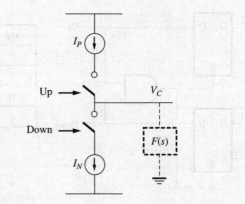

Figure 11.38
Charge-pump and loop filter $F(s)$.

The filter $F(s)$ determines the order and stability of the overall PLL system. Its role is to filter out the high-frequency switching components in the *up/down* signals and deliver a slowly changing control voltage to the VCO. Therefore, it must be designed in the context of the overall feedback control system and not in isolation. Even though the PLL is a highly nonlinear system, it can be analyzed as a linear system when it is in the locked or nearly locked condition. The control system representation is given in Figure 11.39, which we now analyze using linear system theory. The phase is the loop variable in this case, and the phase difference is determined and amplified by K_{PD} in the PFD:

$$v_d = K_{PD}(\theta_{in} - \theta_{out})$$

This is passed through the low-pass filter with a transfer function of $F(s)$. Then the signal passes through the VCO to create the output phase. The relationship between frequency and phase is that phase is the integral of frequency, and the frequency is determined by the control voltage:

$$\theta = \int f dt = \int K_o v_c dt$$

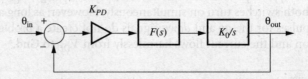

Figure 11.39
Linear feedback control system for PLL.

Therefore, the VCO can be viewed as an integrator that converts the control voltage into a phase. Its transfer function is given by K_0/s. The meaning of this transform is that the VCO introduces a pole into the system transfer function at $s = 0$. Any additional poles in the transfer function of $F(s)$ may lead to instability of the overall system, depending on their exact placement. This is why the loop filter plays such a strong role in the overall stability of the PLL.

We can now determine the two important transfer functions of the system: the open loop gain and the closed loop gain. The open loop gain is obtained by examining the direct path from the input to the output:

$$\frac{\theta_{\text{out}}}{\theta_{\text{in}}}(s) = K_{PD}F(s)\frac{K_0}{s} = G(s)$$

The closed loop gain is obtained by going around the loop once and can be written in terms of the open loop gain:

$$K_{PD}(\theta_{\text{in}}(s) - \theta_{\text{out}}(s))F(s)\frac{K_0}{s} = \theta_{\text{out}}(s)$$

$$(11.9)$$

$$\therefore \frac{\theta_{\text{out}}}{\theta_{\text{in}}}(s) = \frac{K_{PD}F(s)\dfrac{K_0}{s}}{1 + K_{PD}F(s)\dfrac{K_0}{s}} = \frac{G(s)}{1 + G(s)}$$

The classical study of the stability properties of such a system is carried out by analyzing the frequency response of the open loop system. This can be understood by examining Equation (11.9) above. If $G(s)$ in the denominator is equal to -1, the closed loop gain goes to infinity. The condition $G(s) = -1$ occurs when the magnitude of $G(s)$ is 1 and its phase is $-180°$. In practical terms, the system is said to be unstable in this condition. By examining Equation (11.9), the term that determines the stability of the system is the loop filter $F(s)$.

In Figure 11.40, three options are presented for the loop filter. We had assumed that the loop filter could be implemented as a grounded capacitance. This is a first-order filter (with one pole) and it produces a second-order PLL (since the PLL already has one pole due to the integrator). However, the use of a simple capacitor as the loop filter renders the PLL unstable since it introduces two poles at $s = 0$, which immediately sets the phase to $-180°$.

If a resistor is placed in series with the capacitor as in the second diagram, it inserts a zero into the transfer function and this allows the overall frequency response to be stabilized for the PLL. This is also a second-order PLL since the filter is of first-order. When a time-domain simulation is performed with this filter, we would notice that the charge-pump introduces small step discontinuities in the value of V_C as it switches, due to capacitive feedthrough. These discontinuities can be damped by adding a shunt capacitance as in the third diagram. While this is a more complicated filter, it can be shown that the PLL can be stabilized by the proper

$$G(s) = K_{PD} \frac{1}{C_1 s} \frac{K_0}{s}$$

Unstable

$$G(s) = K_{PD} \left(\frac{R_1 C_1 s + 1}{C_1 s} \right) \frac{K_0}{s}$$

Stable

$$G(s) = K_{PD} F(s) \frac{K_0}{s}$$

$$F(s) = \left(\frac{b-1}{b} \right) \left(\frac{s\tau_1 + 1}{sC_1 \left(\frac{s\tau_1}{b} + 1 \right)} \right)$$

Stable

$$b = 1 + C_1/C_2$$

$$\tau_1 = R_1 C_1$$

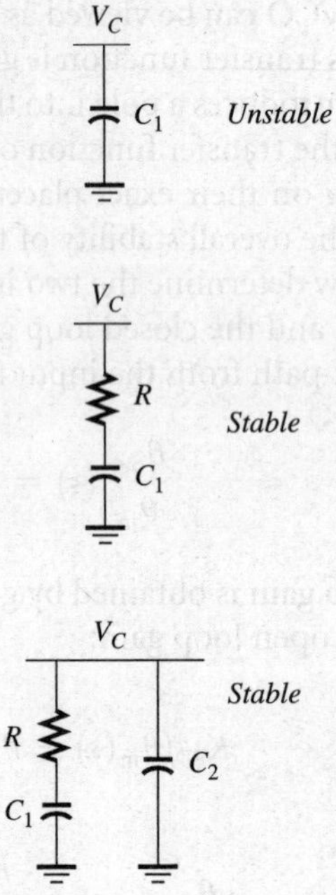

Figure 11.40
Filter options for PLL low-pass filter.

selection of R, C_1, and C_2. Typically $C_2 = (1/10)C_1$. The second-order filter makes the PLL a third-order system. Most on-chip PLLs use this type of filter.

The next block to consider is the VCO which acts as an integrator and generates a periodic output based on a control voltage input. A typical VCO for digital applications is presented in Figure 11.41a. This is a ring oscillator as we have seen before except that we have a controllable delay, τ. The frequency of oscillation is $f = 1/2N\tau$, where N is an odd number. The τ of each stage can be adjusted by the control voltage V_C. In Figure 11.41b, we show a "current-starved" inverter where the control voltage adjusts the amount of current delivered to the inverter to charge and discharge the next stage. As the current varies, the delay through the inverter varies as well. By connecting an odd number of stages in series, the oscillator can be designed to generate the required clock signal. As the control voltage is adjusted, the oscillation frequency changes over a prescribed range. Obviously, this figure is oversimplified compared to the actual VCOs but the basic principle is the same.

Since the output of the VCO generates the internal clock signal, it will have to be buffered so that it can drive the large loads associated with the clock tree. The appropriate buffer sizing methods are required so that the output of the VCO does not directly drive a large load. The last step of the PLL loop is the divider circuit, shown in Figure 11.36. The purpose of this digital block is to reduce the frequency of the VCO output to that of the incoming reference clock so that a proper phase comparison can be carried out.

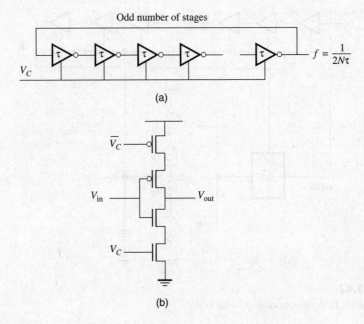

$$f = \frac{1}{2N\tau}$$

(a)

(b)

Figure 11.41

(a) Typical VCO. (b) Current-starved inverter.

This completes our brief look at the PLL. Clearly this is a challenging analog circuit design, especially in the presence of temperature and process variations. A critical design block is the VCO since it generates the clock used by the chip and is prone to *jitter* problems due to supply noise and other factors. As described earlier, jitter is the drift of the clock edge relative to the desired position. Note that the jitter at the PLL input is not propagated to the output since the VCO generates a new clock signal. Therefore, the input jitter is effectively filtered out by PLL. One layout problem is that the PLL is sensitive to the switching noise of other circuits. The interaction with other blocks must be minimized for proper operation. In addition, simulations of such circuits have been known to take a long time to complete. The use of this type of circuit will increase as chips get larger and there are more issues of clock synchronization on chips.

The other useful circuit in digital VLSI designs is a DLL block that synchronizes the data with the clock signal. The PLL can be modified to implement a DLL by a substitution of the VCO with a voltage-controlled delay line (VCDL) (shown in Figure 11.42). The same type of analysis described for the PLL can be applied to the DLL. The circuit utilizes the control signal, V_C, to vary the delay of each inverter. The VCDL circuit can be designed with multiple cascaded stages to construct a delay line. This circuit is popular since it has better stability properties than the PLL and is much easier to design. It can be stabilized using a simple capacitor as the loop filter. However, it transfers input jitter directly to the output. This circuit has been widely used in clock and data recovery applications.

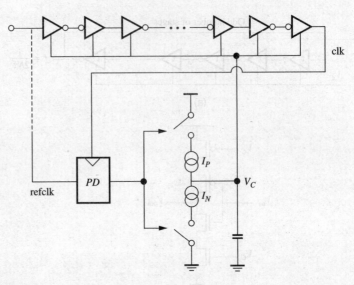

Figure 11.42
DLL with VCDL (Voltage-Controlled-Delay Line).

11.4.2   Clock Distribution Summary

To summarize, the key to proper clock design is to balance as much of the design as possible. First, the clock skew should be minimized by using architectures such as a buffered H-tree. It should be controlled by limiting the maximum and minimum interconnect length, using symmetric tree architectures with equal-sized buffers, and using an *all-or-none* strategy for gated clocks. The last stage of buffering to drive the local flip-flops may not be identical since the fanouts are not necessarily the same. However, the delay through the final buffers should be made the same. The clock edges should be kept as sharp as possible. The proper tradeoffs should be made to shield clock lines with V_{DD} and Gnd to limit crosstalk. The power should be minimized through the careful control of capacitance, and the use of gated clocks. The supply voltage should be regulated through the use of decoupling capacitors, especially in the area of the large clock buffers that switch simultaneously. PLL or DLL circuits should be used to synchronize external and internal clock signals.

Alpha 21264 is a good example of integrating clock hierarchy in its clocking network design, as illustrated in Figure 11.43. The global clock (GCLK) is generated by an on-chip, low-jitter phase-locked loop (PLL). The GCLK signal is routed along a trunk to the center of the die and is distributed by X-trees and H-trees to 16 distributed GCLK drivers located in a windowpane pattern across the chip. Figure 11.44 shows the clock hierarchy of the microprocessor. Local clocks and local conditional clocks (gated clocks) are driven several stages past GCLK. The novelty of this approach is the use of a clock grid structure, much like the power grid structure

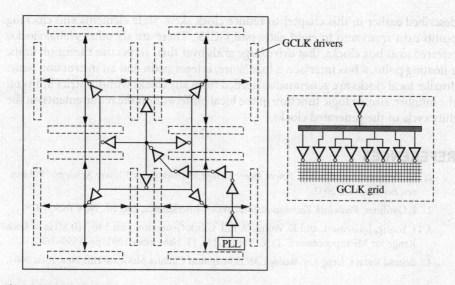

Figure 11.43
Global clock (GCLK) distribution network.

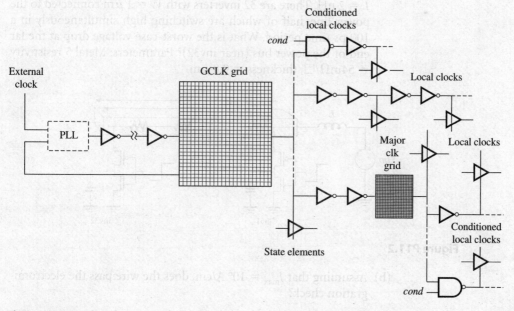

Figure 11.44
Clock hierarchy of 600 MHz alpha microprocessor.

described earlier in this chapter to reduce clock skew. State elements and clocking points exist from zero to eight gates past GCLK. There are six other global clocks, referred to as box clocks, that drive large grids over their respective execution units: a floating point, a bus interface, a load/store, integer pads, and an instruction issue. Smaller local clocks are generated as needed from any clocks without strict limits on the number, size, or logic function of the local buffers or on the requirements on the duty cycle of the generated clocks.

REFERENCES

1. M. Pedram and J. Rabaey, *Power Aware Design Methodologies*. Kluwer Academic Publishers, Boston, MA, 2002.

2. F. Gardiner, *Phaselock Techniques*. John Wiley–Interscience, 2nd ed., New York, 1979.

3. I. Young, J. Greason, and K. Wong, "A PLL Clock Generator with 5 to 110 MHz of Lock Range for Microprocessors," *JSSC*, Vol. 27, No. 11, November 1992, pp. 1599–1607.

4. Behrad Razavi, *Design of Analog CMOS Integrated Circuits*. McGraw-Hill, New York, 2001.

PROBLEMS

P11.1 List several known methods to address *IR* drop problems. Which of these methods are also effective for *Ldi/dt* and EM issues?

P11.2 (a) A 0.4 μm wide wire running 400 μm is used for a power bus in a 0.18 μm technology. It is connected to a pin with an inductance of $L = 2$ nH. There are 32 inverters with $W = 1$ μm connected to the power line, half of which are switching high simultaneously in a 100 ps time period. What is the worst-case voltage drop at the far end of the power bus (near inv32)? Parameters: Metal 5 resistivity = 54mΩ/$\square$, thickness = 0.8 μm.

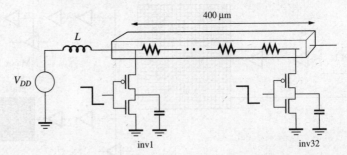

Figure P11.2

(b) Assuming that $J_{max} = 10^6$ A/cm, does the wire pass the electromigration check?

(c) If not, what width of wire is needed to pass the electromigration check?

P11.3 In the simultaneous switching case shown in Figure P11.3, 31 of the 32 output drivers switch from high to low while the one on the far right remains "stable." Assuming that the bonding wire inductance is 10 nH, how much ground bounce is experienced when each inverter discharges 5 pF over 1.8 ns through the chip ground? $V_{DD} = 1.8$ V.

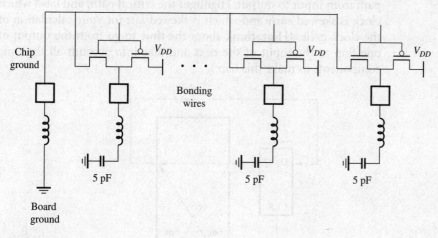

Figure P11.3

P11.4 In the 2-phase non-overlapping clock system shown in Figure P11.4, what is the minimum delay needed between Phi2 falling and Phi1 rising for the system to work properly? Assume that the maximum skew between any of the clocks is 1 ns, and that the delay through the latches is 0. Explain your answer. (Hint: Note that the answer could be positive or negative.) Also, what is the minimum clock cycle?

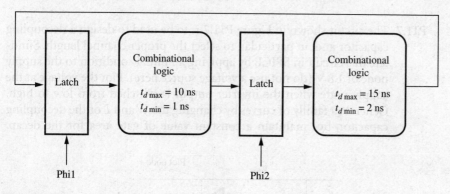

Figure P11.4

P11.5 In the above problem, redo the analysis assuming flip-flops in place of latches and a single clock.

P11.6 In the system shown in Figure P11.6 which uses two edge-triggered flip-flops, find the minimum clock cycle time. Assume that the setup time of the flop is 0.4 ns, the clk-to-q delay is 0.3 ns, and the hold time is 0.1 ns. The worst-case clock skew is 0.6 ns. The dotted lines in the combinational logic (CL) block indicate the longest delay along the path from input to output. Highlight the critical path, and label which clock is skewed *early* and which is skewed *late* for your calculation of the clock cycle. (Hint: think about the time to go from the output of one flop to the input of the next and take into account all the time components to make this trip.)

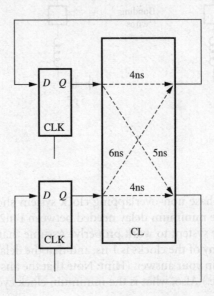

Figure P11.6

P11.7 The circuit shown in Figure P11.7 is to be used to design a decoupling capacitor and, in particular, to select the proper channel length. Simulate this circuit in SPICE by applying an initial condition to the supply node of 1.8 V (do not use a voltage source here). Plot the voltage at the supply node when the inverter output is switched from low to high. Generate a family of curves by changing the W and L of the decoupling capacitor, but maintain a constant value of gate area for the decap.

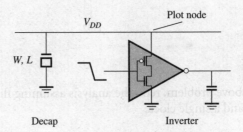

Figure P11.7

What is the optimal value of L according to your results? Assume 0.18 μm technology parameters. You will have to use a nonquasistatic model in SPICE.

P11.8 For the circuit in Figure 11.27, plot the incoming clock signal and the output clock signals. Design the circuit so that it has equal delays from the Clk to both outputs.

P11.9 For the circuit in Figure 11.41b, use SPICE to plot τ versus V_C if $W = 0.5$ μm for all devices. Assume that the inverter drives another identical inverter. Given the results from SPICE, what is the frequency range of the VCO in Figure 11.41a if there are 25 stages?

P11.10 You are required to drive a 10 mm wire with minimum delay. However, your input capacitance must be 12λ (i.e., due to the input capacitance of a 2X inverter). Answer the following questions using rapid "back-of-the-envelope" calculations, and then redo the problem using detailed analysis. Finally, compare the results with SPICE.

(a) First draw a schematic of the circuit involving only inverters and wires that will produce the minimum delay. Your circuit should have inverters that start at 2X and increase in size until they reach the buffers that are inserted to drive the wire segments. Show the entire delay path from end to end.

(b) Size the inverters to produce the minimum delay.

(c) Compute the delay value from the 2X inverter to the end of the wire.

A Brief Introduction to SPICE

J. Chia and R. Saleh

A.1   Introduction

The simple design equations employed throughout the text are useful for "back-of-the-envelope" calculations. Typically, hand calculations are anywhere between 30–50% from the results obtained after chip fabrication. For more accurate analysis, more complex equations can be used with parameters that incorporate process and environmental variations. Unfortunately, calculations with complex equations and a large number of parameters can be time-consuming and error-prone. Instead, CAD tools for the simulation and analysis of integrated circuits are used to obtain detailed solutions. The SPICE program is the most popular tool in industry today. Since it is used throughout this book, a brief tutorial is provided here for those unfamiliar with SPICE. This treatment is only intended to introduce the reader to the SPICE tool. It contains many useful features that are not covered in this appendix. There are many good books and reference manuals that provide a comprehensive study of SPICE. The interested reader should consult these references (see Chapter 3) for more details.

This appendix is most useful after reading Chapters 1, 2, and 3 of the textbook. It describes the input syntax for SPICE so that the simulations described in Chapters 3, 4, 5, and 6 may be better understood. The two most useful types of SPICE analyses for digital circuits are the dc and transient analyses. The dc analysis can be used to generate voltage transfer characteristics, current-voltage characteristics, etc. Transient analysis is used to produce time-domain plots of current or voltage versus time. These are the two types of analyses that are described in this appendix. After describing the syntax of a SPICE input file, two examples are presented to illustrate the use of dc and transient analysis.

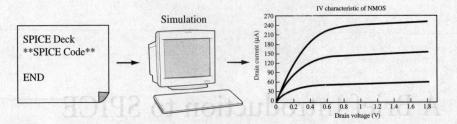

Figure A.1
Typical SPICE design flow.

A.2 Design Flow

Typical SPICE analysis consists of three steps:

1. The circuit is described in SPICE-readable format in a text file known as a SPICE "deck." The deck contains a list of the sources, active elements and passive elements in the circuit, and their respective connections. The deck is also the place where the desired types of analyses (dc, transient) are specified. Today, there are schematic editors that allow you to specify the devices and their connections graphically and then automatically generate the SPICE file from the schematic. This type of input specification should be used if available at your site. We assume that a text file is used as input.

2. The input file is compiled and simulated using the SPICE program. At this point SPICE reads and checks the deck for syntax errors. This is also the stage where the requested simulations are performed. There are many different commercial version of SPICE available. Some run on workstations while others run on personal computers. For the purposes of this textbook, they are all roughly equivalent. We assume a workstation version of SPICE running under the UNIX operating system.

3. Once the deck has been successfully simulated, the results may be analyzed using graphical display programs. SPICE can print out results in text format, but a graphical view of the waveforms is preferred. This form also allows rapid measurement of propagation delays, permits superposition of multiple waveforms on one plot, etc.

Figure A.1 illustrates this design flow.

A.3   Syntax

A sample SPICE deck for an inverter circuit is shown in Figure A.2. Each line will be described briefly and then detailed in the sections to follow.

```
Inverter Circuit
.param Supply=1.8 * Set value of Vdd
.lib 'bsim3v3.cmos.18um' * Set 0.18um library
.opt scale=0.1u * Set lambda (here lambda=0.10)
Vdd   1     0      'Supply'
Vin   2     0      pulse     0    'Supply'   1ns  0ns  0ns  2ns  4ns
Mp  3 2 1 1 pmos L=2 W=8 as=40 ps=4 ad=40 pd=8
Mn  3 2 0 0 nmos L=2 W=4 as=20 ps=4 ad=20 pd=4
Cload       3     0      10fF
* Transient analysis
.tran 50ps 5ns
* Plotting requests
.plot tran V(3)
.end
```

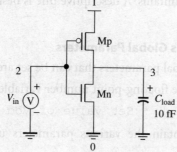

Figure A.2

An example inverter circuit.

A basic SPICE file will contain the following:

1. A title.

   ```
   Inverter Circuit
   ```

2. Settings of various global parameters such as λ, V_{DD}, and the MOS device models to be used. The models to be used are specified by including a library file.

   ```
   .param Supply=1.8 * Set value of Vdd
   .lib 'bsim3v3.cmos.18um' * Set 0.18um library
   .opt scale=0.1u * Set lambda (here lambda=0.10)
   ```

3. A listing of sources, active elements, and passive elements.

```
Vdd 1 0 'Supply'
Mp 3 2 1 1 pmos L=2 W=8 as=40 ps=4 ad=40 pd=8
Mn 3 2 0 0 nmos L=2 W=4 as=20 ps=4 ad=20 pd=4
Cload  3    0    10fF
```

4. Analysis statements (DC, Transient).

```
.tran 50ps 5ns
```

5. Plotting and printing statements.

```
.plot tran V(3)
```

6. Comments.

```
* Transient analysis
```

7. An .end statement.

```
.end
```

A.3.1 Title

The first line of any SPICE file is treated by the compiler as the title of the deck regardless of what the line contains. A descriptive title is best used here with dates, versions, name, etc.

A.3.2 Settings of Various Global Parameters

The three main types of global parameters that can be set are:

1. Parameters, which are floating-point number variables.

```
.param Supply=1.8 * Set value of Vdd
```

2. Libraries, which contain the various parameters used in the MOSFET model.

```
.lib 'bsim3v3.cmos.18um' * Set 0.18um library
```

3. Lambda, the length of the λ unit. Since a 0.18 μm technology is being used, λ is set to 100 nm (for convenience).

```
.opt scale=0.1u * Set lambda (here lambda=0.10)
```

A.3.2.1 Parameters

A parameter in SPICE is a declaration of a global variable that can be assigned to values such as the voltage of a voltage source, the resistance of a resistor or in .dc and .tran commands. The syntax for a parameter declaration is:

```
.param       paramname=realnumber
```

param	All parameter declarations must begin with this.
Paramname	The name of the parameter (e.g.. Supply, Length, Delay).
realnumber	The value of the parameter (e.g., 1.2, 0.1u, 10n).

The example below declares a parameter called "Supply" with a value of 1.8. Note that no units have been assigned. If Supply is assigned to a voltage source, then that voltage source has a value of 1.8 V, if Supply is assigned to an inductor, then the inductor has a value of 1.8 H.

```
.param      Supply=1.8
```

A.3.2.2   Libraries

Libraries contain all the parameter values of the MOS model for a particular technology to be used when designing your circuits. In the past, users could set the model parameters such as oxide thickness, junction capacitances, and doping levels. However, there are so many parameters associated with a model that are tied closely to the foundry service that they are now stored in library files. Users should not adjust these values but should check out the models by generating typical *I-V* curves to ensure that the model libraries are consistent.

Libraries are declared using the .lib command. The syntax for a library call is

```
.lib        '<filepath> filename'
```

`.lib`	All library calls must begin with this.
`filepath`	This is the location of the library file. You should enter this path if the library file is not in the same folder as the deck being compiled. You can use "../" if the library file is in one of the parent directories. You must enclose the path and name in single quotes as shown above.
`filename`	This is the name of the library file. You can use "../" if the library file is in one of the parent directories. You must enclose the path and name in single quotes as shown above.

The example below includes a library called bsim3v3.cmos.18um that is held in the parent directory of the current deck.

```
.lib '../bsim3v3.cmos.18um'
```

A.3.2.3   Specifying Device Sizes in Lambda Units

SPICE provides an .opt scale command that will allow you to more conveniently express the physical dimensions of MOS transistors in units of lambda. The dimensions will be scaled by this value.

```
.opt scale=length
```

`.opt scale`	The lambda declaration must begin with this.
`length`	Value of the unit of lambda in meters.

The example below sets the value of lambda to 0.1 μm.

```
.opt scale=0.1um
```

Later in the description, if the following line is used,

```
Mn 3 2 0 0 nmos L=2 W=4 as=20 ps=4 ad=20 pd=4
```

it is interpreted as a transistor with $L = 2\lambda$, $W = 4\lambda$, $AS = 20\lambda^2$, $PS = 4\lambda$, $AD = 20\lambda^2$ and $PD = 4\lambda$. For scale $= 0.1\ \mu m$, it would have the same effect as using the following line:

```
Mn 3 2 0 0 nmos L=0.2u W=0.4u as=0.2p ps=0.4u ad=0.2p pd=0.4u
```

However, the first description is much easier to read and debug. It also allows you to change the technology dimensions without modifying the circuit description.

A.3.3   Listing of Sources and Active and Passive Elements

The circuit can be constructed by typing a list of sources (voltage or current sources), active elements (diodes and transistors), passive elements (resistors and capacitors), and their associated connection nodes. Each type of source and element is specified on a separate line. Sources and elements are added to the list by specifying:

1. A unique instance name.
2. The nodes to which they are connected.
3. Specific values associated with the element (such as 10 kΩ for a resistor.)
4. A model, if an active element is being specified (such as the BSIM model for MOS transistors).
5. Element specific parameters (such as the width and length of a MOSFET).

A.3.3.1   Instance Name

The instance name of an element is a unique designation that may contain up to 8 alphanumeric characters. The first character of the name must correspond to the type of element that it is being invoked because this is how SPICE will know the type of element you want to describe. For example, the first letter of a resistor instance must begin with the letter R. Any unique combination of characters may follow after.

Table A.1 lists the element type and name convention. 'xxx' can be any combination of up to 7 alphanumeric characters.(This is the syntax for all instance names in SPICE.)

A.3.3.2   Nodes

To specify the connectivity information for the circuit, the nodes to which the element is connected are specified. Most elements require two nodes, while other elements like BJTs and FETs require three or more. In the past, nodes were specified as positive integer values. For a more descriptive input, alphanumeric node names should be used whenever possible.

Table A.1

Syntax of element names

Element Type	Naming Convention	Instance Examples
Voltage Source	Vxxx	V1, VDD, Vsource
Current Source	Ixxx	I2, Isource, ID
Resistor	Rxxx	R5, Rin, Rout
Capacitor	Cxxx	Cg, Cout, Cbig
Inductor	Lxxx	L3, Lself, L1
MOSFET	Mxxx	M1, Mpmos23, Mpu
Diode	Dxxx	D1, Dpn, Dclamp

Note: Node "0" is reserved for the ground node. For some two terminal elements, the "positive" node must be entered before the "negative" node. "Positive" and "negative" do not necessarily refer to the voltage level of the nodes with respect to each other, rather they refer to the designated "+" and "−" side of the element. Voltage sources and diodes are examples of devices that alter their circuit topology if their nodes are specified in different orders. The nodes on the resistors, capacitors, and inductors, on the other hand, may be specified in different order without any effect on the way the circuit behaves. For these elements, it is customary to enter the node that will likely be at the higher voltage as the positive side.

Figure A.3 shows a 10 kΩ resistor named R5 connected between node "5" and ground.

```
R5      5      0      10k
```

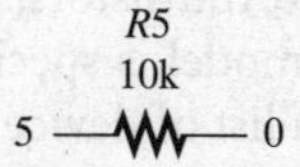

Figure A.3

A resistor passive element.

A.3.3.3 Values

Element values are specified using floating-point numbers. Values that are extremely large or small (e.g., > 1000 or < 0.001 may be specified in exponential format or with engineering prefixes. Table A.2 shows multiplying factors with their associated power-of-ten suffix letter, metric prefixes, and exponential format. The last column shows two equivalent values expressed in engineering and exponential format.

Note: Units (ohms, farads, volts) are not required since SPICE will infer the units based on the type of element (resistors, capacitors, voltage sources). However, they should be specified wherever possible to improve readability. Prefix and exponential formats *cannot* be mixed (e.g., 2E-16P).

Table A.2
SPICE prefixes and exponents

Multiplying Factor	Metric Prefix	Power-of-Ten Suffix Letter	Exponential	SPICE Examples
10^9	Giga	G, g	E9	4.2GHz 4.2E9
10^6	Mega	Meg, meg	E6	.2Meg .2E6
10^3	Kilo	K, k	E3	27kohms 27E3
10^{-3}	Milli	M, m	E-3	273mA 273E-3
10^{-6}	Micro	U, u	E-6	.02us .02E-6
10^{-9}	Nano	N, n	E-9	4ns 4E-9
10^{-12}	Pico	P, p	E-12	95pF 95E-12
10^{-15}	Femto	F, f	E-15	3fF 3E-15

A.3.3.4 Models

For active elements like diodes and transistors, instead of specifying a single value (like resistance or capacitance) a model is specified. The model is added after the nodes have been specified. Then, a list of device dimensions are provided.

Figure A.4 shows a MOS transistor that uses the "nmos" model.

```
Mn   2   3   0   0   nmos l=2 w=4 as=20 ad=20 ps=4 pd=4
```

Figure A.4
A MOS transistor.

Ask your system administrator for the file path and name for the model library.

A.3.3.5 Element Specific Parameters

Elements like MOSFETs have additional parameters like their length and width. To specify these values, provide the parameter to be specified, followed by an equal "=" sign and the value of the parameter as a real number. The syntax of the parameter is the same as that specified in the Values section above. The example to follow specifies an NMOS device named "Mn" connected between nodes 2 and 3, using the model "nmos," with a length of 2λ and a width of 4λ. The areas of the source and drain are typically specified by multiplying the width by 5λ (source/drain extension). The perimeters of the source and drain should be specified as the width of the device in deep submicron technologies.

```
Mn   2   3   0   0   nmos l=2 w=4 as=20 ad=20 ps=4 pd=4
```

Sometimes, there may not be enough space on one line to specify all the parameters. Additional parameters may be placed on subsequent lines by starting the line with the plus "+" sign and then entering the rest of the parameters. The example below specifies the same NMOS device but with the dimensional parameters on a separate line.

```
Mn   2     3     0       0      nmos
+    l=2   w=4   as=20   ad=20   ps=4  pd=4
```

A.3.3.6 Element Syntax

The syntax for the elements are:

A.3.3.6.1 Voltage and Current Sources

```
Vxxx    n+    n-    voltageval
Ixxx    n+    n-    currentval
```

Vxxx Ixxx	The name of the voltage or current source.
n+	The positive node.
n-	The negative node.
voltageval currentval	Voltage or current value of the source. This may be a number or a constant previously declared with a .param command.

Figure A.5 shows a voltage source named "Vsupply" connected between nodes 5 and ground with a value of 15 volts and a current supply named "Isupply" connected between nodes 2 and 3 with a value of 'Icc' amps that was declared with a .param command (not shown).

```
Vsupply   5   0   15
Isupply   2   3   'Icc'
```

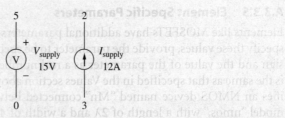

Figure A.5
A voltage and current source.

Sometimes, it is useful to observe the behavior of elements as they are being excited by a trapezoidal waveform. In this case, the PULSE option could be used to specify the parameters of the wave. The syntax for a voltage or current pulse is

```
Vxxx    n+    n-    PULSE    <v1 v2 td tr tf pw per>
Ixxx    n+    n-    PULSE    <v1 v2 td tr tf pw per>
```

Vxxx Ixxx	The name of the voltage or current source.
n+	The positive node.
n-	The negative node.
PULSE	This keyword replaces "voltageval" and signifies that a pulse is being specified.
v1	The initial value of the voltage or current in volts or amps.
v2	The final value of the voltage or current in volts or amps.
td	The delay time in seconds. This is the time of the beginning of the first transition between v1 and v2.
tr	This is the rise time of the pulse, in other words, how long it takes to go from v1 to v2.
tf	This is the fall time of the pulse, in other words, how long it takes to go from v2 to v1.
pw	This is the pulse width of the waveform which is defined as the time the wave remains at v2.
per	This is the period of the waveform.

The example below describes a voltage source called "Vpulse" connected between nodes 3 and 0 that switches between −1 and 1 V. It begins to rise after a delay of 2 ns, with a rise time of 4 ns, a fall time of 3 ns, a pulse width of 20 ns, and a period of 50 ns. A graph of this wave is shown in Figure A.6.

```
Vpulse    3    0    PULSE    -1    1    2ns    4ns    3ns    20ns    50ns
```

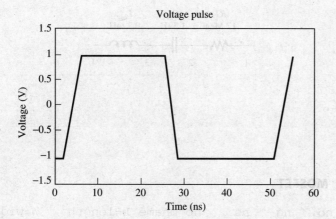

Figure A.6
A pulse waveform.

Another useful source is the piecewise linear source or PWL. The waveform is specified as (time, value) pairs. For the same graph in Figure A.5, the PWL would be specified as follows:

```
Vpulse     3     0    PWL 0 -1 2ns -1 6ns 1 26ns 1 29ns -1
+ 52ns -1 56ns 1
```

A.3.3.6.2   Resistors, Capacitors, and Inductors

```
Rxxx     n+    n-    resistanceval
Cxxx     n+    n-    capacitanceval
Lxxx     n+    n-    inductanceval
```

Rxxx Cxxx Lxxx	The name of the resistor, capacitor, or inductor.
n+	The positive node.
n-	The negative node.
resistanceval capacitanceval inductanceval	Resistance, capacitance, or inductance value of the element.

Figure A.7 shows a 17 MΩ resistor, a 1.5 fF capacitor, and 0.7 mH inductor connected in series.

```
R7      1    2    17Megohms
Cin     2    3    1.5fF
Lbig    3    4    .7mH
```

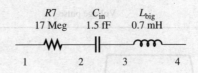

Figure A.7
An *RLC* circuit.

A.3.3.6.3 MOSFET

```
Mxxx    nd    ng    ns    nb mname L=length    W=width
+       AD=drain_area     PD=drain_perimeter
+       AS=source_area    PS=source_perimeter
```

Mxxx	The name of the MOSFET.
nd	The drain node.
ng	The gate node.
ns	The source node.
nb	The bulk node.
mname	The name of the model to be used. This is also where you distinguish between a PMOS and NMOS FET.
length	The length of the MOSFET in units of *m*.
width	The width of the MOSFET in units of *m*
drain_area	The area of the drain diffusion of the MOSFET in units of m^2.
drain_perimeter	The drain perimeter of the MOSFET in units of *m*.
source_area	The area of the source diffusion of the MOSFET in units of m^2.
source_perimeter	The source perimeter of the MOSFET in units of *m*.

Figure A.8 shows a PMOS and an NMOS connected in a transmission gate configuration. Both MOS devices have a $20\lambda^2$ diffusion area and a 5λ diffusion extension. They are both 4λ by 2λ in size.

```
Mp    3    0    2    1    PMOS
+     L=2        W=4
+     AS=20      PS=4
+     AD=20      PD=4
Mn    2    1    3    0    NMOS
+     L=2        W=4
+     AS=20      PS=4
+     AD=20      PD=4
```

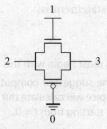

Figure A.8
A transmission gate. For simplicity, the bulk nodes are not shown.

A.3.4   Analysis Statements

In order to instruct SPICE to perform various simulations on a given circuit, SPICE provides analysis commands. The two analyses of particular interest in this book are:

1. transient

2. dc

You may invoke multiple transient and dc requests in your SPICE file.

A.3.4.1   Transient

Transient analysis is used to observe the value of a variable as it changes with time. For example, one may want to view the voltage of the capacitor in an RC network as a step input is applied, or the current through a MOS device as it is switching. For this type of analysis, the user must specify the interval over which the simulation will be performed, and the time step to be used for plotting purposes. SPICE internally solves the differential equations for the circuit numerically and produces very accurate results.

An example of a transient analysis for an RC circuit is shown in Figure A.9.

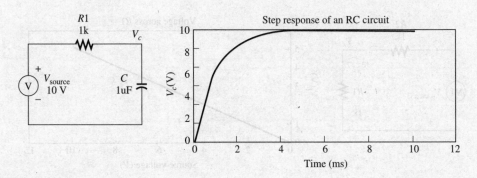

Figure A.9
An RC circuit and a graph of V_c while V_{source} is swept from 0 V to 10 V.

The syntax for the .tran analysis statement is:

```
.tran tstep    tstop
```

.tran	All transient statements must begin with this directive.
tstep	This value represents the suggested computing increment for SPICE. If this value is 1 second, then spice will calculate the variables of the circuit (voltage, current) every 1 second starting from t = 0.
	If the increment unit is extremely large or small, prefixes may be used, (e.g., one millisecond would be 1ms, and 200 nanoseconds would be 200 ns).
tstop	This value represents the time at which transient analysis will stop. If tstep = 1 and tstop = 10, then SPICE will calculate the variables of the circuit (voltage, current) every 1 second starting from t = 0 to t = 10.
	If the increment unit is extremely large or small, prefixes may be used, (e.g., one millisecond would be 1ms, and 200 nanoseconds would be 200 ns).

For the RC circuit example above, the syntax for the command would appear as follows:

```
.tran   1m   10m
```

A.3.4.2   DC

DC analysis is used to observe the value of one variable while another is changing or "sweeping" from one value to another. This is very useful when generating the voltage transfer characteristics of an inverter, or plotting the I-V characteristics of the MOS transistor. In this type of analysis, the user specifies the output variable to be plotted and the variable to be swept from a start value to a stop value, with a given step size. Internally, SPICE carries out the dc solution at each intermediate point between the start and stop values and displays the results.

For example, in the voltage divider circuit in Figure A.10, the voltage V_r between R1 and R2 is observed while V_{source} is swept from 0 V to 10 V.

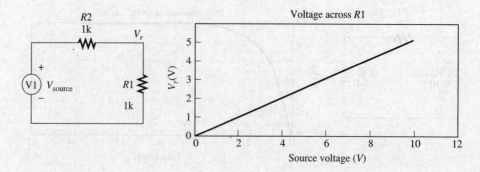

Figure A.10

A graph of V_r while V_{source} is swept from 0 V to 10 V.

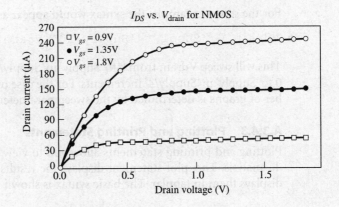

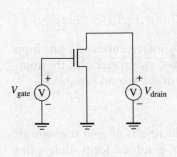

Figure A.11

I_{DS} versus V_{drain} for changing Vgate.

In SPICE, a value can be observed while *two* other values are being swept. This would produce multiple lines on the same graph. In Figure A.11, the drain current is observed while the drain voltage, V_{drain} is swept from 0 to 1.8 V and the gate voltage, V_{gate}, is swept from 0 to 1.8 V.
The syntax for the DC analysis statement is:

```
.dc var1 start stop step <var2 start2 stop2 step2>
```

where everything in <> is optional.

`.dc`	All DC statements must begin with this directive.
`var1`	Name of the variable to be swept (e.g., Vsource).
`start`	The starting value of the sweep (e.g., 0).
`stop`	The end value of the sweep (e.g., 10).
`step`	The magnitude of the increment used to sweep the variable (e.g., 1). The smaller the value, the analysis becomes more accurate but also more time-consuming.
`var2 (optional)`	Name of the second variable to be swept (e.g., R2).
`start2 (optional)`	The starting value of the second sweep (e.g., 1).
`stop2 (optional)`	The end value of the second sweep (e.g., 3).
`step2 (optional)`	The magnitude of the increment used to sweep the second variable (e.g., 1). The smaller the value, the analysis becomes more accurate but also more time-consuming.

For the first voltage divider example above, the syntax for the command would appear as follows:

```
.dc   V1   0   10   1
```

For the second example, the syntax would appear as

```
.dc Vdrain 0 'Supply' 'Supply/20' Vgate 0 'Supply' 'Supply/4'
```

This will sweep Vdrain from 0 to 'Supply' in 'Supply/20' increments, and Vgate from 0 to 'Supply' in 'Supply/4' increments. For the case of two sweep variables, the number of graphs is determined by the sweep parameters of the second variable.

A.3.4.3 Plotting and Printing Statements

Plotting and printing statements allow you to view the results of your transient or dc analysis. The .plot statement displays the results in graphical form while .print displays them in tabular. The basic syntax is shown below:

```
.plot      analysis_type    ov1    <ov2 ... ov32>
.print     analysis_type    ov1    <ov2 ... ov32>
```

where everything in < > is optional.

.plot	All plot statements must begin with this.
.print	All print statements must begin with this.
analysis_type	This is the type of analysis you wish to display, either tran or dc.
ov1	These are the output variables you wish to plot, such as the voltage of a node or the current through an element.

The first example below is for a dc plot request of the voltage at node 5 and the current through the inductor Lself. The second example is a transient print request for the same voltage and current:

```
.plot      dc      V(5)    I(Lself)
.print     tran    V(5)    I(Lself)
```

A.3.4.4 Comments

As in every other coding language, comments are useful to clarify the author's intention of the various lines in the file to the reader. In SPICE, the beginning of a comment is denoted by an asterix (*). Comments can exist on a line by themselves or with SPICE executable statements:

```
* This is a comment **
R5   2   0   10k   * This is also a comment.
```

A.3.4.5 .ic Statement

There are situations where the initial condition of a circuit node must be specified at time $t = 0$ for a meaningful simulation. For this purpose, the .ic statement can be used. It must also be flagged in the .tran line with a "uic" directive so that the initial condition will be used during the simulation. For example, if node 5 must be initially set to 1.8 V, and node 7 set to 0 V, the following lines would be used:

```
.ic   V(5)=1.8   V(7)=0
.tran 50ps 5ns uic
```

A.3.4.6   .end Statement

To finish off the deck the .end statement is required to tell SPICE that this is the end of the file. Any lines entered after .end are ignored.

A.4   Complete SPICE Examples

Figure A.12 shows a dc analysis on the *I-V* characteristic of an NMOS by sweeping Vdrain from 0 to 1.8 V at five different values of Vgate:

```
IV Characteristic of NMOS
.param Supply=1.8         * Set value of Vdd
.lib 'bsim3v3.cmos.18um'  * Set 0.18um library
.opt scale=0.1u           * Set lambda (here lambda=0.10)
* Voltage sources
Vdrain   2   0   'Supply'
Vgate    1   0   'Supply'
* A minimum width NMOS transistor
Mn 2 1 0 0 nmos l=2 w=4 as=20 ps=4 ad=20 pd=4
* DC analysis request by sweeping the drain and gate voltage.
.dc Vdrain 0 'Supply' 'Supply/20' Vgate 0 'Supply' 'Supply/4'
* Plotting requests
.plot dc I(Mn)
.end
```

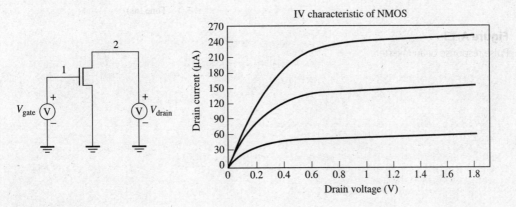

Figure A.12
IV Characteristic of NMOS.

Figure A.13 shows a transient analysis of an inverter by applying a ramp function at the input and viewing the output:

```
Transient Response of an Inverter
.param Supply=1.8          * Set value of Vdd
.lib 'bsim3v3.cmos.18um'   * Set 0.18um library
.opt scale=0.1u            * Set lambda (here lambda=0.10)
Vdd  1    0     'Supply'
Vin  2    0     pulse    0    'Supply'  1n  0n  0n  2n  4n
Mp 3 2 1 1 pmos l=2 w=8 as=40 ps=4 ad=40 pd=8
Mn 3 2 0 0 nmos l=2 w=4 as=20 ps=4 ad=20 pd=4
Cload      3      0      10fF
* Transient analysis
.tran 50ps 5ns
* Plotting requests
.plot tran V(3)
.end
```

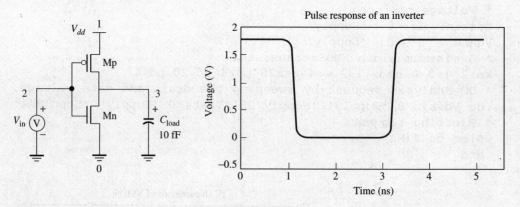

Figure A.13
Pulse response of an inverter.

Index

USEFUL DESIGN PARAMETERS (simplified)

Name	Symbol	0.18 μm		0.13 μm		Units
		NMOS	PMOS	NMOS	PMOS	
Channel Length (rounded for convenience)	L	200	200	100	100	nm
Supply Voltage	V_{DD}	1.8	1.8	1.2	1.2	V
Oxide Thickness	t_{ox}	35	35	22	22	Å
Oxide Capacitance	C_{ox}	1.0	1.0	1.6	1.6	μF/cm^2
Threshold Voltage	V_{T0}	0.5	-0.5	0.4	-0.4	V
Body-Effect Term	γ	0.3	0.3	0.2	0.2	V$^{1/2}$
Fermi Potential	$2|\phi_F|$	0.84	0.84	0.88	0.88	V
Junction Capacitance Coefficient	C_{j0}	1.6	1.6	1.6	1.6	fF/μm^2
Built-In Junction Potential	ϕ_B	0.9	0.9	1.0	1.0	V
Grading Coefficient	m	0.5	0.5	0.5	0.5	—
Nominal Mobility (low vertical field)	μ_0	540	180	540	180	cm^2/V-s
Effective Mobility (high vertical field)	μ_e	270	70	270	70	cm^2/V-s
Critical Field	E_c	6×10^4	24×10^4	6×10^4	24×10^4	V/cm
Critical Field $\times$ L	$E_c L$	1.2	4.8	0.6	2.4	V
Effective Resistance	R_{eff}	12.5	30	12.5	30	kΩ/□

Name	Symbol	Value	Units
Gate Capacitance Coefficient	C_g	2	fF/μm
Self Capacitance Coefficient	C_{eff}	1	fF/μm
Wire Capacitance Coefficient	C_w	0.1–0.25	fF/μm
Al Wire Resistance	$R_{\square}$	25–60	mΩ/□
Cu Wire Resistance	$R_{\square}$	20–40	mΩ/□
Wire Inductance	L_{eff}	0.4–0.5	pH/μm

USEFUL PHYSICAL AND MATERIAL CONSTANTS

Name	Symbol	Value	Units
Electron Charge	q	1.6×10^{-19}	C
Boltzmann's Constant	k	1.38×10^{-23}	J/°K
Room Temperature	T	300	°K (27°C)
Thermal Voltage	$V_{th} = kT/q$	26	mV (at 27°C)
Dielectric Constant of Vacuum	ε_0	8.85×10^{-14}	F/cm
Dielectric Constant of Silicon	ε_{si}	$11.7\,\varepsilon_0$	F/cm
Dielectric Constant of SiO_2	ε_{ox}	$3.97\,\varepsilon_0$	F/cm
Intrinsic Carrier Concentration	n_i	1.45×10^{10}	cm^{-3} (at 27°C)
Carrier Saturation Velocity In Silicon	v_{sat}	8×10^6	cm/s
Aluminum Resistivity	ρ_{Al}	2.7	$\mu\Omega$-cm
Copper Resistivity	ρ_{Cu}	1.7	$\mu\Omega$-cm
Tungsten Resistivity	ρ_W	5.5	$\mu\Omega$-cm

ENGINEERING SCALE FACTORS

G	giga	10^9
M	mega	10^6
k	kilo	10^3
c	centi	10^{-2}
m	milli	10^{-3}
μ	micro	10^{-6}
n	nano	10^{-9}
p	pico	10^{-12}
f	femto	10^{-15}
a	atto	10^{-18}

METER CONVERSION FACTORS

$1\ \mu m = 10^{-4}\ cm = 10^{-6}\ m$

$1\ m = 10^2\ cm = 10^6\ \mu m$

$0.1\ \mu m = 100\ nm$

$1\text{Å} = 10^{-8}\ cm = 10^{-10}\ m$